ENGLISH POLITICAL CARICATURE

TO 1792

THE WORLD IS RVLED & GOVERNED by OPINION.

B.M. 272

Heading to verses by Henry Peacham, 1641. Hollar

pp. 25–26

ENGLISH POLITICAL CARICATURE

TO 1792

A STUDY OF OPINION AND PROPAGANDA

BY

M. DOROTHY GEORGE

LITT.D.

Hon. Fellow of Girton College

★

75191

OXFORD
AT THE CLARENDON PRESS
1959

Oxford University Press, Amen House, London E.C.4

GLASGOW NEW YORK TORONTO MELBOURNE WELLINGTON
BOMBAY CALCUTTA MADRAS KARACHI KUALA LUMPUR
CAPE TOWN IBADAN NAIROBI ACCRA

PRINTED IN GREAT BRITAIN
AT THE UNIVERSITY PRESS, OXFORD
BY VIVIAN RIDLER
PRINTER TO THE UNIVERSITY

PREFACE

IN the vast literature of the subject it might be misleading to select especially relevant works for mention. Some authorities are given in footnotes and in the Index of Artists. Others will be found in the British Museum *Catalogue of Political and Personal Satires* to which the numbers in square brackets in the text refer—volumes i–iv, 1870–83, by F. G. Stephens (art critic and minor Pre-Raphaelite) cover the period to 1770; volumes v–vi, 1935–8, by myself, deal with the years from 1771 to 1792.

I am very grateful to Dr. E. H. Gombrich and Mr. Charles Mitchell for their help and encouragement, and to Mrs. William Martin and Mr. Lawrence Towner for valuable information. I am also much indebted to the Print Room staff of the British Museum, especially to Mr. A. Aspital.

February 1959

CONTENTS

LIST OF ILLUSTRATIONS

Acknowledgements are made to the British Museum for all plates except 12 and 17, which are from the Bodleian Library, Oxford.

Frontispiece. *The World is Ruled and Governed by Opinion*, heading to verses by Henry Peacham, 1641, engraved by Hollar

INTRODUCTION

THE subject of this book is pictorial propaganda in England—the political or controversial print, which, especially in its earlier phases, is distinct from its older relation, comic art. To be politically effective the picture must be capable of rapid production and distribution; the political songs of the Middle Ages had these qualities—only the inventions of paper, printing, and engraving made graphic propaganda possible. There is no need to stress the interest of the outstanding cartoon[1]—to use the modern term—as a vivid occasional illustration of politics. One can scarcely think of Bismarck's dismissal without remembering Tenniel's *Dropping the Pilot*. And of all forms of propaganda the picture can be the most deadly. But, in general, historians—apt to neglect iconography—disregard the wonderful material buried—the word is hardly an exaggeration—in the great mass of English satirical engravings. They reflect the rhythm and tempo of the national life, showing the immediate reactions to events and illuminating opinion and propaganda, with their myths and fantasies, catchwords and slogans. And though many prints were propagandist in the sense that they were intended to influence opinion, deliberate propaganda, paid or organized, is seemingly rare, but sometimes important. The prints were commercial ventures which had to be popular; their great interest is that in the main they reflect opinion. And since they illustrate, not the past, but a sequence of presents in a series of dissolving views, a chronological treatment is imposed.[2]

The object of the book is to find the pattern in the shifting kaleidoscope, not to take the thread of history, as we now see it, and find appropriate illustrations. All political caricature tends to be radical, oppositionist, disruptive. In the eighteenth century and after, the bias against authority was more extreme. Ministerial journalists were inevitably denounced as venal

---

[1] The word was used ironically in this sense by Leech (*Punch*, No. 105) during the 1843 exhibition of cartoons for mural decorations in the new Houses of Parliament. After some time it established itself as the word for a large political drawing in the illustrated papers. M. H. Spielmann, *Encycl. Brit.*, Cambridge, 1911, *s.v.* Cartoon. Leech was anticipated in a plate to the *Westminster Magazine*, 'The Political Cartoon for the Year 1775' [5288].

[2] The prints to be discussed here are chiefly those in the collections of the British Museum. These, of course, are not complete—almost any collection of satirical prints will have some that are not in the Museum. But they contain most of the more important, and the prints are sufficiently representative to be a guide to trends of opinion. Many must have disappeared, especially cheap flimsy woodcuts and the seditious ones that were handed about or posted up surreptitiously. The grosser ones too would tend to be eliminated from collections.

hirelings—a judgement somehow not applicable to the paid hacks of opposition—and any such person as a public relations officer would have been thought an outrage. Johnson's *Dictionary* derivation of Gazetteer speaks for itself: 'It was lately a term of the utmost infamy, being usually applied to Wretches who were hired to vindicate the Court.' Horace Walpole in 1770, deploring the licence of the press, saw no remedy: 'Ministers are and ought to be lawful game, yet the law could not except them as proper to be abused.'[1] Autocracy in France in the *ancien régime* was said to be tempered by epigram, and in Russia by assassination. In England oligarchy was tempered by caricatures as well as by the press.[2]

The prints can be libellous to an extreme degree, and (after the Revolution) with impunity. This was misleading to foreign observers. In 1802 (when English visitors were flocking to France) prints by Gillray disparaging to the Ministry were posted up in Calais to confront travellers going through the passport bureau. 'I felt not a little indignant', wrote Raimbach the engraver, 'at perceiving, in addition to the tone of official arrogance, the wall of an anteroom in which we waited was decorated with the masterly caricatures of Gillray, ridiculing the chief personages of the English administration . . .'[3] In the prints we see how very far *lèse-majesté* could go. It is usual to think of Gillray as the most savagely uninhibited of English caricaturists. He is challenged (though not in wit or ability) by the anonymous engravers of the 1760's and in 1777–80, and again by the caricaturists of 1819–20.

But the prints reflect also a basic patriotism and loyalty, often in conflict with the voice of faction—though faction finds violent expression in these many-sided cartoons which range from naïveté to sophistication. In the mid-nineteenth century Taine found that 'whereas we *suffer* our Government, the English *support* theirs',[4] and the same could probably be said much earlier—the support being consistent with recurrent indignation and contempt, violently expressed, so that at first sight the prints might seem to demonstrate the opposite of this: they belong to 'the history that is present politics', and that, to quote Professor Brogan, 'is mainly composed of envy, malice and all uncharitableness'.[5] As Boyer-Brun said in

---

[1] *Memoirs of the Reign of George III*, 1845, iv. 168.
[2] Cf. 'L'Angleterre est une monarchie composée, mitigée par des caricatures': Charles Nodier quoted Grand-Carteret, *Les Mœurs et la caricature en France*, 1888.
[3] *Memoirs*, 1843, pp. 104 f.
[4] *Notes on England*, trans. E. Hyams, 1957, p. 179. The contrasted use of the extinguisher symbol in France and in England seems significant: see M. D. George, *English Political Caricature 1793–1832: a Study of Opinion and Propaganda*, Oxford, 1959 (hereafter referred to as *E.P.C. 1793–1832*), p. 19, Pl. 8.   [5] *The Study of Politics*, 1946.

1792, 'Les caricatures sont le thermomètre qui indique le degré de l'opinion publique'.[1]

The caricatures are documents in an endless discussion on politics and persons, war and diplomacy. They soon acquired a virtual immunity from prosecution, and a variety and vitality untrammelled by authority, indeed, usually in opposition to it. They were a recognized weapon of controversy, national and sometimes international, to a degree that gives them an importance outside the scope of the modern cartoon. Crises and scandals and vendettas evoked prints and counter-prints, sometimes commissioned by those concerned. Some prints have inscriptions that turn them into graphic pamphlets. They were important also as virtually the only pictorial rendering of passing events. They are history, concrete, personal, and tendentious, seen through contemporary eyes. Like all history they are a seamless web in which the pattern is always changing.

Inseparable from the pictorial pattern of national life found in a sequence of prints is their imagery, the framework of allegory and metaphor which both reflects and colours opinion, which is deeply traditional and yet responds to the fashion of the moment. When English graphic satire established itself it inherited a symbolical language that was international. Allegory was the spirit of the age and all illustration tended to be symbolical. The normal progression for many of these symbols was from the images— pious or ribald—of the Middle Ages, through their Reformation or Renaissance transformations. Though there are earlier examples of the political print in Italy and France, it was Luther who first used pictorial propaganda on a massive scale and in the service of a revolutionary movement. With him it sprang to life, fully armed. He was a pamphleteer of genius, with a great school of wood-engravers, the Cranachs and others, at his disposal, and he had mastered the essentials: he attacked power and pomp in a way dear to the populace. 'The Devil', he wrote, 'knows well that when the foolish people hear high sounding words of abuse, they are taken in and blindly believe them without any further ground or reason.' In a letter of 2 June 1525 he wrote of the efficacy of prints, songs, words, and jests: 'on all the walls, on every sort of paper or playing cards, priests and monks are to be so portrayed that the people are disgusted when they see or hear of the clergy. . . . The clergy have departed from the hearts of the people.' When he ridiculed monks and nuns he was in succession to a traditional art expressed in wood and stone in churches and in illuminated manuscripts, including the margins of Missals and Books of Hours. A worsted

[1] *Histoire des caricatures de la révolte des français*, Paris, 1792.

adversary is apt to over-rate the share of propaganda in his defeat (no need to look farther than to German tributes to British propaganda after World War I): A Catholic historian of Leo X attributes the success of the Reformation to this propaganda in its cruder aspects, and he has a chapter 'Du rire, employé par la Réforme comme instrument de propagande'.[1] It would indeed be hard to find in the later history of graphic satire anything to outstrip Luther's achievement.

Luther's prints ranged from crude images on flysheets appealing to the illiterate to Bible illustrations. Pictorial flysheets circulated in Germany up to the Thirty Years War, but with the revolt of the Netherlands Holland became the chief source of pictorial propaganda. Dutch prints and medals went all over Europe, and since these early satires were largely directed against Spain and the Jesuits they were peculiarly acceptable in England. Reformation images, deriving mainly from Germany and Holland, are found in a long line of anti-clerical prints on the Continent and No-Popery ones in England. Their first appearance in an English guise seems to have been in the illustrations to the Elizabethan editions of Fox's *Book of Martyrs* and in the cuts in Stephen Bateman's *The Doome* in 1581, a chronicle of marvels and portents, related with complete credulity. Some of these militantly Protestant symbols have a special interest and a very long history.

An outstanding example of the medieval image transformed by the Reformation and passing into the language of political allegory is the balance in which the souls of the dead—naked infants—are weighed between good and evil, Heaven and Hell. There were many Reformation versions of the familiar theme. A classic example is a Dutch print copied by Carel Allard: two monks try to drag down a scale containing the papal keys and a book, presumed to be the Summa of Aquinas. But it is hopelessly outweighed by the Bible; on one side stand the Pope and his hierarchy, on the other Huss, Calvin, Melancthon, and Luther. In a variant published in Geneva a demon drags at the Popish scale.[2] There is a similar but simpler English design in the 1576 edition of *Fox's Martyrs* [Pl. 1]: 'A lively picture describyng the weight and substaunce of God's most blessed word, agaynst the doctrines and vanities of mens traditions.' Justice holds the scales in which *Verbum Dei* outweighs 'all the Decreta of the Pope and his Wrath', despite the efforts of a demon. The symbolical and propagandist potency of the contrasted symbols of the Bible and of

---

[1] J. M. V. Audin, *Histoire de Léo X*, Paris, 1844.
[2] Doumergue, *Iconographie calvinienne*, Lausanne, 1909, pp. 183–5.

Popish 'trinkets' or 'trumpery' is manifest in prints of the Great Rebellion. In a long succession of English political prints, countries or persons, documents or symbols are weighed in a balance; the theme is applied to the balance of power and the balance of parties.

Other medieval images appropriated by Reformation artists derived from the *Book of Revelation* which had taken strong hold of the people's imagination. It had been illustrated in block books and their manuscript sources. Dürer had immortalized it on traditional lines. In the first issue (September 1522) of Luther's New Testament with cuts by Cranach, traditional in character, the Pope is Antichrist: the Scarlet Woman or Whore wears the Papal tiara, and so does the Beast with seven heads whose number was 666. Fallen Babylon is clearly Rome with the Castle of Sant'Angelo and other well-known landmarks.[1] A monster with seven heads or more, verging sometimes towards a medieval dragon, sometimes a hydra, sometimes a blend of Beast and hydra, became part of the stock-in-trade of the satirical artist. It may represent a person or persons, or sometimes a grievance, such as Excise or 'Corruption'. Sometimes the monster is explicitly related to Rome and the Beast, as 'Whore' always is. The seven heads and ten crowns were supposed to be Rome's seven hills and ten provinces. Any outstanding *bête noire* is liable to be identified with the Beast.[2] In a very interesting Puritan example (by a Dutch engraver) the seven heads of 'Rome's Monster on his monstrous Beast' [378] are the seven deadly sins as in the Middle Ages.[3] On a memorial medal of Charles I struck in Saxony in 1649, a seven-headed monster rampages above the dead King with the motto *Heu Quaenam Haec Insania Vulgi*! ('Alas what a madness is this of the rabble').[4]

One of the earliest and most noteworthy products of Luther's campaign was the *Passional Christi und Antichristi* with contrasted cuts by Hans Cranach illustrating the life of Christ and the activities of the Pope: Christ washes a poor man's feet; princes kiss the Pope's toe. In English satires, from a cut in *Fox's Martyrs* in 1576 to a poster against Gladstone in 1885,[5] kissing the papal toe recurs as a symbol of abject subservience to Rome. The papal slipper or toe figures repeatedly in the grossly disrespectful cartoons of Italian anti-clerical newspapers in the early years of this century.

[1] In a later edition, at the instance of Frederick the Wise, the tiaras were reduced to harmless crowns, but other details remained, and in the 1534 issue the tiaras were restored.

[2] In English prints one finds Laud, the Stuarts, Cromwell, Bute, the Coalition of Fox and North, and Napoleon.

[3] As in the misericord at New College, Oxford: A. D. Anderson, *Misericords*, 1954, fig. 20.

[4] Hawkins and Grueber, *Medallic Illustrations of the History of Great Britain . . .*, 1885, i. 350–1.   [5] *England's Pope* [B.M. 1850. e. 5/43*].

The famous German Reformation medal or token[1] has had a prolonged influence on graphic satire, if we regard it as the fountain-head of innumerable versions of the reversible head or *phisionomie à double visage*. On the obverse is a profile of the Pope which when inverted becomes the Devil; the reverse is a cardinal-fool, similarly conjoined. It is attributed to the decade from 1537, a counter-token to a Catholic one of Pope and Emperor current during the Diet of Augsburg and the Council of Trent. The motto is *Ecclesia perversa tenet faciem Diaboli*, which suggests Luther as its inspirer, and it has in fact been attributed to his friend, Nicholas van Amsdorf. The little tokens, of which there are many variants, were well known in France, Holland, and England. The design was adapted to pottery, draughtsmen, gems, and seals. It was copied in a cut to Bateman's *The Doome* [Pl. 2]. The double head, so drawn that the nose of one face becomes the chin of the other, was a popular conceit in England and France in the later eighteenth century, sometimes applied to politics, sometimes to such notions as before and after marriage. In political satires the original design was often closely adhered to. In 1761 Henry Fox (a fox) and the Duke of Newcastle are Devil and fool [Pl. 28], and in 1770 Fox, now Lord Holland, is again the Devil with Bute as fool [4416]. In a French print the duc d'Aguillon is conjoined with a fishwife; he was reputed to have joined the Versailles mob on 5 October 1789, disguised as a *poissarde*. In a large bold design of 1871 Napoleon III, violently caricatured, is conjoined with an ass, the two profiles being 'Badinguet allant à la Guerre!!!' and 'Badinguet revenant de la Guerre'.[2] Another favourite device for the double personality which had a long life and many variations, was the body or head vertically divided into contrasted halves, and this was used also to make one person out of two, usually in sinister co-operation—as in the Coalition of Fox and North.

Related to the double-headed image is a profile head of the Pope constructed of emblematical objects disparaging (in Protestant eyes) to the Papacy. This begins with Tobie Stimmer's *Gorgoneum Caput* in 1571; there is a Dutch adaptation (two states); like the Pope-Devil token it was copied in *The Doome* [Pl. 2], and it too has had a prolonged influence on satirical art. On the Catholic side, Arcimboldo produced for Maximilian II a derisory portrait of Calvin; the nose is a frog, the face bits of plucked chicken, the mouth a gaping fish's head, the beard a fish's tail.[3] The genre

[1] F. P. Barnard, *Satirical and Controversial Medals of the Reformation*, Oxford, 1927. He found no engravings of the medals; there are, however, several.   [2] In the London Library.
[3] Now in Stockholm. Doumergue, op. cit., pp. 152–3, pl. xxiii. There is an engraving of a Pope's head constructed of a bell, cups, and plates: *Collection Hennin*, Paris, x. 55.

was used by the German artist Voltz for his famous 'corpse head' of Napoleon which had so many copies and adaptations. The Napoleon print of 1814 (the 'Hieroglyphic Portrait')[1] was imitated in 1871 for an even more venomous head of Napoleon III by Belloguet in a French series, *Pilorie-Phrénologie*, in which there is also an emblematical head of Pius IX. Thus the line of composite emblematical heads reaches from Pope to Pope across three centuries. These heads have analogies with the type of facetious or satirical print, common to folk-prints and satires, and popular both in England and France, in which persons are constructed of appropriate inanimate objects. There are outstanding examples by Hollar [Pl. 4] and Hogarth [Pl. 21].

One medieval image was so familiar that it is unnecessary to seek a specific origin for its adaptation to politics. This is 'Hell Mouth', the fanged and flaming 'jaws of Hell' into which victims are dragged or pushed by demons. In the later Middle Ages the conception was popularized by the Mystery play, where the elaborate movable machinery, the flames and flying demons, made it a favourite scene. The mouth might be round and cavernous, as in the Guthlac Roll at the end of the twelfth century, or long and angular like a crocodile's jaws. It was used repeatedly in English polemical prints for the public enemy of the day; Napoleon and Wellington (in 1832) are both so disposed of. There are other images common—like the balance—to medieval, renaissance, and modern imagery, for instance, the wheel of Fortune or of Time. Death with his javelin persists—the Death of the *Danse Macabre*, the grinning posturing skeleton, not the earlier and more austere figure of *Les trois rois morts et les trois vifs*.

Besides Reformation imagery, chiefly Germanic in origin, there is the renaissance symbolism of the Emblem, Italian in spirit, popularized by the often-translated *Emblemata* of Alciati, first published in 1531. English satirical art was profoundly affected by the popularity of Emblem Books:[2] in form and phraseology seventeenth-century prints are permeated with the art of the Emblem. These books were one of the most typical expressions of allegory. At the end of the sixteenth century illustrations in English books were still rare, but after Geoffrey Whitney's *Choice of Emblems* (printed by Plantin in 1585) Emblem Books became increasingly popular, with Quarles, whose emblems were engraved by William Marshall, as the outstanding emblematist. A typical Emblem Book was a series of little engravings which might range from illustrated metaphors to more elaborate

[1] See *E.P.C. 1793–1832*, Pl. 58.
[2] See Rosemary Freeman, *English Emblem Books*, 1948.

scenes, each with a motto and a moral exposition, usually in verse. The form of the Emblem Book was used by William Blake and adapted to politics by William Hone, so that its influence long survived its seven-teenth-century vogue. Typical emblems (often rooted in the past) were the Eye of Providence with its beam of light, the arm or hand extending from clouds, the lighted candle, the tree (flourishing, decayed, or cut down), Time, the globe, suns and moons (with inset faces), signs of the Zodiac, the Phoenix, the wreath of laurel or oak, or more elaborate illustrations such as the Æsopian fox and grapes, or the fall of Phaeton or of Icarus.

The obligation of political satire to the Emblem Book is expressed in the term 'Emblematical' or 'Hieroglyphical' print, which survived till late in the eighteenth century. But the influence of the emblem was naturally at its height during the first enthusiasm for these books. Many, perhaps most, of the early political prints are emblematical in the strict sense of the term. For instance, *A Rot Among the Bishops*[1] is 'An Ægyptian Dish drest after the English Fashion with a Tribute for Mr. Quarles of never dying memory, set forth in four silent Parables'. By a natural process the word emblem was soon used for any picture with a moral or political significance.

Many emblems were heraldic, and burlesque heraldry is one of the oldest and most long-lived forms of graphic satire: the supporters, the quarterings, the crest, and the motto were great opportunities for insult or ridicule. An early Reformation woodcut from the Cranach studio is a travesty of the papal arms: the Keys are broken, and a hand clutches a money-bag.

The rebus or pictorial writing, a seventeenth-century word for an ancient device, is a variant of the emblem. In England it took shape chiefly in the 'Hieroglyphical Letter', a puzzle print which was sometimes political, sometimes facetious. The most striking examples seem to belong to the later half of the eighteenth century [Pl. 49]; the earliest ones in the British Museum are attributed to 1710 and are non-political. The device is much older. The calligrapher and engraver Palatino published in 1540 an often reprinted guide to scripts and alphabets which included a 'Sonetto Figurato' on four plates, exactly on the principle of the later puzzle-print, verses in which little pictures are interspersed with letters and words. Much earlier again was the rebus in heraldry.

The symbolical frontispiece or title-page, so popular in the seventeenth century, was an extension of the emblem. It is often in an architectural setting; sometimes it is a number of small pictures within a framework

[1] See p. 19.

to symbolize the contents of a book. Emblem-wise, this was usually explained in verse headed 'The Meaning of the Emblem', or 'The Mind of
the Frontispiece', or some such phrase. When a political tract had a frontispiece this was almost always a satirical or at least a symbolical design, and
such prints were sometimes also issued separately.[1] The frontispiece has
great importance in graphic satire. In the first place it was a superb instrument for conveying the bite of a polemical or scurrilous work, a safer and
often more effective medium than words for the expression of dangerous
notions. Secondly, it was a source of political imagery. From its architectural and monumental setting derives a long sequence of satirical monuments in polemical prints.[2] Britannia does not I think, appear in English
graphic satire till after her personification on medals. But, before the
medals, she sits enthroned on her rock in the title-page to Camden's
Britannia (1609), and again, framed in an arch, on the title-page of Dray-
ton's *Poly-Olbion* (1613). And though she was established by the Restoration medals of 1660, there is no better representation of the stereotyped
Britannia of the cartoon than the title-page of Clarendon's *History* (1702).

The folk-print, rare in England in comparison with France and Germany, made its contribution to political imagery. There is the simple
illustration of the proverb or proverbial phrase, such as 'labour in vain' in
which old women with mops and brushes try to 'wash a blackamoor white'.
This was repeatedly used as a political parable from the late eighteenth
century at least. The illustrated metaphor of the nose at the grindstone
was used in English prints for Laud, Charles II, the Pope, Louis XIV,
Britannia, George III and Napoleon. There is also 'Nobody' a bodiless
man whose legs are joined to his shoulders, a folk-print conceit of the early
seventeenth century repeatedly applied to politics [Pl. 58].

Three outstanding folk-print subjects have the special interest that they
were common to England and France and with one possible exception to
Germany, and that they survived with only minor modifications from the
sixteenth or seventeenth to the nineteenth century. The most interesting,
from the political philosophy that underlies it, is that known in England
as 'The Four [or Five—or more] Alls', and in France as *Les Quatre
Vérités*. In the most usual form the four are the King who says 'I rule all',
the parson or bishop ('I pray for all'), the soldier ('I fight for all'), the
farmer or peasant, or—later—John Bull ('I pay for all'). Often there is a
final figure, the Devil or Death, 'I take you all'. In 1803–4 the theme was

---

[1] Conversely, the already published print was sometimes used as a frontispiece.
[2] Cf. Pls. 19, 24; *E.P.C. 1793–1832*, pl. 49.

twice used in a Napoleon satire, *The Three Plagues of Europe*. In 1832 and later variants in crude woodcut were adapted to condemnations of the whole social and political system. The 'Alls' have survived as a device on inn signboards.

The *World Turned Upside Down*—in old French *Le Monde bestorné*—has ancient origins in the marginal drolleries of manuscripts; the tables are turned by, for instance, the hare hunting the hounds or the huntsman, mice pursuing the cat, geese hanging a fox. As a folk-print its standard form is a collection of little oblong scenes, usually sixteen arranged in four rows. As a chapbook the little scenes survived into the nineteenth century. Taylor, the Water Poet, a Royalist, combines a selection of the usual scenes to illustrate two pamphlets,[1] whose political lesson is the reverse of the folk-print spirit—delight in the humiliation of the mighty. Another image for the topsy-turvy world is an inverted terrestrial globe, used both politically and on inn-signs.

It goes without saying that these main streams of influence on pictorial satire were not canalized, that there was much infiltration and cross-fertilization. They were, of course, profoundly affected by the pressure of events and the trend of politics. It is a characteristic of these early English prints that the comic is rare—and that caricature in the strict sense of the word has no place, or almost none. It is important to remember that in the earlier prints it was the idea that was important, not the execution, and that the idea was supplied to the engraver, not by him, though doubtless he often contributed conventional imagery.

Another characteristic of the earlier prints is their association with verse. Elaborate engravings have the form of broadsides with an engraved or printed text. Verses or songs often have headings which range from small woodcuts often from an old block to large engravings. Tradition, and the model of the Emblem Book and the frontispiece, made a verse explanation the natural appendage to a print. What was once general (though not universal) long survived as an occasional practice. Many Napoleon satires are illustrated broadsides, and there are survivals or revivals of the form in the 1820's and 1830's, while for street-papers there was no break in continuity, and woodcuts with a verse commentary only gradually succumbed to a changing world after a long process of degeneration.

Progressively the cartoonists' framework expands as originality gains on convention. Historical parallels and allusions are persistent and revealing.

---

[1] See p. 26.

Literary settings begin with Shakespeare and Milton (in that order) and they keep their supremacy. The next favourites perhaps are *Gulliver* and *Don Quixote*. There are a few popular plays, headed by the *Beggar's Opera*. John Bull joins Britannia, but with a considerable time lag from Arbuthnot's fable of 1712. Repeatedly, the mountain delivers its mouse, the cat pulls chestnuts from the fire. Card-playing, chess, and cock-fighting begin early and are successively followed by ninepins, the race-course, cricket, and pugilism. The Temple of the Constitution is a recurrent symbol, a little outmoded but not displaced by the greater realism of the late eighteenth century.

Not till the fifties of the eighteenth century was the exaggeration of form or feature on which portrait caricature depends used in English political satires. This seems strange, since 'caricatura' or overloading, the French *charge*, began in Italy about 1600 (Leonardo's heads being regarded as grotesques). Annibale Carracci invented both the art and the word and defined the caricaturist's task: 'to grasp the perfect deformity and thus reveal the very essence of a personality. The caricature, like every other work of art, is more true to life than life itself.'[1] From the 1730's, personal caricature, good-humoured and intimate, became fashionable among English dilettanti in Italy and was much influenced by the caricatures of Ghezzi. In the fifties George Townshend began to exercise what Horace Walpole called his 'talent for buffoonery' on political subjects and the word caricatura or caricature established itself as the name for a satirical print. By this time Hogarth had profoundly influenced graphic satire by the scenic story-telling of his print-sequences and had greatly raised the prestige of the engraving. Consequently, the old-fashioned 'hieroglyphical' print, usually dependent on a verbal explanation, with a mass of detail, sometimes intentionally cryptic, gave way gradually to the 'caricature' with an immediate appeal to the eye, sold plain or coloured, but generally coloured. Despite this transformation, much of the old symbolism remained and was adapted to the new look. It is one of Gillray's great merits to combine allegory and fantasy with excellent personal caricature and to subordinate both to his design.

More remains to be said about the transition, which culminated in the classic age of English caricature. In the meantime, how can the long neglect of personal caricature in England be explained? Even Titus Oates, with a chin that would have been a caricaturist's godsend, is favourably, indeed flatteringly, depicted, even when he is 'an incarnate Imp of Hell'. Cartoonists

[1] E. H. Gombrich and F. Kris, *Caricature*, 1940, pp. 10-12.

were as insulting as they knew how to be to a succession of victims from
Sir Giles Mompesson to Sir Robert Walpole, but though these might be
given the attributes of a fiend there was no uglification of feature: their
characteristics are expressed symbolically, or they are put in some discreditable situation—taking a bribe or conferring with the Devil. This was
a convention that long survived. To represent men as animals—a form of
satire common to most ages and countries—is, it may be said, caricature.
'When men's features are drawn with some resemblance to some other
animals the Italians call it to be drawn in caricature', wrote Sir Thomas
Browne in 1690. In Prince Rupert as a wolf [Pl. 11] dressed up as a
cavalier there is something of caricature, but not in the stricter sense—
facial similarity is not attempted. Nor is it when Roger L'Estrange is dog
'Touzer' [Pl. 15], though here there is more of the spirit of mockery.

Was the political climate unfavourable to caricature? Perhaps, and even
after 1660 the prints have more of the spirit of 'the good old cause' of
1641 than of *Hudibras*. Were those who engraved political satire incapable
of (deliberate) personal caricature or were they too deeply wedded to the
emblematical to attempt it? Most of these prints were anonymous and the
work of craftsmen rather than of artists, though a few are by the best
engravers of the day, Hollar, Faithorne, Gaywood, William Marshall.
A gifted amateur, known to history as 'the Protestant Joiner', and ignored
by writers on caricature, has some claim to have made one of the earliest
approaches to the spirit of political caricature in England.[1]

Up to about the middle of the eighteenth century, then, personal caricature remained essentially an Italian art. 'Young man you come from
Italy', the Duchess of Marlborough said to Bubb Dodington in 1710; 'they
tell me of a new invention there called caricatura drawing. Can you find
someone that will make me a caricature of Lady Masham describing her
covered with running sores and ulcers that I may send the Queen to give
her a slight idea of her favourite?'[2] It would seem that the caricature she
envisaged was emblematical in character.[3] In 1742 Gray, writing to Chute
in Florence, remarked on the vogue for graphic satire in England, and
suggested that he should find and dispatch an Italian artist who should

---

[1] See p. 53.

[2] Quoted without reference by Bohun Lynch, *A History of Caricature*, 1926.

[3] By an odd coincidence there is in the British Museum a print (1710) of an ugly old beggar
woman in a London street, sold in 1881 as a caricature of Lady Masham. The print, however,
is one by Laroon the younger of a notorious beggar known as 'Blind Granny' (the caption of
one state of the print). It is just possible that Lady Masham was so travestied, or that the
portrait of a beggar was maliciously handed about as a caricature of the lady. But evidence is
lacking.

visit Holland on the way to learn taste.[1] By the 1780's political caricature was regarded as peculiarly an English art and an English weapon. 'Il faut compter au nombre des privilèges de cette nation', wrote Archenholtz, 'la liberté de faire des gravures satiriques, qui tournent au ridicule les ennemis du jour. Le François les chansonne, le Hollandois plus pesant frappe des medailles; l'Anglois a choisi la gravure, comme le plus propre à donner de la publicité à la satire.'[2]

Though the earliest English prints are scarcely caricatures, seldom intentionally comic, and only by exception works of art, they have a peculiar fascination and they are historic documents. Through their inherited imagery and the pressure of events they treat politics as a struggle between right and wrong, truth and falsehood, and especially between Protestants and Catholics.

[1] *Letters*, ed. D. C. Tovey, 1900, i. 108.
[2] *Tableau de l'Angleterre*, Bruxelles, 1788, i. 149–50. He writes as an eye-witness of events in London between 1771 and 1784.

I

THE GREAT REBELLION: 'THE WORLD IS RULED AND GOVERNED BY OPINION'

THE beginnings of the English polemical print were conditioned by the dissensions between King and Parliament that led to the Great Rebellion, though its ancestral strains were largely continental. There is no special category to be isolated, but a great variety of forms, from the crude woodcut on pamphlet or ballad to the extremely elaborate engraving; 'picture', 'sculpture', 'figure', 'emblem' are the words used. Nor is there any clear distinction between the polemical print and 'straight' illustration. The vogue of Emblem Book and frontispiece established the picture as the natural way to epitomize and stress the content of a book or pamphlet. In the more elaborate prints the aim is to convey symbolically, or in a blend of symbolism and realism, the complexities of a political situation. 'The picture is the Emblem of the Times' is a phrase that recurs. These prints, like the frontispiece and title-page, were usually expounded in verse, sometimes in prose, or a mixture of both. The 'straight' portrait might have an inscription turning it into a satire, and this again was often in verse. All this made the picture a potent form of propaganda, and the output of prints was clearly influenced by the rise and fall of political passions. What light do they throw on the period? They reflect, not of course underlying motives (hidden from contemporaries) but the more emotional and irrational aspects of the conflict. They illuminate its assumptions, prejudices, and illusions—opinions passionately held. When they were deliberate propaganda, they were on occasion directed at the London mob and the apprentices, forces to be reckoned with, and exploited by rumours of plots and Papists.

These civil war satires are interesting also for their imagery. If the symbolism of the Middle Ages and the Reformation was the seed-bed of the English cartoon, its nursery was the graphic satire of the Great Rebellion, when many of the perennial devices of the political caricaturist made a seemingly first appearance.

As a prelude to the English political print we may consider an important

Dutch print by Peter van der Heyden,[1] which belongs to Anglo-Dutch history. It is based on Titian's picture of Diana discovering the unchastity of her nymph Callisto. Queen Elizabeth is Diana (she is also the naked Truth brought to light by Time). Callisto is the Papacy, that is, the lewd nymph who here stands for the Whore of Babylon; she has laid an assortment of baneful eggs; from one crawls a dragon, Gregory XIII; among the other hatchings are a second dragon (the Inquisition), the 'Mort van Paris' (the St. Bartholomew massacre), and Balthasar, the murderer of William the Silent. The date is thus between the murder in July 1584 and (presumably) the death of Gregory XIII in the following April. The four nymphs grouped round Diana in Titian's picture have become the Netherlands provinces in revolt from Spain. Such a tribute to Elizabeth in a Dutch print, at this time, was surely aimed at overcoming her resistance to a Dutch alliance: the pact with the Netherlands followed in August 1585. Was it intended to stress the plea of the Dutch envoys that she should accept the sovereignty of the four provinces? And is it one of those rare prints intended to influence opinion at the highest levels? It is at all events an early print in the long series, Dutch and English, on Anglo-Dutch relations, a recurrent manifestation of a hate-love relationship, as well as a typical contribution to anti-Rome propaganda.

This and other Dutch prints must have circulated in England. When did English graphic satire begin? Coke in his *Reports* (1600–10) mentions the various forms of libel as writings, emblems, and pictures.[2] The year 1621 saw the publication of two outstanding prints, illustrating the two chief grievances of James I's third parliament—Monopolies and the negotiations of the Spanish marriage. Both are English, though one was engraved in Holland; the latter has importance and significance as a classic, repeatedly adapted to meet new alarms of 'Popery' or invasion. This is the *Double Deliveraunce* [Pl. 3] from the two great perils for which Parliament gave thanks in its daily prayers. It is an elaborate engraving 'Invented by Samuell Ward preacher at Ipswich' and 'Imprinted at Amsterdam anno 1621'. Between the dates '1588' and '1605' is an inscription in Latin and English: 'To God. In memorye of the double deliveraunce from yᵉ invincible Navie and yᵉ unmatcheable powder Treason.' On one side of the plate Spanish galleons sail in a horned crescent, assailed by winds and by a single fireship. On the other is the 'Parliament House' towards which 'Faux' advances, dark-lantern in hand.

---

[1] See Frances Yates, 'Queen Elizabeth as Astræa', *Journal of the Warburg Institute*, 1947, x. 76.
[2] Report of the case *de famosis libellis*: Stephen, *History of the Criminal Law*, 1883, ii. 305.

The sun of Jehovah dominates both designs and directs a slanting beam of light upon the lantern. In the centre the Pope, the King of Spain, and others sit in conclave, the Devil presiding: they plot the Powder Treason. Inset is a tiny view of 'Tylburie Camp', where ranks of pikemen are visited by the Queen. Here is a graphic rendering of the Englishman's belief in the intervention of Providence in behalf of his country on the most famous of all occasions. It was also deliberate propaganda against the Spanish marriage, as well as an insult to the King of Spain, and as such it evoked a protest from the Spanish Ambassador which led to Ward's arrest and his examination before the Privy Council. Thomas Scott, a Puritan who, like Ward, could well be termed factious, used the incident in his pamphlet against the proposed marriage of Prince Charles, *Vox Populi, Part II*; this purports to be authentic news from Spain, 'faithfully translated out of the Spanish copy by a well wisher to England and Holland', and the fabrication was widely accepted as fact. Gondomar, 'in the likeness of Matchiavell', reveals to 'the Spanish Parliament . . . His treacherous and subtile Practices to the ruin as well of England as of the Netherlands'. Gondomar remarks, 'and I thinke Ward of Ipswich escaped not safely for his lewd and profane picture of 88 and their Powder Treason . . .'. He advises 'Be sure to have going in the North and West . . . a small rowling Presse for little pictures of Saints. . . . Have a care whensoever any Booke or Picture come out to our prejudice, set some friend to buy them all up, though you burne them forthwith, which fail not to send us of every sort three at the least, for they will be unto us of great use.' This (and other remarks in the long tract) is early testimony to the propaganda value of the picture (already established on the Continent). Scott illustrated his own pamphlet with three plates to authenticate his fabrication and curdle Protestant blood: Gondomar making his report; an 'infernal conclave' in Spain; a conference of English 'Jesuits and Priests' (names in full) plotting to deliver England to Spain. These and other prints reflect both the extent to which England was bedevilled by alarms of Popery and plots (potent from their element of fact) and the propaganda value of such scares. In the public mind recent history was largely a succession of plots. Plots are the subject of an elaborate print, *c.* 1627, *Popish Plots and Treasons, from the Beginning of the Reign of Queen Elizabeth* [13]. There are sixteen little scenes, arranged chronologically, most of them assassination plots. Number 12 is the Armada, number 16 the Powder Plot. In a final scene the Prince of Wales returns after the failure of the marriage overtures, and the whole is summed up in an elaborate tailpiece of the True Church trampling on the malignant

Church of Rome and Spain. Here, with the fires of Smithfield, is the background of Civil War emotions as well as of the achievements of Oates and Bedloe.

Contemporary copies and adaptations of the *Double Deliveraunce* show its immediate impact. The most remarkable is in needlework, a close copy of the original by Dame Dorothy Selby, 'a Dorcas'.[1] On her tomb, carved by Edward Marshall, is an incised slab with the same scene and verses.[2] Surely this must be the only popular print to survive both in silk and in stone. Recurring adaptations, in whole or in part, until the early nineteenth century, symbolizing threats of invasion, 'hellish conclaves' or 'consults' (in Popish Plot language), or encroachments of Popery, are vivid examples of historical memory, as well as illustrations of the extent to which engravers drew upon a repertory of old prints. The Powder Plot detail was revived when fears of Popery became acute; probably every Fifth of November Guy derives remotely from Ward's 'Faux' of 1621.

The other print of that year, *The Description of Giles Mompesson, late Knight* . . . [91], is less spectacular but foreshadows the long series of pictorial attacks on the scapegoat and *bête noire*. It depicts the fate of Sir Giles Mompesson who was probably the original of Sir Giles Overreach in Massinger's play, *A New Way to Pay Old Debts*. He was impeached and sentenced for the most hated of the monopolies, that for the licensing of inns. Monopolies, theoretically suppressed, survived the Act of 1624 by virtue of an enormous loophole to become a source of revenue in the eleven years personal rule. The wrath they engendered is fully documented in prints of 1641. In the interval there are very few; indeed, for the first hundred years of the English polemical print—say from 1620 to 1720—prints were more or less sporadic, chiefly a product of civil strife, war, or near-rebellion.

With the opening of the Long Parliament the polemical print comes into its own, a product of the ferment of ideas. In the pamphlet war that preceded the fighting war prints pick out the highlights as seen by the man in the street, or so it would seem. Speaking very roughly, some 150 extant prints belong to 1641 or the last weeks of 1640, as compared with about 50 for 1642,[3] with fluctuating but smaller totals thereafter, dwindling away

---

[1] Photograph in V. and A., No. 71047. See J. L. Nevinson, 'English Domestic Embroidery Pictures', *Walpole Society*, xxviii. 1 ff.

[2] Sir E. Harrison, *History of Ightham Church*, 1932, p. 16.

[3] This reverses the relative proportion, as between 1641 and 1642, of the tracts collected by Thomason. The outbreak of war seems to have impeded the craft of the engraver, but not of the printer.

after 1653. In the complicated variety of Great Rebellion prints it is dangerous to generalize, but some things stand out. First, and especially at the beginning, Parliament and the Puritans have the best of it; Royalist prints are rare and generally cautious: prints voiced the then dominant opinion in London; they did not lend themselves like ballads (which are predominantly Royalist) to clandestine production and sale. And one must presume the disappearance of many cheap woodcuts on flimsy paper.[1] As the Royalist reaction gained ground, prints became scarcer. Secondly, though anti-Royalist, the prints are not anti-monarchical (with some exceptions to be considered later), and Charles is treated with respect. Thirdly, the prevailing approach is religious, or at least sectarian or ecclesiastical, with fear of Popery as the overriding theme.

In the simplified panorama of the prints the main preoccupations at the opening of the Long Parliament appear as hatred of Prelacy and the Court of High Commission (with the glorification of the Protestant Martyrs, Bastwick, Burton, and Prynne), the grievance of Monopolies, the fate of Strafford. It was Laud's misfortune to be involved in all these things, and he is the chief target of pictorial insult. The mighty explosion of hatred is graphically expressed in prints well designed to fan the flame. The attack is part of the attack on bishops in general, especially after these had made their protest and were imprisoned in the Tower at the end of 1641. The pervading theory is that Prelacy was not merely half-way to Popery, as many believed, but a cloak for Popery in its most dangerous form, a standing conspiracy to deliver England to Rome, with Laud as conspirator in chief. More rationally, Laud is the cruel but defeated enemy of Bastwick and the others; he is responsible for all grievances, the cause of the trouble with the Scots—'the little wheele that turns all' in fact. He is in the long succession of 'evil counsellors' and 'over great subjects' who are resented as upstarts, a line of attack to which all Ministers of the Crown were liable, and which is repeatedly expressed by a comparison of the bugbear of the moment with Wolsey. This was particularly applicable to Laud, reputed to aim at a Cardinal's hat. *Canterburies Dreame* . . . [198] is illustrated by a cut of Wolsey's ghost lamenting the fate of those who, like himself, had tried 'to set the mitre on a level with the Crown'. From the first, Laud is threatened with execution, and at the end of his long imprisonment there is exultation at his death. To study the prints is to see him as a sacrifice to popular resentment and a frenzied fear of Rome, but it must be remem-

---

[1] The woodcuts that survive are on pamphlets or broadsides; cuts bound with copies of *Eikon Basilike* are an exception; see p. 35.

bered that those who were anxious to preserve the hierarchy found it prudent to make a scapegoat of the Archbishop.

Many, if not most, of the forms of pictorial insult used in the seventeenth century were directed against Laud. In 1641 the illustrated squib in the form of a play was new (it was used against George IV in 1820). The topics of *A New Play called Canterburie—his Change of Diot* [174] are Laud's treatment of Burton and the others, his supposed intrigues with Rome, and his punishment by direct action. Each act is headed by a woodcut. In the first he dines off the ears of the three Protestant Martyrs, having himself cut them off. In the second, attempting to sharpen his knife at a carpenter's grindstone, he is seized by its owner, who holds his nose to the stone; 'A Jesuit, a Confessor' (Father Philips) staunches his face with holy water. In the third (repeated on the title) priest and Archbishop have been seized and popped into a cage by the carpenter and his wife, while Archie Armstrong, the King's jester, laughs at them—he had been dismissed from Court for disrespect to Laud. These last two cuts anticipate a number of punitive cages and grindstones. An engraving by Marshall of Laud tied to a post by a rope round his neck was copied several times on inflammatory tracts and broadsides: to quote one [161] where he is threatened with the gallows:

> By wicked counsels faine he would have set
> The Scots and us together by the eares;
> A Patriarks place, the Levite long'd to get
> to sit bith Pope, in one of *Peters* chairse.
>   And haveing dranke so deepe of Babels cup,
>   Was it not time d'ee thinke to chaine him up?

Such things were rabble raising, and Laud complained, not only of libels and ballads 'sung up and down the streets . . . as full of falsehood as of gall', but of 'base pictures . . . putting me in a cage and fastning me to a post by a chaine at my shoulder. And divers of these libels made men sport in taverns and ale-houses, where too many were as drunck with malice as with the liquor they sucked in.'[1]

The adaptation of the Emblem Book to politics is exceptional; a striking example, typical of opinion in 1641, is Thomas Stirry's *A Rot amongst the Bishops, Or, a Terrible Tempest in the Sea of Canterbury, Set forth in lively Emblems to please the judicious Reader* [190]. The four 'Emblems' are expounded in verse. First, the ship 'High Commission' sails towards the

---

[1] H. Trevor Roper, *Archbishop Laud*, 1940, p. 412.

mouth of Hell; on board are Laud, Bishop Wren, and those hated officials Doctors Duck and Lamb (often depicted); Laud's notorious 'etcetera oath' has been thrown into the sea, which is 'The Church and Common-wealth of England'. Next, the ship is blasted by lightning from the hand of Justice. The last two are realistic: Laud going to the Tower; Laud looking from the Tower towards a gallows. It was natural that among the exulta-tions at his death in 1645 there should be, as in 1641, a print [420] in which he enters Hell Mouth in the medieval manner, this time in company with a Pope, a cardinal, a monk, and a bishop (it is interesting to note that this is described as 'Charons ferry-boat').

Laud is explicitly connected with Rome and Antichrist in a venomous pamphlet published to coincide with his attainder and anticipating the verdict, *A Prophecie Of the Life, Reigne and Death of William Laud . . . by an Exposition on part of the 13 and 15 Chapters of the Revelation . . .* [408], one of the many expositions of the 'Number of the Beast' in relation to public enemies—applied, needless to say, with special virtuosity to Napoleon. Laud sits in a chair of state; on his antlered forehead is the number 666; the Devil offers him a cardinal's hat: one servant attends with Popish 'trinkets', another with a roll of tobacco signifying the tobacco patent. In the eighteenth and early nineteenth centuries the disgorging of spoils was often depicted in the most literal manner: examples are Napoleon, Suvórof (in 1799), Lord Melville (in 1805). Laud suffers the indignity in a print of *c.* 1641 [412]; superintended by Henry Burton he is forced to throw up the tobacco patent, his 'canons and constitutions', and is threatened with the hangman. The theme is elaborated in *The Bishops Potion* [177], one of the tracts illustrated by the cut of Laud tied to a post.

Laudian prints (there are many more) have been considered at some length because, to judge from the prints, no other topic or person during the Great Rebellion was such a public obsession for so long. The attitude towards him is something of an opinion-gauge. When, in 1651, his *Sermons* were published, it is clear that there had been a change of mental climate. And when, in 1653, he is actually enshrined in a frontispiece as a pendant to Charles I, one might guess (apart from other evidence) that the change had gathered momentum.

Prints on Strafford can hardly be separated from those on Laud; their association was familiar to all. One of the relatively few without Laud is a woodcut in which he is rowed across the Styx to be welcomed in Hades by Noy, the Attorney-General who had escaped retribution by dying in

1632. This is on a pamphlet, *A Description of the passage of Thomas late Earle of Strafford over the River of Styx . . .* [197]. The small cut anticipates some notable prints in which Charon ferries the defeated or the departed —a convenient device for depicting *bêtes noires* in Hell: Gillray used it for a ribald satire on the defeat of the Whigs in 1807; Napoleon and many Bonapartists are received by Robespierre and others in an elaborate French travesty (in 1815) of part of Michelangelo's *Last Judgment*.

The prints suggest that in 1640-1 resentment at monopolies was a mass-emotion second only to fear of Rome and hatred of Laud. And Laud was traduced as a monopolist. He was accused in Parliament by Harbottle Grimston of 'sharking and taking in the tobacco shops' (through a licensing system). 'The Projector and the Patentee' were partners in infamy: they stood for shady devices secured by intrigue and Court favour to exploit the public under various pretexts of regulating trade and securing quality. For the Crown there was unparliamentary revenue (not very much), with a huge rake-off for the lucky few. The citizen suffered in his purse and his liberties by high prices, shortages, inferior quality, and vexatious regulations. Such was the case against patents of monopoly, experienced in countless individual grievances. (A case has been made for them and some were not without a quota of good intentions.) An engraving by Hollar [Pl. 4], copied and adapted in other prints, symbolizes the Patentee (the description was applied also to the Projector—'Mr. Tenterhooke'). It is a striking example of the application to politics of the folk-print in which persons are constructed of objects connected with their calling. A man with a wolf's head has fish-hook fingers which pull strings attached to money bags; his legs are screws. The rest of the body is made up of things that had been the subjects of monopoly: wine, playing-cards, coals, soap, pins, &c. He is a 'Wolfe like devourer of the Common wealth / That robs by Patent, worse than any stealth / . . . Strong scrues support him that hath scru'd us all / And now we live, to see this strong man fall.'

Though this and some other prints are comprehensive indictments, the most hated of the Monopolies was that of wine, and the public rage was directed against the cousins Kilvert and Abel, Projector and Patentee of the grant. More particularly at Abel: 'every man limnes his picture, and scarce any stationer in Towne, but has some Pamphlet, Sonnet or Ballet in his praise'. Thus a broadside of 1641 associating the 'downfall of wines' with the death of Strafford and the imprisonment of Laud. Abel and Kilvert were imprisoned by order of Parliament in 1640. A portrait of

Alderman Abel with a wine-barrel under his arm (copied from a plate by Hollar) is one of three which decorate a well-known verse pamphlet by Thomas Heywood: '*Reader, Here you'le plainly see Judgment perverted by these three: A Priest, A Judge, A Patentee.*' The priest of course is Laud, the judge is Sir Robert Berkley who justified ship money and was impeached in February 1641.

All the prints on Monopolies record the downfall of the Patentee: in 1641 Monopolies officially ceased, to be replaced (from 1643) by the parliamentary levy of excise duties—which were to acquire a deep and lasting hatred. Portraits by Hollar of Abel, and of Prynne, Bastwick, and Burton, have inscriptions recording the crimes of the first, the virtues and sufferings of the others; these and many other prints illustrate the extent to which the first actions of the Long Parliament appeared as punishment of evil-doers and succour of the righteous—a turning of tables which in the case of bishops was also a rescue from Popery. An interesting representation of the deliverance from Rome is Hollar's print of Time carrying the Pope 'backe to *Rome*' [Pl. 5]: 'This trunke of trash & Romish Trumperies.' These include a bishop's mitre and cap.

For 1641 then the prints reflect the news of the day to a greater extent than after the outbreak of war. Besides the main preoccupations with Laud, Strafford, and Monopolies, there was the flight abroad, first of Windebank to France and then of Lord Finch to The Hague, and both men were often associated with Laud. A portrait of Finch with wings did duty several times. Another favourite subject, in its own right as well as in relation to Laud, was the end of the Court of High Commission and the disappearance of the Ecclesiastical Courts; prints and pamphlets exult at the cessation of interference with religious exercises and with matters of every-day life. In a tract of 1641 there is an illuminating summary of the chief news: *Old Newes newly revived: or, The Discovery of all occurrences Happened since the beginning of the Parliament: As the confusion of Patents, the Deputies death, Canterburies imprisonment, Secretary Windebank, L. Finch, Doctor Roane, Sir John Sucklin and his associates flight, the fall of Wines, the desolation of Doctors Commons, the misery of the Papists, Judge Barckleyes imprisonment, and the ruine of Alderman Abels Monopoly. Most exactly compiled in a short discourse between Mr. Inquisitive a Countrey Gentleman, and Master Intelligencer, a Newesmonger.* The woodcut on the title attempts to summarize this summary. The tenor of the tract is exultation at the unmixed blessings bestowed by Parliament, notably immediate relief from the vexations suffered in the Ecclesiastical Courts. The speakers adjourn to a tavern to drink the health of Parliament in wine at a reduced price.

This was a spirit that could not survive the impact of war and heavy taxes. The near-unanimity of the prints of 1641 was broken, not by open defence of what in the prevailing mood was scarcely defensible, but in attacks on the sudden 'Swarme of Sectaries', and the preaching of illiterate tradesmen and mechanics. The proliferation of sects and congregations, suddenly freed from restrictions, and preaching that was eccentric and fanatical, lent themselves to ridicule; most of the early pamphlets are anonymous, but John Taylor the Water Poet signed several and wrote others, and engaged in violent controversy with Henry Walker, the leather-seller (or ironmonger) with a London congregation who was to become a chaplain to Cromwell, and a leading London journalist, but who has no place in the *D.N.B.*[1] Most of the tracts are unillustrated, but some cuts stand out, because each did duty several times and they convey the spirit of this pamphlet campaign. There is the tub-preacher holding forth to a congregation originally at the Nag's Head in Coleman street, but adapted also to other localities. This illustrates Taylor's doggerel tract: *A Swarm of Sectaries |and Schismatiques: Wherein is discovered their strange preach- (or prating) of such as are by their trades Coblers, Tinkers, Pedlars, Weavers, Sowgelders and Chymney-Sweepers* (an interesting list of the callings at the bottom of the social ladder). It served also for *Lucifers Lacky . . .* [210] on the 'dissembling Brownist'[2] with the added motto, 'When Women Preach and Coblers Pray, / The Fiends in Hell make holiday.' The tub-preacher was to become (in word and picture) a symbol of the ranting nonconformist. *Religions Enemies, with a Brief and Ingenious Relation, as by Anabaptists, Brownists, Papists, Familists, Atheists, and Foolists, sawcily presuming to tosse Religion in a Blanquet* [245] is another of Taylor's tracts. The tossers, who toss the Bible, are the first four of the title. This is interesting as an early attempt to associate Popery, not with Anglicanism but with the sects, and also for the appropriation of the Bible as an Anglican emblem. The Puritans had made their own this embodiment of Truth versus Error—often symbolized by Prayer Book or Mass Book. Parliamentary troops sometimes went into action with banners on which a Bible was depicted. On a broadside of 1641, *Good Newes for all*

[1] See J. B. Williams, 'Henry Walker, Journalist of the Commonwealth', *Nineteenth Century*, Mar. 1908.

[2] The name Independent had not yet established itself, and the usual term was Brownist from Robert Browne, died *c.* 1633, the separatist regarded as the founder of Independency (or Congregationalism).

True-Hearted Subjects [226], is the device of the Arms of the City combined with an open Bible. When the Bible became an attribute of the dead King it was one of the indications of the massive shift of opinion in 1649. At first, the attack on the sectaries was Anglican-Royalist and chiefly voiced by such a light-weight as John Taylor. But from 1644, when toleration became a great national issue as between Presbyterians and Independents, pamphleteering against the sects was taken up by Presbyterians and became altogether more important.

As against the preaching cobblers the retort was denunciation of the fat idle priest, pluralist, and non-resident. This traditional theme (never less appropriate) was expressed in a simple symbolism [Pl. 6], used and elaborated by the political anti-clericals of the eighteenth and nineteenth centuries [Pl. 23].

If the Royalist stereotype of a Puritan was a ranting preacher, that of the Puritan for his adversaries was a 'Popish Cavalier', raffish and dissipated. The debauched and roistering Cavalier is admirably portrayed in a broadside dated 1641, *The Sucklington Faction: or (Sucklings) Roaring Boyes* [Pl. 7]: 'Here sits the prodigall Children; the younger brethren (Luk. 15. 2) acting yᵉ parts of hotspur Cavaliers and disguised dingthriftes, habiting themselves after the fashions of the world, as one that is to travaile into a farre Countrey.' They are prodigal sons, proud, profligate, indolent, and drunken. The engraving (with a satirical verse on tobacco) has an expressive realism, Hogarthian in spirit and competence, unlike the allegorical designs of the period. Here are the younger sons who haunted the Court, flouted their elders, and formed Sir John Suckling's much derided troop of gorgeously dressed and ineffective soldiers who accompanied Charles to Scotland in 1639. The use of the word Cavalier is noteworthy. With 'Round-Head' it was a new term in the winter of 1641–2. Lilly the astrologer, speaking of what he saw that Christmas, writes: 'The Courtiers againe, wearing long Haire and lockes, and always sworded, at last were called by these men [Puritans] Cavaliers, and so after this broken language all that adhered unto the Parliament were termed Round-heads; all that took part . . . for his Majestie, cavaliers, few of the vulgar knowing the sense of the word Cavalier.'[1] 'Round-Head' (as it was first written) was much resented, and a counter-term 'Rattle-Head' was produced but failed to establish itself. A little pamphlet war developed in 1642, well illustrated in a broadside [Pl. 8] in which the Roundhead (a Puritan minister) is 'Sound-Head', the 'Priestly-Prelate' is 'Rattle-Head', and the true

[1] *Monarchy and No Monarchy*, 1652, p. 107.

Roundhead is a 'Balld-pate Fryar'. The Rattle-Head, half-Bishop, half-Jesuit, rejects Truth (the Bible) and accepts a crucifix from the friar:

> See heer, Malignants Foolerie
> Retorted on them properly,
> The Sound-Head, Round-Head, Rattle-Head
> Well plac'd, where best is merited.

The bisected body, sometimes Janus-headed, was then and long remained a favourite device to indicate a double personality, a secret enemy, a hypocrite, a Mr. Facing-both-ways. In Great Rebellion prints it is chiefly used, as here, and as in *The Kingdomes Monster* [Pl. 9] for the crypto-Papist. Archbishop Williams (in 1642)[1] dressed as soldier *cum* bishop-Jesuit is one of a succession of bisected soldier-clerics.

At the end of 1642 'The unheard of invention of the Round-heads' was attributed in *Magna Britannia Divisa* [143] to 'the dissolute Scollers of Oxford and Cambridge' who were 'Authors of the Round-Heads and of 27 other Masques and Disguisements, heads, cheefs, extravagant opinions or Religions in England . . .'. John Taylor (no scholar) describes the round-head in *Heads of all Fashions . . . allegorically showing the diversities of Religion in these distempered times*:

> But as this head is understood of late
> Some hold it acarce a friend to th'King and State,
> And some suppose it whereso'er it lurch
> To be a great disturber of the Church.

The Rattle-Heads do not seem to have made a corresponding protest against the term Malignant. Whatever may have been the material and moral strength of the two sides on the outbreak of war, Henry Peacham, a Royalist, admitted that opinion, as voiced in pamphlet and broadside, was hostile: the retort was to represent it as fickle and confused. This is the tenor of a very interesting plate by Hollar on the pamphlet war, *The World is Ruled & Governed by Opinion* [Frontispiece], which illustrates lines by Peacham. Opinion, with the world on her lap, sits in her tree, which is watered by Folly; its fruits, 'shaken off with everie little wind', are 'idle books and libells' (pamphlets and broadsides with titles belonging to 1641) which 'in everie street in everie stall you find'. On her arm is a chameleon, her emblem because it 'can assume all Cullors saving white' —that is, except truth. She is blinded by her hat in which is a turret

---

[1] In Hollar's portrait [340 and 341].

representing the Tower of Babel. Below the design is a dialogue: Opinion answers Viator's questions. Asked if she cannot remedy the confusion, she answers,

> Ah no then should I perish in the throng
> O' th giddie Vulgar, without feare or shame
> Who censure all thinges bee they right or wrong. . . .
> Because that Follie giveth life to these
> I but retaile the fruites of idle Aire
> Sith now all Humors utter what they please
> To th' loathing loading of each Mart and Faire:

Some of John Taylor's tracts are among the papers in the tree, as well as counter-tracts by Henry Walker. Peacham carried the argument farther in *Square-Caps turned into Round-Heads: or, the Bishops Vindication and the Brownists Conviction. Being a Dialogue between Time, and Opinion, shewing the folly of the one and the worthiness of the other* [338]. This, Peacham's last work, is remarkable (in 1642) for its open defence of bishops, especially the Archbishop. Opinion, with her chameleon, turns a wheel so that five heads of Roundheads are uppermost, and five bishop's caps below:

> Time doth Opinion call into accompt,
> Who turnes the Bishops downe and Round-Heads mount:
> Upon Her lofty Wheele their Noddels are;
> But her Camelian feedeth upon aire.

The chameleon was an emblem of duplicity and inconstancy from its changing colour, nimble tongue, and supposed capacity to live on air.[1] Here Opinion replaces the traditional Fortune or Time. John Taylor, in the same year, expresses a similar notion—an inverted world—in the ancient imagery that illustrates *Mad Fashions, Od Fashions, All out of Fashions, or the Emblems of these Distracted times* [Pl. 6].

In 1642 the pamphlet war was slipping into the fighting war and in August the King set up his standard at Nottingham. By the end of the year it was apparent that neither side would get an easy victory. This is the background for a Civil War print of a type much rarer than the broadside and pamphlet illustrations that multiplied after 1640—the large, elaborate engraving intended to depict the complexities of a political situation. Among the relatively few extant the most ambitious is *Magna*

---

[1] In *Magna Britannia Divisa* (see below) Archbishop Williams and Bishops Duppa and Towers are 'the Prelatical Camelions'.

[2] Taylor uses the same cut for a tract of 1647 *A Plea for Prerogative: or, Give Caesar his Due* . . . [E. 154/24].

Britannia Divisa [143], dated 31 December 1642, with an Amsterdam imprint. To discuss it at length would be to plunge into the intricacies of home and foreign affairs, but the general purport is clear. It is an attempt —violently partisan—to depict the causes, events, and personalities of the war—'this Popish War'. The design is on two large sheets (probably intended to be pasted side by side on a wall) with lengthy marginal explanations printed in French and English. The genre is continental and there are analogies with that remarkable production the *Mappemonde Nouvelle Papistique* of 1566 (printed at Geneva and dedicated to Queen Elizabeth).[1] This is on sixteen sheets intended to form a large wall-map. Figures and buildings seen from above are grouped in a symbolical map which is framed in the gaping jaws of Hell—an interesting application of the ancient device. So too the Civil War print, also *contre-Rome*, is an extremely complicated view of places and people in a vaguely geographical setting. But this print, though linked with the past, foreshadows the future; in its mass of political allusions it outdoes the intricacies of English eighteenth-century cartoons. The viewpoint is ultra-Presbyterian: a die-hard aversion to the peace-talks of 1642–3, combined with seeming respect for the King who is the victim of evil counsellors and foreign intrigue. There are many allusions to foreign affairs, notably Richelieu's attitude to Spain, his death, and even the conspiracy of Cinq-mars. On one sheet is the *Professio Christiana, or the King and the Parliament;* on the other the *Processio Romana, or King without his Parliament*. On the first are the achievements of the parliamentary side from events in Scotland in 1637–9, beginning with a view of Edinburgh Castle. The King's unsuccessful attack on Hull in April 1642 is depicted: on the banner of the town is an angel with an open book, *Biblia Sacra*. In another group Charles receives gifts of money and plate for the war (against himself), and an army, 'raised by the King and Parliament',[2] is put under the Earl of Essex 'for the defence of the Protestant Religion, the securitie of his Majesties person and Parlement, the preservation of the laws, liberties and peace of the Kingdom . . . against the aggression violence and oppression of this Procession'. The war is thus between Christianity and Rome. The details are explained in notes numbered from A to V.

On the other sheet, and in even greater profusion of detail, is a long pro-

[1] Reproduced in part, Grand-Carteret, *L'Histoire, la Vie . . .*, Paris, 1927, ii. 122, and attributed to Pierre Eskrich. There is said to be an impression in the British Museum, but I have traced only the explanatory text (190 pp.).

[2] Cf. *The Whigs Idol . . .*, a Tory ballad on Presbyterians, *c.* 1709, who (in 1642) 'Yet drew for *King* and Parliament!! / As if the Wind could stand *North South*'; see p. 72.

cession or masque containing groups and single figures numbered from 1
to 90. Since this is a 'Popish War' and the Procession 'a Bloudy Plot', it is
headed by monks with a processional cross: 'The Episcopal War' (in Scotland) is identified with 'the Roman religion': the Irish rebellion is prominent. Friars, Jesuits, Father Philips (the Queen's confessor), Papal
emissaries, the Pope, and cardinals are depicted. The Pope is treated with
crudity: he is laden with the 'Masse-God'; the usual 'trinkets' or 'trumpery' are excreted by his mule, with the unusual addition of 'Gregorian
Almanacks', that is, the reformed calendar accepted only in Catholic
countries. The mule excretes also dispensations directing princes 'to keep
no faith with heretiques'—a phrase that echoes through No-Popery propaganda for another two centuries. His conclave is voiced by cardinals, who
blow through trumpets 'To Kings and Princes Let your Government be
arbitrary, abuse the goodnesse of your People, hold them in ignorance, use
them like Beasts, and (this Procession finisht) we shall make you carry the
sadle and they the Pack-sadle.' With these 'Perfidious Counsels and tyrannical advices' is associated the invention and use of the term Round-Head
already noted. The procession ends at the Tower, where Laud and Bishop
Wren and other Malignant prisoners are 'the timpanists of this confusion':
unable to take part they ring the bells. The climax is a view of the Church
on a pinnacle, reformed by 'a good Synod' (then sitting at Westminster):
bishops who 'daunce on the Sabath day' are falling 'to their Episcopall
down-fall within the abisses', while two (Presbyterian) ministers climb the
hill to replace them. Here is Milton's 'New Presbyter' displacing the 'Old
Priest'. This ecclesiastical extremism is combined with a quasi-loyalist
attitude consistent with the conventions of the Parliamentarians, and prophetic of the combination of Presbyterians and Royalists that led to the
Restoration. It may be significant that the King's attempted arrest of the
five members is absent. Hollar's pictorial map of the three kingdoms [144]
is another political survey, less complicated, and devoted half to British,
half to Imperial and Bohemian history—one of the English episodes is the
attempt to arrest Pym and the others, as a pendant to the defenestration
of Prague.

Prints illustrating incidents of the war are few, the concern is with persons, with plots (there is a very elaborate one on Waller's Plot), and with
the dangers of Popery which meant especially soldiers from Ireland. A
notable example is *The Kingdomes Monster uncloaked from Heaven: The
Popish Conspirators, Malignant Plotters, and cruell Irish* . . . [Pl. 9],
a nightmare vision of fear and hate. Two hands reach down to draw aside

a cloak and reveal the Monster: on three stalk-like necks are three clusters of heads representing 'Papist Conspiritors', 'Bloudy Irish', and 'Mallignant-Plotters'; the body is half-Papist, half-Cavalier, and the Monster is about to destroy—with fire and sword—the Church, the Parliament, the Kingdom, and the City.

At this time (September 1643) Newcastle's 'Papist Army' had defeated the Fairfaxes in Yorkshire and negotiations were afoot for Irish troops (they were sent to Cheshire in November). Reinforcements from Ireland were a continual source of hope for one side and dread for the other. As the Irish scene shifted, these might be either from the King's troops in Ireland or be recruited from Irish rebels—'the bloudy Irish'. A broadside of 1642 ridicules the first: *The English-Irish Souldier With his new Discipline* . . . [Pl. 10]. There is an interesting analogy with a print of a Hessian in America laden with food in 1778, *A Hessian Grenadeir* [5483]; both express contemptuous dislike of the forces of the Crown, and it is noteworthy that on both occasions the thieving soldier was an enormity. With the formation of the New Model Army (April 1645) the contrast between the forces of King and Parliament became more glaring; as the Royalists admitted, 'In our Army we have the sins of men (drinking and wenching) but in yours you have those of devils, spiritual pride and rebellion.' Two broadsides illustrate the contrast: *The Mercenary Souldier* and *The Zealous Souldier*.[1] One is a Cavalier, cloaked and sworded, the other a man in improbable armour, brandishing a huge sword. One says, 'I came not forth to do my countrey good / I came to rob and take my fill of pleasure. . . .' The other asks, 'can one happier Die / Then for to fall in Battaile, to maintaine / Gods worship, Truth, extirpate Popery. . . .'

Prince Rupert was the Cavalier's hero, the Roundhead's bugbear, and, despite his Protestant antecedents and former popularity, it is only the bugbear that figures here, usually with his famous white poodle, Boy, who was credited with supercanine powers. A minor bugbear was Colonel Lunsford, and legendary atrocities were attributed to both. To quote Cleveland's *Rupertismus* on these pamphlet tales of horror:

> They fear the giblets of his train, they fear
> Even his dog, that four-legged Cavalier
> He that devours the scraps that Lunsford makes
> Whose picture feeds upon the child in steaks, ...

The shooting of Boy at Marston Moor by a soldier 'who had skill in

[1] B.M., 669, f. 10/49, 50.

Necromancy' is the subject of *A Dogs Elegy, Or Ruperts Tears . . .*, [395], with 'Witch, Pope and Devill' as chief mourners. The most virulent attack on Rupert is *Englands Wolfe with Eagles Claws* [Pl. 11], illustrating a broadside published after his departure from England, and interesting as an approach to caricature.

With the end of the first Civil War in 1646 the prints reflect growing disillusionment, a sharpening of the issues as between the two parties, and new and growing animosities between Parliament and Army, Presbyterian and Independent. In the prints this last is the dominant subject of 1646–7. The Army was mainly Independent, though with many other sects, and the Independents stood for freedom of conscience and complete toleration for the sects (Popery and Prelacy always excepted); the Presbyterians, with their majority in Parliament, were for a State Church, rigidly organized and utterly intolerant, and were anxious to disband the Army and so leave themselves supreme. The split, or rather chasm, was manifest with Parliament's rejection of the Army's plea for 'tender consciences', and the Army was further embittered by the Parliament's attitude towards their arrears of pay. Despite the constitutional issues involved, the religious and sectarian aspects of the controversy dominate the prints, and, as always, each side associates the other with Popery, and assumes for itself the part of champion against Rome. The situation is strikingly displayed in a pictorial broadside of September 1646, *The Watchmans Warning-Peece, or Parliament Souldiers Predilection, shewing*[1]

> That if our Armies lay down Arms
> Before the Work is at an End
> We may expect
> Yet worser Harms
> More pretious Lives and States to spend.

Reason walks in a rocky landscape menaced by enemies—Papists, a dragon (the Pope), a spotted leopard (Prelacy), and by a still more crafty adversary explained in the last verse:

> The crooked serpent creeps upon the Earth,
> An Antichristian Presbyter by birth
> His head from Rome, his taile and body so
> With them to Aye-Perdition he shall go.

Watchman's plea is for London to be guarded by an army. The 'Antichristian Presbyter' had already been attacked in April in a pictorial broad-

[1] B.M., E. 354/10.

side, *Dictated Thoughts* [647], a protest against intolerance and an emblematical plea for 'tender consciences'. Pope, Priest, and Presbyter, linked by a chain, stab 'Tender Conscience' to the heart. A Presbyterian retort followed, but not till November: *A Reply to Dictated Thoughtes by a More Proper Emblem* [653]; an Independent takes the place of Presbyter, and is styled 'Profane Libertin or advocate for a general Toleration', he has a double face and tramples on the Bible. He and two others, the Pope and a bishop with the 'Liturgie', stab a burning heart representing the 'honest hearts' which they unite to wound.

The same engraving was used for another Presbyterian thrust, *Proper Persecution* . . . [657] directed especially against Richard Overton, a Leveller who had attacked the Westminster Assembly of Presbyterian divines (the Synod) in pamphlets signed Martin Marpriest (professing to be the son of Martin Marprelate (John Penry), enemy of the Elizabethan bishops). Overton was attacked in yet another anti-toleration print, *The Picture of an English Persecutor, or A foole ridden Ante Presbeterian Sectary* [670]; he crawls on hands and knees with a fool riding on his back. It must be remembered that Presbyterian intolerance was extreme indeed. To quote one of their divines, 'To let men serve God according to their own persuasion is to cast out one devil that seven more might enter.'[1] The Presbyterians had taken up the Anglican theme of 1641–2 against sectaries and schismatics; the most comprehensive attack was in Thomas Edwards's *Gangræna*. The conflict evoked Milton's sonnet 'On the new forcers of conscience under the Long PARLIAMENT', with the famous last line, '*New Presbyter* is but *Old Priest* writ large'. Presbyterian attacks include a broadside (January 1647), *A Catalogue of the severall Sects and Opinions in England and other Nations* [666] with portraits of twelve sectaries; the first is a Jesuit (with Guy Faux's lantern); six, the Independent, is 'Libertin' wearing a sword and breaking the Tables of the Law; the last is 'Divorcer' (surely intended for Milton), who is thrashing his wife.

Royalists naturally cashed in on the dissensions of their enemies. In December 1646 Samuel Sheppard produced a verse tract, *The Times displayed in Six Sestyads* [656] with a print of 'Three Grand Enimies of Church and State'. These are 'Profane Liberty' (an Independent), 'Envious Hypocresie' (a Presbyterian with six masks) and 'Jesuiticall Pollicie'. Daniel Featley's Anglican contribution (in 1645) had been *Dippers Dipt* with a striking title-page.

A pictorial plea for unity followed in March, *A Pious And Seasonable*

---

[1] Quoted, C. H. Firth, *Cromwell*, 1934, p. 152.

Perswasive to the Sonnes of Zion Soveraignely useful for Composing their Unbrotherly Devisions [675]. An Independent, 'a Godly dissenting Brother', takes the hand of 'a Godly Brother of the Presbyterian way', to the dismay of a 'Romish Prelate' (Anglican) and an 'English Jesuite', who watch together, saying, 'Ah lass wee are utterly undone, our designe is spoyled, they are agreed.'

However, the rift between the Godly Brothers and between Parliament and Army deepened, while both sides manœuvred for possession of the King, who was trying to play off one against the other. Charles, who was handed over by the Scottish army to a Parliamentary Commissioner at the end of January, was brought to Holmby House. There, forestalling the secret intentions of the Presbyterians, he was seized by Cornet Joyce (2 June) and taken to Newmarket. The Army marched towards London, and Parliament was forced to temporize and then to yield. But this was deeply resented by the citizens, apprentices, and mob. The Presbyterians prepared to fight, putting their weak forces under Major-General Massey. The futile attempt to resist Fairfax's veterans is the subject of a cocksure pamphlet [686] decorated by a cut of two fighting cocks (one of many political cockfights): 'Presbyterian John revived' against 'Independent Craven a dying.' In the language of pamphlets and squibs the Presbyterian was now 'Sir John Presbyter', or 'Presbyterian Jack', or 'Mr Persecutor' and was a target for both Independents and Royalists. An early example of burlesque heraldry (1647 or later) is *Atchievement of Sir John Presbyter* [702], a Royalist satire, bitterly hostile to sectaries and Presbyterians, and using, as became customary, the jargon of heraldry for the elaboration of insults.

Besides these envenomed exchanges between the Godly Brothers, there is a more subtle exposition of the Independent *versus* Presbyterian theme in an emblematical design of October 1647, *Truth flatters not: Plaine dealing the best* [697]. Four figures are dominated by the eye and sword of Jehovah: they are 'Heresie' (the Pope on his seven-headed Beast), 'Prelate', 'Priste' holding a crown upon a sword, who is clearly though not quite explicitly a Presbyterian minister, in fact, 'Old Priest writ large'; a weathercock in his hat indicates his recent veering towards royalism. Last is 'Veritie', a woman holding a Bible and saying, 'Learne of mee to be meeke and lowlie.' It is made plain that she is an Independent or a sectarian preacher by the fact that 'Scorner', a Cavalier, points at her saying, 'A silly tubb preacher.' Each speaks, under compulsion to speak truth. The 'Priste'-Presbyterian:

I hate the Pope, his poysoned cup,
      and trinkets all.
The Bishops deeds, and Romish weeds
      to me are gall.
Yet well I know, what Layicks owe
      unto our Coat,
Reverence all way, good livings pay,
      is our just lot.
Sects and unlearned, up-start Jackes
      doth us defraud,
Who to our shame, our power and name,
      have over-aw'd.

This line of attack is exceptional among the imputations of Popery and Prelacy.

There is a note of triumph in John Spittlehouse's *Rome Ruin'd by Whitehall . . . a Confutation of the three Degrees of Popery, viz. Papacy, Prelacy, and Presbitery . . .* In a plate headed 'An Emblem of Antichrist in his threefould Hierarchies . . .' a triple-headed Pope—Cerberus—stands between 'Presbiter' and 'Prellat'. All three deplore their ruin. This is an Army viewpoint, with a dedication to Fairfax. Published at the end of 1650, it represents the achievements of Independents over Presbyterians by the King's death and Cromwell's victories.

To return to 1647. Alongside the bitter controversies between the Godly Brothers, we can trace in the prints the growth of Royalism and, perhaps, the counter-trend towards republicanism. In January the common interest of Parliament, Synod, and Army is expressed (optimistically) in what may have been a plea for unity. In *Englands Miraculous Preservation Emblematically Described, Erected for a perpetual Monument to Posterity* [660], Royalists, dying and dead, submerge in the water surrounding an ark which contains the Houses of Parliament and the Westminster Assembly; the Queen floats siren-like next Charles. There are six medallion portraits of generals, including Fairfax and Cromwell. A very different view is that of a print dedicated to the Earl of Northumberland, undated, but probably belonging to 1646: *Syons Calamitye or Englands Miserye Hieroglyphically delineated* [373]. Disillusionment, war-weariness, Anglicanism, and moderate Royalism are expressed in a complicated symbolism expounded in verse beginning 'Alas Poore England!'. Two buckets in a well indicate the alternations of opinion.

Similar disillusionment is the note of a broadside (February 1647) by a Somerset country gentleman with a grievance—Humphrey Willis. His

Royalism is sharpened by resentment at the jack-in-office and the new rich, and he uses imagery for a topsy-turvy world to illustrate verses: *Times Whirligig, or, The Blew-new-made-Gentleman mounted* [668]. A Committee-man tramples on an inverted globe saying, 'Take him Marshal'; at the North–South Pole is an orb without the crown. The verses are a plea for peace: 'arbitrary power' was the only thing to fight against and that fight has succeeded 'Beyond what we could hope or wish . . . / If we sometimes had from our Prince / A lash or two, what have we since? . . . O what an ague hath this land / Look how it shakes, how tottering stands; / How pants for some Physitian . . .'. *The Committee Man* [228] is a spectacled owl in a frankly Royalist print of about the same date which deplores revolutionary change: 'O Tempora, O Mores . . .'.

On the King's imprisonment little more remains than a crude cut that served for several loyal pamphlets; Charles looks from a barred window in Carisbrooke Castle, saying, 'Behold your King'. The execution evoked a flood of loyal papers, not only in English, but in Dutch, German, French, and Latin, some with conventional illustrations. Here, it is the plate to *Eikon Basilike* [Pl. 12] that demands attention as supreme among political-allegorical frontispieces—not aesthetically, but as an historical document, and as probably the most effective piece of pictorial propaganda of the Great Rebellion. First, for its association with the famous book and as part of its message. Then, for its multiplied variants and adaptations, and finally as a design with a life of its own. In a minor degree it shares the prolonged controversy that has raged round the authorship of 'The King's Book';[1] was Marshall's plate designed by Charles or by Dr. Gauden? By the Doctor, if we are to believe his own letter to Clarendon: 'this book and figure were wholly and only of my invention making and designe . . .'. But Royston, who printed the earliest editions, said that the design was sent him by the King: 'his Majestie sent another figure to bee engraven on copper and annexed to the Booke . . .'. And according to Dr. Edward Hooker[2] the King 'drew' the frontispiece and 'pencilled' the mottoes on the right side, he and Marshall supplying those for the rock and the palm-tree. Drawing was one of the King's accomplishments, and there is the

---

[1] This account is based on Dr. F. F. Madan's *New Bibliography of the Eikon Basilike . . .*, Oxford, 1950. His conclusion is that loose papers written by the King reached Gauden, who on his own initiative used them as the basis for a book, and sent the completed manuscript to Charles at Newport. After some hesitation the King accepted this as what he intended to write, and 'corrected and heightened' it for the Press. This has not been univerally accepted so that the controversy is even yet not ended.

[2] Corrector of the Press to William Dugard and author of the *Apothegmata Carolina* 1649, extracts from the *Eikon*.

perhaps suggestive fact that the text chosen for his coronation service had been 'Be thou faithful unto death and I will give thee a crown of Life'. It seems possible that the design, or part of it, was his.[1] It replaced an earlier one sent to Royston: three crowns indented on a crown of thorns. Three crowns remained the core of the symbolism of the famous plate, which from the first was an essential part of the book. Kneeling before an open Bible,[2] Charles spurns the world, rejects a crown of gold, accepts a crown of martyrdom, awaits a crown of glory. The other half of the design is a characteristic example of the emblem. The palm, weighted but erect, and the storm-beaten rock symbolize the King's faith and steadfastness. The palm was believed to have the power of straightening itself against a weight, and Dryden, alluding to Marshall's plate, transferred the imagery to Cromwell:

> His palms, though under weights they did not stand,
> Still thrived; no winter could his laurels fade.[3]

The rapid printing of edition after edition by different printers involved repeated re-engravings and copies of the plate: thirty-five pre-Restoration variants have been traced. Seven were engraved by Marshall; the boldness of his signature is an early indication of the immunity of the artist as compared with author and printer. Three of the others, one a crude woodcut, cannot be connected with any edition and were probably made for the printsellers; each has survived only from having been inserted in a single copy of the *Eikon*, and more variants of these perishable separate prints may have existed. Adaptations of the design were made for editions printed outside England—some of great interest. There were post-Restoration adaptations and in 1703 the original version illustrated a broadside of the King's sayings. An enlarged copy was made for a mid-eighteenth-century printseller, a cartoon, cheaply produced as if for a wide circulation; two versions exist, with different inscriptions. The one in the British Museum Print Room is *The Emblem of the Royal Martyr King*

---

[1] The profile of the first version has a more amateurish look than the three-quarter face which Marshall introduced when he re-engraved the plate.

[2] To stress that he was a good Protestant. The point is made in two of the verse 'Explanations' of the frontispiece:

> That hee's no Papist neither, look before him,
> Gods word, no Missal there, doth so declare him.

And:

> [Charles speaks] . . . my book upon my bord,
> Explains my heart, my hope is in thy Word.

[3] *Heroick Stanzas upon Oliver Cromwell*, 1659.

Charles y^e *first in his sufferings*; there is no reference to the *Eikon*. The famous design survived also in more remarkable forms. With the Restoration it apparently blossomed into stained-glass windows and paintings in churches. Two embroidery pictures still survive; one is in the V. & A. In this the design is enriched by the standing figure of a youthful Charles II, armed and erect, hand on his sword, as a pendant to the kneeling King; two angels hold a crown above his head. This oriflamme must have been kept carefully hidden before the Restoration.

The *Eikon* frontispiece figures in its own right in a pamphlet published early in 1649: *Frontispiece of the Kings Book opened. With a Poem annexed: the In-Security of Princes*. This contains also two of the sets of explanatory verses that were an important adjunct of the plate, as of most 'emblems'. For the *Eikon* no less than six were printed or engraved, five being connected with specific editions, one known only from the pamphlet. A seventh exists in manuscript in Thomason's hand.[1] Such verses were a perfect medium for loyal sentiments, and surely there must be others in the commonplace books so often found among seventeenth-century manuscripts in country houses.

In 1649 two other frontispieces played leading parts in the controversy that sprang up over the *Eikon*. But this was not the controversy based on conflict of evidence: that began only in 1690, when Dr. Gauden's claim to have written the book and the acceptance of his authorship by Charles II and his brother were first made known. The problem was different in 1649—the urgent need to discredit a book so damaging to the régime, so daunting to the regicides. Milton declared in *Eikonoklastes* that its influence was such that all except some few were 'ready to fall flatt and give adoration to the Kings image and memory'. The publication, immediately after the execution, written in the first person, but unsigned, astonished the country, indeed Europe. Only one line of attack was really practicable: to declare the book spurious and father it upon some ambitious cleric. Hence the first (anonymous) attack; the title parodies that of the *Eikon*: ΕΙΚωΝ Α'Α ΛΗΘΙΝΗ, *The Portraiture of Truths most sacred Majesty ... Wherin the false coulours are wash'd off, wherewith the Painter-stainer had Bedawbed Truth, the late King, and the Parliament in his counterfeit Piece.* There could be no better testimony to the effect of the *Eikon*: in 'many before well affected persons ... I found an Idol-worship crept in among you and found you adoring the counterfeit Pourtraicture of one you sometimes knew no Saint ...'. The author is alleged to be a 'court parasite

---

[1] 'Explayning the frontispiece of the Kings Book.' [B.M., E. 550/4.]

preaching up prerogative . . .'. The gist of the argument is in the frontispiece and its accompanying doggerel: a hand from the upper margin draws aside a curtain to reveal the author, a cleric in a doctor's cap:

> The curtain's drawne: all may perceive the plot,
> And him who truely the blacke babe[1] begot. . . .
> Presumptuous Preist, to skip into the throne,
> And make the *King*, his bastard issue owne
>> The Authour therefore hath conceiv'd it meet
>> The Doctor should doe penaunce in this sheet.

The retort was rapid,[2] considering that a plate had to be engraved, ΕΙΚΩΝ Η ΠΙΣΤΗ, *Or, the faithfull Pourtraicture of a loyal Subject, in vindication of Eikon Basilike . . . In answer to an insolent book.* . . . Charles sits, hand on an open book, an elbow resting on a skull. A man in a fool's cap is about to snatch off the crown and replace it by a doctor's cap, but is restrained by a Cavalier. The verses begin as before and end:

> Though as a King in's actions he did shine
> Yet in his writings he may be divine
>> Do not then say one skips into the throne
>> The Doctor and the King may both be one.[3]

This seems to point prophetically to the double authorship theory, but the Cavalier of course makes a complimentary play upon words.

Many more examples of the political frontispiece could be cited. Its introduction into a non-political book is noteworthy. Marshall's plate to the second edition of Quarles' *The Shepheards Oracles* (a posthumous work of 1646) is frankly Royalist. The Tree of Religion is defended by Charles with sword and sceptre and watered by a bishop, while it is attacked by a Jesuit and by Protestant dissenters. One of these, standing in a tub, fires at the tree; he has already transfixed on his spear a bishop's cap, the Liturgy, and 'Cannons'. Others try to root it up. The branches are Faith, Hope, Charity, and Good Works, and the last two are being cut off. A protecting hand descends from Heaven. The usual verse explanation is absent and the only allusion in the text is to

> . . . these base sycophants that lye
> Close gnawing at the root, as well as those
> That with the Romish Axe, strike downright blows
> On the main body of Religions Tree. . . .

[1] The *Eikon* in its dark binding was sometimes stigmatized as 'the black babe'.

[2] Thomason acquired the tracts on 26 Aug. and 11 Sept. This seems to disqualify Endymion Porter (buried 20 Aug.) as author of the second.

[3] The verses seem to be the model for those on print and counter-print on the Sacheverell controversy, see p. 69.

After the King's death the situation called for official propaganda on the grand scale to counteract the shock to the country. On the highest level this was supplied by Milton, who as Secretary for Foreign Tongues was the chief literary supporter of the new Commonwealth. There were also severe measures of press control. A wave of pictorial propaganda from 1649 and especially in 1651–2 has signs of official inspiration, its purpose being to discredit the Stuarts and build up Cromwell. There are reasons to connect this with Henry Walker, John Taylor's adversary, now a leading journalist and one of Cromwell's chaplains; he was to show himself a shameless time-server in 1660 when he produced a sanctimonious eulogy of Charles II. Out of a set of four pictorial broadsides two have been attributed to Walker, on grounds of style and imprint.[1] On the same grounds the fourth should also be his. Besides these, Walker's printer published two portrait-broadsides listing Cromwell's achievements, the portrait engraved from the painting by Robert Walker of Cromwell as a victorious general, one version of which is now in the National Portrait Gallery. In this anti-monarchical propaganda three interlaced lines of approach are conspicuous. One was the use of astrology and of 'prophecies', allegedly ancient, to show that monarcy was doomed to end with Charles I. Another was to discredit the Stuarts by attacks on James I and his Court, sometimes also on Charles I (as in Milton's *Tenure of Kings and Magistrates*), and by accounts of the violent deaths of Stuart sovereigns. The third, pictorially the most striking, is found on broadsides on Charles II's relations with the Scots. Resentment at the prospect of an invasion of Scots, perhaps also of the still more dreaded Irish, produced an excellent climate for anti-monarchical propaganda.

The first, February 1651, is *The True Manner of the Crowning of Charles the Second King of Scotland . . . Together with a declaration of his life . . . and a close view of his Court and Counsell.* On this is an engraved equestrian portrait of Charles II in armour with a battle raging in the background. The text, besides imputations on the young man's character and conduct, is propaganda on the usual lines: 'What are the great fruitlesse boastings of *English* Malignants, the vaine hopes of *Irish* Papists . . .'. The second, July 1651, livelier than the vituperative manifestoes attributed to Walker, has a print, often reproduced, but without attention to its context. The design is effectively simple, with a certain humour unusual in Civil

[1] J. B. Williams (Muddiman) in *Camb. Hist. Engl. Lit.* vii. 355–6. He thinks that Robert Ibbitson rarely published any other author's writings, but he published official papers. In 1653 he was put forward for the office of printer to the Council of State, but did not get it: H. R. Plomer, *Dictionary of Booksellers and Printers . . ., 1641–67*, 1907.

War prints. Picture and text are an excellent rendering of the situation and a clever appeal to anti-Scottish sentiment. And it has a second string in its use of prophecy: *Old Sayings and Predictions verified and fulfilled, touching the young King of Scotland and his Gued Subjects* [812] is illustrated by 'The Scots holding their young Kings nose to yᵉ grinstone'. The verses begin:

> This Embleme needs no learned Exposition,
> The World knows well the sad condition
> Of regall Power, and Prerogative
> Dead, and dethron'd in *England*, now alive
> In *Scotland*, where they seeme to love the Lad,
> If hee'l be more obsequious than his Dad,
> And Act according to Kirk Principles,
> More subtile then were Delphick Oracles, . . .

There is a final appeal to 'true *English* hearts' to make a speedy end of 'these wars', that 'the *Scots* (though late) may see / What 'tis attends the STEWARDS family'. Then follows an 'old Prophesie of a Jesuite [*sic*] in Hen. VII time, of all the Kings and Queens that should succeed in *England* thus, Mars, Puer, Alecto, Virgo, Vulpes, Leo, Nullus'—no King will succeed Charles I. This 'prophecy' was worked hard in 1651–2.[1] It was inscribed on a portrait of Charles I which is the frontispiece to a scurrilous production, *The None-such Charles, his Character*[2]—a title appropriated from Fabian Philipps's royalist tract. And it appeared again on the portraits of James I prefixed to two libellous publications by Sir Anthony Weldon, one being *A Cat may look at a King*: a woodcut of a cat looks across at the portrait. Robert Vaughan in 1651 (unaware of the rout of Worcester) engraved a counter-print to Republican manifestoes, a 'picture' with a 'traiterous inscription' for which he was indicted at the Middlesex Sessions:[3] 'Charles Sonne of Charles the Martyr . . . Nowe in the head of a gallant and numerous army of the valliant and faithfull Scottes marching by the favour and mightines of his maker, towards the possession of the rest of his fathers Crownes . . .'.

The chief astrologer of the day, William Lilly, came into action in

---

[1] Another 'prophecy' in 1651 is *The Black Dutch Almanack or Predictions and Astronomicall Observations foreshewing what will further happen to the King of Scots and other Kings and Commonwealths . . .* This professed to include an old prophecy found in Dutch; in a rhyming jingle it foretold the flight of Charles from Britain, never to return.

[2] Probably by John Hall, appointed official writer at a salary of £100 a year: J. B. Williams, *History of English Journalism*, 1908, p. 103.

[3] On 14 Oct. 1651: a jury acquitted him on 28 Apr. 1652: Jeaffreson, *Middlesex County Records*, 1888, iii. 206, 287.

August 1651 with *Monarchy or no Monarchy in England. Grebner, his Prophecy.* This contains emphatic approval of Charles's execution and a prophecy that England should no more be governed by a king. He professes to embody his predictions in sixteen 'Enigmaticall' plates, which he would have explained, he says, 'had the courtesie of the present times deserved it at my hands'. The end of monarchy (a mole sniffing at a crown) and the overthrow of pulpits and preachers—presumably Presbyterians—are depicted. Though after 1660 Lilly declared himself a crypto-Royalist who had given secret aid to Charles I, his *Monarchy* was Republican propaganda. Was it commissioned? It seems not unlikely; in 1648 he had been officially called upon to attend the siege of Colchester to encourage the soldiers with prophecies of speedy victory. He also contributed in 1651 to the disparagement of Stuart kings in his *True History of King James and King Charles I.*

To return to the Charles II broadsides. The title of the third, *A Mad Designe* [814], November 1651, has had some publicity through its adoption by David Low as a generic name for cartoon.[1] But in the political language of the day 'design' connotes plan (bad or good), scheme, conspiracy, and here it clearly refers to the subject of the print: Charles intends to appeal for foreign and papal aid. The broadside, attributed to Walker, is a complicated emblematical representation of Charles's fate after Worcester, combined with an attack on Scots and Presbyterians. It is a processional design, with analogies to *Magna Britannia Divisa*, filled with personal allusions and allegations of Popish intrigue.

The fourth broadside, October 1652, exulting over 'the rout of Worcester', symbolizes the destruction of monarchy. In *The Woefull Mirrour of Monarchy* [813] Death triumphs. There is a 'List of the Family from which Charles the second king of Scotland descended, that sat in the fatall Throne of *Scotland* and came to untimely ends'. Starting with Charles I, this goes backwards to the legendary kings (fourth century B.C.) imagined by the Scottish historians Boece and Buchanan. The number of the Beast, 666, is applied comprehensively to Charles II and his ancestors; James I and his elder son are said, as often at this time, to have been poisoned. (This was a crime attributed to Charles I and Buckingham.) Hatred of the Scots had a propaganda value that is exploited in the frontispiece to *The*

---

[1] Low follows M. H. Spielmann (*Encycl. Brit.* 11th ed. *s.v.* Cartoon) who writes 'The Mad Designe' of the reign of Charles I [*sic*] became the 'cartoon' of the reign of Queen Victoria. Low adds, 'the unappreciative monarch [Charles I] was moved to anger against "these Madde Designes"': *British Cartoonists*, 1942, p. 8. Titles of tracts illustrate contemporary usage: *The Pretended Design of Levelling* . . . 1647; *Designes Unmasqued* . . . 1669.

Dissembling Scot Set forth in his true Coulours . . . [852], 1 February 1653, an early example of the *bête noire* whose body is inscribed with all manner of vices and crimes; Charles Fox and Napoleon, among others, were thus indicted. The Scot is 'Persecutor', that is, Presbyterian.

From 1653 polemical prints are scarce. Cromwell's expulsion of the Long Parliament is applauded in an illustrated broadside, *The Parliament Routed: or, Here's a House to be let* [856], with an introductory quatrain which ends 'O Lord protect the Generall, that He / May be the Agent of our Unitie'.[1] English attacks on Cromwell hardly begin before 1660. But there are many Dutch pictorial insults, and in these the whole anti-Cromwell legend may be found: he is tyrant, hypocrite, self-seeker, man of blood; he is vain and arrogant. The King's execution figures often in these prints; it is usually Fairfax who is executioner-in-chief—he is, for instance, Cromwell's hound, 'the bloodhound Fairfax'. In 1656 Cromwell is Antichrist, on the seven-headed Beast [897], and the extent to which he remained an obsession with the Dutch is seen in his reappearance in prints of 1780 as the embodiment of English arrogance and violence. In England, too, Cromwell is one of those few who survive in folk-memory and graphic satire as cautionary embodiments of political crimes. In the long-drawn-out chorus of pictorial dispraise there are a few exceptions—marking crises of resentment at military or diplomatic failure.

In the war of 1651–4, as in other wars, the Dutch used the satirical print and the medal as national weapons. The war-engendered hate was reinforced, not only by commercial jealousies, but by Stuart associations due to Princess Mary's marriage to William of Orange and to the Cavalier colony in Holland, with Charles II's headquarters there. Royalist propaganda flowed from Dutch presses. In their use of graphic satire the Dutch were far in advance of their adversaries, and English counter-prints were few. Only three survive in the national collection, notably a complicated allegory in the Dutch manner which heads a broadside of 1652, *Dr. Dorislaws Ghost, Presented by Time to unmask the Vizards of the Hollanders* [837]; one item in this represents the long resented 'Massacre at Amboyna' in 1623, adapted from the frontispiece to *A True Relation . . . of the Massacre* [839], published in November 1651; another incident in the plate (taken from the *Double Deliveraunce*) is 'the treacherous assault of Van Tromp upon the English ships'. The tenor of the print is Dutch craft and cruelty. Dorislaus, Commonwealth emissary to Holland, had been

---

[1] See the remarkable emblematic tribute to Cromwell by Faithorne, 1658, *The Embleme of Englands Distractions*, reproduced *History Today*, viii. 603. In B.M.

murdered by Royalists at The Hague. It seems strange that a Dutch version was published at Amsterdam in the same year. Finally, in January 1654 there was *The Great Butter Box* [854], a coarse and clumsy pictorial broadside which is a grosser rendering of the gibes that had appeared in Marvell's *The Character of Holland* written, as official poet,[1] in 1653, in which the country is 'This undisgested vomit of the sea', its governors (Hogan Mogan) 'the hogs, as all their subjects boors', and the Dutch skipper 'butter Coloss, Tunned up with several towns of beer'.

Occasional English prints before 1660 suggest the approach, desired or dreaded, of the Restoration. Resentment at Puritan rule speaks for itself in the title of a tract published at Christmas 1652, *The Vindication of Christmas. Or his Twelve Yeares Observations upon the Times, concerning the lamentable Game called Sweepstake: acted by General Plunder, and Major General Tax: . . . a Description of that oppressing Ringworm called Excize; and the manner how our high and mighty Christmas-Ale that formerly would knock down Hercules, & trip up the heels of a Giant, strook into a deep Consumption with a blow from Westminster.* This has a woodcut of Christmas (in a long robe and bearded) repulsed by a soldier and welcomed by a countryman [848]. By an Act of 1644 the day was to be kept as a fast on the ground that it was a heathen festival. Another sign of the times is open defence of the Anglican Church—when Dr. Gauden (a time-server who had taken the Covenant and kept his benefices) came into the open in 1653 with *Hieraspistes, a Defence of the Ministry and Ministers of the Church of England*, it was clear that the weather was changing: in the frontispiece Charles I and Laud (with a Bible) are martyrs defending the faith. Edward Chisenhale was a Royalist who had been fined for delinquency; his *Catholick History* in the same year is a glorification of the Church of England; in the frontispiece the Church is *Veritas*, the Romish Church (with Pope and Devil) is *Vanitas*.

The often-used device of ghosts in colloquy served for a sequence of tracts. In March 1658 there was an anti-monarchical dialogue between Henry VIII and Charles I in Windsor Chapel [910]: both confess to many crimes. (Here one is reminded of the macabre scene in the chapel in 1813 when the two coffins were opened in the presence of the Regent.) But in June 1659 the ghosts of Charles and Cromwell [924] meet: 'Oliver the late usurping Pretender' entreats the King for pardon. And, in March 1661, the ghosts of Cromwell and Bradshaw meet at Tyburn [947], with those of other regicides, exhumed or executed.

---

[1] Legouis, *André Marvell, Poète, Puritain, Patriote*, 1928, p. 176.

With the Restoration there was an outburst of squibs and lampoons and violent diatribes against the regicides, and it was inevitable that Cromwell should be Antichrist. In a satirical portrait he is 'the true Emblem of Antichrist', and this is also the theme of a tract by Abraham Nelson, professedly written in 1654, published in 1660, *A Perfect description of Antichrist . . . wherein is plainely shewed that Oliver Cromwell was Antichrist*.

These Great Rebellion prints, miscellaneous as they are, fall into successive phases. First, an outburst of pictorial pamphleteering—violent opinions, suddenly freed from restrictions and violently expressed. The spirit is Puritan-Presbyterian with a few relatively cautious Royalist-Anglican prints. Hollar's allegory, *The World is Ruled & Governed by Opinion* [Frontispiece] stands out as significant though far from typical. Secondly, the bitter strife between Presbyterian and Independent dominates the scene, and is fought out in print and counter-print, with an occasional plea for unity in face of the enemy, while an occasional Royalist print tries to turn the discord to advantage. With the crisis of the King's death the enormous effect of *Eikon Basilike*, despite press restrictions, is reflected in the many variants of the frontispiece. To counteract the sense of outrage in the country there is evidence of deliberate propaganda in a sequence of illustrated broadsides which are anti-monarchical, anti-Stuart, in some degree anti-Presbyterian, and there is reason to believe that these were officially or semi-officially inspired. On the constitutional crises that followed there is almost nothing, apart from approval of Cromwell's expulsion of the Rump in April 1653. Until 1660 attacks on Cromwell are almost wholly Dutch; the many Dutch prints insulting to the Commonwealth and the Protector, before and during the naval war, evoked a very limited pictorial retort.

Throughout, the constitutional and legal aspects of the struggle are barely touched on. There is one little *Plea for Prerogative*,[1] one or two incidental allusions to 'Arbitrary Government'; but the Star Chamber is not mentioned. There are protests against a topsy-turvy world, resentment at the upstart, especially the 'Committee Man', and at the attempt to make, Christmas a fast day. The approach to such topics is almost wholly Royalist, although a majority of the prints are Puritan in spirit. Controversies are seen in terms of religion: the changes are rung on Popery, Prelacy, Presbyterian, Independent, sectaries. Doubtless the prevailing imagery, with its personification of qualities—Hypocrisy, Vanity, Verity,

[1] By John Taylor; see p. 26, n. 2.

Discord, and the like—was peculiarly suited to religious themes, but then the imagery reflected the mental and moral climate. Not till the 1660 edition of Clement Walker's *History of Independency Part II* (for which he was imprisoned in 1649) have I found any of those symbols of the Constitution which belong to the graphic imagery of the eighteenth century: in the frontispiece Cromwell, poised insecurely on a globe which rests on Hell Mouth, directs the cutting down and rooting up of the 'Royall Oake of Brittayne'; the fruits of the tree, besides *Eikon Basilike* and the Bible, are 'Magna Charta',[1] 'Statutes', and 'Reportes'—emblems of liberty and law. Liberty indeed, destined to a dominant role in English political imagery, appears only in the guise of 'Profane Liberty' or 'Libertin' (otherwise Congregationalist). Yet the Great Seal of the Commonwealth had the legend 'In the first Year of Freedom'. It is noteworthy that Liberty had long been an important Dutch symbol. On a medal of 1575 the Hat of Liberty (afterwards to acquire the form of cap—the *pileus* that French Revolutionary symbolism transformed into a Phrygian cap) has the motto *Libertas aurea cujus Habenas ratio*, 'Golden Liberty whose reins are held by Reason'.

In the matter of imagery, though devices of the later cartoonists have been noted, there are striking absences. No Britannia, despite her appearance on title-pages; no British Lion with one partial exception. In fact these symbols were ready to hand. The Dutch Lion was well established, but the corresponding Dutch emblem for England was a dog, and long remained so (in happier days it had been a rose).[2] In Dutch prints Anglo-Dutch wars are fights between the Dutch Lion and English Dog. The partial exception is a plate by Hollar illustrating complimentary verses by Henry Peacham on the marriage of Princess Mary in 1641, *En Surculis Arbor*.[3] The two lions rampant face each other, their paws supporting an orange tree (another political emblem making an appearance):

> Two Lions sterne, one red the other gold
> The Holland and our English heere you see,
> The Orange Tree do equallie uphold,
> In perfect League and endless Amitie. . . .

But here the English Lion is still partly at least heraldic.

Britannia reached the political print by way of the medal. First, a Dutch

---

[1] 'Magna Charta' appears in the tribute to Cromwell by Faithorne, 1658, see p. 41 n.

[2] On a Dutch medal of 1587 is a plough drawn by a pair of oxen; on one is the Belgic Lion, on the other a rose for England: Van Loon, *Hist. métallique des pays bas*, La Haye, 1732–7, i. 371.

[3] B.M., C. 20. f. 2/288.

satirical medal of 1655 (obverse, the head of Cromwell); the Protector kneels with his head in Britannia's lap, presenting his bared back to the French and Spanish Ambassadors, who obsequiously compete for an alliance with England. The medal has another interest. It was copied for an English satirical print of 1739, an attack on Walpole, *The Naked Truth* [2417]: '. . . so submissive were those great powers in those days and so much aw'd that they dreaded a frown from the Protector'.[1]

On English medals Britannia first appeared on those struck in 1660 for the Restoration: always seated by the sea, sometimes on a globe; usually with shield and spear (as on the famous naval medal for which Frances Stuart sat in 1667 and which became the form stereotyped on the penny). That is to say, she derived from coins of the Roman occupation;[2] first, from Hadrian's *as* of A.D. 119—a Græco-Roman personification of the country—and also on coins (A.D. 140–3) of Antonius Pius when she was seated either on a rock or a floating globe.[3] We shall find her (seemingly) first appearance in an English political print in a copy of a Dutch satire.

And although Irish, Welsh, and Scots are attacked in the prints on political grounds, only the Scot has a distinctive appearance or dress, and that is limited to his cap. The Scots were 'blue caps' as Falstaff calls them, and in the prints described every (conspicuous) Scot wears a flat round cap coloured blue, as yet the only use of colour. The Scot is not 'Sawney',[4] but 'Jockey'[5]—otherwise ne'erdoweel or beggar. Both Scots and Welsh speak dialect, very slight in the case of the Scot, but the Welshman uses a burlesqued Anglo-Welsh according to the literary and theatrical conventions of the day.

[1] Inscription on the second state [894], title, *The Difference of Times between those Times and these Times.* Cf. pp. 98, 108.

[2] J. M. C. Toynbee, *The Hadrianic School, a Chapter in the History of Græco-Roman Art,* 1934, pp. 55 ff.

[3] The coin of A.D. 155, on which she is *Britannia capta*, seated dejectedly on a rock, spear and shield beside her, and with dishevelled hair, has a resemblance (probably fortuitous) to some of the Britannias of the cartoonist. This was the form known to Henry Peacham:

> With hair dishevelled and in mournful case
> Who spurnes a shippe with scepter in her hand,
> Thus Britain's drawne, in old Antiquities
> What time the Romanes, overran her land
> Who first devis'd her sitting in this plight,
> As then their Captive, and abandon'd quite.
> *Minerva Britannia*, 1612, p. 108.

[4] The earliest instance of Sawney in the *O.E.D.* is 1700, but cf. Lacy's play, *Sawney the Scot* (1667): J. O. Bartley, *Teague, Shenkin and Sawney*, Cork, 1954, p. 89.

[5] The Scots are 'the Bretheren Blue' and 'the Jockies' in verses (attributed to Cleveland) in the first number of *Mercurius Pragmaticus for King Charles II*, 10–17 Sept. 1649: J. B. Williams, *History of English Journalism*, 1908, p. 85.

CHARLES II. THE PLOT

AFTER the Restoration pictorial propaganda has three main pre-occupations. First, invective against the regicides, ridicule of the Rump. Pictorially, all is loyalty; but the seditious press was causing uneasiness. Secondly, attacks on the Dutch, more especially during the two wars, retaliation for a Dutch caricature campaign against England, during one of the more violent phases of the hate-love relationship. Thirdly, the grand crisis, exploding in the Popish Plot and culminating in the Exclusion Bills. The reign, beginning as it did with the Declaration of Breda, was a prolonged struggle between the King and a changing, but (till 1681) formidable, opposition for the support of public opinion, an opposition always latent and becoming apparent as early as 1667. Finance, ecclesiastical divisions and legacies of the Civil War were the foundation, but the conflict was inflamed by the intrigues of Louis XIV and the skill of his ambassadors, acting on the constant principle that Charles and his Parliament must never be on good terms.[1] The press was of supreme importance: prints had only a small part among the mass of publications in which pamphlets, verse satires, lampoons, ballads, squibs, 'prophecies', and 'dying speeches' had the major share, together with sermons and the many libels circulated in manuscript. But prints illuminate key points, and those on the Popish Plot have a notable place in the history of English graphic satire.

The anti-regicide phase of 1660–1 provokes comparisons with the anti-Laudian phase of 1640–1 and after—speaking always in terms of prints. Though the mood and the issues differed, there are some striking analogies, with Hugh Peters corresponding to Laud as arch-villain and chief target. Peters had been the outstanding Cromwellian cleric, a leader of the Independents and an army chaplain whose preaching was unrestrained even by the standards of the day—a 'Pulpit Incendiary' who had inflamed minds during the King's trial. He was regarded as the embodiment of the

---

[1] Barillon to Louis XIV, on 2 Feb. 1682, N.S.: 'The greatest security your Majesty can have is based on the difficulty, not to say impossibility, of a reconciliation with parliament. This reconciliation can never be to the interest of your Majesty, it must ever be traversed with care and secrecy by those who serve your Majesty.' P.R.O. Paris (Baschet) Transcripts.

violence and fanaticism of the Interregnum. Like Laud he was the subject of macabre jests and crude ferocity. In one print [967–8] he stands upon the Book of Common Prayer, the Articles, Canons, Homilies, a crown and mitre; he draws towards himself huge money-bags covered with inscriptions denoting the contributions and sequestrations of the war. A devil whispers in his ear; behind is a church, standing for St. Paul's; Peters says: 'Make it a Stable let it out to yᵉ Jews.' In one of several satirical portraits [971]—and here the comparison is with Archbishop Williams—he is dressed half in armour, half in a minister's gown (he had been colonel of a regiment of foot in Cromwell's army in Ireland).[1] In the background are allusions to his horrible execution; he hangs from a gibbet with the legend *Inde Pendens*, a pun much admired and often repeated. If Peters corresponds to Laud, Cromwell evokes comparisons with Strafford—the Protector with the Deputy.

All this connotes that turning of the wheel of Fortune or of Time so longed for by the Royalists. And this is the theme of a large crude woodcut [965], used for two verse broadsides; it expresses the mood of 1660 and has something of a folk-print character. As in 1641, here is the turning of tables, but in reverse. The grandees of the Interregnum, whose punishment was pending, are now shut up in the pound, travestied as animals: *The Tryall of Traytors, or, The Rump in the Pound, Wherein is presented the Lively Shapes and Bloody Actings of the Chief of those Grand Traytors who subscribed to the horrid Murder of that Blessed Martyr Charles. . . .* They are dominated by a wheel, containing a map of the world, between 'Hasilrig the Fox' (who turns it) and Speaker Lenthall as an ass. The animals are flanked by the Devil—'The Rumps Scout'—and by Harrison, a squirrel, who looks from a prison window. With the characteristic inconsequence of folk symbolism[2] the delighted spectator is dressed as a fool: he is 'Jack Spy-Knave' who 'laughs to see / These Traytors pounded and himself so free. / Thus is poor *England* freed from future harms. . . .' There is much praise for Monck. The verses begin: 'Behold and view, Times wheel is turned round / *Subjects* are free, whilst *Traytors* in the *Pound* / Do ly, for bloody Murder. . . .' As Peacham had prophesied in 1642, Time has called Opinion to account.

When Puritan rule was followed by the two most frivolous decades of English national life, we should expect changes in the political print. And

---

[1] J. B. Williams, *History of English Journalism*, 1908, p. 127 and n.

[2] There is also characteristic carelessness as to the roles of the characters, all classed as regicides: Haselrig (fox), Lenthall (ass), Scobell (cat), Desborough (boar), Hewson (bear), Vane (wolf), John Cook (ram), Peters (buck), Thomas Scott (goat).

so there are, though old preoccupations persist, especially fanatic fear of Popery. A new form of political satire—new in England—was the adaptation of the pictorial playing-card to politics—when printed in sheets they became wall-decorations. The seemingly first example is a set on the Rump Parliament, which is apparently pre-Restoration (*c.* 1659) and was probably made in Holland for the Cavalier colony. This treats serious subjects with a levity that was new. On the ten of clubs Cromwell kneels: 'Oliver seeking his God while the King is murthered by his order'; in the background is the execution. That there were grosser prints than any that have survived is clear from the attack on the Rump 'hung up' in the Exchange, and described by Pepys (on 7 February) as an example of the 'great and general contempt' for it among both 'good and bad'.

But the Dutch had gone farther in the use of levity and ridicule. On 28 November 1663 Pepys recorded: 'I have been told two or three times, but to day for certain I am told how in Holland publickly they have pictured our King with reproach. One way is with his pockets turned the wrong side outward, hanging out empty; another with two courtiers picking of his pockets; and a third leading of two ladies, while others abuse him; which amounts to great contempt.' This was part of a campaign of disparagement. Relations with the Dutch were dominated by naval and commercial rivalry with interests clashing in most parts of the world, each with bitter grievances against the other. Mutual antipathies were tempered (or sharpened) by the old idea of a Protestant league against the Catholic powers, sanctioned and sanctified by the memory of Elizabeth's pact with the Netherlands. English prints express detestation of the Hollanders as ungrateful, treacherous, and altogether contemptible. The Dutch use of prints in foreign countries to discredit the English is the subject of a diatribe by Dr. Samuel Collins provoked by his experiences in Moscow, where from 1660 to 1669 he was physician to the Tsar.

The Dutch [he writes] like locusts swarm in Moscow and eat the bread out of the Englishmens mouths, they are more in number, and richer, and spare no gift to attain their ends.

He goes on:

The Hollanders have another advantage by rendering the English cheap and ridiculous by their lying pictures and libelling pamphlets, this makes the Russians think us a ruined Nation. They represent us by a Lyon painted with three crowns reversed and without a tail, and by many Mastive Dogs, whose ears are cropped and tails cut, with many such scandalous prints, being more ingenious in the use of their Pencils than Pens. These stories take much with a barbarous people. . . .[1]

Henry Stubbe maintained that Dutch pictorial insults were a justification for the war of 1672. He cites Dr. Collins and reproduces the humiliated British Lion—three crowns were an emblem on Restoration medals.

For these insolent Hollanders have advanced themselves to their present grandeur and height as well as vastness of trade [so he writes in 1672 when the Dutch saved themselves from invasion by cutting the dykes] by affronting the high merchants . . . defaming and abusing their Prince and by exposing them to scorn and derision by ridiculous pictures and odious medals. . . . It is no justification for the States General to say that these are for the most part the actions of individuals. . . . It is enough . . . that the States themselves published some and that no solicitations and complaints could make them recall, or suppress the others.[2]

Stubbe continues in his second pamphlet, *A Further Justification of the present War* . . . :

The Provocations of the Dutch by their Pictures, Medals and Monuments (all publick and authorized by the States, or commonly tolerated) were such as would have justified a more early War. . . . There was not a Port in Europe wherein the drunken Dutch sea-men and their officers did not revile and abuse our English merchants and others of our Countrymen . . . trayling the English Colours defiled with Excrements through their streets and at the stern of their Boats. . . . Whereby foreigners were perswaded that the Dutch had totally destroyed the naval strength of these Realms in general and themselves the sovereigns of the British seas. Curious prints were divulged every where of the English Phœbus [Phaeton] being overthrown, not by the Thunderbolts of Jove, but Valour of the United Provinces. Britannia, or Old England, was no longer seated on her Globe, with her Feet in the Sea, but prostrate on the dry Land, Holland being mounted on an Elephant and trampling on her. Also a Boor cutting of the Tailes of the English Mastifes whereof some ran away, others sate licking their Soares, others stood barking at a distance. Another Boor was employing his Hatchet to kill a multitude of Adders with this Inscription: The English Dogs and Vipers destroyed by the Valour of the Hollanders in such a manner that they shall give the World no further Trouble. By these Artifices not only the Merchants of England have been discouraged in their Trading, the foreign Princes alienated from her, and their Subjects induced to believe that the English were so odious, so detestable a People, that they deserved not to be considered in place of Commerce.

He concludes that all this has 'done England more Prejudice than their

---

[1] Collins, *Survey of Muscovy*, ch. 26.
[2] Henry Stubbe, *A Justification of the present War against the United Netherlands*, 1672.

Ships and Canons'. Stubbe illustrates his two tracts with copies of the prints he describes. One [Pl. 13] is a composite of dovetailed subjects which had probably (in Holland) been first issued separately, and comparison with the Dutch original shows that the copy, though inferior and slightly reduced, is accurate. Here are Phaeton (overthrown by the seven arrows of the United Provinces), Britannia, the mutilated English curs, the adders, and a peering Jesuit. There is also a menacing or inquisitive bear, then standing for any northern country—usually Sweden. A fox wearing a ribbon (looking up at the Jesuit) is supposed to be Charles II. This is the earliest example known to me of Britannia in a satirical print: she holds a peacock, emblem of pride; she has slipped from her globe and is trampled on by the Dutch Maid, who holds a victor's palm branch and leans against 'her Elephant'.

As in Oliver's time, English retorts to Dutch graphic satire made a poor showing. Marvell's *Character of Holland* was reprinted as a broadside for both wars—in 1665 and 1672—probably without the author's consent. The strain of coarse invective begun in *Butter Box* continued. Insults to the country and its inhabitants were piled up in two pictorial verse broadsides, *The Dutch Boare Dissected, or a Description of Hogg-Land* . . . [1028] and *The Egg of Dutch Rebellion* [1045] (partly an attack on the De Witts). The Dutch are fat clumsy fellows, addicted to cheese, brandy, and herrings. They return England's former aid with 'base Pranks'. They are frogs or 'froglanders', or live in a land cumbered with frogs (anticipating many later caricatures on frog-Dutchmen). Both broadsides exude jealousy of Dutch commercial achievements. In *The Low Estate of the Low-Countrey Countess of Holland on her Death-Bed* . . . [1040] the country is personified by an old woman, aged a hundred, dropsical—that is swamped by the cutting of the dykes—and *in extremis*. Addiction to satirical prints and medals is implied:

> She that on Pictures doted so, may here
> Herself the Picture see of a *dear year*

but even now there is hope—'a Doctor from the Hague;' . . .

> Who knows what vertues in an *Orange* dwell
> An Orange only tis can make her well. . . .[1]

Meanwhile the opposition to Charles was swelling, aided by a campaign of disparagement for which the material was all too abundant. The anti-

---

[1] By the revolution of July 1672 William of Orange became Stadtholder, Captain General, and Admiral.

thesis between the Court and the Country parties had been established, with the dissenting interest as the backbone of the Country Party, and associated with the doctrine of the wholesale corruption of members of Parliament by the Government—pensioners were 'state vermin',[1] and the Court Party, like the Anglican clergy, were 'Popishly affected'. The term 'Patriot', assumed by the Opposition, already had the significance of the days of Wilkes and Dr. Johnson. The Anglican viewpoint was expressed by South in a sermon: 'What can be expected if a company of bold, crafty, designing villains shall be incessantly buzzing into the rabble's ears tyranny and arbitrary power, pensioners and evil counsellors on the one hand, and pointing out themselves for the only patrons of liberty and property and the redressers of grievances on the other?'[2]

Even before the Press Act (for the licensing of presses and publications) expired in 1679 propaganda was carried to heights—or depths—seldom equalled. This was a revolutionary agitation, directed at the populace. Oates's bombshell almost coincided with the revelations (contrived by Barillon and the Opposition) which showed that Danby had taken part in Charles's intrigues with Louis XIV, involving demands for French gold in return for the dissolution of Parliament. Both revelations came as a climax to the long campaign by the Opposition to show the country that the Court party designed 'to change religion and government'—to introduce Popery and Slavery. Of course there was some foundation for this, but the Whigs (as they were now to be called) relied largely on misrepresentation. The most damaging of all the stories was that James and the Jesuits had started the fire of 1666 and others since then—unfortunately there had been many in London. This was propagated in a series of 'Fire Libels' from 1667 onwards, at first secretly; after the Plot new and enlarged versions came out openly. Bedloe's *Narrative*, one of the Plot classics, was largely compiled from these libels. The frontispiece to *Pyrotechnica Loyalana* ... [1030], published in 1667, gives some idea of this propaganda, though James does not appear. It is a medley of Jesuits setting fire to the globe with fireballs, with the Pope plying bellows, Jesuits storing combustibles in a cellar, and 'G.Faux' with his lantern entering another cellar; Hubert[3] is there with his fireball. Thus the Plot was prepared for.

---

[1] Vermin as a term of abuse dates from 1562: *O.E.D.* Cf. Rolle, *Abridgement*, 1656: 'He is a corrupt man, he is a Vermine in the Commonwealth'. 'Vermin'—human rats or insects—recur in these prints, notably in 1831.

[2] *Sermons*, vi. 56–57 (preached *temp.* James II).

[3] Hubert, a Frenchman, 'a mopish besotted fellow', was hanged on his own confession that he had started the fire with a fireball, having been hired to do it: Pepys, *Diary*, 24 Feb. 1667. Analogies with Van der Lubbe and the burning of the Reichstag are striking.

Nevertheless, it nearly miscarried at the beginning, through its own absurdities and the scepticism of the chief victim, the King. But Godfrey's murder had a shattering effect; he was the London magistrate to whom Oates had made his depositions and it was everywhere accepted as an attempt by Jesuits to 'stifle the Plot'. The agitation against Papists rose to panic heights, Protestants were taught to expect a general massacre, and Londoners expected to be burnt in their beds, maidservants being allegedly bribed to introduce fireballs. All this was taken as proof of a design to introduce Popery and Slavery and was aimed mainly at the Duke of York as a 'Popish Successor'.

The propaganda is spotlighted by the prints. 'Among other ways [of expressing horror of Popery] this of exposing their Hellish Contrivances by Picture was not thought the most contemptible'; thus the 'Explanation' of a large Plot broadside in twelve scenes [1088]. There are Popish Plot playing-cards, fifty-two little designs, sold either as cards or on sheets 'fit to adorn studies and houses'. Some of the designs were used also on an almanack 'which may not unfitly be called the Christian Almanack fit for Shops Houses and Studies . . . the price Sixpence'.[1] There are many Popish Plot prints, often in a sequence of little designs on the various episodes; these usually include a 'consult' in Rome (Pope, Devil, and an eavesdropping Oates); Godfrey's murder is a central theme, treated with much imaginative detail. There are of course emblematic portraits of Oates as the saviour of the nation. An adaptation of the Emblem Book to the Plot is *The Protestants Vade Mecum or Popery display'd in its proper Colours in thirty Emblems . . .*[2] beginning with Jesuits in counsel in the reign of Henry VIII, number viii is 'King Charles the First murder'd' (Oates had made the Jesuits responsible for this). The burning of London is number ix; all the rest are on the Plot, with four on Godfrey, whose murder remains a great unsolved mystery.

The spirit of the campaign as carried on from the Whig headquarters at the Green Ribbon Club (at the King's Head tavern at the Fleet Street end of Chancery Lane) is well conveyed in the elaborate prints on the Pope burnings on Queen Elizabeth's accession day, 17 November, which took place at Temple Bar in 1679, 1680, and 1681, after torchlight processions from Aldgate, *The Solemn Mock Procession of the Pope, Cardinalls, Jesuits, Fryers*, &c. . . . [1072, 1084, 1085]. A leading feature in the procession of pageants was Godfrey's dead body supported on a horse by one of the

---

[1] Advertisement, *True Domestic Intelligence*, 26 Dec. 1679, quoted, Willshire, *Catalogue of Playing and other Cards in the British Museum*, 1876, p. 244.   [2] B.M., G. 18365.

'murderers', a Jesuit: 'the manner he was carried from Somerset House to Primrose Hill'. Another pageant was 'the Popes Chief Physitian with *Jesuites Powder* in one hand . . .' exclaiming 'This for 15 thousand Pound', to show that he was Wakeman, the Queen's physician whose acquittal on a charge of conspiring with the Queen to poison the King had been the first—and bitterly resented—check to the Plot. In 1680 there were additional pageants, the Meal Tub plotters, Roger L'Estrange and four 'Protestants in Masquerade', a retort to his cartoon and his pamphlets. There was seemingly no print in 1681.

With Roger L'Estrange and his enemy, Stephen Colledge, we come to what from our viewpoint is the core of the Plot, a group of prints, one by L'Estrange, six by Colledge, unique in the history of English graphic satire as weapons in a campaign for and against revolution by men taking leading parts in the struggle. At first almost alone L'Estrange resisted the tide of propaganda that had seemed irresistible. This old Cavalier and high Tory was a brilliant pamphleteer and journalist whose pen had made many enemies.[1] Colledge, 'the Protestant Joiner' and maker of the 'Protestant flail', was a very active agent of Shaftesbury and the Green Ribbon Club: his trial for treason and his 'Dying Speech' made him a minor Protestant martyr. These seven prints have more claim than those so far produced to be considered cartoons in the modern sense. L'Estrange may or may not have done more than 'invent' the design and write the verses, but Colledge's prints were almost certainly drawn and engraved by himself.[2] How far he was the 'inventor' is another matter. Appropriately, this foretaste of the cartoon coincides with the appearance of 'Whigs' and 'Tories' and the first great struggle between parties in Parliament. And though to use the word cartoon before the mid-nineteenth century is an anachronism, the term is almost indispensable.

There were two main lines of counter-attack on the Whig campaign.

[1] He is the Sheva of Nahum Tate's sequel to *Absalom and Achitophel*:

> Wakeful as Judah's Lion for the Crown;
> Who for that Cause still combats in his Age,
> For which his youth with danger did engage.

[2] Six were mentioned at his trial and in L'Estrange's *Notes upon Stephen Colledge*; there may be others (see p. 55, n. 3). These attributions lack absolute proof: the chief witness against him was the perjured Dugdale. But his authorship was accepted as common knowledge, undisputed except by his denial at the trial and in his 'Declaration' of 24 Aug. (*Cal. S.P. Dom. 1680–1*, p. 416) which was not repeated in his 'Dying Speech'. A large bundle of prints and the drawing for *Raree Show* were found in his house. Stylistically, the prints are the work of an excellent craftsman; I believe that the Pope-burning print of 1680 [1085, original in C. 20. f. 6/26] is his. 'His Vein lay much toward *Doggerel* and Designing, as he has plentifully given the World to understand in his Learned *Drawings* . . .': L'Estrange, ibid., p. 28.

One was to throw doubt on the Plot witnesses; at first this was highly dangerous. It was to 'sham the Plot', to be a 'Papist in masquerade', and risk being denounced by Oates and thrown into one of the lethal London prisons. The other, also risky at first,[1] was to 'turn all to '41' as the phrase went. L'Estrange used both with consummate skill. A famous Whig pamphlet gave him his chance at the end of 1679 and he published anonymously (but the author was unmistakable) his *Answer . . . to the Appeal from the Country to the City for the Preservation of His Majestys Person, Liberty, Property, and the Protestant Religion.* This notorious pamphlet is significantly signed Junius Brutus and has the motto *Salus Populi suprema Lex.* It was a frank appeal to religious bigotry and pointed to armed resistance to arbitrary government and a Popish Successor. Readers were to picture the inevitable consequences of a Popish king: London burnt 'by the same Popish malice which set it on fire before', the Tower guns battering down their houses, their dearest relations burning at Smithfield, 'troops of Papists ravishing your wives and daughters and dashing your little childrens brains out . . .'. To this vision L'Estrange retorted: 'Imagine you see the whole nation in a flame, and brought to the same extremities of fire and sword by the same schismatical and republican malice which embroiled it before.' He then instanced with chapter and verse the bogus Popish scares during the Troubles. The Plot is mastered, 'there's hardly a Catholic dares shew his head', but 'the Kings authority is visibly arraigned'. He followed up this with his cartoon, *The Committee; or Popery in Masquerade* [Pl. 14] which appeared early in 1680. This is a satirical representation of 1641 and after with a pointed application to Whig tactics. The Committee are representatives of different sects with John Presbyter as chairman. A plotting cabal, the Junto in debate, look down on them from a balcony 'T'inspire and push an Enthusiast Rabble'; these join hands across the room with a seditious Lord Mayor with the Pope beside him. The deluded rabble, grouped round the Committee, have banners inscribed 'A thorough Reformation', 'Liberty Property' (a first appearance in a print for this slogan), and 'Religion'. Discarded on the ground are 'Magna Charta', 'Biblia Sacra', 'Councills', 'Laud against Fisher', and 'Hooker'—that is the Law, the Truth, and the Church. There are other incidents and allusions. The verses make some shrewd hits:

> *First*, make the *People* Sure; and That must be
> By Pleas for Conscience, Common Liberty:

[1] Narcissus Luttrell records in Feb. 1680 'about this time many libels were thrown about to disaffect the King and his people and turn all to 41'. (Apparently they could not be sold openly.)

By which Means, we secure a Popu'lar Voyce
For *Knights*, and *Burgesses*, in the next Choyce . . .
In the mean while, the Pulpits and the Presses
Must ring of *Popery*, *Grievances*, *Addresses*,
Plots of all *Sorts*, Invasions, Massacres, . . .

lines directly applicable to 1679–80 as well as to 1641. But the Whig campaign was concerted, engineered, and financed in a way hitherto unknown —by subscriptions among the Party and by secret contributions from Barillon the French Ambassador. When L'Estrange impugned John Presbyter he could not know that Barillon was shortly to buy up two Presbyterian preachers of repute in the City (to guard against their being gained over by the Court or by the interests of the Prince of Orange). Such people, he wrote to Louis, 'have great power, especially in this country, and they can inspire others with their sentiments without shewing by what motives they act or who is directing them'. Some weeks later he adds that the money has been well spent—they will be useful because 'the City of London is in part led by them, and the rest of England models itself on London'.[1]

With his tireless and very clever pen L'Estrange was the chief enemy of the Plot, the Court's chief defender, and, with the doubtful exception of the Pope and the Duke, the Whigs' chief bugbear—burned in effigy, assailed in pamphlets and lampoons, and the principal target of Stephen Colledge, who portrayed him as a runaway cur—'I should be ungrateful', he wrote, 'If I should not acknowledge the Honor he has done me, in divers of his emblematical pictures. He has presented the World with six Tousers, and L'Estrange with four pair of Gallows.'[2] Three of the Tousers[3] survive. The first, *Strange's Case, Strangly Altered* [Pl. 15], was produced when he had found it necessary, in October 1680, to escape the attentions of Oates and Parliament by retreating, first to Edinburgh and then to Holland, returning in February. As a runaway cur, scourged by the Devil, a broom tied to his tail (symbol for Henry Brome, his bookseller-publisher), and with a pen and emblems of Popery on his head, he eludes the hangman and deserts his patrons and masters, who are the Pope, 'Mack' (the Duke of York), and two ecclesiastics. The verses and the

---

[1] P.R.O., Paris Transcripts, 3 June, 1 July, 30 Sept., 1680, N.S.

[2] *Notes upon Stephen Colledge*, 1681, p. 29.

[3] A fourth Touser (used for two broadsides) is in Colledge's vein, and may be his, though it is a woodcut: *Romes Hunting-Match for III Kingdomes* [1094–5]. Another Touser belongs to 1682 and cannot be his. L'Estrange figures in the Pope-burning print of 1680, which I believe to be by Colledge.

inscription, in the guise of an advertisement for 'a *Strange* old *Yorkish Tike*', are facetiously abusive—the puns and jests strike a note new in prints (though not in pamphlets). Another Touser, *The Time-Servers* . . . [1112], followed the dismissal of the Oxford Parliament: effigies of 'An Irish Tory and a Popish Priest, and the Cur Towzer . . . all on the speed for Rome. . . .' Towzer barks 'forty one'. But the most important of Colledge's prints are the two he did for the meeting of the Oxford Parliament.

At this climax of the struggle between the Whigs and the Court the situation for the public at large—for what L'Estrange called 'the sober part of the nation'—had resolved itself into the question, was there a scheme for Popery and Arbitrary Government as the Whigs maintained, or was there a Whig design against the Monarchy and the Church, as the King and the Tories believed, and L'Estrange and a very few others re-iterated in print? The Whigs were confident, the Tories almost in despair. It was openly said, Barillon reported to Louis, 'that if the King leaves London he will not be able to return when he pleases'.[1] The Whigs' violence, their electioneering tactics,[2] their pamphleteering, their reliance on the monstrous fabrications of the Plot, proved their undoing: people came to believe that the King was in more danger from the fanatics than from the Papists.

Colledge's prints are central to this appeal to the public that underlay the proceedings at Oxford in March 1681. 'A most scandalous libel against the Government for which with other things Colledge was most justly executed'[3] was the verdict of the Whiggish Luttrell on *Raree Show* [Pl. 16]. The song, coarse and crude, but clever, gives an idea of the tavern gibes of the Green Ribbonites—they can be matched in meaning, though not in expression, in lines attributed to Marvell.[4] It was sung repeatedly with explanations by Colledge in a gathering of Whig City notables, at Lord Lovelace's house on the way to Oxford. With the print (the two are inseparable) it shows, L'Estrange thought, 'the designs of the Party' and 'looks like a song of triumph'. The King is Leviathan, embodiment of ab-solute rule—'Child of Heathen *Hobbs*, with a hey, with a hey'. His clothes are patterned with faces like the all-powerful giant on the title-page of Hobbes's book. But he is also a raree-show man with his pack on his back,

---

[1] P.R.O. Paris Transcripts, 30 Jan. 1681, N.S.

[2] M. D. George, 'Elections and Electioneering 1679–81', *Eng. Hist. Rev.* 1930.

[3] Written on his copy of the print. Dryden, *Works*, ed. Scott and Saintsbury, 1882–92, vii. 2 (where the words of *Raree Show* are printed).

[4] *Advice to a Painter to draw the Duke by*, probably by Henry Savile. Margoliouth, *The Poems and Letters of Andrew Marvell*, Oxford, 1927, i. 321.

a peep-show containing the Parliament which he is carrying off to Oxford. And he is doublefaced, half Papist, half Protestant. The song is put into the mouths of Leviathan and Topham, the Sergeant at Arms whom the Commons had been dispatching all over the country to make arrests. The King walks confidently, bent on Popery and Arbitrary Government. Topham:

> That monstrous Foul *Beast*, with a hey, with a hey,
> Has *Houses Twain* in's Chest, with a ho,

If they want to get out, says the King, they must vote 'To yield up all they have, and *Tower Lords* to save . . .', that is, the Catholic peers, of whom only Stafford was tried and executed for the Plot (in December 1680). The bubbles he blows through a long pipe symbolize the self-deluding emptiness of his words (a symbolism much used in the eighteenth century and later). Across the bridge, in Oxford, all is changed. 'Methinks he seems to Stagger . . . Who but now did so Swagger . . .'. The pack is too heavy: 'May the mighty weight at's back / Make 's lecherous loyns to crack. . . .' He is stuck in the mire and Topham calls upon '*Cooper*, *Hughs*, and *Snow*' (officers of the Commons who have followed *Raree Show*), to pull him down so that the nation is freed and the Church can now be disposed of. The last verse begins, 'Ha-loo the *Hunts* begun, with a hey, with a hey, / Like Father, Like Son, with a ho'—a song of triumph very like a battle-cry. In the background are the buildings of Oxford with a little alehouse inscribed 'Louse Hall' (name given to a disreputable resort kept by one 'Mother Louse'[1] frequented by members of the University). Colledge explained that this stood for Whitehall 'because of its poverty'. (The Whigs counted on the King's lack of funds, not suspecting the promised subsidy from Louis.) To identify Charles with Leviathan was a stroke of wit reflecting the intense interest taken in Hobbes's book.

Like *Raree Show*, the print by Colledge known as 'Mack' or 'Mackninny' (one of the 'Tousers') illustrates the confidence with which the Whigs went to Oxford. The title speaks for itself: *A Prospect of a Popish Successor: Displayed by Hell-bred Cruelty: Popish Villainy: strange Divinity: Intended Slavery: Old Englands Misery: &c.* [1110]. James, half devil, half Papist, blows flames through a cruciform trumpet to burn London and the 'Provost House' (Edinburgh), saying, 'Thus Ile Govern Hereticks or Godfrey um.' He holds a torch to a fire where martyrs burn at the stake. A 'Church Papist' (Bishop Mews), half bishop, half Pope, stands upon a Bible; he holds out a scroll, 'A Free Pardon (in spite of God)

---

[1] David Loggan engraved a satirical portrait of her standing in front of Louse Hall [797].

for Plotters, Traytors, Murderers, Burners, Rake-hells, Tormentors, What-soever.' In the other hand is a crosier with which he pushes three ministers out of a church, saying, 'Out Fanaticks, In Popery' (Colledge was a Pres-byterian for whom Episcopacy meant Popery). Astride the roof of a second church are four clerics and a bishop riding post haste to Rome, led by a Jesuit and followed by a devil: 'They must goe the Devill Drives: Tantivy, Tantivy, Tantivy.'[1] The devil drops 'A Pen for Towzer' upon a dog, L'Estrange, which fawns on a second Jesuit, wears a cross and rosary, and barks 'Presbiters, the Plotters, Bow, Wow, Wow.' A broom, 'H.B.', is tied to his tail, a fiddle to his back, and he holds a scroll: 'Discoveries Mas-querads [his cartoon] Dialogues Apeals strange cases.' He is 'Touzer, old Ban dogg, of the Popes; but maingie...'. Below the title is the inscription 'Though Hell, Rome, and France; Have united their Powers: We defye them all Three (Sir) The Parliament's Ours: March the 21st 1680'. [1681.]

There is little doubt that these and other prints by Colledge were part of the Whig campaign:

The faction had another Order regimented [wrote Roger North], being a Detachment from the libelling Garrison in *London*, who had in Charge the Train of Artillery (if I may so term it) the Tongue and Pen Managery. . . . Besides, there was a Magazine provided for Ammunition, Libels, Lampoons, Satyrs, Pictures and Sing-songs, for the service at *Oxford*. Some adapted to deceive Men of Fortune and Education, well penned, and, perhaps, in Heroic Verse, others for the Rabble and drunken, sottish Clubs, in Ballad Doggerel, with witty Picture affixed, in dainty Conceit and Proportion; notable Eloquence for the eye! One was the King, for a Raree Show, with his box of Parliament Motions at his Back and the Saints pulling him down into a Ditch. . . . Another was called *Mac-Ninny*. . . .[2]

As propaganda both erred, like Milton's *Eikonoklastes*, in being acceptable only to party zealots.

Two other prints by Colledge are earlier, December 1680 and February 1681. In *The Contents (Hats for Caps) Contented* [1087] bishops eagerly exchange their academic caps for cardinal's hats, and their leader, Bishop Mews (who, as in 'Mack', has a patch on the cheek), kisses the Pope's toe. The other is a Plot satire, *The Catholick Gamesters or a Double Match of Bowleing* [1077].[3] The Popish Lords (then in the Tower) aim ostensibly at ninepins, actually at Godfrey, while the King looks on.

---

[1] A word for a rapid gallop, applied to Romanizing High Churchmen and high Tories. It is thought that this print is the origin of the word so used and its derivatives. *O.E.D.*

[2] *Examen*, 1740, pp. 100–1.

[3] This has the first example known to me of a device that became very popular, though not

Colledge's prints have the distinction of being the only ones to figure in an English trial for treason, a trial in which the designs of the Whigs were an issue and in which Colledge defended himself with the most remarkable skill. *Raree Show* and 'Mack' strikingly exemplify not only the violence which engendered the strong Tory reaction, but the over-confidence of the Party. The Whigs went down to Oxford assured of their power to control events, pass the Exclusion Bill, and make the King into 'a Doge of Venice' or otherwise dispose of him: 'The Parliament's Ours', as Colledge put it. The King turned the tables by dissolving Parliament, and the leaders fled to places of safety, hanged in the rope that Charles had so lavishly allowed them. How much the promise of French gold had to do with the King's victory is not here relevant: it was unknown, and if known might have undermined the popularity which was the true basis of what Roger North called a second Restoration. Surely never was the tide of opinion more completely turned. It was something more than a recoil from the excesses of the Plot; the legal conservatism, perhaps decisive in 1640-1 and 1659-60, was potent in 1681.

In literature Dryden was as characteristic of the later period of the reign as Marvell of the earlier. How does the change show itself in the prints? An expiring flare-up of the Plot was expressed (early in April 1681) in *The Happy Instruments of England's Preservation* [Pl. 17]; a print combining a view of 'The Infernall Conclave' with an apotheosis of the four chief witnesses, protected by angels. Oates says—protesting too much—'My testimony still triumphs.' Wakeman walks off from the Consult with his bribe 'to Poyson the K—'; a woman goes off with instructions 'to turn the plot upon the Presbyterians' (she is Mrs. Cellier, 'the Popish Midwife'). A tiny execution scene on Tower Hill is inscribed 'Exit Viscount Stafford'. The Whigs' bitter resentment at the reaction—so dangerous to themselves—is illustrated in 1682 in *A New Ballad, With the Definition of the Word Tory* [1121] attacking the Tories and their two propagandists, 'Towzer' and Nat Thompson, whose woodcut effigies decorate the song. Though beginning 'See how the *Tories* drives their trade / Clokes all with Fourty One', it is ostentatiously loyal: the last verse opens 'But Heaven praise our Great Monarch / And the Partner of his Bed', recently accused of conspiring to poison her husband. Far indeed from *Raree Show*.

---

for many years, the satirical or facetious signature or imprint, namely 'Printed at the half-way house that stood between Bothwell Bridge and Holy-Rood', a cryptic allusion to the Duke of York.

Despite much high-Tory pamphleteering and despite the mass of verse satires on Shaftesbury and the discredited Whigs, cartooning seems to have temporarily died with Colledge. Then as later it was essentially the voice of opposition to authority. There is a set of Rye House Plot playing-cards and also an illustrated broadside on the Plot [1123] with seven little scenes, one being 'E. Shaftesbury dictating his measures' to Oates, now discredited. The fervent loyalty of the period is reflected in an outcrop of historical compilations on the Great Rebellion with emblematical frontispieces, probably issued also as separate plates. One is Nalson's *Impartial Collection of the Great Affairs of State* . . ., each of the two volumes (1682–3) with a frontispiece by Robert White expounded in verse. First, Britannia, seated and weeping, is approached by a diabolical figure, half Puritan, half Jesuit, with his cloven hoof on a Bible [1122]. In the second [748], there is a gesticulating crowd in the foreground interspersed with pikemen; behind is the House of Commons (menaced by lightning) and there is also a ship from which men throw Charles I into a stormy sea. 'But see the temper of this barbarous Croud / Whom nothing satisfies but spoil, and Bloud.' By the same author in 1684 is *A True Copy of the Journal of the High Court of Justice for the Tryal of K. Charles* [743]. Cromwell, in armour and with the legs and claws of a wolf, sits in a triumphal car driven by the Devil and drawn by griffins. On the point of his sword he balances a pair of scales: 'Liberty' (a bunch of feathers) outweighs solid emblems of the monarchy and the Church. His wheels crush the bodies of Justice and of the decapitated king. Three weeping women, chained and crowned, represent the three kingdoms. *Arbitrary Government display'd in the Tyrannick Usurpation of the Rump Parliament, and Oliver Cromwell* was published in 1683 as a counter-thrust to accusations against Charles II. The frontispiece, 'The Common wealth ruleing with a standing Army' [1127], is a remarkable example of graphic allegory on a tiny scale. The Commonwealth is a dragon, 'a most horrid picture' of Arbitrary Government; its fruits (excreted) are monthly assessments, loan money, taxes, excise, and other incidents of the Interregnum. The monster is about to devour 'Food for a Commonwealth': symbols of Laws, Customs, Episcopacy, Monarchy, Statutes, Magna Charta, Prerogatives, Privileges, Liberties, 'Church land & tythe, gaine [money] nobility & House of Peres.' With a chain—'Liberties'—(its tail) it encircles a group, who exclaim 'O wonderfull Reformation'. The body encloses the Parliament and tiny armed troops cover the neck.

Edward Pettit's *Visions of Government* . . . 1684 represents the anti-

French attitude of high-Tories, and this is well summarized in the frontis-piece [1130]. Taking a sword from an angel, Charles II tramples on a monster marked with a fleur-de-lis and with three heads—those of a sec-tary, a Jesuit, and a heathen Turk. Britannia, armed and helmeted, stands by. It would seem that she is now well established as a familiar symbol. The book is dedicated to the Duke of York: the flood of loyalty that sur-rounded Charles II in his last years overflowed to the advantage of James, who profited by the calumnies with which the Whigs had assailed him,[1] but it was manifest that dread of Popery was still active. In *Visions of the Reformation* . . . 1683 [1126] Pettit accepts a theory put forward in Popish Plot days by the Whigs—that the Jesuits were wirepullers 'in every parti-cular of that Rebellion', and were responsible for the King's death. A double-headed Presbyter is painting out the Royal Arms and replacing them with the Arms of the Commonwealth, while the Pope steals the crown. The sectary-Papist was a favourite Tory emblem, a counter to the double-faced Anglican or 'Papist in Masquerade' of the Whigs.

---

[1] These were not confined to crude publications like the 'Fire libels'; 'Mack' was much more typical of attacks on James than *Raree Show* was *vis-à-vis* Charles. There was, for instance, *Nostradamus' Prophecy* (Jan. 1672), frankly Republican or Haringtonian, and attributed, though doubtfully, to Marvell:

> Fire-balls shall fly, but few shall see the train,
> As far as from Whitehall to Pudding Lane . . .

Merlin Revived or an old Prophecy found in a Manuscript in Pontefract Castle . . . was published as a broadside shortly before the Oxford Parliament and pointed to the death, if not the execu-tion, of the Duke of York:

> A Senate then shall end the Strife
> And Atropos shall cut a Life,
> Rome then from England fast shall fly . . .

Accusations of arson were made in Parliament to support the Exclusion Bills by prominent Whigs, for example by Goodwin Wharton (11 Nov. 1680), and by Henry Booth (7 Jan. 1681): *Grey's Debates*, vii. 448; viii. 260. The Whig *canards* were summarized in Monmouth's declara-tion in 1685; they included poisoning Charles II and murdering the Earl of Essex (who cut his throat in the Tower).

THE REVOLUTION. HIGH CHURCH AND LOW CHURCH

LOYALTY marked the beginning of James II's reign and was expressed in prints attacking Oates, sentenced for perjury to the pillory, flogging, and imprisonment. In one of these [1142] he is 'an incarnate Imp of Hell', dressed half as Jesuit, half as Turk. Loyalty again is the ostensible note of a set of playing-cards on Monmouth's Rebellion, but these have signs of a very different attitude, discreetly masked by tributes to correct opinion. 'Madam Lisle executed' and 'The Godly Maids of Taunton presenting their colours upon their knees to the Duke of Monmouth' suggest covert anger at savagery in the West, while 'The late Duke of Monmouths Standard Fear Nothing but God' implies, one suspects, sympathy with the Rebellion. The hatred roused by Judge Jeffreys is illustrated in prints over a long period.

The Revolution and the flight of James, with the wars that followed, are almost wholly the subjects of Dutch prints. In the French wars, satirical prints—officially inspired—were used on both sides as weapons of offence, with William III and Louis XIV as rival champions. Caricature—a word now possibly permissible if incorrect—became international—a war of prints. In this the advantage was overwhelmingly with Holland. Besides native artists, with Romeyn de Hooghe at their head, French Protestant refugees contributed to the campaign against 'Universal Monarchy' and the Jesuits. Medals were part of the graphic warfare. This is an important stage in the history of the cartoon. Prints were numerous, large, and striking (though usually over-complicated). More conspicuously than before, ridicule was used for the deflation of pomp and majesty. The ageing *Roi Soleil* was manifestly vulnerable and his mistresses were introduced with zest and spite. This was international propaganda: the Dutch prints generally had titles and inscriptions in both Dutch and French, sometimes in Dutch and English or in all three languages. There were also some German contributions and copies. Many professed falsely to be published in France, some states were printed in London (or have London imprints). But though James, his wife, his infant (depicted as the son of a miller) with

'Father Peters' (Petre), figure repeatedly in these Dutch prints, it is remarkable that English artists had almost no share in a pictorial war which thus remains outside an account of the English cartoon.

Very few English prints on the Revolution survive. The most striking is one on the capture of Judge Jeffreys, *The Lord Chancellor taken disguisd in Wapping* [1179 A]; this has the character of a cartoon, and four copies of the original, two English and two Dutch, attest its popularity. The shouts of the angry crowd are noteworthy: 'Remember ye West', 'Remember Mr Cornish' (the Presbyterian Alderman executed for the Rye House Plot), 'Remember Maudlin Colledge' (it was remembered in 1745). A devil claws at the face of what may be a disguised and prostrate Jesuit. There is one tribute to the Prince of Orange which does associate the Revolution with the war against France: *Englands Memorial. Of its Wounderfull deliverance from French tiranny and Popish oppression, Performed through Allmighty Gods infinite goodness and Mercy. By His Highness William Henry of Nassau, the High & Mighty Prince of Orange, 1688* [1186] is an allegorical design with reminiscences of *The Double Deliveraunce* and of Civil War prints. An orange-tree centres the plate; falling oranges knock down Jeffreys and remove James's crown, while Father Peters, the Queen, and her infant flee, and Louis XIV murders his Protestant subjects. There are Jesuits, devils, demon winds; the Eye of Providence beams on the tree and on the Church of England. In *The Protestant Grind-Stone* [1255] 'King' and 'Queen' press the Pope's nose to the stone, which is turned by two bishops; 'Schomberg' and two men identified as Bishop Burnet and Halifax stand by, while the Devil, a Jesuit, a monk, friar, and cardinal look on dismayed. The presence of William's commander-in-chief in Ireland connects the print with the Irish campaign. This is also the chief aspect of almost the sole surviving English contribution to the European war of prints. *The Usurpers Habit* [1267] is a portrait of Louis XIV with his dress covered with representations of battles, towns, and fortresses: 'the thefts and conquests' of France. He is seated and has taken off his hat, representing the little town of Limerick which he has been forced to surrender; there is a list of twenty-four places in French occupation whose recapture is prophesied in a verse tribute to William, ending,

> This mighty Work for William is Design'd
> The Scourge of France, and Darling of Mankind.

It is interesting to find a German copy of the *Double Deliveraunce*, with emblematical additions and verses in German, English, and Latin. This is 'invented by Samuel Ward Preacher of Ipswich, now repeated by Transmariner an. 1689', the title: *The Papists Powder-Treason. Deo Trin. Uni. Britanniæ bis ultori* [43, 1223]. This version was used again in 1740.

There are two sets of Revolution playing-cards, one Orangist, the other ultra-Whig, having some subjects in common: Judge Jeffreys and the Seven Bishops, which, to judge from the prints, connote the aspects of the reign that moved the public most deeply. Both sets have some significant themes. On the ace of hearts in the first set Charles II and a confidante receive treasure chests and money-bags from a French deputation: '£500 thousand pound sent from France to keep of the sitting of the Parliament.' In the second, which gives more attention to Papists and Jesuits, one of James's crimes is the punishment of Oates—the Revolution brought him a pardon and pension. Another villainy of James, shared by Charles II (names are not given), is 'The Earle of Essex's throat cut' (imprisoned for the Rye House Plot he committed suicide, evoking the Whig *canard* that he was murdered). The Assassination Plot was the subject of an old-fashioned allegorical print, *The Triumph of Providence over Hell, France, & Rome* . . . [1296]. Its many details include Louis XIV disgorging conquests and the Eye of Providence shining down on William in his travelling coach.

With Anne's reign and the War of the Spanish Succession the prints show rather less detachment from continental battles. A set of playing-cards on the war has some interesting themes. On the ace of hearts is *The French King's Dream*: by the bed are three cats; one fat for pampered favourites, one lean for the people 'exhausted by heavy Impositions', one blind for the King's Council, 'at their witts end'. This fable was repeated in 1800 with George III (who lets his Ministers govern) as both the dreamer and the blind cat [9551]. On the Knave of diamonds is the first English print on comparative national characteristics, one of a long line; a Frenchman, 'F', and an Englishman, 'E', fight, one for Ambition the other for Liberty, while a Dutchman, 'D', stoops to pick up the coins they drop.[1] This aspersion on the Dutch represents a persistent prejudice, often repeated in the prints. Throughout the eighteenth century the Dutch are selfish neutrals and war profiteers. At this date the imputation connotes more a state of mind than a fact, but it reflects acute mutual grievances.

Except for these cards, prints on the war are copied from continental

---

[1] Stephens interprets 'D' as the Duke of Marlborough taking bribes. This is not consistent with the tenor of the cards whose main subject is Marlborough's victories. There is also a card on official corruption which Stephens interprets, I think wrongly, as the Duke's peculations.

ones. *A Bridle for the French King, or an Emblem of the present Warr* [1463] is 'Done from the Original brought from Vienna'. Queen Anne, attended by a griffin, pursues Louis with a bridle, while Holland seizes him by the throat; the Emperor, aloft on a pedestal between Justice and Hope, says, 'Tyrant in vain thou dost oppose thy Spight / England & Holland both maintain my Right'.[1] Copies of Dutch prints were interpolated in the last volume of the 1707 edition of *Poems on Affairs of State*, perhaps as a device for giving novelty to a compilation many times reissued (with variations) from 1697. They are: 'A Collection of some satyrical Prints publish'd beyond Sea relating to the Affairs of Europe, since the French King plac'd his Grandson on the Throne of Spain, with their Explanations in English.' They are chiefly on continental aspects of the war; the exception is the second print: *The Sun in an Eclipse or Lewis XIV eclips'd by Queen Anne*; in the centre of a complicated design she clips the wings of the Gallic Cock. An eclipse of the sun coincided with the battle of Ramillies and evoked a number of Dutch emblematical prints on the terror of *le Roi Soleil*, 'Louis Soleiller', at such an omen. It is worth noting that this copy from the Dutch was in its turn adapted in a German print.

The sparsity and conventionality of the English prints on the wars with France suggest an isolationist frame of mind puzzled by conflicting loyalties—as if interest in the struggle against 'Universal Monarchy' had been hampered by old animosities and new grievances. Suddenly, after eighteen or twenty years of meagre pictorial output in the face of great events, there was an outburst of activity, unequalled for many years to come. The growing antagonism between Whig and Tory—now equated with High Church and Low Church—exploded in 1709 over the impeachment of Dr. Sacheverell for two high-Tory sermons, declared by the Commons to be scurrilous and seditious. A Ministry which had at last become purely Whig after starting as mainly Tory, and which had had the upper hand in a very active pamphlet and newspaper war, suddenly found itself overwhelmed by an outburst of popular disapproval in which Sacheverell became a martyred hero. This produced a pictorial war, more in tune with popular opinion than the literary war, and giving a striking view of the passions involved and the matters at stake. For the issue, seemingly trivial, was fundamental: the doctrine of passive obedience versus the Whig principle of the right of resistance, at a time when the Tory theory, taken to a logical conclusion, would seem to point to a repudiation of the Revolution and the Hanoverian succession. But the Tories were no slaves to logic, and

[1] Copied in woodcut for a broadside, on paper watermarked 1707.

F

the Church had established itself in popular favour by its stand against the Romanizing activities of James. The Tories maintained that the Whig doctrine led to rebellion: 'The Roundhead's Steps the Whigs persue.'[1] All this was a hotbed for graphic satire.

The sudden activity evoked a Tory diatribe against pictorial defamation which rates the power of the print very high: the author of *The Picture of Malice or a true Account of Dr. Sacheverell's Enemies* . . . calls the print 'a Dutch talisman . . . with a virtue far exceeding that of the Palladium, not only of guarding their cities and provinces, but also of annoying their enemies, and preserving a true balance amongst the neighbouring powers around'. And he breaks into verse which credits the print with destroying the prestige of Louis XIV, defaming Charles II, and revolutionizing the popular (pre-Reformation) attitude to the Pope:

> Swifter than heretofore the Print effac'd
> The pomp of mightiest Monarchs, and dethron'd
> The dread idea of royal majesty;
> Dwindling the prince below the pigmy size
> Witness the once Great Louis in youthful pride,
> And Charles of happy days, who both confess'd
> The magic power of mezzotinto shade. . . .[2]

Two pictorial broadsides of 1706, Whiggish, but professing allegiance to the Church, devotion to the Queen, illustrate the growing tension and show how politics had invaded everyday life. *The Oxford Almanack Explained* [1462] attacks the Tory politics introduced into the pictorial Almanack for the year; one of many items in the complicated print is the rout of the Tories, stigmatized as '*Papists, Nonjurors,* and *Jacobites,* Enemies of the Queen, Church, and Protestant Succession, appearing in very envious and deceitful postures towards the Oak and Orange-Tree &c, yet necessitated to be packing up their Popish trinkets to be gone . . .'. The other, *The High-Church Hieroglyphick* . . . [1465], denounces an inn sign, 'the sign of the Embleme Put up at . . . Stoke by *Naland* in *Suffolk.*' On the sign (as depicted in the print) demons undermine the Church, while clerics support it:

> With Brawny Shoulders strive to underprop,
> And keep the vast declining Fabrick Up:

---

[1] *Roundheads & Whigs Compar'd* [1494].

[2] The new art of mezzotint had been little used for political prints; probably the writer had in mind the series of twenty-four mezzotint caricature portraits published in Holland, *Les Héros de la Ligue* of 1691, the first being Louis XIV, travestied as *le Roi Soleil*, and with James II as *Le Roi Jacques Délogé*.

> The *High-Tantivy-Priests*, the *Tacking Elves*
> Who would, to Ruin *England*, Damn themselves.
> See the *Non-Cons*, and *Moderate-Churchmen* Laugh
> To find themselves by High-Church Fall, more safe.

The Whiggish 'moderate churchman', latitudinarian and with a tenderness for dissent, was the Tories' bugbear, attacked as an enemy of Church and Monarchy. The High Church attitude is symbolized in an undated print, *A Trimmer* [1231], several times re-issued with alterations, and probably current from the Revolution throughout Anne's reign at least. This 'half Priest half Puritan' is a split personality: 'One Legg a Pulpitt holds, a Tubb the other.'[1] 'Trimmer' has no relation to Halifax's famous 'Character', but is used, much as L'Estrange had done after the Rye House Plot, for dissenters who had conformed to the Church from interest; it expresses Tory aversion to Whiggish Revolution bishops (Burnet the most outstanding). This divided personality is a basic device of English graphic satire, and the thesis that the Low Church 'Moderate Churchman' was at heart a Presbyterian whose symbol is the tub-preacher—'still a Rebel if he durst' [1233], was central to High Church propaganda; expressed for instance in *A British Janus, Anglicé A Timeserver* [Pl. 18].

But it is odd to find the Tory author of *The Picture of Malice* already quoted asserting that 'the chief means by which all the lower order of that sort of men call'd Whigs shall ever be found to act for the ruin of a potent adversary are these three—by the Print, the Canto or Doggrell Poem, and by the Libell [pamphlet]. . . .' And that of the three the print, 'if not the first, has yet been the chief machine which his enemies have employ'd against the Doctor.' The object of his reprobation is a print of Sacheverell composing the sermon he preached at St. Paul's, inspired by the Devil and instructed by the Pope, *The High Church Champion, and His Two Seconds* [1498], the inscription

> . . . Such pamper'd Priests plead ye Pretenders Cause
> Support his faction, and dispise the Laws,
> And cry High Church is ruin'd and undone,
> If Persecution dont through Britain run.
>   What tho' this Emblem may have little in it
>   Yet since ye bought ye Sermon, buy ye Print.

Far from prints being the Whigs' 'chief machine' they were used much more by the Tories in their campaign for the Doctor. High Church

---

[1] See C. Mitchell, *Hogarth's Peregrination*, Oxford, 1952, p. xxix.

propaganda descended to rabble raising; there were alehouse gatherings, toasts, cries of 'High Church and Sacheverell', bonfires, riots, and attacks on dissenters' chapels. In the national collection there are at least five times as many High Church prints as Low Church ones between 1700 and 1711, not counting a set of pro-Sacheverell playing-cards—fifty-two little designs. And the Whig print usually evoked one or more counter-prints.

The Low Church champion was inevitably Dr. Hoadley, a far abler controversialist than Sacheverell, but far inferior in appearance and popular appeal. Many years later he figured in prints (not High Church ones) as a time-serving prelate. Only once is he favourably portrayed: in *The Living Man's Elegie* . . . [Pl. 19] two angels hold his portrait. This exultation at the sentence on Sacheverell forbidding him to preach (for three years) is a counter-print to a Tory retort to the *High Church Champion*: in *To the unknown Author of the High Church Champion* [1501] Sacheverell's portrait had been similarly upheld. Hoadley was made the embodiment of faction, rebellion, and profane Latitudinarianism. In *Guess att my Meaning* [1503], yet another counter-thrust to *The High Church Champion*, Hoadley writes his Whiggish sermon, while Cromwell stands by with an axe; on his shelves are books embodying his principles: 'Lock of Government [sic]', 'Sydney of Government',[1] 'Faction display'd' (by Defoe), 'Milton' (his (republican) prose works edited by Toland), 'Harringtons Oceana', 'Hobbs Leviathan', 'Burnets Pastoral Letter' (burnt by order of Parliament for maintaining that William's right to the crown was by conquest). In a similar print, the *Apparition* . . . [1569], the ghost of Cromwell introduces another Low Church library with a few more titles: 'Observator', 'Review' (Defoe's paper had defended Sacheverell's impeachment), 'Atheism', 'Fanaticism', and 'Against ye Trinity'. Hoadley's doctrines were in fact all that the High Church abhorred as subversive of religion[2] as well as of civil obedience.

These political libraries are an innovation, favoured in later prints (especially in the form of punning titles); hitherto there had been little beyond the Bible, the Prayer Book, and *Eikon Basilike*. In the lively controversy allegories were used that were to become classic themes of English political caricature. The coach, with its horses, driver, postilion, passengers, destination, victims, and vicissitudes, was a splendid vehicle for political allusions. Its substitution for the earlier notion of the symbolical

---

[1] See below, p. 160 and n.

[2] This became more apparent with the Low Church ascendancy after Anne's death, when Hoadley's sermon (Mar. 1717) 'On the Kingdom of Christ' precipitated the Bangorian controversy, a violent pamphlet war, which evoked (apparently) no pictorial war.

car (which recurs from time to time) marks a stage towards modernity, and its first appearance seems to be *Needs must when the Devil drives; or, An Emblem of what we must expect if High Church gets uppermost* [1496]. 'Perkin', the Pretender, is the passenger; Sacheverell is postilion blowing on a posthorn 'Tantive hi Oh' to show that he rides headlong to Rome; the leaders, 'Passive Obedience' and 'Non-Resistance', trample on the prostrate body of 'Property', while the next pair, Philip Stubbs and Francis Higgins (clerics partnered with Sacheverell in another Whig print [1535], *The 3 Pillars of ye Church*) trample on 'Liberty', while the coach and the wheelers—'Slavery' and 'Popery'—pass over 'Toleration' and 'Moderation'. Fixed to the coach are a gallows and wooden shoes, emblems of French despotism. The verses expand and expound the design (with the telling lines 'Your Lands will be to Monks and Fryers given') and were answered in the similar verses of the counter-print, *Like Coachman, Like Cause, or An Emblem Of what we must expect, if Low-Church gets uppermost* [1497]. The Devil again drives, the coach is the Commonwealth, emblazoned with its arms—with a calf's head for crest, and with gallows, axe, and 'Covenant' behind. Cromwell, the passenger, says 'No Monarchy'. Hoadly (prematurely a bishop) is postilion; the leaders, 'Moderation' and 'Occasional Conformity', trample on 'Common Prayer' and on 'Episcopacy' personified in Laud. The next pair, 'Presbytery' and 'Rebellion', trample on 'Loyalty' embodied in Strafford. The wheelers, 'Republican Tirany' and 'Slavery', tread down 'Magna Charta' and 'Liberty of the Subject', while under the coach lies Charles I, or 'Monarchy'. These allusions are stressed by the background, the buildings of Whitehall. The verses of the first print end,

> Let who will say there's nothing in this print,
> I'll swear the Doctor and the Devil's in 't.

The retort:

> Let who will say there's nothing in this print,
> I'll swear the Devil and Old Noll is in 't.[1]

The calves' heads and axes, accusations of regicide and republicanism, are symbols recurring in pro-Sacheverell prints. There is no doubt that on 30 January some ultra-Whigs or old Commonwealths' men and Independents did from time to time dine off calves' heads (representing King Charles's head) with appropriate republican toasts, as a demonstration

---

[1] These verses and similar ones on other Sacheverell prints seem to derive from the *Eikon Basilike* pamphlets of 1649, see p. 37, or there is a pattern for such doggerel, common to both.

against the official fast for the day, with its Prayer Book service for the Royal Martyr.[1]

Another new theme used in some famous later prints is the funeral procession. *The Funeral of the Low-Church or the Whig's last Will and Testament* [1531] is interesting as one of the earliest election prints. A Whig makes his will, while deathbed consolation and false hopes are provided by three journalists, Defoe, Steele, and Ridpath ('Observator'); the pall on the coffin is decorated with calves' heads and axes. The verses are spoken by the dying man whose party has been routed at the election:

> . . . Triumphant Tories now assume their Powers
> And fill those Places which we once call'd ours
> Whilst we Poor Whigs our wretched Fate bemoan
> And wish we'd left Sacheverell alone—

one of the few veracious pronouncements of the pictorial war.

The prominence given to journalists on this and other prints is a sign of a new age. The three attacked here are also 'The Three Champions' in *The British Censor* [1512] a broadside headed by their portraits:

> Three Brethren in Iniquity
> That vex *the Church* and spight the *Monarchy*.

Steele's association with the other two is deplored, 'But siding with *the Party overcome*':

> Him with the *Brittish Libellers* I join,
> Nor envy him the Company of Fellows,
> That have the *Pillory* disgrac'd and may *the Gallows*.

Ridpath, 'a scotch rogue' as Swift called him in a letter to Stella, was obnoxious as an aggressive journalist and a Presbyterian foe of Episcopalians in Scotland, but the chief enemy was Defoe. *Faction Display'd* [1508], the title taken from his poem, is an attack on Whigs as Presbyterians, Latitudinarians and Deists: a seven-headed monster attacks Sacheverell; its central head is the Pope, and 'The Whore of Babylon' sits on its tail, playing a fiddle. The others are Hoadley, Defoe, Richard Baxter, Ridpath, Tindal, and Toland. They have identifying labels, the Pope has 'Solemn League and Covenant', Toland has 'Milton'; Defoe, 'Review'.

The election of four Tories for the City of London in 1710 was an outstanding feature of the Whig *débâcle*, and is the subject of two Tory prints,

---

[1] Some rowdy young aristocrats were mobbed for such a feast in 1735. Sylas Neville records his own tavern dinners on calves' heads with regicide toasts, in the seventies and later. *Diary*, ed. B. Cozens-Hardy, Oxford, 1950, pp. 96–97, &c.

Wonders upon Wonders . . . [1549] and *Londons Happynes in Four Loyal-Members* [1550]. Both have verses repudiating 'Perkin' and professing devotion to the house of Hanover. (There is no overt Jacobitism in the Tory prints.)

But the advance in English graphic satire produced by High Church and Low Church excitements was not followed up for many years. There is almost nothing on the Peace (though there were many Dutch prints), on the accession of the Hanoverians and the Tory rout, or on the Fifteen. A rather crude Jacobite's coat of arms [1601] seems to belong to Anne's reign; the supporters are Louis XIV and the Pope. Another coat of arms, 'The Traytor's', was advertised and described in the *Flying Post* of 10 August 1714, the traitor being Harley.[1]

Despite innovations the Sacheverell prints mark the end of an age, not the beginning of a new one. Prints were still sporadic, called out by specific excitements. More significantly, the excitements tend to be religious—politics and religion being still interwoven, and dominated by memories of '41 and '49. From the Stuarts to the Hanoverians the shift is from prints mainly ecclesiastical or sectarian to prints mainly secular. In 1670 Dr. Samuel Parker had maintained that only religious questions were capable of stirring the populace:

People are never serious in their exception against any Publick Law, unless in matters of Religion; and in that case they study for reasons to disobey, because it gratifies their Pride and Vanity to seem more knowing that their Governours in that part of Wisdom that they think most valuable. Self conceit and Spiritual Pride are strange Temptations to Disobedience. . . . But if Princes will suffer themselves to be controuled by the Pride and Insolence of these contentious Zealots, they do but tempt them to slight both their Persons and their Government.[2]

This was a plea for enforced conformity to the Church based on 'the Violence of Godly Madness' during the Troubles. The populace that had clamoured against Laud and Prelacy in 1641 were clamouring in 1710 for High Church and Sacheverell. Throughout, Popery was the main enemy with the Jesuits as arch-villains, for reasons ranging from hysteria ('there is a kind of Spell in the word Popery, it transforms Man into a Beast'),[3] through memories of the fires of Smithfield and of Popish Plots and Treasons real and fabricated, to the belief that the doctrines of resistance and tyrannicide were shared by the Church of Rome and Commonwealthsmen.

[1] T. Wright, *Caricature History of the Georges*, 1868, p. 10.
[2] *A Discourse of Ecclesiastical Politie* . . ., pp. 309, 311.
[3] L'Estrange, *History of the Plot*, 1680.

From 1640 to 1710 (roughly speaking) a majority of prints attack the Anglican Church, or the Presbyterians, or the Independents, or dissent in general, each being associated with Rome. Jack Presbyter was the Anglicans' chief enemy: the Presbyterians were the most powerful of the Nonconformists, the richest; they had claims to consideration for their attitude in 1659–60; they were the most disposed to infiltrate the Church (like 'The Trimmer') and, it was alleged, disrupt it from within. Most incorrectly, they were associated with Cromwell and regicide, on grounds that are pungently expressed in *The Whigs Idol, or Geneva Ballad* [1509], a Sacheverell broadside headed by Hoadley's portrait decked out with regicide and republican emblems. The 'Idol' is Jack Presbyter:

> When Monarchy began to Bleed,
> And *Treason* had a fine New name
> And *Thames* was *balderdash'd* with *Tweed*,
> And Pulpits did like Beacons flame;
> When *Jeroboam's* Calves were rear'd,
> And Laud was neither lov'd nor fear'd,
> This *Gospel Comet* first appear'd.
>
> Soone his unhallow'd Finger strip'd
> His Sov'reign Liege of Power and Land,
> And having smote his Master slip'd
> His Sword into his Fellows hand,
> But he that wears his Eys may note,
> Ofttimes the Butcher binds a Goat,
> And leaves his Boy to cut his Throat.

The last (fourteenth) verse ends:

> Yet when all's said one thing I'll swear,
> No subject like the old Cavalier,
> No Traitor like *Jack* ———.

IV

WALPOLE AND AFTER

THE lack of political prints in the first six years of George I's reign is surprising: rival political clubs at Tory alehouses and Whig mughouses found outlets in mobbing and rioting, bonfires and processions; the cry of 'High Church and Ormonde' replaced 'High Church and Sacheverell'. The ecclesiastical disputes blew up again at the end of 1717 in the so-called Bangorian Controversy provoked by a Low-Church-Latitudinarian sermon by Hoadley. For two years this raged in a pamphlet war that invaded the theatre, but not, it would seem, the print-shops. It died away in a public madness made for caricature—the South Sea Bubble —the Stock Exchange boom and crash produced by the inflation and collapse of shares in the South Sea Company and of other undertakings, for the most part schemes floated for the mere purpose of speculation from which brokers and buyers expected a quick profit. The similar but vaster crisis in France connected with John Law's Mississippi scheme had already been the subject of a few French prints and a mass of Dutch ones— the speculating mania having raged in Holland. Many of these were copied or imitated for the English market, but there were also some notable English satires. These Bubble prints are a landmark in English cartoon history. They were aimed at the amusement of the general public, a few of them became part of the regular stock in trade of a famous print-shop, Thomas Bowles in St. Paul's Churchyard, and were still for sale in the nineteenth century. Secondly, Hogarth, aged 23 and still a bookseller's hack, produced two emblematical satires, which stand out among the mass of Bubble prints, though compared with his own later engravings they are undistinguished. The context of all these prints is the baneful character of stock-jobbing; this was, and long remained, axiomatic: 'the pernicious art of Stock Jobbing', as it was called in a parliamentary report on the boom and crash of 1697-8, a wave of speculation followed by the expulsion of stockbrokers from the Royal Exchange so that they were forced to frequent Exchange Alley with headquarters in Garraway's coffee house.

The Bubblers Bubbl'd or the Devil take the Hindmost [1625] was the first of the English prints, advertised on 21 June 1720, that is, while South Sea stock was still rising, though Law's system was collapsing. This is based on a Dutch satire, but (as in all these adaptations) the allusions and inscriptions are English. A rather simplified woodcut version was published by Dicey of Northampton, a famous purveyor of broadsides and chapbooks. It is typical of very many prints: an architectural setting, sometimes topographical and, if so, usually represented the *rue Quincampoix* (scene of French stock-jobbing), Exchange Alley, or, as here, a Dutch building; there is a combination of allegory and realism with Fortune and Folly taking leading roles among the infatuated public. Almost always there are allusions to specific projects, under their own or derisive titles. *Bubblers Bubbl'd* has a list of forty-two actual schemes, '*cum multis aliis*', headed by 'Robin's Fishery for Gudgeons', the South Sea Company—Robin being Robert Knight the cashier. Sometimes fantasies are included as in *The Bubblers Mirrour* [1621]: 'Air Pump for the Brain' and 'Engine to remove S. Sea House to Moorfields'—that is, to the madhouse. Much is made of the imagery of the air—objects are air-borne or wind-tossed or cloudborne or inflated—there are castles in the air, kites, flying ships, as well as bubbles. These symbols of false hopes were to reappear in the prints on the early balloons and aeronauts. They figure in an adaptation by Pine from the Dutch, *The Bubblers-Kingdom in the Aireal-World* [1622], where Icarus drops his feathered wings and his shares in the Temple Mills (an old-established business that weathered the crash) and London Assurance (one of the two flotations of 1720 that still survive).

Two pairs of prints stand out as completely English in design, both published by Thomas Bowles early in 1721. One pair, in mezzotint, represents the lucky and the unlucky gambler; each print is called *The Bubblers Mirrour or Englands Folly*; to one title is added the word *Joy* [1620], to the other *Grief* [1621]. Each is a half length portrait of a speculator registering emotion, one fortunate, the other ruined. Each has a symbolical coat of arms framed in bottomless cornucopias, foretelling disaster for one man, recording it for the other; the supporters of the first are two foxes and the crest is a head in a fool's cap. In the other the supporters are asses and the crest is a Janus-head. The margins are covered with inscriptions: 'A List of the Bubbles, with the prices they were subscribed at and what each sold at when Highest. Together with Satyrical Epigrams on each by ye Author of ye S-Sea Ballad.' The same heading is repeated on the other print but the Bubbles are different. The Epigrams appear also on the set of Bubble playing-cards which are possibly the last pack of satirical cards.[1]

---

[1] Historical and instructional cards continued, but these were no longer polemical or topical. There were playing-cards on Byng [3370] in 1756, but no set has survived.

(There is also a quite different Dutch set.) The English set is interesting, each card concerned with an actual promotion, with a little picture—realistic or symbolical—and four lines of satirical verse. For instance the eight of spades is 'Puckles Machine', an effective-looking machine-gun and its operator—the 'Epigram':

> A rare invention to Destroy the Crowd,
> Of Fools at home instead of Foes abroad
> Fear not my Freinds, this Terrible Machine,
> They're only Wounded that have Shares therein.

The other pair of prints—in broadside form—give a still more comprehensive survey of Bubbles: again both have the same title, *The Bubblers Medley or a Sketch of the Times Being Europes Memorial for the Year 1720*, and both contain, arranged in the manner of medleys, copies of Bubble prints, Dutch and English, some probably designed for the medley, with a setting of other engravings sold by Bowles, including a playing-card. In each there is a famous Bubble broadside; on one [1610] is 'Bubble Poem', headed by a group of speculators in front of Garraway's, the words are from Swift's *The South Sea Bubble* (80 lines out of 228). On the other [1611] besides much other verse is 'A South Sea Ballad', the song sung in the London streets with much effect from the late summer of 1720. This is headed by another view of speculators in Change Alley—a lucky one goes first to the Herald's Office to get a coat of arms, 'and then in quest of a title'. An unlucky one tears his hair: 'Self Wife and Children all Undone.' In the first medley is a view of the Mint Coffee House crowded with defaulters (an excellent view of a coffee house interior); one says, 'And I sold a Bear of 500000, but Stock rising whipt over here and will never pay the Difference.' The Stock Exchange bear was at first, not the speculator but the stock—the skin sold before the bear was caught. The Mint in Southwark was a liberty which, as a place of sanctuary, was the resort of desperate characters.

Hogarth's pair of Bubble prints belong to 1721 and were many times reprinted during the century. *The Lottery* [1730] is an allegory without allusion to recent events, a satire on national credit, the mania for gambling and the State Lotteries. These began in 1709, although in 1698 lotteries had been prohibited as common nuisances. The other, though within the general convention of Bubble prints with its fantastic mixture of allegory and realism, differs from them in several ways: *An Emblematic Print on the South Sea Scheme* [Pl. 20 a] has no allusions to specific bubbles: the ruin of trade and of the City of London are attributed to the corruption of the times and the malign and fiendish power of money. The setting is between the base of the Monument on the right and Guildhall on the left, indicated by a figure of Gog (or Magog) on a balcony; in the middle distance is a merry-go-round in action and in the distance, St. Paul's. From the balcony hangs a mutilated figure of Fortune from which the Devil scythes off fragments for the eager throng below. Among the crowd Hogarth has introduced personal caricatures: a dwarfish and deformed Alexander Pope rifles the pockets of a fat man with a child's hornbook hanging at his belt who is supposed to be Gay—a South Sea loser (he invested £1,000, saw it rise to a nominal value of £20,000 and vanish), while Pope had been lucky. The inscription on the Monument attributing the fire of 1666 to the Papists has been altered: 'This Monument was erected in memory of the destruction of the City by the South Sea in 1720.' Two giant foxes on the pedestal look down at the scene below, where Trade is a dying woman, Honesty is being broken on the wheel, and Honour is being scourged by Villainy—figures deriving from designs by Callot. There are other incidents: women eagerly crowd into a building topped by antlers to raffle for husbands with their 'Lottery fortunes'. A Jew, a Catholic priest, and a dissenting minister crouch over a game of hustle cap—a form of pitch and toss—their religious differences forgotten:

> . . . Thus when the Shepherds are at play,
>   Their flocks must surely go astray
>   The woful Cause y^t in these Times,
>   Honour, & Honesty are Crimes,
>   That publickly are punish'd by
>   Self Interest, and Vilany;
>   So much for Monys magic power
> Guess at the Rest you find out more.

This connotes an attitude altogether different from Hogarth's incursion into politics more than thirty years later except that on both occasions he resents injury to trade. That it represents a considered point of view may perhaps be gathered from his 'Hieroglyphic Print', *Some of the Principal Inhabitants of ye Moon* [Pl. 21], in 1724, a design in a circle as if seen through a telescope. This is one of the most striking examples of persons constructed of appropriate or symbolical objects, composites as they were afterwards called. Monarchy, Episcopacy, and Law are derided. The Monarch's face is a coin (a crown piece), he wears a pantomime crown, a collar of bubbles, and is spineless compared with the other two, and less regal than the bishop, the central figure who sits with one foot arrogantly on a stool, while the other is a cloven hoof. The bishop's face is a Jew's harp, that of the judge next him a mallet; the judge's foot rests on a Bible which is tied to a pump-handle, pumping coin into an episcopal chest, with its episcopal coat of arms, namely a knife and form. The pump-handle is attached also to the Jew's harp, regulating its note—money is all-powerful. A rope collar-wise round the judge's shoulders indicates his character; thus the three magnates respectively personify nullity, avarice and gluttony, cruelty. They are poised precariously above a platform resting on clouds and are flanked at a lower level by great officers of the Court and by two foppish persons of quality. The former are made of mirrors (with candle-sconces for arms) and firescreens—they are mere Court furniture. A tea-pot, goblet, fan, and hooped petticoat make up the lady whose companion consists of a wig and suit of clothes with a disk for face on which are armorial bearings. The figures have letters showing that Hogarth intended to supply an explanation. As it stands it is a bitter gibe at the hierarchy and the world of fashion. The context was the sense of national decadence and widespread but unfathomed corruption which was the aftermath of the South Sea débâcle.

The inordinate rise of South Sea stock had started with attempts to pay off the National Debt by juggling State obligations from one fund to another, with corrupt profits and bribes for the highly placed—Ministers and the King's mistresses. To the public it was a gigantic swindle. When Walpole was called in to restore credit (though we now know he did not in fact do so)[1] his retraint of vindictiveness and policy of compromise and moderation were extremely unwelcome to those who thirsted for blood. From the outset of his career as chief Minister he was charged with the corrupt protection of the guilty. He was nicknamed 'the Screen'; insulting paragraphs appeared in the papers and were embodied in prints. These Screen prints begin the long series of attacks on the Ministry in power which were the main theme of political caricature up to the fall of the Coalition in 1783 and always tended to recur. By convention Ministers and their supporters were placemen and venal exploiters of the public, while the Opposition were patriots—the Ins and the Outs indeed were known as the parties of Corruption and Opposition; this was the old anti-thesis between Court and Country that had been so potent a slogan be-tween 1667 and 1681, and was deeply rooted in the ancient tradition of the over-great subject. Walpole's methods provided ample material for this

[1] J. H. Plumb, *Sir Robert Walpole*, 1956, ch. viii.

Opposition propaganda which was the more formidable because ministerial propaganda was always attacked as venal, so that public opinion was normally anti-ministerial and liable to be stampeded into violence.

The South Sea incident which especially inflamed the public was the absconding of Knight the cashier in January 1721, taking with him a book credited with the blackest secrets. At the instigation of the British Resident in Brussels he was arrested and imprisoned in Antwerp; the Brabanters, relying on an ancient privilege, refused to give him up, and he soon escaped. This was alleged and believed to be a put-up affair to protect the guilty, managed by Walpole and paid for by the King's mistress, the Duchess of Kendal. On 4 March a libellous mock advertisement appeared in the *Post Boy*: 'To be sold, A Large Commodious Skreen, something the worse for wear.'[1] Other papers took up and expanded the notion. Walpole was 'Robert Skreen' in the *Daily Post* on the 27th. The *London Journal* in the same month elaborated the idea in a paragraph engraved on one of the Screen prints, together with more threats and insults: *A True Picture of the Famous* SKREEN *describ'd in the London Journal, No. 85* [Pl. 20 *b*]. On a tall screen with several leaves are pictures (compared with those on the shield of Achilles) representing the crimes and the punishments with which Walpole is charged and menaced. He is threatened with the fate of the de Witts—murder by the mob—as well as with Tower Hill; there are allusions to brazen effrontery (Friar Bacon's Brazen Head) and bribe-taking. Sheltering behind the screen but revealed by cast shadows are Walpole himself and other guilty men and women. On the wall is a map of Antwerp. Doggerel below the design gives 'Advice':

> . . . Remember Gaviston: on Spencer [Despenser] think;
> The Cup is full and somebody must drink:
> Justice and Vengeance is the common Cry,
> Guilt makes it terrible to live or die,
> To palliate Roguery never more be seen,
> They're doubly Guilty whom ye Guilty Screen.

The Brabant Skreen [1712] was an even more elaborately explicit attack, and the verses, quoted from the *London Journal*, No. 92, appeal to the King to rid himself of a traitor:

> Let no curs't Traitor tho of High Degree
> Eclipse the Beams of Sacred Majesty! . . .

On the screen are eight incriminating scenes and on the wall is a picture

---

[1] See C. D. Realey, *Early Opposition to Sir Robert Walpole*, 1931.

of the 'Joyful Entry' (*Joyeuse Entrée* to Antwerp 1514, origin of the Brabanters' privileges under the Empire).

At the beginning and the end of his career Walpole was threatened with the fate of Piers Gaveston and in 1742 the Screen theme of 1721 was revived. Both the Screen prints of 1721 were closely copied by a plagiarist, a sign of popularity. A cruder attack on Knight was also copied in a second print and given still wider circulation by its reproduction in woodcut for two successive numbers of the *Weekly Journal or British Gazetteer*. This is *Lucipher's New Row-Barge* [Pl. 10 *b*] in which devils take the fugitive cashier to the gaping mouth of Hell. Two lines of the inscription convey its tenor: 'Impov'rish Thousands by some Publick Fraud, / And worship Intrest as your only God.'

The screen was a convenient device for attacking Walpole without risky explicitness—a precaution soon dropped. It figures in an interesting print on the general election of 1722, *The Prevailing Candidate, or the Election carried by Bribery and the Devil* [1717]. On each of seven leaves of the screen is the date of one of the years of the late Parliament, each with its reprehensible enactment. These include the Septennial Act and the 'Act to indemnify S.S. V. . . . .ns' (Villains). Emerging from the screen—that is, dispatched by Walpole—and escorted by the Devil, is the candidate. He holds a money bag and takes the hand of a 'Knave . . . who has pow'r to command / All the Votes in the Corporation'. The knave is shackled by a chain; his conscience-stricken wife is reassured by a parson who 'avers brib'ry no Sin, / Since mony's a family blessing'. Two boys attend the candidate, one proffers a wooden shoe, emblem of French slavery. On 31 March, when the election was in full swing, this was advertised in the *Post Boy* with two other prints: 'Britannia stript by a Villain to which is added the true phiz of a late Member.' Both are on the same plate [1720–1], the Villain being a South Sea Director who gives Britannia a small purse and makes off for 'a distant Shore' with a large one; the 'late Member', depicted as Punch, has ruined the nation. Walpole was repeatedly Punch in later prints.

But the nation was clearly not ruined; prosperity and peace with Walpole's policy of conciliating his adversaries produced a period of calm after the excitements of 1721–2 when the Opposition had deluged the country with pamphlets and newspapers, and there had been close co-operation between newspapers and print-shops. In the placid interval the art of graphic satire advanced; its range was extended to ridicule the taste of the town, foreign musicians, the opera, the theatre, masquerades, topics which became part of the caricaturist's repertory. In 1726 came one of those sensations that from time to time invaded the print-shops—the controversy over Mary Tofts, who professed to have given birth to rabbits. In all this, Hogarth's prints stand out, and he produced one of a number of satires on the amazing credulity of the medical profession. The lighter touch of these social satires gradually influenced the political cartoon.

At the end of 1726 the birth of the weekly *Craftsman* was a sign that the halcyon period would end. There were reports of the imminent fall of Walpole and when George I died suddenly in June 1727 a new Ministry was expected. The elections were carried on with much animosity and disorder and there were seditious ballads, but the only surviving election print has no personal allusions. *Ready Mony the prevailing Candidate, or the Humours of an Election* [1798] is a commentary on the usual conduct of a country election; bribes, kisses for the elector's wife, chairing the member, with verses elaborating the contrast between the obsequious candidate and the arrogant elected person, a theme recurring in prints for more than a century.

Not till 1730 do pictorial thrusts at Walpole approach the animosity of 1721, although the *Craftsman* had been ruthlessly attacking his foreign policy and of course charging him with corruption. An ostensible panegyric in the form of a monument with figures, ironical in its extravagance, is clearly bitter denigration. In form and title it echoes a satire on the despicable Francis Charteris, classic eighteenth-century profligate, just convicted of rape. *To the Glory of the R^t Honble. Sr Robert Walpole* [1842] is a companion print to *To the Glory of Colonel Don Francisco, upon his delivery out of Goal* [1841]. On a second state some inscriptions are altered to leave no doubt of the print's hostile intention.[1] It was copied as part of the more savage campaign of 1741–2 [2500].

Next year the essays in the *Craftsman* were reissued in seven volumes, each with a satirical frontispiece. All these were reprinted together on a single sheet [1822], headed *Robin's Game or Seven's the Main. Being An Explanation of Caleb D'Anver's Seven Egyptian Hieroglyphicks Prefixed to the Seven Volumnes of the Craftsman*, with the motto, *Jacta est Alea*. This was the folding plate to (and title of) a shilling pamphlet 'containing a Key to the State Hieroglyphicks and a description of the Seven Volumes . . . with Remarks thereon', the whole edition being too dear 'to be every Body's

---

[1] Stephens interprets the first state as praise of Walpole: 'BOBBY the *Screen*' (among others) was attacked for the very unpopular pardon to Charteris; *Ballad on Colonel Francisco Rape-Master General* . . .: M. Percival, *Walpole Ballads*, Oxford, 1918, p. 35.

Money', and the 'Enigmatical Frontispieces . . . set it above the ordinary Reader's Understanding'. The so-called explanations are elaborate interpretations, ostensibly speculative—insults only slightly veiled. The composite plate was also published separately as a large broadside, the title altered to *Robin's Reign . . .* [1822].

One of these designs (pl. to vol. v) is the first pictorial attack on Walpole's foreign policy, using the ancient theme of the balance. Walpole, 'a pitiful dirty looking scoundrel', completely subservient to Cardinal Fleury, throws appeasing documents into his scale to be hopelessly outweighed by French emblems of sovereignty and sea-power. The Gallic Cock crows on the back of the sleeping British Lion, a recurrent device of the cartoonist. In another design (pl. to vol. iii) there is a printing press, the first of many pictorial tributes to this palladium of liberty. 'I hope there will be no attempt to construe my Explanations as Libels', ran the introduction. But proceedings were taken: *Robin's Game* together with a play, *The Fall of Mortimer*, and a ballad, *The Chelsea Monarch or Money Rules All*, were presented by the Middlesex Grand Jury in July 1731 as 'false, infamous, scandalous, seditious and treasonable libels'.[1] Since the second revival, by Wilkes, of this old play was to have dire consequences, something must be said of it here. Walpole had already figured as Gaveston; the comparison with Mortimer was still more venomous: each the favourite of a queen consort, the fate of one is prophesied for the other. The lines, with seditious alterations from the original, seemed horribly pat and were received with dismaying applause:

Tis full three years since *Mortimer* began
To lord it over us by the Queen's vile Favour . . .
In this short space, he and his brother Devil [Horatio Walpole]
Have made, undone, new fram'd, shuffled and tost
The antient Customs of our native Soil
So very often that the Kingdom staggers
Under the heavy Burthen of the Charge. [Act i, sc. i.]

With the Excise scheme of 1733 graphic satire was fully established as a standing instrument of propaganda. Popular agitation reached a new climax, which, though probably less than in the Popish Plot frenzy, perhaps than in the Sacheverell ferment, was geared more explicitly to party politics. Popular clamour against some ministerial measure or project is a recurrent theme of eighteenth-century politics. Hungry Outs eager to

---

[1] Percival, op. cit., pp. xx–xxi, 50.

supplant the Ins carried on the art and craft of agitation in newspapers, ballads, prints, and by organized petitioning and other devices, always fomented by cries of Liberty in danger. That famous slogan, 'Liberty and Property and No Excise', was first heard in 1733. To the Opposition who had been hammering at Walpole ('King Bob', 'Robin', 'Blue String', 'Volpone', and the like) as an arrogant Colossus, enemy of trade, a source of corruption, and himself in corrupt subservience to France, the Excise scheme was a godsend. It was also a menace. If carried, the country gentlemen would be propitiated by the reduction of the Land Tax, trade would be encouraged to the greater glory of Walpole. The word Excise—hated instrument of the Interregnum—was enough to set the agitation going. By a legerdemain which is apparent in the prints people were induced to believe that the excise—limited to wine and tobacco, the duty being transferred from customs—would become a General Excise, that an army of excise officers (actually 126 for the whole of England) would be a new 'standing army' with access to every house at any time, and that the result would be slavery and wooden shoes.

Ballads and prints were used to create the myth of the Excise Monster. *Britannia Excisa* [1936], a ballad attributed to Pulteney, was illustrated in woodcut with one of the long succession of many-headed monsters of English political folklore. A scaly creature, blend of hydra, medieval dragon, and Beast of Revelation, with webbed wings and the claws of a bird of prey, draws Walpole's coach, turning one of its seven heads to vomit coins into his lap, while the others gulp at the necessities of life—a leg of mutton, a sheep, a tankard, a goblet, a tobacco pipe. At the bonfires which celebrated the withdrawal of the Bill an Excise dragon was burnt:

> Your Liberties, Properties, now are secur'd,
> Which late were in Danger of being immur'd;
> The *Merchants* and *Vintners* their Trade may pursue,
> And not dread the Plague of a Raskally Crew.
> > For no new EXCISE,
> > With five hundred Eyes,
> Shall henceforth your Wives or your Daughters surprize
> For if they had Licence to gage all your *Stocks*
> May also pretend to gage under their Smocks.

In this display of propaganda and agitation some familiar devices of the cartoonist made a seemingly first appearance. Liberty with her cap and spear was to establish herself by stages during the Seven Years War, the

Wilkite disturbances, and the dispute with America. (After this she seldom appears, the cap and spear become emblems in their own right—or occasional attributes of Britannia.) She appears first in an Excise print (her cap is still a hat in the Dutch convention); together with Trade (a merchant holding a ship) she attends maypole rejoicings at the defeat of Excise in *The Noble Stand: Or the Glorious CCIIII . . .* [1921]—the large minority (204–265) that voted against the motion for the Bill.

One of the most interesting of the prints is *Excise in Triumph* [Pl. 22]. Walpole is a fat exciseman enthroned on a barrel and drawn by an emaciated British Lion, yoked, and shod with wooden shoes, but expressing angry resentment, an excellent example of the noble creature's capacity for registering emotion. Walpole's truck passes over a document—Magna Charta, reduced to infamy. One of the new standing army rides a mutilated unicorn which walks beside the Lion, while others are drawn up behind. Excise prints were adapted to fans; on one fan leaf (only a fragment survives) Walpole is compared to Wolsey: 'Wolsey and his Successor here in one behold. Both served their Masters, both their Country sold' [1925].

Every phase of the uproar is illustrated—the large minority against the Bill, the City petitioners escorted by a mob, and Walpole's unlucky comment (always remembered against him) that they were 'sturdy beggars'; the rejoicings, the bonfires, the burning in effigy. The 'Progress' of some *bête noire* from lowly beginnings to undeserved eminence and final retribution, in a sequence of little scenes is a device still alive. It was inevitably used against Napoleon; the first example in these prints is *R–b–n's Progress in Eight Scenes . . .* [1938], probably inspired by Hogarth's *Rake's Progress*;[1] this begins with his criminal ambition and ends with Excise: precariously poised on a pyramid he scatters bribes, while his effigy hangs over a bonfire.

Even Walpole's favourable reception in Norfolk was elaborately ridiculed, first in *Fog's Journal* (28 July), then in a ballad, and finally in a print [1931] on which the ballad is quoted, a good example of the close relationship between these instruments of propaganda. Walpole as a quack doctor, his brother Horatio beside him as his zany, enters Norwich in his gig (the quack was the eighteenth-century embodiment of riches got by humbug and chicane). He holds three papers: 'Excise', 'A Cure for Religion', 'A Cure for Trade'. The zany proclaims his master's feats; the mob retort, 'that's nothing he has cur'd a whole Bench of Bishops of Religion'; '. . . Why he has almost cur'd a whole Nation of their Trade.'

[1] See below, p. 113.

The bishop was still, and long remained, a target for satire; indeed, the attitude of the prints to the Church and the clergy is a sort of gauge of currents of opinion. The line of attack was very different from that of the seventeenth century; he is no Tantivy-Tory or Popish prelate, but an ambitious worldling and a subservient tool of Walpole—arrogant, pompous, overfed. In 1731 there was an incident that evoked an outburst of ridicule. Archbishop Wake was reported ill: a broadside ballad illustrated with a woodcut described the competition for the succession: *First Oars to L—b—th; or, who strives for Preferment* [2867];[1] according to the *Craftsman* two hawkers were arrested for selling it. Three bishops, each in a Thames wherry (sculler), race each other across the river. The rivals are Hoadley (Salisbury), Gibson (London), Blackburne (York). Similar engravings of the race were sold separately, and verses relate the outcome: 'The man whose place each thought to take / Is yet alive and still a WAKE.' There were similar satires and prints when Wake died (in 1737) and again when Archbishop Potter died (in 1747).

The ancient theme of the pluralist inevitably recurs. In 1737 Archbishop Wake, book in hand, drives *An Ass Loaded with* (Church)[2] *Preferments* [2269] turning away from a poor kneeling parson. The ass (with the head of Wake's son-in-law) has panniers laden with church offices including the 'Sine-cure of Bray'. He is contrasted with 'Good antient Pastors'; today, 'A supple Conscience and a Front of Brass / For highest Honours fits the heaviest Ass.' *The Pluralist* [Pl. 23] in 1744 is in the classic form of a cleric grabbing at churches: having placed hands and feet on four, he looks greedily at a fifth: 'For what can Priestly Avarice aswage? . . . Let Curates drudge the lazy Drone to serve. . . .'

In 1736 there was an attempt, well-intentioned but unfortunate, to check the appalling evil of gin. Three prints are noteworthy as the first of the satires on gin and beer which recurrently spotlight the social and political environment. Nothing afterwards was to approach them, or the agitation they illustrate, for levity and brutality in the face of tragedy (except that in 1751 one was reprinted). Gin, cheap, fiery, lethal, was distilled anywhere, sold anywhere in the most brutalizing conditions. Repeated protests from magistrates on the devastation caused led at last to action, futile in 1729, drastic in 1736 with a Gin Act intended to stop the retailing of gin altogether, by a prohibitive duty and a retailer's

---

[1] Stevens has misdated the print 1747; M. Percival shows that the date is May 1731: op. cit., p. 54.
[2] Depicted.

licence of £50. It was violently attacked in Parliament by Pulteney and the Patriots, was passed but was defeated by the distillers and the London mob. On the date that the Act was to take effect retail dealers draped their signs with black and organized mock lyings in State and funeral processions for 'Madam Geneva' or 'Mrs. Gin'. Hence *The Funeral Procession of Madam Geneva* . . . [2277] which is dedicated by 'a Lover of Trade' to 'those Melancholly Sufferers the Distillers'. This is a parish funeral; the chief mourner is one Loddy, an almost naked beggar and a familiar character; distillers follow, and in front ragged women drink and fight. In *The Lamentable Fall of Madam Geneva* [2278] she is dead drunk and prostrate, with bottle and glass. Though the spirit is entirely different this foreshadows Hogarth's contrast between gin and beer in 1751. One of the burlesqued monuments (made out of the implements of distilling) beloved by cartoonists is depicted in *To the Mortal Memory of Madam Geneva* . . . [Pl. 24]. She was the 'kind comfort of the starving Poor', to quote from verses engraved below another print: 'Queen Gin: for whom they'd Sacrifice / Their Shirts, or Smocks, nay both their Eyes' [2278]. The theme of all these prints is that gin alone could produce that absolute (and degraded) drunkenness which was the only solace of the very poor who could not afford beer. Behind the agitation were the interests of publicans, farmers, and landlords, and the opportunity to attack Walpole. Of course Madam Geneva was not dead. She survived, at first under ironically defiant names—'Parliament Brandy', 'Strip-me-naked', 'The Last Shift', 'Cholick Water', and the like. Then openly, after gin riots ('No Gin, No King') and a war on informers.

Pictorial attack on the reigning sovereign is, so far, exceptional : as a rule Ministers can do no right, Kings, little wrong, a convention that makes exceptions noteworthy. George II was unpopular in 1737; his fits of rage, when he would kick his hat about, were well known. *Æneas in a Storm* [2326] shows the King's ship tempest-tost, while Britannia waits his return to England from Hanover; one of the winds in the clouds is kicking a hat. Much more disrespectful is *The Festival of the Golden Rump* [2327] in the same year. This is one of those prints deriving from the frequent 'dreams' and 'visions' dear to the *Craftsman* and other papers, in which the more elaborate fantasies of the Opposition wits were embodied. It is based on 'The Vision of the Golden Rump' in *Common Sense or the Englishman's Journal* (written by Lord Chesterfield and others) for 19 March: the King is a 'pagod' on an altar, a satyr with a golden rump; his high priestess (the Queen) tried to appease him 'when he lifted up his cloven hoof to correct his domesticks'. Walpole is his chief magician in a robe embroidered with the words 'Auri sacra Fames'. The Order of the Bath (instituted in 1725) is also ridiculed in the text and in the print, which is unbelievably gross. Disrespect could hardly go farther and one must suppose that the authors were emboldened by the support of the Prince, then enjoying popularity at his father's expense. Disrespect was again displayed in 1738, in *Solomon in his Glory* [2348] where George II dallies with Madame Walmoden, the sceptre falling from his hand, while a pugdog plays with his mourning hatband for Queen Caroline, whose portrait is on the wall.

Ever since 1731 grievances against Spain had been piling up, with a swelling stream of anti-Walpole propaganda and a growing demand for war. This increasingly appears in the prints from 1737 and only a few out of very many can be noticed here. *Slavery* [2355, *c.* 1738], inscribed 'To the Worthy and most injur'd Merchants of Great Britain', is noteworthy for the first Shakespeare quotation: John of Gaunt's speech in *Richard II* from 'This fortress built by Nature for herself' to '. . . bound in with shame / With inky-blots & rotten parchment bonds'—very apt to Walpole's hated treaties and the Convention of Pardo. A Spaniard drives four Britons in a plough, while Walpole forces the British Lion to follow; in the middle distance another Spaniard cuts off Jenkins's ear, while a Spanish ship fires at an unresisting vessel. The famous ear appears repeatedly, for instance in another scene by the sea which adorns a song with music: *The Present State of Little Britain* [2335*],

> Britons where is your great Magnanimity, where's your boasted Courage
> flown (*bis*)
> Quite perverted to Pu-si-la-ni-mi-ty, Scarce to call your Souls your own
> (*bis*).

Britannia sits on a canon which is inscribed 'Open my lips', words from what was then known as 'Cromwell's device'; the canon speaks: 'O Lord open thou my Lips and my Mouth shall show forth thy Praise.' Inland, a Spaniard cuts off the ear of the kneeling Jenkins, and stuffs a paper, 'Convention', down his throat—an attack on Walpole's bitterly resented attempt to settle mutual grievances by negotiation.

Hostilities with Spain produced the usual exasperation with the Dutch. *Hocus Pocus, or the Political Jugglers* [2419], dated 8 October 1739 (war was declared on 29 October), contains typical complaints of selfish neutrality: a Dutchman rifles the pockets of an Englishman who is fighting with a Spaniard, while a pug (Holland) runs off with the bone for which two other dogs are fighting. And again in the same print, 'Sly Hogan takes a neutral course / Yet helps yᵉ Spaniards with his stores.' The same theme is that of a crude street ballad, *The Whimsical Age or the Political Jugglers*,[1] where the three dogs and the bone reappear:

> Mynheer would have little to do,
> But cunningly crys out forbariance sir,
> He's nought but the gelt in his view,
> While England and spain are at variance sir.

The declaration of war did nothing to lessen the frenzied distrust of Walpole. In 1740 the coming general election loomed over politics, moving the Opposition to further flights of propaganda, and the print-sellers took full advantage of the public mood. Campaigning prints were produced on both sides, remarkable for a kind of sophistication that was new. *The Stature of a Great Man or the English Colossus* [Pl. 25], published in March, is a bold design and the first direct illustration of a passage from Shakespeare. Walpole 'doth bestride the Narrow World', with the familiar quotation from *Julius Caesar* engraved below; the 'dear Brutus' of the original becomes 'dear P......y' (Pulteney). As usual Walpole is accused of subservience to Fleury, preventing the ships from fighting, destroying trade, raiding the sinking fund, and so on. The design illustrates the developing art of the cartoon. *The Cardinal in the Dumps* [2454] demands mention for its recognition of Anglo-French rivalry on the American continent, normally outside the cartoonist's horizon till the eve of the Seven Years War. Fleury and Walpole are both dismayed at Vernon's capture of Portobello; the former says, 'G—d, he'll take all our Aquisitions in America.' 'The Head of the Colossus' is on a pole.

The theme of Walpole as 'Prime Minister', an office, alien to the Constitution, which he had assumed, and for which, with other things, he deserved the axe, was prominent in 1740. It was implicit in the *Colossus*, more explicit in *The Cardinal* . . ., the direct thesis of the *Life and Death of Pierce Gaveston . . . Grand Favorite and Prime Minister To that Unfortunate Prince, Edward II . . . With Political Remarks by way of Caution to all Crowned Heads and Evil Ministers . . .* [2462]. The 'caution' was enforced by a frontispiece by George Bickham (who also published the book). Walpole, without his wig, stands by a block, holding a dying confession on which the word 'Corruption' is legible; a soldier stands by to represent the standing army.

---

[1] M. Percival, op. cit., pp. 158–61.

With the pending election, pro-Walpole propaganda makes a first appearance in two prints of 1740. One is yet another appeal to history: in *The Patriot-Statesman* [2459] Burghley conducts Walpole ('like *Burleigh*, shining with victorious Rays') to the temple of Fame; they are under the protection of Pallas, who drives away Envy, Discord, &c. This heads a broadside where the comparison of the two statesmen is seriously elaborated in a speech against faction put into the mouth of Elizabeth. Different editions and states, well worn, show that this was widely circulated: it can hardly have been effective against the general belief that the glorious past was being betrayed, and that all praise of Ministers was venal. Johnson's *London* (in 1738) expresses the mood of the time:

> Struck with the seat that gave Eliza birth,
> We kneel and kiss the consecrated earth,
> In pleasing dreams the blissful age renew,
> And call Britannia's glories back to view,
> Behold her cross triumphant on the main,
> The guard of commerce and the dread of Spain,
> Ere masquerades debauched, excise opprest,
> Or English honour grew a standing jest

And:

> Here let those reign whom pensions can incite
> To vote a patriot black, a courtier white,
> Explain their country's dear-bought rights away,
> And plead for pirates in the face of day.

In its day, *London* was a (Tory) political pamphlet. Another appeal to the age of Elizabeth was the reprinting, in January 1740, of the *Double Deliveraunce* [Pl. 3], that is, of the version of 1689, with the title *Spayne and Rome defeated* [2456].

The other ministerial effort was a defence of the Walpolean system in the guise of an attack on the *Craftsman*; the editor, Nicholas Amhurst, 'Caleb D'Anvers', is a tinker, crying, 'Constitutions to mend', the first of a line of political tinkers who damage the pot with every patch. Here is another instance of newspaper, print, and ballad in co-operation: in February the theme was broached in the *Daily Gazetteer*, which advertised the print in June: *The Itinerant Handy-Craftsman, or Caleb Turn'd Tinker* [2448]. A ballad followed, *The Tinker Turn'd Politician; or Caleb's Metamorphosis*,[1] and finally fourteen stanzas of the ballad were printed in the *Gazetteer* in March 1741. The theme was that the Place Bills, Bribery Bill,

[1] M. Percival, op. cit., p. 198.

&c., of the past fifty years were harmful tinkering with the Constitution. Lines from *Hudibras* on the print point the moral:

> Faults still they find with That or This
> And something always is amiss;
> As if Government was intended
> For nothing else but to be mended.

The *Craftsman* retorted that the 'tinkering' could be harmful only to the 'constitution of a Particular Ministry'.

This was shadow-boxing compared with the grand crisis of 13 February 1741, when a motion, 'the Motion', for the removal of Walpole from his Majesty's presence and councils for ever was made in both Houses. The tale of his misdeeds was a rehearsal of familiar accusations. This had been foreshadowed in the winter by a large and important print, *The Evil Genius of England in Several Scenes relating to the War* [2418], dated 6 December and still advertised on 24 February. The high hopes of Opposition were dashed by the Minister's unexpectedly large majority; 290 to 106 in the Commons, 108 to 59 in the Lords. The Walpolean triumph was celebrated in a famous print, *The Motion* [Pl. 26], which produced a sequence of prints and counter-prints, forming one of the peaks of English pictorial polemics. It is noteworthy too for the first full use of a device that at once became popular; the verse explanation is in the patter of a Savoyard raree-showman, admirably suited to the fantasies of propaganda.[1] This elaborate print, using the coach allegory with a new realism and with a topographical setting, the buildings of Whitehall, was advertised in the *Gazetteer* on 21 February. Sandys (who made the motion in the Commons) drops a Place Bill, dismayed at the reckless driving of the Duke of Argyll (whose speech in seconding Carteret's motion in the Lords had been impolitically violent). At Argyll's feet crouches a 'Spaniel curr', Bubb Dodington; the passenger, Carteret, cries, 'Let me get out:' Pulteney in the foreground wheels off a barrow-load of 'Patriot' propaganda, leading 'de Puppies by de Nose', first of many illustrations of this metaphor. The verses begin:

> Who be dat de Box do sit on?
> Tis John, de Hero of *North-Britain*
> Who out of Place, does Place-men spit on
> Doodle Doodle do

[1] It probably derived from ballads. Cf. *The Raree-Show-Man. Or His Box and Magick Lanthorn Expos'd* ... and *The Englishman's Answer to the Magick Lanthorn*. Madden Collection, Cambridge University Lib., III, nos. 1606, 1537. *The Raree Showman* is depicted in *The First Heat of the European Race* [2333]; his first appearance (as Charles II) was in 1681; see pp. 56–57.

They end:

> So Sirs, we have shewn you all de *Hero's*
> Who put you together by the Ear-os,
> And frighten you so with groundless Fear-o's
>   Doodle . . .

The Motion also encouraged a fashion for the characterization of individuals in a way that was new: Lyttelton is described: 'Who be dat astride de Pony / So long, so lank, so lean and bony.' Published at 3*d.*, *The Motion* was clearly subsidized, the usual price being 6*d.*, or perhaps a shilling. A woodcut version was 'sold by all the Booksellers of London and Westminster' and the design was adapted to a fan mount. A similar design [2478] is attributed to Gravelot, and may well be the original version; in this there is a riverside setting; evidently Walpole's house at Chelsea. It is one of the rare prints that can be ascribed to ministerial inspiration at the highest level. 'Tell me dear now', Horace Walpole wrote to Conway from Florence ('extremely diverted' by it), 'who made the design, and who took the likenesses, they are admirable. . . .'[1]

The print reflects the situation: the Walpolean elation and the momentary dejection of Opposition. But as the text of the famous motion served to point and concentrate election propaganda, so the print gave opportunities to the Opposition artists. The war of pictures was at its height in March and had ended by the dissolution of Parliament on 27 April. It was seemingly an affair of the initiated: M.P.s, journalists, political clubs, and coffee houses. *The Motion* was followed by *The Grounds*, *The Motive*, *The Protest*, and *The Reason* (for the Motion),[2] all setting out the case against Sir Robert: placemen, bribery, peculation, servile bishops, taxes, excise, standing army, the Gin Act, damage to trade and manufactures. There are attacks on Ralph Freeman, editor of the *Gazetteer*[3] called 'the Court Evil' (from Henry Fielding's paper, the *Champion*). In *The Grounds* Walpole's son Robert (Volpone Junior) drives the 'Money Press', a massive chest on wheels drawn by yoked placemen, which crushes 'Liberty', 'Honesty', 'Trade', and 'Manufactures'. Volpone stands on the chest, making coins pour into it by slashing at the body of his child, 'Sinking Fund'. He is 'de Grand Projector of Great Britain'. Verse 14:

> Who be de Groupes of Swordsmen, Gownsmen, and other dat escort him?
> Dey be his Creatures in de State, Church, Army and Revenue, dat court him
> For as dey depend on him, dey must needs support him.

---

[1] *Letters*, ed. Toynbee, i. 96 (25 Mar. 1741); was the author George Townshend? See below, p. 115.　　[2] 2484, 2485, 2488, 2491.　　[3] Cf. Johnson's definition, p. 2.

The other prints are on similar lines, each with special items of interest. *The Negotiator's* [2463], 'a brave gallante show', published in March, belongs to the same set, but is concerned with foreign affairs in a complicated way; George II and Charles Albert, who was claiming the Austrian Succession, are on a see-saw among the other powers; Frederick tramples on Silesia; 'Bohemia' (Maria Theresa) weeps. Walpole, with one foot in a grave—that is, tottering to his fall—clings to a pacifist policy and begs the bellicose Philip of Spain to listen to the (ostensibly) peace-loving Fleury.

The Walpolean counter-prints attack the Opposition leaders and their Press. In *The Political Libertines, or Motion upon Motion* [2490] Pulteney leads *The Champion* by the nose, that is, Henry Fielding who is further identified by holding his play, 'Pasquin'. In *The Funeral of Faction* [2487] who 'dy'd of a disappointment on feb yᵉ 13, 1741', the procession is led by Caleb D'Anvers (Amhurst) with his 'Craftsman' banner. Other newspapermen follow with their papers, including the *Champion* and the *Daily Post*. They carry Faction to 'the Family Vault', the tomb of Wat Tyler, Jack Straw, Jack Cade, and Kett. On a memorial stone are the figures by which the famous motion was defeated. The important point is made (in verses which by exception are not the showman's) that the defeat has dashed the hopes of 'Perkin' in 'Old England'. In *The Acquital* [2486] Pulteney and others impotently throw their darts at Walpole; these are 'Want of Place', 'Want of Pension', 'Resentment', 'Sham Patriotism', and the like. And in the more allegorical *Truth and Moderation* [2489] of 21 April the crowd of assailants is led by 'Vain Conceit'. Ministerial print-shop propaganda of this kind is rare.

With the Dissolution there was a slackening of prints until the new Parliament met on 1 December, and the more sophisticated personalities cease, but during the interval there were some interesting satires on foreign affairs. The sensation of the election was the defiance of the Court in the supposedly safe Westminster, by Admiral Vernon and a Patriot colleague. This was the first of the famous Westminster elections where Opposition challenged potent ministerial interests with the cry that they represented the 'Sense of the People', and where both sides could command powerful mobs. George Bickham dedicated the first of many prints of the Covent Garden hustings [2497] 'to the brave Admiral Vernon, and his worthy Colleague': they are for 'the Glory of Britain'—their opponents for 'Excise'. Nevertheless, the Court prevailed, but the closing of the poll under the protection of a party of Guards gave opportunity for an election petition, carried against Walpole by a majority of two. In the new election two Patriots were unopposed; two exulting broadsides followed. In *The Triumph of Justice* [2501], dedicated to 'the Independent Electors of Westminster', the Prince of Wales presides over Walpole's tomb, and in *The Banner of Liberty* [2505], an illustration to the text of the election petition, Liberty drives away Slavery.

Walpole's fall is celebrated with exulting prints. Like Laud, and in the traditional manner, he disgorges his spoils in *The Political Vomit for the Ease of Britain* [2531], a print with a Dutch copy. And in *Brother Robert under his Last Purgation* [2533] a vision foretells his execution, which, seemingly, was now no longer merely visionary. In *From One House to Another* [2536] 'Sir Blew String' is driven by Justice to the Lords: 'The Country claims its due, Protection's vain.' But doubts soon prevail. The Patriots are now Placemen or would-be Placemen, and in *The Promotion* [2535] Walpole laughs at the distribution of offices and honours. The demand for vengeance was general: the populace held him guilty of the crimes so often stressed in newspapers, ballads, and prints. But proof was lacking. Had he robbed the Sinking Fund for himself? Had he given treasonous orders to admirals? Would the Screen operate again, as after the South Sea? A secret committee of 21 was appointed at last to investigate and a ballad in April voices fears and hopes: *The Secret Committee*:[1]

> In great expectation
> Thus prays the whole *Nation*
> No Screen in the SECRET COMMITTEE.

Pictorially, Walpole's career as Minister begins and ends with 'The Screen'. Four prints on this theme in 1742 are extant. First [2539], Walpole as Punch exults at the defeat by two votes on 9 March of the first motion for a secret committee; a picture on the screen anticipates his imprisonment and death; among the many allusions to national grievances is the first on the hard lot of the half-pay officer while commissions were given to boys. Shameful episodes are displayed on a tall folding screen in two other prints. *The Screen* [2540] has the sub-title, 'A New Screen for an Old one', and its advertisement in the *London Evening Post* announces that 'The Old Screen' in 1721 [Pl. 20 *b*] is 'to be had'. Walpole (now Lord Orford) behind the screen, is still Punch, pulling the strings of puppet M.P.s; Pulteney, 'Dear William', is informed:

> ... He was the *Punch* at first you saw;
> He gives the other Puppets Law,

1 Percival, op. cit., pp. 180–2.

And by his secret Strings he still
Governs the others as he will;
And all the Difference that is known.
You only *hear another Tone:*
The *Puppet Man,*—behind the *Screen,*
Is the same man,—although not seen.

(Quoted on the print from the *London Evening Post.*)

In *The Night Visit, or the Relapse: With the Pranks of Bob Fox the Jugler* [2559] twenty-three charges against Lord Orford are depicted on the screen. In front, George II consults him on the management of his Ministers: 'Mix and divide them' is the reply. The King's protection of the fallen Minister is symbolized in *Touch me not; or B—bs Defiance* [2551], a Janus-head of Walpole and the King is seen as if in a glass; the former defies Justice herself: 'Touch me, Madam, if you dare.'

> . . . I and the King the haughty W—lsey cry'd,
> And All ye Malice of his Foes defy'd;
> But R——n, haughtier still (t'evade Disaster)
> Cries, Touch me if you can,—and not my M——r.

The fabric of misrepresentation and exaggeration built up by propaganda and given visual substance in the prints led naturally to clamour for Walpole's punishment, for comprehensive Place Bills, for 'no standing armies' and (inconsistently) for vigorous conduct of the war; it led of course to anger with the new placemen and ex-Patriots. Some of this was directed against Pulteney. But it was manifested also in a flurry of Radicalism: popular constituencies, led by London, sent instructions to their members demanding the things they had been led to expect. They ordered them to vote for the punishment of Walpole, for shorter Parliaments, against decay of trade, and also against the export of wool, and so on. These instructions are the subject of *London's Conduct stands the Test* . . . [2577] in which unresponsive M.P.s rely on 'lesser Boroughs' and are double-faced; there is a 'Ministerial Forge' where a smith is hammering out the 'Lie of the Day', articles are being prepared for 'the Gazetteer', and instruments of oppression are stored for future use: 'Tax Skrews', 'Tax Bridles', 'Law Pincers', 'Hanover Bridles', and the like. A counter-print followed on 30 November, *Bristol and Nottingham against London: or the Funeral of City Faction* [2570], more defiant than propagandist, and adapted from *The Funeral of Faction*; the tomb is the same, the newspaper banners are the same. A satyr burns the London Instructions in a bonfire, Discord flies off, Walpole laughs and his supporters shout derisively, 'Impeachers ha ha', 'Instructors ha ha'.

Disillusionment was complete. It is impossible here to follow the prints on the ministerial shufflings of the next few years. These were mainly anti-ministerial, but the Opposition was not sufficiently powerful to whip up popular clamour. One development must be noted—Pitt's growing importance. He makes a first appearance among the noisy clamourers for office in *The Claims of the Broad Bottoms* [3579] dated 1 March 1743; he hopes 'to be puff'd into something by and by. . . . Am I not an Orator? Make me Secretary at War.' His public repute, the occasional breaks in the popularity that was so vital to his policy and career, are vividly illuminated. His first achievement of office in 1746, with a consequent volte-face on the Hanover question, evoked violent attacks, summarized in a ballad by Hanbury Williams, *The Unembarrassed Countenance.*

> He bellow'd and roar'd at the Troops of Hanover . . .
> That no man was honest who gave them a vote . . .
>
> But nature had given him ne'er to be Harrass'd
> An unfeeling heart, and a front unembarrass'd.

The gibes of the song are repeated in *This is the Unembarrassed Countenance or, an Irish Post Face* [2854]—Pitt had just been appointed joint Vice-Treasurer of Ireland.

A main cause of discontent was the disappointing course of the war, and the use of Hanoverian troops. Dettingen brought this to a head—the English fight, and fast—Hanoverians rest, and feast—such is the theme of two prints [2583-4] on *The H—v—n Confectioner General*, that is, Baron Ilten, general of the Hanoverians, who was accused of preventing the Guards from following up the victory. In the second, George II, as the White Horse of Hanover, rides the fainting British Lion, who complains that he is starving on 'bon pour Nicole', a bitter catch phrase connoting the contemptuous words of a Frenchman on giving bread to his horse, Nicole, while the English troops were without it. Ilten lurks behind a tree; the English pursue the French, the Hanoverians are stationary: 'We will not be commanded by ye English.' Lord Marischal, the Jacobite, sent a similar print to an unknown correspondent, saying that it was widely circulated in England. He explains allusions to 'starve donc' and 'bon pour Nicole' as things which 'vraies ou fausses, font un grand effet sur le peuple'.[1] These anti-Hanoverian prints were in effect Jacobitish propaganda—perhaps Jacobite productions.

The reactions evoked by the Forty-five are vividly illustrated, with No Popery as the leading theme, especially at first, and much is made of the supposed threat to abbey lands. *The Invasion, or Perkins Triumph* [2636] is 'a Protestant Print. Inscrib'd to all true Lovers of their Religion & Liberty', and is an adaptation of an anti-Sacheverell print of 1710, *Needs Must when the Devil Drives*. As before 'Perkin' (now Perkin II) is in the coach; as before, two of the horses are 'Passive Obedience' and 'Non-Resistance'; the others are 'Superstition', 'Rebellion', 'Hereditary Right', 'Arbitrary Power'. Perkin holds a mask, sign that his *Declaration* (in which he declared himself 'utterly averse to all persecution') is a snare. The King of France drives, with the Pope as postilion; behind, as footmen, are the Devil and two monks. A monk carries the banner of the Inquisition, another superintends the burning of a heretic. A band of Scots follow the coach with the banner of Slavery and Wooden Shoes. The coach drives over Britannia, who drops her purse and other emblems of Property, and also over personifications of Religion (with a Bible), and Law (with Magna Charta). The verses, in the *Eikon*-Sacheverell pattern, conclude:

> Our Laws, Religion, Liberties, a Prey
> To Gallic Fury and Tyrannic Sway,
> Our Lands to dronish Monks and Fryars given,
> Who make a Mammon Merchandise of Heaven,
> These lively Emblems grace our Poignant Print,
> If these are nothing—the Devil's in't.

A more poignant attempt to curdle Protestant blood followed in October, *The Procession, or the Popes Nursling riding in Triumph* [2658]. Perkin and the Pope are drawn in a car by asses, wolves, and tigers; Louis XV drives, shouting, 'Universal Monarchy'; the Bourbon menace is combined with ultra-Protestant propaganda at its most extreme. A Spaniard shouts, 'Gibraltar and P. Mahon is ours'; others cry, 'Tame the Proud Britons', 'The Trade of the World is ours', 'Cape Breton restor'd' (it had just been taken from France). There are many other items, and emblems of 'Popish Errors Rage and Infernal Cruelty' include 'Bulls and Indulgences Fines Tortures Excommunications Death by Fire and Sword'. All the Church lands are to be reclaimed. But in the background is a view of York Minster, with a regiment of parsons led by Archbishop Herring, who

---

[1] Quoted from the *Stuart Papers* (4 Nov. 1743), Mahon, *History of England*, 1858, iii, appendix, p. xiii.

has discarded mitre and robes for military dress. (On news of Prestonpans Herring had convened the county and set on foot an association of volunteers.) In a patriotic print, *The Mitred Champion: or, the Church Militant* [2634], he is dressed (like Archbishop Williams in 1642) half as soldier, half as bishop; exclaiming 'Religion! Liberty! My Country', he leads a body of armed clerics, with an officer who shouts 'King George and yᵉ Church of England for ever'. But this was travestied in a counter-print [2635] with the words of the militant Herring altered to 'My (Mitre),[1] my Lands, My Gold, Church'. The armed clergy lack enthusiasm; one says, 'I'll be Vicar of Bray still'; another, 'I've 12 Children but no lands'. The apathy of the volunteers is illustrated in *Briton's Association Against the Pope's Bulls* [2661]. The Pretender leads from Edinburgh a herd of bulls snorting out 'Excommunications, Indulgences, Massacres, Jure Divino, Decretals'. A medallion of Henry VIII has the legend 'Ho ho abby lands again'. The print is bisected by the river Tweed, with Jacobites marching on Scottish soil. Neptune, saying 'the true Spirit of Liberty', presents Britannia with a palm of victory. Soldiers are marching north, some prepared to fight, but one says, 'I wont go out of yᵉ Parish'; another, 'Agod I'd go five miles to fight', and the chaplain complains, 'I wish they'd go to Dinner'.

All the post-rebellion Jacobite prints—quite a number from 1746 to 1750—attack the Duke of Cumberland. In December 1746 he is *The Butcher* [Pl. 27] in a caricature 'taken from yᵉ Sign of a Butcher in yᵉ Butcher Row'—one of those prints of persons constructed of appropriate objects. Actually, it is adapted from a print of a butcher [2470], one of a set of such composite figures. There is a symbolical border with satyr's head, and fire-brands, in the background are blazing buildings, and the figure is given a military dress. It is constructed of an ox on its hindlegs, with the head of a calf; the body is a butcher's tray, in one hand is a cleaver, in the other a slaughterer's axe—as in the original. But on the soldier's tunic is a star and an epaulette formed of butcher's hooks (anticipating Napoleon's famous emblematical epaulette[2]). The verses, with omissions and one significant alteration, are as on the original; they end:

> His axe, Knives, Clever, is prepar'd for fight,
> And Death & Slaughter are his sole delight
> Thus arm'd he Terror all aroᵈ doth* spread
> Had he not borrow'd from a Calf his Head.
> (* 'would' in original.)

---

[1] Depicted.   [2] See *E.P.C. 1793–1832*, Pl. 57.

The favourite approach is to contrast the Duke and the Pretender. A sequence of prints and counter-prints—though which is print and which counter-print we can only guess—may begin with a loyalist one, *The agreeable Contrast between the British Hero, and the Italian Fugitive* [2832]. Cumberland and Britannia address the Pretender, who sits reading: she says, 'Vain Tool, behold here at thy Feet / Your broken Hopes and Cullodens Defeat.' A Jacobite manifesto followed (or preceded) this: *The Agreeable Contrast. Shews that a Greyhound is more agreeable than an Elephant, & a Genteel personage More agreeably Pleasing than a Clumsey one* . . . [2833]. The graceful Chevalier, who turns to admire Flora Macdonald, is accompanied by a greyhound, while Cumberland's corpulence is set off by an elephant; the Duke, who has a butcher's knife and apron, deserts 'a town trollop'.

A climax of Jacobitism is expressed in a print without date or title [2834]. The Pretender, in Highland dress, stands with a cap of Liberty beside him, behind are a tent and Scottish soldiers; a lamb stands on a wolf. Cumberland holds a bloody axe and is surrounded with emblems of savagery; the crown falls from a plant which is probably intended for a turnip, emblem of Hanover. Britannia sits between them holding a balance in which 'Mercy' outweighs 'Butchery'. Below is Hamlet's speech to the Queen, beginning, 'Look here upon this Picture and on this', abridged, and adapted to 'two Princes', instead of two brothers. Another savagely Jacobite print (in 1749) was suggested by a gift of wild animals from Maria Theresa to Cumberland. In *The Prodigal Son. or; the Brute among the Beasts; to feed Swine* [3014], Cumberland sits near a horned owl wearing a Garter ribbon, which stands on a human heart and a skull inscribed 'Col . . . .n' (Culloden). A huge goat and a boar symbolize the Duke's character; a draggled British Lion is in a cage. The food—'like my own'— that the Duke chooses for his beasts is blood. The Prince of Wales is 'yᵉ hornified owl' (seemingly an early allusion to Bute and the Princess), the Chevalier is the 'Lyon of England' who will 'chase to yᵉ Forest yᵉ bloodhounds again'.

Meanwhile, the peacemakers at Aix-la-Chapelle incurred the customary dispraise. The most obnoxious proviso was for the return to France of Cape Breton, 'the people's darling acquisition', with the humiliating condition that two hostages were to be given for its surrender. Among the prints on the negotiators and the terms two stand out. *Tempora mutantur, et Nos mutamur in illis* [3015] in December 1748 is one of those bitter comparisons with the glorious past. A Frenchman points to the two hostages:

'Dis for de Glory of de Grand Monarch.' A plenipotentiary, presumably Lord Sandwich, says, 'Dam Posterity I'll get Money'; he has stabbed the British Lion and the Hanoverian Horse is licking its blood, while the Gallic Cock crows; a 'poor distressed Sailor' begs from a defeatist admiral. At these shocking sights Cromwell, Henry V, and Edward III rise from their graves to say: 'Was it for this I sought the Lord and Fought'; 'Agincourt's forgot'; 'And Creci likewise'.

The Contrast 1749 [3028] satirizes the grand display of fireworks in the Green Park to celebrate the peace. The comparison is between the disgruntled Englishman who has got 'No Money, with Fireworks', and the elated Dutchman who has 'Money, with Commerce'. They face each other, one with empty pockets and a burnt-out pavilion behind him (a casualty of the display), the other with over-full pockets and with sunlit ships in the background. The Dutchman jeers: 'Myn Heer You have been at War what have you got?' In the public mind the Dutch had been laggards in war, intent always on their seaborne trade. This traditional attitude had been vividly expressed in *The Benefit of Neutrality* [2665],[1] dated 26 December 1745. A cow represents Power; an Englishman tries to pull it away by the tail from a Frenchman and a Spaniard who have seized it by the horns, while an unregarded Dutchman sits quietly milking: 'A neutral Cur, who sees the Fray / Steals in and bears the Bone away.'

During the political stagnation of the mid-eighteenth century, Opposition functioned feebly under the patronage of the Prince of Wales (till his death in 1751). The prints register discontent ranging from disgruntlement to Jacobite rancour. Modish folly, connoting national decadence, was symbolized in a fashionable toy: the *pantin*, a manikin suspended on a string with movable arms and legs (a similar symbolism was given to another toy some forty years later).[2] A languidly fashionable company dangle these objects in *Pantin à la Mode* [3017], a print with cautionary verses: Britain aspired like Rome to excel 'in Arts and Arms', 'Till Gallic Influence / Bid Foppery rise, and turn'd the Scale of Sense'. *Folly Triumphant* . . . [3068] is a broadside in a similar vein with attacks on (alleged) imbecilities: 'Folly, playing with his *Pantin*, in his Triumphal Car, drawn by a *Butterfly*, and *a Locust*, Emblems of Pride and Poverty.' The follies include the firework display in the Green Park, the new Mansion House, Westminster Bridge with its defective arch and

---

[1] Probably the origin of an important print of 1778; see below, pp. 153-4.
[2] The bandelure or *émigrette* (the yo-yo of the twentieth century), supposed occupation of *émigrés* at Coblentz.

foreign (Swiss) architect, as well as the grand hoax of the century, the Bottle Conjuror[1] which was the subject of many prints and for at least seventy years a recurrent symbol for political humbug.

[1] An advertisement (11 Jan. 1749, *General Advertiser*, &c.) that a man would, among other marvels, get into a quart bottle at the Haymarket Theatre attracted crowds; it was a hoax by the Duke of Montagu to test public credulity. Cf. p. 148.

V

FROM PEACE TO WAR

WITH the sudden death of the Prince of Wales in 1751, Opposition almost ceased to exist, but in 1753 the calm was broken by one of those storms against the Ministry of the day, blown up against the Pelhams by agitation against the Act for permitting the naturalization of foreign Jews. 'No Jews, no wooden shoes', was the slogan. Bishops who had voted for the Bill were assailed as Deists, and, with its other supporters, alleged to have been heavily bribed. The many prints on this burning question display the facets of a peculiarly crude manifestation of anti-semitism. A general election was imminent, and the Act, passed in June, was repealed in December. In *Vox Populi Vox Dei, or the Jew Act Repealed* [3202] Christianity is menaced by a 'Mob of Jews & Deists', and by a bishop who holds a bribe of £1,000. The verses begin, 'God's Word declares the Jews a Vagrant race.' On the eve of the election Henry Pelham died: in *His Arrival at his Country Retirement & Reception* [3264] he enters Hell, greeted by predecessors and demons; his crimes, and above all the Jew Act, are greater than those of the other villains: Walpole, Wolsey, Judge Jeffreys, and Machiavelli.

The Jew Act and its slogans echoed through the elections, and even cost some candidates their seats, notoriously in London and Oxfordshire (as the prints record). But ministerial influence was of course all-powerful, and in *The Compleat Vermin-catcher of G— B—n, or the old Trap new baited* [3269], published at the beginning of the elections in April 1754, Newcastle, who had succeeded his brother, fishes down the chimney of the House of Commons; his line is baited with 'Titles, Bribes, Places, Pensions, Secret Commissions, Army, Navy, Excise'. Eager aspirants hasten from all quarters.

Impending war, after the uneasy peace, soon dominated the scene. In *The Grand Monarque in a Fright; or, the British Lion roused from his Lethargy* [3284], dated 4 April 1755, it is clear that this is an American crisis, with the Ohio Valley in dispute, and that the West and East Indies are involved. Newcastle feebly listens to the blandishments of the Governor of Canada, de la Jonquière, who begs him to drug and pacify the awaking Lion. Louis is double-faced, making apparent concessions while ordering his Minister to use the chain of forts on the Ohio to drive off the Lion. Verses begin: 'France trembles at the British Lion's Roar / And Lewis' treach'rus Wiles deceive no more.' In June competition for the Ohio Valley is again the theme of *The American Moose-Deer, or away to the River Ohio* [3280].

Eve-of-war hostilities are the subject of a pair of prints by Boitard (a Frenchman), *British Rights maintained; or French Ambition dismantled* [3331] and *British Resentment, or the French fairly coopt in Louisbourg* [3332], one published in August, the other in September, and both reflecting the premature rejoicings and exaggerated hopes caused by the small engagement off Newfoundland under Boscawen. In both, Mars and Neptune aid Britain and the Lion worsts the Cock. In the first Britannia holds the staff and cap of Liberty; her Lion plants its paws on feathers stripped from the Cock, and these include Ohio and Quebec. The 'Genius of France' laments: 'Ave Maria que ferons nous! after our Massacres, and Persecutions, Must Heretics possess this promis'd Land. . . .'A falling star is inscribed 'Universal Monarchy—ha! ha! ha'. In the second, Britannia, listening to 'the complaints of her injured Americans, receives them into her protection': two noble savages kneel at her feet. The Cock disgorges French positions including Niagara, Crown Point, and Ohio, but not Quebec. A dismayed Frenchman watches a canon inscribed with 'Cromwell's Device'.

In *Half-Peace* [3334] and *Half-War* [3335] published in November the note has altered. In one, while France is eager to fight, an Englishman relies on treaties, and his sword is padlocked by the Hanoverian Horse. In the other, an Englishman tries to snatch Nova Scotia from a Frenchman who threatens to retaliate in Germany. Backwardness in fighting the French in America is the theme of *Oliver Cromwell's Ghost* [3340]. His portrait heads a broadside in which his spirit protests to the dithering Ministry and recites the exploits of Admiral Blake.

With the formal declaration of war on 18 May 1756 and the disasters that followed there was a swelling demand for the dismissal of the Ministry and the appointment of Pitt, embodiment of the discontents, antipathies, and aspirations of the country. In the crescendo of indignation prints multiplied as never before—they are literally to be counted in hundreds. The new development of 'cards' began in the summer, and George Townshend embarked on a campaign of 'caricaturas' published by Darly, a joint enterprise against the Ministry.[1] The political rebus—the pictograph

[1] See pp. 115-17.

letter—sprang into popularity, a device for combining the lampoon, the print, and the puzzle. The main themes are a corrupt, treacherous, and inept Ministry, the loss of Minorca, the employment in England of two regiments of mercenaries—Hessians and Hanoverians—instead of a national militia, the poisonous effects of French luxuries: 'A vain, luxurious and selfish EFFEMINACY' was the chief cause, according to 'Estimate Brown', of national degeneracy and misfortunes, in the book that went through seven editions in 1757.[1]

Ministers were caricatured, sometimes as animals—Henry Fox almost always with a fox's head and brush denoting craftiness—Newcastle was often a goose or an old woman, sometimes an ass, the dupe of Fox, and misled by his own sinister and all-powerful secretary, Andrew Stone. The first of the 'cards' is *The Pillars of the State* [Pl. 28a] by Townshend. Newcastle and Fox face each other, both wearing fleur-de-lis badges; behind each is a gallows and from this pair of 'pillars' hangs a chain supporting an inverted ship with the Gallic Cock crowing on its keel; 'Gallus so near' is a punning allusion to their French predilections and their coming fate. A favourite quotation from the *Beggar's Opera*, in a seemingly first appearance—'Brother Brother; we are both in the Wrong'—shows that they are a pair of thieves. Ministers were also the Knaves of a pack of cards; Newcastle, Spades, is *Mons.r Dupe* [3504]; Fox, Hearts, is *Mons.r Surecard* [3506], cunning and subtle; fleurs-de-lis grow at the feet of both. Anson, the gambler, is Diamonds, with a die in his hand [3535]; and Hardwicke, the Chancellor, is Clubs, *Null Marriage* [3522] with a bag of French gold, and pilloried also for his Marriage Act (which stopped some notorious abuses from irregular and unlicensed marriages). In the same series of prints he was also *The Vulture* [3502], preying on the vitals of the nation, an enemy of Liberty, Loyalty, and Justice. But Anson and Hardwicke are subsidiary villains, far less frequently attacked than Fox and Newcastle—the main theme of the cards is condemnation of these two as knave and fool [Pl. 28b], or fox and goose.

The national anger expressed in these and very many other prints went deeper than the inflated fury against Walpole, and this is recognized in *Poor Robin's Prophecy* [3383]. Sir Robert's apparition terrifies the timid Newcastle in one of the many rebuses. His words are in 'Hieroglyphick Characters' and in verse which ends 'When things are so bad that they can't be well worse / You'll wish for poor Robin who so oft you did Curse'. The comment, added in 1757, 'A Remonstrance of a deceased

---

[1] *An Estimate of the Manners and Principles of the Times*, 1757.

Minister to a People whose Complaints were rather numerous than well founded.' Another 'Hieroglyphick' (rebus) is *Oliver Cromwells Speach to the Ass & Fox 1756* [3508], an item in the Cromwell legend:

Those men that love their King & Country should not let Knaves or Fools govern, but let the Axe & Halter reward their maleadministration. Suffer not the French to frighten you, but arm your Militia, let them be your defence and be to 'em as I was. . . . I made them fear and the Dutch too. Liberty was then secur'd and no treason traitors suffer'd to rule. . . . I was a great Rogue to be sure but I had a head for it. You are such silly monkeys that you can not slip your necks out of the noose. . . .

Hengist & Horsa [3346], title of one of Darly's cards, repeats the names given to the two regiments of mercenaries, Hessians and Hanoverians, imported as a defence against France. They reflect the blackest suspicions against Ministers, who were thought to have raised this 'standing army' as a protection for themselves against national indignation. Hence the unusual excursion into fifth-century history for a parallel in the Saxon invaders who came to aid the Britons and stayed to pillage and conquer. Ministers watch their victim, the weeping Britannia, threatened by two German soldiers: 'These Foreign Friends will bleed me to death Oh! my Country. . . .' The popular demand was for a national militia as a 'constitutional' force which would be a protection against a standing army.

Between June 1756 and the following March, when he was executed, Byng is the subject of over fifty prints, almost all savagely abusive. Squibs, lampoons, and ballads abounded, and were collected into a volume of *Bungiana*. A popular street ballad is typical:

Draw nigh, my good folks, whilst to you I sing,
Great Blakeney betrayed by Newcastle and Byng.
Before, such a story ne'er has been told;
We're bought all my friends, by shining French gold.
To the block with Newcastle, and the yard arm with Byng
Tar a rara ra ra ra ra ra ra ras ring.

Newcastle, trembling for himself, did his best to concentrate anger on the Admiral and pressed for his immediate trial and execution. Opposition groups at once began to blame Ministers and were eager to prove Byng's guilt in order to discredit them for his appointment. Mass emotions were stirred and placards were posted in London 'Hang Byng or look to your King'. Most of the prints are concerned with the joint guilt of Ministers and Admiral. The former were accused of selling Minorca to the French, as in a rebus, *A Letter from an Auctioneer in Town to his Friend in the Country*

[3356]; other places will soon be cheaply disposed of; by exception Byng is not mentioned. *Byng Return'd; or the Council of Expedients* [3367] is an indictment ranging over a variety of subjects: guilt is fixed on the Ministry in four historical pictures of betrayals to France. Besides 'Portmahon' (Minorca) are 'Boulogne betray'd by the E. of Warwick in the Reign of Edward the 6th' (at the peace of 1550), 'Calais betray'd by the Council in the Reign of Queen Mary', 'Dunkirk sold by the Council in the Reign of Chas the 2^d'. Sovereigns are ostentatiously exempted from blame and this corresponds to the seeming popularity with cartoonists of George II, despite Pitt's alliance with Leicester House and the Princess Dowager. One of Darly's cards is *Optimus* [3537], the King's head crowned with laurel, with the inscription 'Britons behold the best of Kings'.

Accusations of luxury—peculiarly applicable to Newcastle with his extravagance and his famous and indispensable cook—were no mere garnish to the more concrete crimes: it was alleged that Ministers were reluctant to resist France for fear of being cut off from French imports. In *Birdlime for Bunglers, or the French way of Catching Fools* [3434] a Frenchman scatters bait for Ministers to scramble for, money and tickets inscribed 'Cooks, Valets, Dancers, Fiddlers', while he holds 'bird cages', that is, scourges and wooden shoes. Newcastle has a bag of '8,000,000', a sum often repeated in the prints and connoting money 'well nigh sunk the last year and not any material service done the Kingdom, but loading the Nation with heavy Taxes' [3479]. Anson, the ruined gambler, rushes forward, tied to an E. O. (roulette) table which he overturns, and Byng lies crushed under the avidly competing Ministers. Irreligion and frivolity in high places are stressed in an emblematical print foretelling national ruin, *Britannia in Distress under a Tott'ring Fabrick with a Cumberous Load* [Pl. 30], an elaborate indictment of Ministers. These 'Degenerate Britons' pull down the Pillars of the State, a fabric already breaking under a burden of pensioned parasites; the ropes they use are 'Minorca Lost, America Neglected, Trade not Protected'. 'Manufacturers in the Dumps' are seated on the ground.

These and very many more prints of the summer and autumn merge with those of the autumn and winter illustrating the growing inevitability of Pitt's appointment, as first Fox and then Newcastle resigned and Pitt would agree to no coalition with either. In *The Fox in the Pit* [3399], Fox, a fox carrying a goose inscribed '8,000,000', has been chased into a pit by a man on a horse inscribed 'Integrity', who shouts 'Justice'; the goose cries, 'I'm in Tophet.' The pit was 'designed by Nature to destroy every thing of a crafty or subtle disposition'. A generation later the same play on words was used for the sons of Pitt and Fox. Pitt's career introduces a new conception to graphic satire—the Patriot Minister.

Tributes to Pitt soon gave way to satires on the confusion that followed his dismissal in April. Byng had been sacrificed,[1] despite Pitt's support for a motion that the verdict should be laid before the House. The chief bug-bears in this interregnum were Fox and Cumberland. It may be noted here that no one goes through such violent alternations of favour and dis-favour as Cumberland, and no one but Bute is more consistently dis-praised than Fox. A famous print after Townshend appeared in April, deriding Fox's attempt to form a Ministry, *The Recruiting Serjeant, or Brittanniais Happy Prospect* [3581]. Fox calls for 'Gentlemen Voluntiers willing to serve under Military Government'; his drummer boy is Wel-bore Ellis (called by Horace Walpole Fox's jackal). The recruits are Lord Sandwich with a cricket bat, the fat Bubb Dodington in a coat patterned with fleurs-de-lis, and Lord Winchilsea carrying a rudder.[2] The grotesque patron of this group is Cumberland, posturing absurdly in a little temple topped by the Hanoverian Horse which tramples on Britannia. He had precipitated Pitt's fall by refusing to accept the command in Hanover while he was Minister.

Fox's intrigues are the subject of *Guy Vaux the 2^d* [Pl. 29 a] (16 December 1756) where a fox advances conspiratorially on the House of Commons; this is an adaptation from the *Double Deliveraunce* of 1621, an anticipation of 'Guy Vaux' prints of his son Charles a generation later. Charles Fox, one of the most caricatured of English politicians, made his first appearance in 1757, aged eight, in two prints: his father had secured for his sons a reversion to a lucrative sinecure held by Bubb Dodington. In *The Sturdy Beggar* [Pl. 29b], Stephen, the elder fox-cub, asks, 'Daddy won't he die soon, Sir', And Charles adds, 'He's too fat to live long.' Oddly prophetic is *The Bawd of the Nation or the Way to Grow Rich* [3636], in which Fox, while distributing honours to the grief of Honour (personified), encourages his children in reckless extravagance: Stephen pours money through a gridiron, while Charles begs 'Let me try'.

[1] Byng's monument in the church of Southill is inscribed: 'To the perpetual Disgrace of Publick Justice, The Honourable John Byng, Esq. Admiral of the Blue, Fell a Martyr to political Persecution, March 14, in the Year, 1757, when Bravery and Loyalty were insufficient Securities for the Life and Honour of a Naval Officer.' Transcribed by Boswell, *Life of Johnson*, Oxford, i, 1934, p. 315.

[2] It is a strange fact that two of these figures, Winchilsea and Dodington, are apparently copied from drawings by Hogarth in the manuscript of *The Analysis of Beauty* published 1753, which seems to decide the question of priority.

During the negotiations behind the scenes while gold boxes were raining upon Pitt there were by exception one or two anti-Pitt satires. One made a sensation; it is interesting as an example of the political print inspired by a leading actor in the drama and intended to influence events; and remarkable too for its inside knowledge and its insolence. This is *The Treaty or Shabears[1] Administration* [3608] published on 1 June. Newcastle sits on a turnstile, one of whose four arms is tied to a table on which is a royal crown. Pitt and Temple ('Gawkee') bow obsequiously to the Duke, while Bute attitudinizes; standing behind is a young man wearing a Garter ribbon. The point is made clear in the verses:

> See Gawkee & P——t how they Sue for a place,
> See, perch'd on a turnstile his unsteady Grace, . . .
> See a blue ribbon'd, silly, proud, son of a W——e,
> See a strutting Scotch Peer, of whom I could say more.
> Then see in the corner a strong hempen string
> That Shall hang the Vile D— if he leave his good K—.

In later states of the print an attempt was made to show that the young man—clearly the Prince of Wales—was Newcastle's nephew Lord Lincoln. 'I enclose a most extraordinary print', Walpole wrote to Mann. 'Mr. Fox has found a caricaturist equal to George Townshend, and who manages royal personages with at least as little ceremony.'[2] The facts behind the print were that Bute was taking the chief part in the difficult task of bringing Newcastle and Pitt together, playing on the Duke's dread of a Fox–Cumberland coalition and his desire to be on terms with the future—that is to be *persona grata* at Leicester House. The imputation against the Prince's mother reflects the rumour—indeed belief—that Bute was her lover; admittedly there was no evidence for this, it was assumed in order to explain his favour at Leicester House.[3] The scandal was to be inflated and exploited to a monstrous degree.

Another Foxite print was an attempt to ridicule the presentation of the Freedom of the City to Pitt and Legge; in *Will Quixote and his Squire going in triumph to the City* [3598] they drive together like mountebanks in an ornate and canopied coach; the scene is the Strand with Temple Bar in the distance. A bystander says, 'No, by G—d, wee are glad you are out.' It is a strange coincidence that in a Foxite print of 1784 the younger Pitt

---

[1] John Shebbeare, a pamphleteer and hack partisan who 'made a pious resolution of writing himself into a place or the pillory'. *Walpole Letters*, ed. Toynbee, iv. 26.

[2] *Letters*, ed. Toynbee, Oxford, iv. 58 (June 1757).

[3] *Letters from George III to Lord Bute, 1756–1766*, ed. R. Sedgwick, 1939, show that it was not the Princess but her son who was infatuated with the tutor.

was caricatured making a mock-triumphal procession to receive the Freedom of the City in another gold box.

During the great coalition polemical caricature slackened, with the two chief *bêtes noires*, Newcastle and Fox, protected by Pitt's prestige, and in the years of victory it almost ceased. But not at first. Despondency verging on despair was the climate of 1757. The prevailing mood on the eve of Pitt's appointment is well summarized in a print called *Without* [3605]; twelve little scenes of national and ministerial sins and shortcomings have captions with a blank to be filled with the word 'Without'. A king obscured by clouds is 'Supreme Majesty [Without] Power' (a good illustration of the popular view of the 'Glorious Constitution'). Others are 'Bishops [Without] Religion', 'Commanders [Without] Abilities', 'Colonies[Without]Protection'. Ships and armies are idle, trade languishes, the poor starve. 'We are no longer a nation', wrote Chesterfield on 4 July, 'I never yet saw so dreadful a prospect.' And this was before Cumberland's German fiasco, for which he was pilloried by (among others) Townshend, his former aide-de-camp: as *The Terror of France 1757* [3610] he runs from Marshal d'Estrées across the Weser, crying, 'Oh for my Recruiting Serjeant [Fox] with more men and money.' In the mock procession of *The Triumph of Cæsar* [3615] he has ruined Prussia and destroyed British interests in America, all for the sake of Hanover and to the treasonous delight of Newcastle and Fox.

In the autumn there was another failure, the return of General Mordaunt from the expedition to Rochefort. This disappointment of high hopes is expressed in *Change of Diet. A Ballad: being a Sequel to the Roast Beef of Old England* [3628]; the verses are illustrated by a kitchen interior, with a French cook gorging on beef and an Englishman spitting out frogs. 'Rule Britannia' burns in the grate and a picture of a frog and an ox is inscribed, 'Sic transit Britanniæ Gloria'. The refrain is 'O! le Soupe maigre de Fransa / O! de French Fricassees & Ragout.' Mordaunt is blamed, and there is another contrast between past and present:

> When our Edwards & Henries sate on the Throne,
> The Grand Monarque trembled, whene'er they did frown;
> As Agincourt, Poictiers & Cressy must own.

This expresses a basic sentiment, characteristic of a time when Fielding's 'Roast Beef of Old England'[1] was a sort of national anthem, sung in the gallery between the acts of the play. It should be compared with Hogarth's

---

[1] In *The Grub Street Opera*, 1731.

two invasion prints of the same year. A similar shocking reversal of the Englishman's rights and privileges was depicted in 1801 [9714]. The *mystique* of roast beef is strikingly illustrated in caricatures, but usually in a vein of anti-Gallican complacency.

Among the many attacks on General Mordaunt and the Duke there was one savage thrust at Pitt, a bitter sequel to *Will Quixote and His Squire*, and presumably Foxite propaganda. This is *England's Benifit Night Or Pyt & Boxes put Together* [3640]. A Frenchman obsequiously presents Pitt with the Freedom of Rochefort, another does the same to Legge; and both promise their best endeavours in the service of France. The British Lion growls, 'Oh! how I am Decieved by Those Two false Prophets Curst, Damn'd & Decietfull men my Eyes are now Open'd.'

Blame for British generals was soon succeeded by praise for Prussian victories and the glorification of Frederick as the Protestant hero. In *The Difference* [3671], dated 1758, Prussian victories are contrasted with British humiliation; the cap of Liberty crowned with laurel has been transported to Prussia. Frederick taunts a degraded Britannia with failure at Rochefort, while England is given up to 'Mammon'. Once again 'heros defunct' rise from the grave to record their indignation—they are Raleigh, Cromwell, and Drake.

There are also a few prints on the situation in Europe not primarily concerned with English politics. *The Cricket Players of Europe*, June 1757 [2506, 3591], is the first cricket field cartoon—there are not many. Maria Theresa bowls, Frederick of Prussia bats, Louis XV prepares to catch him out; the 'She Bear', a fat Empress Elizabeth, rushes towards Maria Theresa, saying, '. . . if you are tired I will bowl for you.' Turkey as well as other European powers, not all easy to identify, have their roles. The umpires (both dishonest) are Spain and Holland, the latter as usual a self-regarding neutral, and the issue is highly doubtful. One of the many 'Balance' prints shows the outcome; in *The Ballance turnd: or the Russian Cat-arse-trophy* [3675] dated October 1758, the Kings of Prussia and England—'Value against Number'—completely outweigh a scale overcrowded with 'The Unnatural Confederates', despite the furtive attempts of Holland to pull it down; the King of Poland and the Tsarina are falling. This is a tribute to Frederick's defeat of the Russians at Zorndorf in August.

Victory in Europe is the subject of *The Court Cards of 1759, or Hearts is Trump & has Won the Game* [3699]. The twelve cards are in two lines, red above, black below. George II, 'Optimus' as before, is King of Hearts, saying to his Knave, Pitt, 'I've won the Game My Dear Will & care not an Ace for Europe.' Pitt, who holds the cap of Liberty on a staff, answers, 'My Liege You've Hearts enough left yet for another Rubber.' The Queen of Hearts is Britannia; King, Queen, and Knave of Diamonds are Frederick II, the City of London, and Ferdinand of Brunswick. The black suits, France, Austria, Poland, admit that they are beaten. The Knave of Spades is Holland: 'I never play but I cheat.' The Knave of Clubs, Marshal de Belleisle, says, 'We can play no more I've no more Cards or Counters.' He was taken prisoner at Minden.

This is the only good-humoured allusion to the battle. There are many Minden prints, all concerned with the failure of Lord George Sackville (afterwards Germain), in command of the British cavalry, to obey the order to charge. It was the situation at Dettingen in reverse, and another example of the unfortunate consequences of Anglo-Hanoverian jealousies. The clamour against Sackville recalled that against Byng, but was less bedevilled with politics (in fact he was protected by the Court). In *The Cowardly Soldier, & the Runaway Ghost* [3687] he and Byng's ghost meet on the field of Minden. In later prints in which Germain appears, and there are many, he is never mentioned without some cruel allusion to the battle.

For the moment the topic was thrust aside by more resounding victories. On 16 October news reached London of the capture of Quebec. Then came Hawke's victory at Quiberon Bay on 20 November, celebrated in (for instance) *Britons Glory, or Admiral Hawke Triumphant* [3688]. *The Grand Fair at Versaile, or France in a Consternation* [3679] illustrates in seven little scenes a French squib on both calamities : the deeds of Joan of Arc are contrasted with the fatal influence of Mme de Pompadour. The squib is engraved below: 'Batteaux plats à vendre / Soldats à louer / Ministre à pendre / Generaux à rouer / O France! la Sexe Femelle / Fit toujours ton destinée / Ton bonheur vint d'une Pucelle, / Ton Malheur vient d'une Catin.' Horace Walpole supplied an English version—the last two lines:

> O France! still your fate you may lay at Pitt's door;
> You were sav'd by a Maid, and undone by a ———.[1]

The situation in Europe is the subject of *1760* [3745], a confused survey in which Frederick controls the Russian Bear, Maria Theresa falls, saying, 'I have crackt my Crown . . .', France begs Spain for aid and the British Lion insults the Gallic Cock. This was explained as indicating 'the com-

---

[1] *Letters*, ed. Toynbee, Oxford, iv. 305.

mon Humbugg of confederate Nations, who having almost exhausted their Blood and Treasure in the support of a destructive War, are yet resolved to persist, tho' they expose their Shame and Weakness to their very enemies'. Thus the reign ended in a blaze of glory, with Pitt at the zenith of his reputation.

VI

HOGARTH AND ENGLISH CARICATURE— MID-CENTURY DEVELOPMENTS

ONLY in the last three decades of the century was the transformation from the emblematical print to the political caricature complete. The engraving, complicated and sometimes cryptic, seldom comic, conceived in black and white and heavily cross-hatched, had been succeeded by a bold design, immediately striking to the eye, intended (usually) to amuse, and sold plain or coloured but commonly coloured. But important progress towards this development was made in the mid-century. The changes are associated, first with Hogarth, who has been called the father of English caricature (paradoxical as this seems for one who disparaged caricature). Secondly, with the amateur, who introduced the Italian art of *caricatura*. Thirdly, there was the enterprise of print-sellers who took advantage of political turmoil and amateur talent. There were also some interesting developments of imagery.

Hogarth's influence was fundamental. In his own satirical and humorous masterpieces he painted and then engraved—to use his own words—'the customs, manners, fashions, characters and Humours of the present age'.[1] These great sequences raised the standards of engraving and the prestige of the print; they were raised also by 'Hogarth's Act', the Act he obtained in 1735 for securing to engravers copyright in their designs and protecting them from victimization by print-sellers. Despite loopholes, this revolutionized the status of the engraver and was to the ultimate advantage of the print-seller, since prints became an important British export.

The impact of personal caricature, introduced from Italy, at first as a fashionable art practised by the virtuosi and their friends, was not welcomed by Hogarth—adversary of connoisseurs. Arthur Pond, virtuoso, artist, and picture dealer, etched twenty-five caricature portraits after Ghezzi and others from 1736 to 1747. And in 1743 Hogarth published his *Characters & Caricaturas* [2591], 'Being perpetually plagued from the mistakes made among the illiterate by the similarities in the sound of the words. . . .' (Here one remembers that in 1732 Hogarth had 'made a

[1] Joseph Burke, *William Hogarth. The Analysis of Beauty*, Oxford, 1955, p. 208.

Characateur' of a Billingsgate porter.[1]) 'Caricatura' is represented by heads by Ghezzi, Annibale Caracci, and Leonardo, all copied from etchings by Pond. For 'Character' Hogarth copied heads from Raphael's cartoons and from his own *Marriage à la Mode*. 'For a further explanation of the Difference', he inscribed on the plate, 'See yᵉ Preface to Joʰ Andrews.' Here Fielding had distinguished between the 'comic history painting' of his friend Hogarth, whose true excellence consisted in 'the exactest copying of nature', and caricatura, with 'all distortions and exaggerations . . . within its proper province'. The distinction was vital to Hogarth, disparaged by jealous rivals—'the whole nest of phiz-mongers'—who, had taught their friends to run down his men's portraits as 'charicatures'. And his expressive realism was not to be confounded with the crudities of caricaturists. His own 'manner of designing' he called 'the Comic and Moral'.

But caricature and the burlesque were destined to transform the emblematical print, and here the amateur made his contribution with drawing that was incorrect and expressive, an art superbly practised by Max Beerbohm. It was an amateur, George Townshend, afterwards Marquis, who in 1756 introduced caricature into political satires (though there had been earlier approaches to this); his vein was ribaldry and buffoonery. It was natural that Hogarth, both as craftsman and artist, should think little of such productions.

The print-sellers (in 1756) used the words 'Character' and 'Caricatura' indiscriminately for collections of prints by Townshend and others, and in 1758 Hogarth returned to the distinction with *The Bench* [3662]. He elaborated his thesis in a long inscription which begins, 'There are hardly any two things more essentially different. . . .' His own comment on this print was, ' I have ever considered the knowledge of character, either high or low, to be the most sublime part of the art of painting or sculpture, and caricatura as the lowest; indeed as much so as the wild attempts of children—yet so it is, that the two words from being similar in sound are often confounded.'[2] (It would seem rather that no firm line can be drawn between the two, his own *Portrait of John Wilkes Esquire* [Pl. 36] might be taken as a superb example of either: Hogarth called it 'The Monster Caricatura that so sorely gall'd . . . the Heaven born Wilkes'.) An ironical dedication of a later state of *The Bench* to the 'Honble Coll.

    [1] *Hogarth's Peregrination*, ed. Charles Mitchell, Oxford, 1952, p. 3.
    [2] Quoted, Nichols, *Anecdotes of William Hogarth*, 1833, pp. 66–67. See J. Burke, *William Hogarth. The Analysis of Beauty*, Oxford, 1955, pp. li–lii.

T...s...d' implies contempt, or perhaps resentment for plates attacking himself, attributed (doubtfully) to Townshend.

Hogarth practised most of the categories into which the satiric prints of his day can be classed, and gave an impetus to the comic in doing so. These prints are a small part of his *œuvre* but important in the development of English graphic satire. The well-established form of burlesque heraldry is assimilated to caricature in *The Undertakers Arms, or a Consultation of Physicians* [2299], in 1736, a satire on notorious quacks (with portraits) and on the medical profession. The travesty of the picture was to be brilliantly applied to politics by Gillray: Hogarth introduced the genre in England in 1725 with his parody [1764] of Kent's altar-piece in St. Clement Danes, where it had been violently attacked as a Jacobite manifesto: 'a popish paultry Piece of Trumpery' containing a portrait of 'the wife of the Pensioner of the Whore of Babylon'.[1] He ridicules both the protest and his enemy Kent in his elaborate joke: 'Tis not the Pretender's Wife and Children as some weak bretheren imagine ... Nor St Cecilia as the Connoisseurs believe, but a Choir of Angells playing in Consort.' And in his *Paul before Felix* [3173], in 1751, 'Designed in the rediculous Manber of Rembrant', he burlesqued the Dutch masters and parodied his own attempt at the grand manner, the *Paul before Felix* painted for Lincoln's Inn Hall. *The five Orders of Perriwigs* ... [3812] in 1761 was a satire on 'Athenian' Stuart's forthcoming *Antiquities of Athens Measured and Delineated* ..., and ridicules antiquarians and their learned and costly publications, the heads ranging from portraits (a flattering one of the Queen) to caricature. What an admirable example of the emblematical print and the *singerie* is *The Tailpiece to the Artist's Catalogue* [3809] with the affected ape-connoisseur watering the dead work of the dead masters.

These jokes are not political. Until *The Times* in 1762 his political plates were scarcely polemical. The emblematical South Sea prints of 1721 are more the work of a moralist than a politician; the same could be said of the hieroglyphical fantasy of 1724. After 1724 none of his prints conforms to the anti-ministerial convention. On the contrary. After the appearance of *The Rake's Progress*[2] in 1735, Hogarth was pressed 'by the Patriots in Opposition to Sir Robert Walpole to design a series of prints, to be intitled *The Statesman's Progress*, but he, scorning to prostitute his art to the purposes of faction, rejected their offer.'[3] Horace Walpole in his *Anec-*

---

[1] *A Letter from a Parishioner ... to the ... Bishop of London*, 1725.
[2] Here Hogarth seems to have given birth to a phrase: *The Oxford Dictionary of Quotations* attributes 'rake's progress' to Thackeray (*Pendennis*).
[3] Hawkins, *Life of Johnson*, 1787, p. 500 n. Cf. p. 83.

dotes of Painting calls this 'a very lucrative offer that was made to engage him in a set of prints against the head of a Court party'. He refused. In 1735 he had expressed his gratitude for Hogarth's Act in an emblematical tribute to the British Constitution: he published the plate of a royal crown irradiating a group of coronets, mitres, the bag of the Great Seal, the mace, the Speaker's hat, &c., with the Act itself and a long inscription beginning, 'In humble and grateful Acknowledgement of the Grace and Goodness of the Legislature. . . .' Hogarth was exceptional (in 1735) in being 'a warm partisan of George II'.[1] The story of the King's displeasure at the artist's treatment of his Guards in *The March to Finchley* is probably apocryphal.[2]

The classic expression of the time-honoured John Bullish contrast between English beef and liberty, and French *soupe-maigre* and slavery, is *The Gate of Calais. O the Roast Beef of Old England* [3050], with political allusions in the refugee Highlander and the degraded Irishman in the French service. 'To sum up all', he wrote, 'poverty, slavery, and innate insolence, covered with an affectation of politeness, give you even here a true picture of the manners of the whole nation.' Caricature intrudes on character in the persons of the fat friar and the lean cook: 'I meant to display to my own countrymen the striking difference between the food, priests, soldiers etc. of the two nations. . . .' This was in 1749, and reflects feelings roused by 1745. The contrast was given a more direct political application in 1756: the two plates of *The Invasion* [3446, 3454] are the antithesis of the voluble pessimism and defeatism of that year. Hogarth advertised them in March and again in September (in the full spate of anti-Byng satires): 'Two prints desin'd and etch'd by William Hogarth. One representing the preparations on the French Coast for an intended Invasion, the other, a View of the Preparations making in England in order to oppose the wicked Design of our Enemies: Proper to be stuck up in publick places, both in Town and Country, at this juncture'—and we may be sure they were stuck up, and at other junctures—in 1759, before Quiberon, for instance. In one there is a sledge-load of Popish furniture ('trumpery'): instruments of torture, gibbet, &c., a figure of 'St. Antoni' and a 'Plan pour un Monastere dans Black Friars à Londres'. An officer roasts frogs spitted on his sword, pointing to a flag: 'Vengeance et le Bon Bier et Bon Beuf de Angleterre.' In the other [Pl. 31], British soldiers and a sailor amuse themselves in a carefree way outside an inn while a sergeant measures a recruit; one of them is drawing on the wall a caricature of the

---

[1] Boswell, *Life of Johnson*, Oxford, 1934, i. 146.
[2] R. B. Becket, *Hogarth*, 1949, p. 18.

French King holding sword and gibbet. The inscriptions are the quint-essence of the patriotism of the day: lines from James Thomson's *Rule Britannia*, and a young fifer playing 'God save Great George our King' (then a novelty): verses by Garrick end:

> Britons to arms! and let em come, . . .
> No Power can stand the deadly Stroke
> That's given from Hands & Hearts of Oak
> With Liberty to back em.

This is in the vein of patriotic prints of 1803: it was as much opposed to the political satires of 1756 as *The Times* was to those of 1762. More could not be said.

The well-known *Beer Street* [3126] and *Gin Lane* [3136] in 1751 were political in the sense that they were produced to support a ministerial measure against the unlimited sale of gin (which was in fact a turning-point), while other prints attacked the Act as they did that of 1736. 'Bear St and Gin Lane were done when the dredfull consequences of gin drinking was at its height', he wrote in his Autobiographical Notes. The four prints of *The Election* are a generalized satire on election brutality and corruption, in which both sides are involved—no longer Whig and Tory but 'Old Interest' and 'New Interest'. Money is poured out from the Treasury, it is true, but that was a commonplace. The series is seemingly a protest not only against the conduct of elections, but against senseless party rancour and meaningless slogans, a theme that underlies some of his other prints. That the intention was not anti-ministerial is shown also by the dedications, the first (in 1755) to the hated Henry Fox. Hogarth's political prints of 1762–3 and the imbroglio with Wilkes are part of the history of the time, to be considered in their context.

The acknowledged share of the amateur in the cartoon began in 1756[1]—the joint enterprise of George Townshend, Matthew Darly (who was artist, print-seller, drawing-master, and designer of *chinoiserie* decorations and furniture), and his wife Mary, also an artist and a print-seller. She taught etching and caricature, and in 1763 published a little guide to the art (engraved by herself),[2] in which she included examples of the work of her pupils and clients, among whom was Townshend. At first in partnership with one Edwards, Mat Darly began in August 1756 to publish a new

---

[1] A reference to Townshend in the *Public Advertiser*, 5 June 1765, may imply that he was credited with *The Motion* (see p. 90). At that time he was only 18, but there is something in the design which suggests that it may have been based on a drawing by him; especially in view of the close association of Walpoles and Townshends. George Townshend's step-grandmother was Walpole's favourite sister. [2] Copy in B.M. Print Room.

form of political print; this was the 'card', a small design about 2½ by 4 inches on pasteboard, convenient for sending by post in the manner of a picture postcard. Cards were sold at 6*d*., and had a great vogue; sometimes they were original designs, sometimes reduced versions of larger prints. The size made them relatively free from over-elaboration and they were generally humorous. They began as part of the campaign against Newcastle and Fox. Horace Walpole attributed the invention to George Townshend, who certainly designed the first of the series: 'A new species of this manufacture [satiric prints] now first appeared, invented by George Townshend; they were caricaturas on cards. The original one, which had amazing vent, was of Newcastle and Fox, looking at each other, and crying, with Peachum in the *Beggar's Opera*, 'Brother, Brother we are both in the wrong'.[1] Townshend's etching for this is in Mary Darly's book. Elaborated as *The Pillars of the State* [Pl. 28 *a*] it begins the series. A comparison with the 'Pillars of the State' in *Britannia in Distress* [Pl. 30] spotlights the contrast between the old school and the new.

The Darlys gave a longer life to the cards by reprinting them in little volumes as *A Political & Satyrical History* . . . first, of the years 1756–7 and then in a succession of books of which there was a bewildering number of editions and volumes up to 1766, as well as imitations and piracies (one called *England's Remembrancer*) by other publishers. In this way many prints circulated in a number of versions: in their original form (either a large print or a card or sometimes both), in one of Darly's volumes with added comments (reprinted with additions from year to year) and again in a rival series. In these books the term caricature for political print became established. At first, in 1756, caricatura was used for the person depicted, almost at once for the print itself, and caricature very soon replaced caricatura.

The work of the amateur was essential to the enterprise—a source of prestige and inside information as well as of pupils. A volume for 1756–60 contains 'An Explanatory Key to every Print: rendering the whole full and significant', and professes to be 'Drawn and Etch'd by some of the most eminent Parties interested therein'. In a volume published in 1763 the imprint was followed by 'Where Sketches or Hints, sent Post Paid, will have due Honour shewn them'. Some of the sketches and hints, usually anonymous, sent to print-sellers in Gillray's day have survived; probably from Darly's time onwards they were never negligible. The publication line of an illustrated broadside against Bute continues,

[1] Memoirs of the Reign of George II, ii. 68. See above, p. 101.

'who returns the unknown Author Thanks for the Above, and shall be greatly obliged to him for any future Favours of the same kind'.

Mary Darly's book was intended for the amateur; following Hogarth, she begins with the 'Difference between Character and Caricature':

'Caricature is the burlesque of Character, or an exaggeration of nature, when not very pleasing, it's a manner of drawing that was, and still is, held in great esteem by the Italians and French, some of our Nobility and Gentry at this time do equal if not excel anything that ever has been done in any other Country, tis a diverting species of designing, and will certainly keep those that practise it out of the hipps or Vapours, and that it may have that effect on her Friends is the wish of My Darly.

The innovations of Townshend and the Darly's were a response to political rancour; developments in imagery followed. Britannia and the British Lion had already expressed almost every conceivable change of mood and fortune. Both were commonly subjected to injury and insult, not stopping at murder. Britannia had acquired the cap and staff of Liberty as occasional attributes—but in general only to be deprived of them. Occasionally the Lion personifies the King—displacing the Hanoverian Horse, which had several times reflected George II's unpopularity and sometimes stands for George III. The first mention of John Bull in the prints seems to be in 1756 [3467], when Andrew Stone sells by auction 'all the valuable effects of John Bull Me[rchant] . . . leaving of Trade', Minorca having 'cost Mr Bull a great deal of money'. This is a long time-lag from Arbuthnot's invention of John Bull.[1] Here, in 1756, John Bull is England, and it is not for a considerable time that he acquires his secondary character of typical Englishman—though some equivalent to Sawney, Teague (Paddy was later), and Taffy was clearly needed—supplied sometimes by 'Jack English' (as in 3829), once by 'Will' [4008], a seeming tribute to Pitt, and once, perspicaciously, by 'Jack Afterthought' [4020]. In 1757 [3548] Britannia, brutally murdered, was 'the Lady of John Bull Esqr' (a relationship which occasionally recurs). After this John does not reappear in the prints till 1762, and then always in connexion with the peace negotiations. He appears when caricature and the comic are encroaching on allegory and symbol, for which Britannia is more suitable. He is first depicted (previously he had been only mentioned) in an imitation of the inn sign, as *A Poor Man Loaded with Mischief or John Bull and his Sister*

[1] *Law is a Bottomless Pit, exemplified in the case of the Lord Strutt, John Bull, Nicholas Frog., and Lewis Baboon, who spent all they had in a Law Suit* [the War of the Spanish Succession], Mar. 1712. Rearranged with other John Bull pamphlets as *The History of John Bull* in *Miscellanies* (by Pope and Swift), 1727.

Peg [3904]—Peg being Scotland. An ox or bull long continued to be a symbol for John Bull, especially when slaughter or mutilation or murderous anger was to be depicted: this imagery dates seemingly from 1762: in the *Caledonian Slaughter-House or the Death of John Bull* [3907] Bute prepares to give 'the fatal blow'. It is interesting to note that in 1819 Wellington was depicted (by Cruikshank) as the Bull's executioner.[1] In *The Smithfield Bargain or Scotch Salesman* [3942] Bute hands over to France 'the English Bull' garlanded for sacrifice. In a complicated satire by Paul Sandby (without a title) against Bute, Hogarth, and others John Bull is a bull-headed man [3910]. In yet another on the approaching peace Bute shaves 'Master' Bull in a barber's shop [3959]—the first of many political shavings (executed especially by and on Napoleon). 'The Bull-dog of England' is an animal appearing for the first time in 1762 [3987]. At this time, and for long afterwards, John Bull (like the British Lion) was occasionally the King, as in *The Three Roads to John Bull's Farm* [3926]. In *John Bull's House sett in Flames* [3890] the house is St. James's Palace, the incendiary is Bute. *A Catalogue of the Kitchen Furniture of John Bull Esqr leaving of House-keeping, now selling by Auction* [3990] is one of many satires on economies in the royal household.

A development which was to have a great influence on caricature was the use of colour. Every now and then among the mid-century prints there is a coloured impression. When or by whom the colour was applied we do not know, but from time to time a print is inscribed '6d. plain, 1s. coloured', or the like. The first examples known to me are a print of 1748 [3019] and two of 1750 [3086, 3091]; they remain rare during the fifties and sixties. In 1762 two volumes of *The British Antidote*[2] were advertised on a print [4004] at '10s. 6d. coloured, 5s. plain', but this was exceptional —single volumes are repeatedly advertised at 2s. 6d. with no mention of colour. The *Public Advertiser* (7 December 1762) adds to a list of the contents of the *Antidote*, 'The above prints may be had BUTIFULLY coloured, framed and glazed, or in a volume.'

While the cartoon was slowly altering, the old-fashioned explanation in verse was becoming less frequent—it was unsuited to the format of the card. The pictorial broadside in which the text was at least as important as the print continued to appear, but less often. The political ballad had become comparatively rare—supplanted by the newspaper. But it is characteristic of these prints that nothing was lost. Old symbols, old allegories, old forms were absorbed and adapted.

[1] See *E.P.C. 1793–1832*, Pl. 74.   [2] See p. 120.

VII

PITT, BUTE, AND GEORGE III

THE new reign opened with a loyal print, an apotheosis of the young King enthroned among clouds: *Long live his Most Excellent Brittanic Majesty, King George the Third, or Down with the Devil, Pope, French King, and Pretender* [3732]; all are prostrate at his feet. But politics soon intrude. The cartoonists expanded a penetrating epigram, attributed to a physician's wife and current in December 1760: 'that the great question was whether the King would burn in his Chamber *Scotch*-coal, *Newcastle* Coal or *Pitt* Coal'. Hence, *The Quere? Which will give the best heat to a British Constitution PITT: Newcastle or Scotch Coal* [3735]. Fires burn on three altars; Bute's fire, on 'a kind of new rais'd alter', warms only Scots. On Pitt's is the motto which is his appellation in many prints—*Pro Patria non sibi*. Newcastle's altar is inscribed *Pro sibi non patria* and its fire was 'smother'd in the year 57, & is too much decay'd to break out with Vigour . . . & never was universally esteem'd except by French cooks & so not fit to be us'd'—a legend that does him less than justice. Britannia's *Answer to the Quere* [3737], dated 1760, is a rebus: '. . . As my King is a Briton born let no northern Hero or Frenchified sham Patriot ever dare to separate our mutual love. . . .' She adds a list of 'Negatives': 'no Pitt no Money, no German Connections, no religious Humbug [Whitefield, much attacked at this time and later], no German petticoat Government, no more mercinary Foreign Generals, nor no [more] War then is Necessary.' An unsophisticated but significant pronouncement.

Aversion to petticoat government and the Scots is also expressed in *The Loyal Beasts, or Visionary Addressers. a Dream* [3740]. George III is 'a youthfull lion' receiving addresses and homage; there are descriptive verses but no names are given. Two at least are obvious. On the King's right 'Is a most dreadful scottish bison', and crouching behind it is a tigress, not mentioned in the verses, but clearly the King's mother—seemingly the first allusion in the new reign to her supposed relations with Bute; later ones left nothing to the imagination. The elements of discord are too clear, and the flames were blown up by controversies over the peace negotiations and by Pitt's resignation. There is no trace in the prints of the short-lived unpopularity that followed his acceptance of a pension, and a

barony for his wife—on the contrary. In *Merit Rewarded or Truth Triumphant* . . . [3814] the King begs Britannia to bestow '3000 p^r Annum' on
Pitt—a most unusual attitude to any pension; the famous letter to Alderman Beckford, his chief supporter in the City, is quoted in full on a scroll
held up by a winged figure: 'I resigned . . . in order not to remain responsible for Measures, which I was no longer allowed to guide.'[1] A
Spaniard muzzles the British Lion which is ridden by a fox—Henry Fox,
who says, 'I ride now post to preferment. . . .' The Gallic Cock prepares
to crow again and de Bussy, the French agent for peace negotiations, hands
out bribes. The print is exceptional in being without a reference to Bute.
Prints multiplied, almost all directed against Bute, and with insults to
the Princess Dowager. Henry Fox's opinion (in 1762) that jealousy of
Scots was the prime motive of opposition to the peace is supported by the
prints:

The Press is with more vehemence than I ever knew set to work against Ld Bute.
And it would be very surprizing to see how quick & fiercely the fire spreads, but
for the consideration that it is fed with great industry, & blown by a national prejudice which is inveterate & universal. . . . A peace is thought necessary to Lord
Bute: therefore a peace or any terms is exclaim'd against. But the true objections,
his being a Scotchman & a Favourite, are avow'd, & on those articles is he most
scurrilously accus'd . . . with as little disguise as ever faction wore boldly
attack'd, & told of his intrigue with the Prss Dowr of Wales—[2]

All this is still more emphatically true of the prints, to whose influence
there is much contemporary testimony.

The volume of the *Political & Satirical History* for the years 1761–3
in which 'cards' and other caricatures were reprinted, took the additional
title *Displaying the Unhappy Influence of Scotch Prevalency.* . . . An imitation of this which appeared in 1762 and subsequently was called *British
Antidote to Caledonian Poison*, and this again was imitated and followed by
The Scots Scourge. . . . These little books contained, besides the prints,
additional inflammatory comment. From 1761 to 1763 and after almost
every print was primarily an attack on Bute,[3] sometimes with Fox as a
secondary villain. Pitt—'English Will' or 'honest Will'—was Bute's anti-
thesis and enemy.

The assault began with 'the Thane' as the lover of the Princess Dowager
of Wales, the King's favourite, and thus the bestower of posts and pensions

[1] See p. 139.

[2] *Life and Letters of Lady Sarah Lennox, 1901*, i. 68 ('Lord Holland's Memoir . . .').

[3] For the contemporary attitude to Bute cf. Butterfield, *George III and the Historians*, 1957,
pp. 45 ff.

to hordes of hungry barbarous Scots to the exclusion of the English. These insults continued, and sharpened the attacks on the peace negotiations: Bute is a Jacobite, with French interests at heart, the enemy of Liberty and Magna Charta. Then came a climax of rage over the Cider Tax, reviving the cry of 'Liberty, Property, and No Excise'. Wilkes and Churchill and a swarm of lesser libellers made these insults their own. Priorities are often doubtful, but very many prints anticipated Churchill's diatribe against the Scots—*The Prophecy of Famine*—probably also the *North Briton*, while others pay tribute to the paper and illustrate its gibes. Prints were largely responsible for the public opinion fostered by skilful propaganda which was the background of Wilkes's triumphs. Their importance is vividly illustrated by two famous plates, one by Hogarth in 1762, the other by his friend Benjamin Wilson in 1766. Only in the prints can we now recover the crescendo of abuse that assailed Bute—its effect on un-instructed opinion, the way in which these cries merged with 'Wilkes and Liberty', and these again with the slogans of the dispute with America.

It seems odd that the Ministry made almost no attempt at pictorial counter-propaganda, though there were ministerial journalists and pam-phleteers (much abused in the prints). Speaking very roughly, there are extant some 400 prints against Bute—not counting all the copies and piracies—and only four on the other side; the uproar caused by the most famous, *The Times* (to be considered later), speaks for itself. *Britannia guided by Justice* [3865] is an openly Butite print which in the then state of opinion could have seemed merely laughable. Justice crowns Bute with laurels and he says that he values not 'the World's Cencure, as I am determin'd to Act with impartiality, with honour and with Honesty'. Any defence of the Ministry was written off as the work of 'hirelings', probably with truth—prints had to be popular to sell on their merits—or demerits. The second ministerial print (*c.* 1762), an attack on Pitt (Bute is not mentioned), was at once alleged to be paid for. This was *Sic Transit Gloria Mundi* [3913] in which he is charged with pride, popularity-mongering, 'changing sides', taxes, and the pension. It was copied for the *Antidote* with the mock signature 'Sawney Scott fecit' and the inscription: 'This Print was trumped up by Sejanus [Bute] and his party against the Great Commoner; whom they have placed on the Globe; blowing . . . bubbles of his Popularity; while the Mob below are sounding his Praise; on the right Side is a Figure modelling a Crown into a Commonwealth's Hat.' Indeed, as the *Briton* showed by being the incentive to the *North Briton*, ministerial propaganda was apt to provoke damaging retaliations. The fourth appeared in 1766.

The Hungry Mob of Scriblers and Etchers [Pl. 32] is an interesting though puzzling attack on Bute's propaganda. He scatters coin to an expectant crowd, one of whom is Samuel Johnson, holding (as in 3979) his pension of '300 Pr Ann.'. It is to be presumed that Smollett (of the *Briton*) and Murphy (of the *Auditor*) are there. Hogarth is an inconspicuous figure with an engraving tool, walking behind the more imposing Mat Darly who holds one of his most insolent prints, 'The Screen' [3825]. Is he—Darly, one of Bute's most inveterate enemies—there to defy Bute? And if so, can the parson be Churchill?—he is not unlike him. And have these 'Patriots' among the hirelings come to be bought off or to defy? The comment on the version in *The Scots Scourge* is, '... He got *this* a pension, and gave *that* a bribe. But his fortune can't silence the ill-natur'd Tribe.'[1]

It is also remarkable, if perhaps natural, that print-sellers as such were not prosecuted for seditious libel. Doubtless the worst prints were too scurrilously obscene to be brought into court or given publicity, but they may have had their influence on Press prosecutions, even on the famous proceedings against No. 45 of the *North Briton*. The *Antidote* challenged the law of libel and the pillory in its 'Humorous Explanation' of *Multum in parvo or a New Card for a Scotch Courtier* [4078]; the figures are 'Droll Caricatures going to receive the Reward due to their Merit; but, who they are, or where they are going, or for what they are going, we dont think it convenient to explain at present, as we have no great inclination to pass our Heads through a certain wooden Machine, invented by a set of arbitrary Men, to punish all those who are wiser than themselves.' Some characters in this print are indeed obscure, but they include Bute, a he-goat wearing a boot, riding a she-goat (the Princess), and their destination is Hell.

In the attacks on Bute history was called in. He was compared with the murdered 'Rhezzio' (Rizzio), reputed lover of Mary Queen of Scots, in, for instance, *The Scotch Colossus...* [3939]; like Walpole, he was Sejanus—favourite and tyrant. He was Macbeth, 'a favourite who murdered his master' [3897]. In *An Antidote by Carr for C-l-d-n* [Caledonian] *Impurities* [3845] Sir Robert Carr, favourite of James I, rises from the grave holding axe and halter to say (incorrectly), 'These were my doom for

---

[1] Nichols lists the plate among the attacks on Hogarth for *The Times*, but in another of those attacks, *The Fire of Faction* [3955], in which Hogarth blows up the fire with bellows, the fuel includes not only *The Times*, *The Briton*, and the *Auditor*, but the *Hungry Mob*.

Ad-lt-y, Oppression, Injustice. . . .' In *The Highland Seer, or the Political Vision* [3867], Bute starts from the Princess's bed to hear the warnings of five ghosts. First is Roger Mortimer: 'Let not ambitious Love they Heart ensnare/Lest thou the Fate of Mortimer should share.' The others are William (i.e. Peter) des Roches, Bishop of Winchester, Hubert de Burgh, Simon de Montfort, and Elizabeth's Earl of Essex. They illustrate some odd historical notions as well as the hatred attaching to a favourite. The design is headed by lines beginning:

> Is there a Curse on human kind
> So pestilent, at once, to Prince and People,
> As the base servile Vermin of a Court.

On his resignation, in *Sawney below Stairs* [4048], one of the many Charon prints, Bute is welcomed in Hades by Roger Mortimer, Wolsey, Walpole (because of Excise), Sejanus, the two 'Spencers' (Despensers), and Count Bruhl, the allegedly treasonous Minister of Maria Theresa.

The punning symbol for Bute was the jack boot, and this often contains two little figures, the Princess and her supposed lover. A typical print, and an example of the Townshend manner, is *The Loaded Boot* . . . [Pl. 33], drawn by White Horse and zebra, that is, by the King and Queen. The Princess's symbol was the petticoat, usually of tartan, and the emblem of petticoat government. These two objects became fuel for many bonfires. A new device to give verisimilitude to slander was the 'transparency', a device ascribed to Townshend, a print so folded that one design was superimposed on another, which became visible, as part of the whole, when held to the light. Thus, what is behind a curtain [3824], or a screen [3825] or inside a tent is revealed. In *The Scotch Tent, or True Contrast* [3912] not only Bute and the Princess but George III are discovered, the King with a petticoat suspended over his head and holding a scroll, *amor vincit omnia*. They are engaged upon a 'Scotch & French Scheme . . . to hurt King and Country' which the Duke of Cumberland swears to resist. All three are crudely scurrilous and all have been attributed to George Townshend. It seems astonishing that the last was openly advertised as published by Mary Darly.

The famous road from Scotland to England is the scene of *We are all a comeing, or Scotch Coal for ever* [3823]. Hungry aspirants crowd a public coach, others ride or drive or plod on foot. There is the inevitable joke about the 'scotch fiddle' or the itch (scabies) which was to be worked hard sixty years later to deride George IV's highly successful visit to Scotland.

The reduced version of the print in the *Political & Satirical History* is described as 'a droll caricature of the Expeditions of the Locusts to the English Canaan which (they cry'd out) flow'd with Milk and Brimstone' [a cure for scabies]. There is a sequel, *We are all Come, or Scotch Coal burns longer than Pitt or Newcastle Coal* [3858]. A lucky Scot who has waxed fat in England holds up a sign to his countrymen, the root of a tree entwined with thistles and supporting a big irradiated boot, 'the root of all evil'. In this scene of rejoicing the Scots make inflammatory remarks, as, 'They say we shall have all the places of Profit & the English may go starve': 'Let em send the English to Canada . . .' (a gibe at the peace—Canada was represented as a very bad bargain).

No terms could have been acceptable when it was reiterated that Bute and Bedford were betraying the country to France, and peace was 'the approaching ignominious event'.[1] Bute was allegedly a Jacobite, and, or, bribed, Bedford selfishly intent on a reduction of the Land Tax. This was 'The Peace (but not of God) which passeth all Understanding' [3926]. A gross attack on Bute called *Gisbal, Lord of Hebron* [3848] is inscribed (on reduced versions in the *Political & Satirical History*), 'This is the Man that eas'd Brittain of a War, which, if continued must have finally ruin'd our Enemies, 'tis to him we owe our happy disunion, the Excise, extended Œconomy, &c. &c. &.' In *The Congress; or, a Device to lower the Land-tax* [3887] Bute marches under 'the Standard of England'—a petticoat and a boot—and hands over to a Frenchman 'Guadelupe, Martinico, &c &c &c &c &c &c', saying, 'Tak aw again Mounseir, and gie us back what ye please.' The other gives back 'Barren Canada' and 'Part of Newfoundland', adding, '. . . Now tank de grand Monarque for his royale bountee.'

To personify the Beast of *Revelation* was reserved for the most execrated of *bêtes noires*. In a print of December 1762, *The Vision or the M–n–st–l Monster* [3983], Bute was described in a parody of Biblical language (a form of humour that became very popular): '. . . I saw a Beast rise up out of the Sea from the North, and many who were Sons of Corruption worshipped yͤ Beast. . . .' Pictorially, the creature does not conform to the canon—he has not seven heads, but a dog's head wearing a Scots bonnet and an earl's coronet. He is a hideous dragon with webbed wings, claws, scaly neck, and three tails. One leg is a fox which devours a soldier (Henry Fox was Paymaster), the other is a goose (the Duke of Bedford as peace negotiator). The monster devours Britannia and Habeas Corpus and tears

---

[1] *London Evening Post*, 16–18 Sept. 1762.

at Magna Charta. An imp, Hogarth, is preparing to paint a flattering portrait of the monster, one of many attacks for *The Times*.

A further stage, if that were possible, in anti-Bute clamour was reached with the budget (22 March) and the introduction of a Cider Tax. The cry of 'Liberty, Property, and No Excise' was renewed, and there was a fresh outbreak of bonfires in which boot and petticoat were burned. As in 1733, but with even less excuse, the tax was represented (pictorially) as a general excise. The print-sellers battened on the new topic and the anti-Excise propaganda was loud, libellous, and long-drawn-out. One print must suffice here—not typical of the others, but an interesting example of the emblematical figure made of appropriate objects—*An Exciseman made out of ye Necessaries of Life now Tax'd* . . . [Pl. 34] has the head of a knave in a pack of cards and is made up of taxed objects; a setting sun, 'Light', connotes the Window Tax, and the ground at the exciseman's feet represents the Land Tax. This is seemingly the first of the innumerable prints on the general burden of taxation.

Bute quailed before the storm of abuse and resigned on 8 April, despite his unshaken majority. For many years he remained a political bogy: the favourite, the personification of 'secret influence'. This widely held belief lost all touch with reality from 1765, but persisted as part of the Whig doctrine of an attempt by George III to regain the power of the Crown and subvert the Constitution by ruling through 'King's Friends' and so bypass the Cabinet. All this is fully illustrated and exaggerated in the prints, where Bute remains a prime villain throughout the war with America—indeed for about thirty years.[1] The note was set as soon as he resigned in a print with a title highly disrespectful to the King: *The S—— Puppitt Shew or the whole Play of King Solomon the Wise* [4049]. Bute and the Devil are on the stage, drawing back a curtain to display a row of puppets among whom are the King and his mother. Bute says, 'Tho I am out it's known for Certain,/I prompt 'em still behind the Curtain.' The King: 'War is no more & Smileing Peace/Shall Taxes thro the Land encrease.'

Bute's resignation was quickly followed by the unfortunate proceedings against Wilkes and the printers for No. 45 of the *North Briton*, the opening of the vendetta between the King and Wilkes which had followed the vendetta of Wilkes against Bute, to whom he attributed his failure to become either ambassador to Constantinople or Governor of Canada. But

---

[1] In *The National Assembly or Meeting of the Three Estates* [7623] in 1790 by Dent, where King, Lords and Commons are travestied as animals, with George III as 'The King of the Beasts'; Bute is prominent as 'The Secret Beast'.

first, to consider the related topic of the treatment of the King in the prints, a by-product of the attitude to Bute and the Princess. There are a few indications of popularity in 1760, but commonly, from 1761, George III is represented as weak and stupid. Occasional identification with the British Lion or John Bull is not a suspension of blame. In *The State Ballance or Political See-Saw* [3843] the King and his mother (with a big boot in her lap) sink, while Pitt and Newcastle rise, though Cumberland in the middle tries to 'Preserve the Equilibrium'. George holds a map of Scotland showing 'Bute I', and says,'Tho they have blinded me yet I find I am sinking in national Esteem'; Britannia lies prostrate, her cap of Liberty has fallen off. Bute drives the Princess in *The Triumphal Car or Scota's—— Victory 1762* [3846], while the King, personification of Folly, stands behind as footman, holding a rattle and a fool's cap and saying, 'I am nobody.' They drive over Magna Charta, Trade, and Laws. In *The Masquerade; or the Political Bagpiper* [3880] Bute and the Princess sit on the throne while the King stands by, playing the Scotch fiddle; in the version in *The Political & Satyrical History* he says,'I'll play any tune you bid me', while Bute remarks, 'He's as soft as wax. . . .' With unpopularity for George III goes praise for George II and for the King's father and uncle, Frederick and Cumberland, who are popular as enemies of Bute, and are 'Sons of Great George' [3907]. The King is blinded by his mother who holds her fan before his eyes and asks 'dear Sawney' for a pinch of snuff—that is 'Scotch Snuff with French Opium' [3927]. As *The Four Nonparells* [3934] King, Queen, Princess, and Bute dance round a maypole to a Highlander's piping. This is on a verse broadside which openly derides the King:

> The first Nonparell, grown so famous of late,
> Renown'd for his Wisdom, in matters of State;
> In Politicks skilfull, in Judgment so Sound,
> There's none can excel him search all ye World round.

This is in the vein of ironic toasts in the City to Wit, Beauty, Virtue, and Honour, that is, to King, Queen, Princess, and Bute.[1]

The old grindstone theme was called in, and in *Scotch Impudence or the Northern Grinder* [3938] Bute drags the King towards the stone. One of many indications that the King was expected to rule as well as reign is *The Tenant's Complaint to David Simple, of Noodle Hall, Esq* [4021] in which no less than fifteen tenants state their grievances; these are interesting but

---

[1] Walpole, *Memoirs of the reign of George III*, 1945, i. 274.

too long to quote here. The squire (George III) answers, 'you know good people, I don't trouble myself about my Estate, I leave the management to my Stewards & Clerks, if they supply me with mony that's sufficient'. He holds by the hand a fat little boy—the future George IV—and in his arms is the infant Frederick. 'Leo Britannicus' is clearly the King in *The Lyon Entranced* [3922] where the Lion, dead or doped, lies in state with Britannia as chief mourner, but only in the *Antidote* version is this made obvious by an 'Explanation': 'When Princes suffer themselves to be thrown into an inglorious Lethargy by the Arts of designing Favourites, it is a certain Sign the D——n is plac'd upon a weak Foundation.' In 'a curious caricature card', *The Lion made Ridiculous by Sawney & Jenny* [3962], the Lion is on his hindlegs wearing a petticoat, jack boots, and a Scots cap topped by a fleur-de-lis, while the Princess holds a thistle and Bute leads him by the nose. This was openly published by Mary Darly. *John a Boot's Asses* [3979] is a daring satire which by exception is without imprint—but it was openly copied for the *Scots Scourge*; Bute rides an ass, the Princess; tied to its tail is a second ass, blindfolded, to represent the King. A climax of insult, also copied for the *Scots Scourge*, was reached in *The Opposition* [4036]; the British Lion with the head of a mule (the King) drags a cartload of Englishmen uphill. Bute, riding a she-goat, the Princess, is one of a group pulling at the Lion's rein, while another group pull in the opposite direction. One of the latter says, 'Tis an obstinate Creature, he'll be guided by none, but that d—d Scotchman, & his villainous gang': another says, 'I'm tired with pulling, so he may go to Hell his own way.' One of the men in the cart remarks, 'If ye Cart overturns I hope ye Animal that draws it may break his neck in ye fall.' Here, by exception (till much later) the King is charged not with weakness but obstinacy: verses begin, 'Some say he's a Lion & some say a mule,/But most people say he's an obstinate fool.'

Most of these prints were attacks on the peace negotiations of 1762; most contain gross insults to the King's mother. In others she was the chief target. She was, for instance, *The Wanton Widow* [3851]; in 1769 she was the Queen in *Hamlet* directing Bute to pour poison into her sleeping son's ear [4329]. These flights are related to a theme with which Wilkes was especially connected; the identification of Bute with Roger Mortimer, lover of Isabella, Queen of Edward II, thereby comparing the Princess to a queen who had murdered her husband and ruled England with her lover. This was elaborated, broadened, and coarsened in the prints, but it was exploited also (perhaps first) by Wilkes in No. 5 of the *North Briton* in

July 1762. He followed this up in March by republishing the old play used against Walpole, *The Fall of Mortimer*, with a dedication to Bute: '. . . wherever the name of Roger Mortimer shall be mentioned, that of Bute will follow to the latest time. . . . I wish you my Lord the most exquisite pleasures under the Cyprian myrtle. . . .' George had learned (in 1756) of the calumnies against his mother, and he wrote to Bute: 'They have also treated my Mother in a cruel manner (which I shall never forget nor forgive to the day of my death. . .). I do therefore here in the presence of Our Almighy Lord promise that I will remember the insults, and never will forgive anyone who shall venture to speak disrespectfully of her.'[1] Is it surprising that the young, inexperienced King was obsessed by hatred of Wilkes, or that his Ministers struck at the *North Briton* at the first opportunity, given by No. 45 (25 April 1763), with its remarks on the untruthfulness of the King's Speech on the peace, though this was blamed on the Minister (no longer Bute but Grenville). It was not one of Wilkes's most effective squibs. Is it not probable that the dominant motive was revenge for No. 5 and desire to stop the stream of insult against Bute and the Princess?[2] The use of General Warrants made Wilkes a martyr of Liberty and started a sequence of great issues. But before this Wilkes had embarked on a vendetta against Hogarth for his print *The Times* [Pl. 35].

Hogarth threw his bombshell, the third of the four Butite prints, on 7 September, 1762, and it duly exploded to his own damage. It was similar in spirit to the attack on Pitt (*Sic Transit Gloria Mundi*), but far more comprehensive and thoroughgoing—a protest against warmongering and demagogy, against factious attacks on the negotiators of the peace. The complicated design is filled with emblematical details, but the main theme is clear. A street is in flames, the flames of war and faction; one set of people try to put out the fire, others blow it up and obstruct the firemen. Incidentally, there is an excellent view of a contemporary fire-engine, fed by hose and buckets and worked by pumping. The chief fireman, whose badge, a crown and G.R., indicates the King, stands on the engine, directing a jet of water at a blazing terrestrial globe, the sign of the nearest burning house. The other houses also have signs, a fleur-de-lis, an eagle, and so on, to identify the countries at war. Scotsmen, one being Bute, are among the firemen. Newcastle furiously drives a wheelbarrow at the hose

---

[1] *Letters from George III to Lord Bute, 1756–1766*, ed. R. Sedgwick, 1939, p. 3.

[2] The dismissal of the Grenville-Bedford Ministry in 1765 for their insult to the Princess in excluding her from the Regency Bill seems to support this.

and the legs of a Scot, his barrow is heaped with *North Britons* and *Monitors*—fuel for the fire. Standing on the stilts of popularity and surrounded by a clamouring mob among whom are three adoring Aldermen, is Pitt, blowing at the blazing globe with bellows. A millstone, marked '3000£ per annum' (the pension) hangs from his neck. Across the way is the 'Temple Coffee House'; Lord Temple, Pitt's brother-in-law and Wilkes's patron, with a blank face (to suggest his unpredictable and factious disposition), squirts water at the King's back from a window. From the attic windows, and very small in scale (to show that they are garretteers, or insignificant literary hacks), Wilkes and Churchill also aim their squirts at the King. In the foreground Frederick of Prussia plays the fiddle, delighting in the conflagration, regardless of his wretched subjects who surround him, having fled from a burning house; one is a dying woman with a new-born infant. As a pendant to this group is a contented Dutchman, fat with the spoils of neutral trade. A dove with an olive branch flies above the clouds and flames. There are other details, including a building with a number of emblematical sign-boards, some obscure; on one is a picture of soldiers—evidently the militia—marching to the tune of 'the Norfolk jig' and signed 'G. T. fecit'. In this, according to Wilkes,[1] Hogarth 'vents his spleen upon Mr George Townshend and the gentlemen of Norfolk'. Townshend (like Pitt) had been an uncompromising advocate of the Militia Bill: attempts to levy the Militia had caused riots. *The Times* seems to be a counter-print to *John Bull's House sett in Flames* [3890]; St. James's Palace is burning, Bute, the incendiary, escapes in a shirt, and Pitt works the engine.

The uproar caused by *The Times* shows the importance of cartoons, especially one by Hogarth. It reflects also the enormity of his challenge to public opinion. Wilkes devoted a whole number—17—of the *North Briton* to a vicious attack. The cartoonists outdid themselves in elaborate pictorial invective; among them was Hogarth's old enemy Paul Sandby. At least thirteen vengeful prints rapidly followed *The Times*, most of which appeared again in versions made for the *Political & Satirical History* and the *Antidote*. In Sandby's *The Boot & the Blockhead* [3977] Hogarth, feebly passionate, protests to Churchill against the *North Briton* article. 'This Caricature', runs the explanation to Darly's version, 'shews the exaltation of a Scotch Blockhead, which infatuated the greatest droll genius in the World to fall down and worship and even daub his own Character to whitewash the Black Boot; and forgot himself so far as to aim at injuring the most

---

[1] *North Briton*, No. 17.

K

exalted *English* Patriot that ever was, till the bold and honest North Briton nipped him in the Bud. But they say he has Scotch fitts at intervals.' In *Tit for Tat* . . . [3978] there are more of the customary insults to Bute and the Princess. Hogarth is at his easel painting a big irradiated boot, and has defaced a portrait of Pitt 'by order of my L——'; he says, 'any thing for money. I'll gild this Scotch Sign & make it look Glorious, & I'll daub the other sign to efface its Beauty & make it as black as a Jack Boot.' His 'Line of Beauty' (theme of his *Analysis of Beauty*) is ridiculed, and in other prints becomes the line of 'Buty' or 'Booty'. He is *The Butefyer* [3971] and he is credited with a pension of £300 a year. The foundation for this was his office (contemptuously derided by Wilkes) of 'Serjeant Painter of all the King's Works' at a fee of £10 a year, which, 'one way or another', was worth, he said, £200 a year. He got it in 1757 on the death of his brother-in-law. His own explanation of his motives carries conviction. He had lost money by an illness, and the war abroad and 'contentions at home' had interfered with the sale of his prints. So it was necessary to 'do some timed thing' (cash in on the mania for political prints): 'this produce the Print call The Times the subject of which tended to Peace and unanimity and so put the opposers of this humane purpose in a light which gave offence to the Fomenters of distruction in the minds of the people. . . .'[1] Surely one of the least successful attempts at peace and unanimity ever made.

All this time the cartoonists had paid little attention to Wilkes—the *North Briton* was associated not with him but with Churchill—which must have galled one so avid of notoriety. 'I am excellently pourtrayed in Saturday's *Briton*', he wrote to his publisher (29 August 1762). 'Why do not the print-shops take me . . . I am an incomparable subject for a print. . . .'[2] It was not till the affair of General Warrants that the cry 'Wilkes and Liberty' was heard. Here Hogarth struck back. On the second appearance in Westminster Hall before Chief Justice Pratt (6 May) Hogarth made the sketch for the famous portrait, *John Wilkes Esq' Drawn from the Life, and Etch'd in Aquafortis* [Pl. 36]; beside the Patriot are two numbers of the *North Briton*, 17 and 45; Wilkes is the embodiment of Mephistophelean cunning and impudent demagogy and for the first time the cap and staff of Liberty are sardonic symbols. This was a portrait, as Hogarth wrote, 'done as like as I could as to feature at the same time some indication of his mind, [it] fully answerd my purpose the ridiculous was

---

[1] Joseph Burke, *Wm. Hogarth. The Analysis of Beauty*, Oxford, 1955, p. 221.
[2] G. Nobbe, *The North Briton, A Study on Political Propaganda*, New York, 1939, p. 85.

apparent to every Eye a Brutus a saviour of his country with such an aspect was [so] arrant a Joke that it set every body else a laughing gauld him and his adherents to death. . . .'[1] A copper-plate printer told Nichols that nearly 4,000 impressions were worked off in a few weeks. The papers were, as Hogarth said, 'stufft with evectives' (invectives). Wilkes reprinted No. 17 and added a caricature portrait of 'William Hogarth Esq[r], Cut in Wood, from the Life' [4053]. Churchill published his verse satire, *The Epistle to William Hogarth:*

> Lurking, most ruffian-like, behind a screen,
> So plac'd all things to see, himself unseen,
> Virtue, with due contempt, saw Hogarth stand,
> The murd'rous pencil in his palsied hand.

Hogarth retorted with *The Bruiser, C. Churchill (once the Rev[d]) in the Character of a Russian Hercules, Regaling Himself after having Kill'd the Monster Caricatura that so Sorely Gall'd his Virtuous Friend, the Heaven born Wilkes* [4084]. Besides the caricature of Churchill as a bear clutching a tankard of porter and a knotted club, there was added in the two final states (not often reproduced) a tiny picture (on the palette) in which Hogarth renews his attack on Pitt: against a pyramidal tomb is a reclining statue of Pitt flanked by Gog and Magog, the Guildhall giants, one of whom holds a crown over the head of the City's idol. Hogarth stands in the foreground flogging a dancing bear, Churchill, and holding a rope attached to a performing ape, Wilkes, which rides cock horse on the staff of Liberty. Nine more cartoons (at least)[2] followed, attacking Hogarth, with savage gibes at his wife and his work, for instance, *Tit for Tat or W[m] Hogarth Esqr Principal Pannel Painter to his Majesty* [4054].

The fateful quarrel between Wilkes and the Ministry went on, with Bute, now called Mortimer, as enemy in chief, though behind the curtain. Until the Stamp Act controversy the cartoonists ignored Grenville. The Wilkes affair produced two more *bêtes noires*, Sandwich and Chief Justice Mansfield. One had already been caricatured by Townshend as a creature of Fox (in *The Recruiting Serjeant*), the other (then Murray) had been attacked in 1756–7 as Newcastle's Attorney General. But now both became villains in their own right. Sandwich was execrated as Jemmy Twitcher (in the *Beggar's Opera*) who had peached on his boon companion and

---

[1] Joseph Burke, op. cit., p. 221.

[2] With the thirteen that followed *The Times* this makes twenty-two in the British Museum, not counting copies in the *Antidote* and the *Scots Scourge*. Mr. Peter Quennell estimates the total at over twenty-five: *Hogarth's Progress*, 1955, p. 278.

fellow rake in the affair of the *Essay on Woman* (the privately printed parody which Walpole called 'bawdy and blasphemous to the last degree'). Mansfield got the sobriquet of Judge Jeffreys for the sentences on Wilkes and on John Williams who had reprinted No. 45 after it had been burnt by order of Parliament. All this is illustrated. *The Execution* [4066] is a striking print in which Sandwich, trampling on the muzzled British Lion, drags the manacled and half-naked Britannia by a noose round her neck; in his pocket is a paper, 'Blasphemy'; Fox, now Lord Holland, scatters bribes, treads on Magna Charta, and cries 'Twitch-her, Twitch-her Jemmy Twitcher'. Britannia's spear is broken, her shield half hidden by a huge Scottish thistle.

> What has Britannia left to hope
> When Graceless Twitcher pulls the rope?
> When old Corruption holds the bribe
> And Gold secures the venal tribe.

The pillorying of John Williams (14 February 1765) is the subject of a number of prints, including *The Pillory Triumphant* [4115]. In a scene in Palace Yard, Williams, under a 'Scotch Yoke', is protected by an angel. The jack boot and a Scots bonnet are being suspended from an improvised gibbet to the shouts of the 'sons of *Wilkes* and *Liberty*'. Williams had published some of the more savage anti-Bute prints and his imprint is on perhaps the most venomous anti-British cartoon of the whole American War.[1]

A different note is sounded in another print of 1765 when efforts were being made to induce Pitt to take office and so rid the King of Grenville. Pitt was at Hayes, suffering from gout and severe nervous irritation, and was being exacting and difficult. Therefore in May the King sent his uncle, Cumberland, to negotiate in person, but the overture, like others, ended in failure. This is the subject of *The Courier* [4121]. Cumberland gallops along 'The Road to Hays', towards Pitt's house, which is represented as a hovel; from the open door projects a huge gouty foot resting on a stool; a pair of crutches leans against the wall. The hovel has a sign, 'Popularity the Blown Bladder by W. P.' Behind Cumberland is another public house, with the sign of the Crown, proprietor 'I. Bull' (George III) and with the names M—d and B—e (for Mansfield and Bute). The hovel symbolizes Pitt's theatrical economies when he left office in 1761. Thus blame is distributed all round.

[1] *The Closet* [5470] in **1778.**

In July 1765, with Pitt still obdurate, Grenville was dismissed and the Rockingham Whigs came in. Their year of office was marked by one thing, the repeal of the Stamp Act, and this produced an outburst of important prints. This was the first issue between England and America to come before the public. In these prints the pattern of popular attitudes to the dispute and the war is already apparent. From first to last Bute is made responsible for 'stamping' and then for coercing America. The causes of the Colonies and of Wilkes are treated as one, with General Warrants and the Stamp Act as linked tyrannies. The prints illustrate the extent to which relations with the Colonies were bedevilled by Wilkes and Liberty.

Little attention was paid to the Act when it passed in March 1765, but reactions in America—'Non-Intercourse' and damage to trade—produced a demand for repeal. The agitation had much in common with other agitations—against Excise, against the Jew Act, and the Cider Tax. Like them it was promoted by vested interests, fomented by mobbing and cries of Liberty in danger, carried on by organized petitioning, backed up by Press propaganda and satirical prints. Like them it was successful. But there were important differences: the issues were far wider, the agitation was not anti-ministerial—Rockingham, in office, adopted the cause of repeal. And while the prints on the other agitations are unanimous, Stamp Act ones are not. In these prints America is personified for seemingly the first time, sometimes as a Red Indian in war-paint, or as a blend of Indian and Amazon, sometimes as a woman resembling Britannia (her mother) but younger and more buxom.

The first[1] Stamp Act print—one in which Grenville makes a first appearance—was advertised in October 1765, *The Great Financier, or British Œconomy for the Years 1763, 1764, 1766* [Pl. 37]. Grenville holds up a balance in which pettifogging economies are far outweighed by 'Debts 140 Millions'. Pitt is behind him, leaning on a crutch and saying, 'Conquests will ballance it'; he points to sacrifices of the peace, which Grenville drops to the ground: 'Guardalupe, Martinico, Havanna' as well as 'Newfoundland Fishery' and 'Philipines'. Behind Pitt is America, a suppliant Indian with a yoke on her neck inscribed 'Taxed without Representation'; she holds a bag of 'Dollars', saying, 'Commerce will outweigh it.' Behind her are tax collectors; one helps himself to dollars, saying, 'We must obey orders'; his companion answers, 'Dam'me Jack better pillage the French.' Grenville's servant, wearing a fool's cap inscribed 'Œconomy', drops

---

[1] F. G. Stephens thought *The Last Shift* [4118, n.d.] the first: I think it can hardly be earlier than 1775.

candle ends into the scale thereby robbing a hungry cat (economy was much disparaged as a Scottish failing carried out in the royal kitchens). On the right is a prison from which hang chains inscribed 'General Warrants'; Britannia sits dejectedly at the gate while Grenville's ape, wearing his master's collar, pulls away the stone on which she sits and breaks the spear from which her cap of Liberty has fallen. France and Spain rejoice. Ships are for sale, with brooms at the mast-heads, a usual item in Stamp Act prints.

The Deplorable State of America or Sc—h Government [4119] was advertised on 2 January, and some weeks earlier (11 November) in the *Boston Gazette*,[1] where there was a long description, an interesting example of the extension of this graphic propaganda to the Colonies. Britannia offers Pandora's box, the Stamp Act, to America (an Indian), the latter turns to Minerva: 'Secure Me, O, Goddess, for I abhor it as Death'; she answers, 'Take it not.' Liberty lies prostrate, menaced by a serpent emerging from a huge Scottish thistle. Mercury (commerce) flies off, saying to America, 'It is with Reluctance I leave ye.' In the sky is an irradiated boot to which the King of France proffers a bribe: 'Take this, and let thy banefull Influence be poured down upon them.' Ships of course are to be sold, and a gallows is prepared for 'Stamp Men' who find themselves compelled to rob or starve.

Two prints followed which deserve special attention; by a lucky chance we know how and why they were produced.[2] Both are by Benjamin Wilson, a leading, perhaps the leading, portrait painter of the day, who was making a large income and enjoyed the profitable patronage of the Duke of York. He was also an inventor and a F.R.S., and an etcher whose fake Rembrandts tricked 'certain artists and amateurs who imagined themselves to be connoisseurs'. Something well above the level of the ordinary satirical print might be expected. This is not so, but the success he achieved is remarkable. The first, in February, was produced, Wilson says, 'In order to please Lord Rockingham . . . who had promised to take care of him.' This was *The Tomb-Stone* [Pl. 38], commemorating Cumberland, go-between in the negotiations for the Ministry, who had died in October. 'Here lieth the Body of William Duke of Cumberland &c lamented by his Country, which he twice Sav'd. First . . . at the Battle of Culloden, and after by selecting a Ministry, out of those virtuous few, who gloriously withstood

---

[1] R. T. H. Halsey, 'Impolitical Prints', *Bulletin of the New York Public Library*, Nov. 1939.
[2] From the manuscript autobiography incorporated (against his instructions) in Randolph's *Life* of Wilson's son, Sir Robert Wilson, 1862.

General Warrants, American Stamps, Extensions of Excise—&c &c &c.'
Britannia and America flank the inscription, weeping figures in bas relief,
surrounded by military trophies. Bute—'Sejanus'—and his friends dance
exultantly on the lid of the sarcophagus; he is between Bedford and Grenville, from whose pockets hang 'Stamps', 'Reversions', 'Pensions', and
'Cyder Tax'. Dancing with them is a little dog in parson's dress—'Anti-
Sejanus'—who is held up by Sandwich. He is Dr. Scott, Sandwich's
chaplain, who had 'hackneyed his pen in support of the Stamps'. Bagpipe
music is provided by a bulky Scotch demon, a monster who is balanced on
the left by Lord Temple with a blank face as in *The Times*. He holds a
huge 'Oriflame' of discord and says to Grenville, 'Stamp away Brother.'
Others pilloried are Halifax (for General Warrants) and two bishops who
think it prudent to 'stay a little' before joining the dance. The print, says
Wilson, was 'very successful in its object' so that 'Mr. Edmund Burke
[then Rockingham's secretary] and Grey Cooper [Secretary to the Treasury]
pressed him much to try another political print'. Wilson responded with
The Repeal, Or, the Funeral of Miss Americ- Stamp [Pl. 39] published,
he says, within ten minutes of the repeal of the Act (8 March). Here
then is one of the very few prints known to have been officially inspired.
Its success was immediate and remarkable. Wilson states that in four days
he sold above 2,000 at a shilling apiece. He could not keep pace with the
demand and on the fifth day two pirated copies came out at half the price:
'credible persons' told him that 16,000 of these were sold. Actually, there
are four piracies in the British Museum, besides a reduced copy in the
Antidote. Seven versions were exhibited in the New York Public Library[1]
in November 1939. It was described in the newspapers and a long facetious
description is quoted in Benjamin Franklin's *Memoirs*. A funeral procession
makes its way towards a tomb inscribed 'Within this Family Vault; Lie
interred, it is to be hoped never to rise again, The Star Chamber Court,
Ship Money—Excise Money and all Imports without Parliament, The Act
de Hæritico [*sic*] Comburendo, Hearth Mon Gener Warrants And [a blank
for Miss Americ- Stamp] which tended to alienate the Affection of Englishmen to their Country.' Above the tomb two skulls of traitors (as those
displayed on Temple Bar) associate not only Bute but the Stamp Act with
Jacobitism. Anti-Sejanus heads the procession reading the burial service,
two legal *bêtes noires* follow, Wedderburn and Fletcher Norton, with black
processional flags decorated with 'Stamps'—a device of Scottish thistle

[1] Horace Walpole's copy of the print, now in the Library, has the names of the 'Mourners'
in his handwriting.

and Jacobite white rose. Grenville carries the infant's coffin, and is followed by the chief mourner, Bute—' Sejanus'. Next come Bedford and Temple, Halifax and Sandwich, and two bishops. Now that Non Intercourse is over, the Thames-side warehouses are open again, ships are ready to sail—the *Rockingham*, the *Grafton*, the *Conway*, named after those who had carried repeal. A big chest is being shipped containing 'a statue of Mr Pitt'.

Wilson's two prints embody the main points of the propaganda against the Stamp Act—the only American tax except the Tea Tax to be mentioned in the prints. They stress the firmly held delusions that Bute and his following were responsible for 'stamping' America, that the Stamp Act and General Warrants were linked tyrannies, and that the causes of America and Wilkes were one. (All this was developed with great virtuosity in later prints which treat the tax as if it were still valid and ignore the provision that the money was to be used only for the defence of America.) They were not propaganda for repeal—that issue was decided before they were published, but self-regarding panegyrics of the Ministry by an expectant.

The propaganda that prevailed against much contrary opinion was that of the commercial and industrial interests alarmed at the check to trade. To this was added the tireless lobbying of Benjamin Franklin to show 'that the Colonies cannot be forced to submit to the Stamp Act but at an Expence greater than the Profit'. He pointed his arguments by a famous cartoon 'invented' by himself and printed on cards on which he wrote his messages to 'Men in Power'. This was *Magna Britannia—Her Colonies Reduced*, engraved at the end of 1765 and used in the early weeks of 1766.[1] A mutilated Britannia has slipped from her globe, her amputated limbs lie beside her—they are Virginia and Pennsylvania (with a hand from which an olive branch has dropped), New York and New England, the last a leg from which a spear points at the helpless body. Her ships are for sale and a legend, *Date Obolum Belisario*, shows that she is destitute, reduced to beg for alms. Nothing suggests that this was ever for sale in England. None of the original cards has been traced, but in August 1768 an English copy was published without comment in Almon's *Political Register*: *The Colonies Reduced* and *Its Companion* [Pl. 40], a second design, to show the guilt of

---

[1] This account is based on Edwin Wolfe's article, 'Benjamin Franklin's Stamp Act cartoon', *Proceedings of the American Philosophical Society*, vol. xcix, pp. 388–96 (Dec. 1955). I am indebted to Mr. Lawrence Towner, editor of the *William and Mary Quarterly*, for information about this. Franklin wrote to his partner, David Hall, on 28 Feb.: 'I enclose you some of the cards on which I have lately wrote all my messages.' According to a contemporary inscription on the American version he also 'employ'd a Waiter to put one of them in each Mans hand as he entered the House the day preceding the great debate': op. cit., p. 390.

Bute, who stabs Britannia in the back and delivers her up to Spain: 'Now I shew you her Weakness you may strike Home.' Britannia threatens America who throws herself into the arms of Louis XV who will thus become 'King of de whole World'. A Dutchman runs off with her shipping trade.

Franklin's card was copied in America with a lengthy explanation, probably in 1767—perhaps later. It would have been appropriate to the Olive Branch Petition of 1775. A French version would seem to belong to the years of war with England (years covered by Franklin's residence at Passy)—or to the eve of war. A large Dutch adaptation, *Grande Bretagne mutilé ou horrible mais vraie répresentation* . . ., is similar in spirit to prints of 1780; an Englishman mourning the loss of his trade has been introduced.[1]

Just before *The Tomb-Stone*, one of the hitherto rare satires against Pitt had appeared, *The Colossus* [4162], in which he is attacked for his eloquent denunciations of the Stamp Act. This was advertised as 'A Character not a Carricature, called the Statesman in Stilts; or American Colossus. 'Tis true 'tis Pity, and Pity 'tis true. Shakespeare.' As in Hogarth's *The Times* Pitt is on stilts; one, 'Sedition', is hooked and extends over 'New York'; the other, 'Popularity', is planted in the City and among the merchants in the 'Royal Exchange'. One crutch, entwined with serpents, is over the House of Commons; the other is his 'Pension' and is among bubbles: 'Patriotism, M. Charta, Continental Connections, War, Peace, Gold Boxes, Minority, Majority.' Above Pitt's head is a 'Common-Wealth' hat. On an air-borne temple is Lord Temple, as Fame, blowing bubbles that fall and disappear: 'Publick Spirit, Honesty and Loyalty.'

Much more characteristic of Stamp Act prints is *The State of the Nation A.D. 1765* [4130, n.d.], a scene by the sea with Britannia weeping on the shoulder of an angry America, while Grenville rushes forward to enforce the Stamp Act but is stopped by Pitt, who holds the staff and cap of Liberty. Mansfield, directed by Bute, menaces Britannia, but is checked by Pratt who insists, 'No General Warrants.' In another scene by the sea, *Goody Bull or the Second Part of the Repeal* [4142, not by Wilson], Britannia (Mrs. Bull) resents the success of America: 'Oh the Hussy, She dares me to my Very face.' Pitt rebukes her—'Why you Old Devil, what have you a Mind to turn your Daughter a Drift.' Across the ocean is Pitt's statue: 'To the Memory of Will Pitt Esqr who Delivered America from Slavery by the repeal of the Stamp Act 1766. Honour Inv^t Liberty fecit.'

[1] Cf. the French, Dutch, and American versions of an English cartoon of 1778, pp. 153-4.

Men surround the statue shouting for Pitt, for King George, and for Liberty and against Twitchers, Sejanuses, and anti-Sejanuses: 'Wilkes, England and America for ever.'

But for a short time, after Pitt had succeeded Rockingham, his American policy shared his own unpopularity and one or two of the many anti-Pitt prints are also anti-American. This was the Ministry which Pitt—now Chatham—intended to transcend party divisions by combining 'men in favour with the public' with 'men in favour at court'. His title, according to Horace Walpole, 'blasted all the affection which his country had borne to him, and which he had deserved so well. . . . The people . . . thought he had sold them for a title.'[1] The prints suggest that they thought he had sold them to Lord Bute. Thomas Hollis wrote to America on 1 October 1766 of 'the recent unparalleled prostitution of the once magnanimous and almost divine * * * * * * *, who now is totally lost in parchment and BUTISM'.[2]

There is a conventional tribute to Chatham and Pratt (now Camden) on their promotions, with attributes of Liberty and Justice, and figures of Fame and prostrate Envy. This is *Britannia's Glory* [4144]. There is a naïve print in which Chatham and Bute clasp hands before an enthroned Britannia: *Britannia's Affection for her Children or Envy Expos'd* [4157]— the fourth and last Butite print. Otherwise the chorus of dispraise is complete and prolonged. Chatham is *The Hypocrite unmaskd or the Double Pensioner* . . . [4146], supporting Bute on his shoulders; he has discarded his crutches and a hypocrite's mask. In *The Cat's Paw* [4148] Bute, a big monkey, forces a cat to pull chestnuts out of the fire. A royal crown over the fireplace is surmounted by thistles and white roses. By exception, Bute is omitted from *The Triumph of America* [Pl. 41]. Down a steep slope Chatham drives a Red Indian Amazon in a triumphal car, with his crutch, topped by a coronet, beside him. He lashes at the leaders who are about to plunge over a cliff from which Britannia has already fallen. His team are members of his oddly chosen Ministry, the leaders 'Crafty' (Shelburne—a first appearance) and 'Royal Oak' (Grafton, descendant of Charles II). The next pair are 'Weathercock, a fine showy horse' (Charles Townshend) and 'Surly' (Lord Northington). The wheelers are 'Prudence' (Conway) and 'Prerogative formerly known by the name of Liberty' (Pratt, now Camden, who as Pitt's Chancellor shared his unpopularity). The postilion (on Crafty) is an American Indian.

[1] *Memoirs of the Reign of George III*, 1845, ii. 358.
[2] *Memoirs of Thomas Hollis*, 1780, i. 340.

Another of the few anti-American prints is *The New Country Dance as Danced at C****, July the 30th, 1766* [4147] advertised in September, and as the title shows a satire on Pitt's appointment. Courtiers and Ministers dance while George III plays the fiddle. Bute, dancing with the Princess, leads Chatham on a string. The latter, hobbling on a crutch, says to America, 'I stood staunch to your cause.' America, who is a half-naked young woman holding a bottle of 'Rum' (a unique attribute) answers, 'Yes we finely hum'd Old England.' Britannia has fallen awkwardly and says, 'I'll dance no longer if America takes the lead.' Wilkes is carried off to Paris by a witch on a broomstick. The many other characters include the Kings of France and Spain who announce their intentions of not fulfilling the obligations of the peace of Paris, now they have 'got a Friend at Court'. Another aspect of the reaction against Chatham is stressed in a rebus, a *Hieroglyphic Epistle from Beelzebub . . .* [4145]: 'Your pretended Poverty, Your selling your horses your acceptance of a Pension and now a Place and a Peerage, are Convincing Proofs of what vast Knowledge you have in men and things and indicates that no man can be a good Politician without thinking of himself. . .' (a gibe at the *Pro Patria non sibi* motto); Lord Bath (Pulteney), a fellow renegade, sends him greetings from Pandemonium.

The most interesting of this group of prints is a complicated and cruel satire advertised in March 1767, *P * * * and Proteus, or a Political Flight to the Moon* [4163] with the sub-title *Mutatas dicere Formas* and the motto *Quem Deus vult perdere prius dementat*. Chatham is symbolized in a number of forms, first as a kite flying to the moon by a 'Via Lunatica', with Bute holding the string on which is a lantern inscribed 'Privilege' and 'Prerogative'. Inscriptions on the kite include 'as I do not guide I am not responsible' (a gibe at his letter to Beckford in 1761[1] which points to his present incapacity for affairs of State); 'A Project for annexing the Empire of the Moon to the Crown of . . . . ;' 'The Family Compact between the Sun and Moon discover'd' (his schemes of empire are derided). The King watches the kite with a half-witted stare, crying, 'Emperor of the Moon O la.' The papers on the kite's tail are 'Patriot, Post, Places, Pension, Peerage, Popularity'. Chatham is also a savage bull, and has knocked down his brother-in-law Lord Temple, and threatens Wilkes, who drops the staff and cap of Liberty. He is a cormorant swallowing 'Posts, Pensions, Titles' and emitting 'Grants, Bounties, Reversions, Dukes, Hard Taxes, Undigested Subsidies'. He is also a weeping crocodile, fawning on the King and saying, 'so good so gracious Hoh oh oh'. There is an inscription:

[1] See p. 120.

> Sir! He can turn! and turn! and yet go on!
> And turn again! and he can Weep Sir Weep
> And be Obedient as you see, Obedient,
> Very Obedient.

Thus was his grandiloquent respect for the Crown derided.

After a short spell of furious energy Chatham relapsed into what was then called suppressed gout, and might now be called manic depression, quite unable to leave his country house. At last he recovered sufficiently to press his resignation on the King, and in October 1768 Grafton became actual as well as nominal leader.

VIII

WILKES AND LIBERTY

A NEW phase in cartoon history began in 1767, the monthly magazine illustrated by satirical engravings; this succeeded the vogue for 'cards' and 'Political & Satyrical' histories. John Almon—journalist, bookseller, and militant Wilkite—started the fashion with his *Political Register* in May, the plates illustrating the more extreme contents or sometimes prudently left to speak for themselves. The *Oxford Magazine* followed in January 1768; it had a longer life and a gradual decline in acrimony. Two ephemeral and aggressive publications belong to 1768–70; the *Freeholders Magazine* and the *London Museum*; the old-established *London Magazine* introduced polemical prints. In the seventies other magazines appeared and disappeared, notably the *Westminster Magazine* in December 1772. The vogue passed, but from time to time, especially in the early nineteenth century, there were magazines in which folding caricature plates were an important feature.

For cartoonists politics continued to be aspects of Wilkes and Liberty with Bute as arch-villain; till after 1770 every incident of the Wilkes saga is illustrated: the Middlesex elections, the riots, the imprisonment, the feud between the City and Crown, Ministers, and Commons, the stirrings of Radicalism manifested in meetings, petitions, and Addresses. The Press was in one of its more violent phases with the *Letters of Junius* as the highlight of much pamphleteering. The context of fable and mass-emotion surrounding the important issues at stake is conveyed in the prints as no-where else. Preoccupation with Bute became more fantastic than ever, and the thesis of a ministerial design to enslave both Britain and America gained ground. In the Colonies revolutionary unrest had been in conflict with much traditional loyalty to the Crown, but in 1768–9 the Americans received a barrage of inflammatory news about Wilkes which turned George III into a tyrant. The Sons of Liberty in America had fraternal relations with Wilkite organizations in England; Americans vied with the English in gifts to the prisoner during his comfortable sojourn in the King's Bench. It was in the summer of 1769 that the new township in Pennsylvania was called Wilkes-Barré in honour of Wilkes and Colonel Barré—defenders of the Colonial cause. 'The Wilkite thesis, that coercion in the Colonies was the complement of a royal scheme to subvert Liberty in the Motherland through "corruption" of Parliament, carried increasing conviction in Boston, Philadelphia, Charleston and Williamsburg, as the conflicts of the 1760's continued into the early 1770's.'[1] In England cartoonists in the main still held to their picture of a blindfolded King.

After the repeal of the Stamp Act public interest in the Colonies waned, despite increasing unrest in America, but prints illustrate the way in which conflicts there were aspects of Wilkes and Liberty. They illuminate the passions and propaganda (powerfully aided by ministerial ineptitude) by which a vendetta between George III and his Ministers on one side and Wilkes and Opposition groups on the other, was transformed into a great constitutional issue, highly damaging to relations with the Colonies. In June 1769 the *Political Register* produced twin designs: *What may be doing Abroad—What is doing at Home* [4287]. The sovereigns of France, Spain, Prussia, and Austria agree on the partition of Great Britain and her possessions: George III weeps at the shameful consultations of his Ministers on the Wilkes affair—both very far-fetched notions; one of many crimes attributed to Grafton is 'The Reduceing of Boston by the Military'—that is, the landing of troops after the riots of 1768.

The Triumverate or Britannia in Distress [4298] is a complicated allegorical fantasy on the petition of the Livery of London to the King on 5 July 1769. The Triumvirate are Grafton (enthroned), George III, and Bute who holds the sceptre he has taken from the King. Britannia is in chains, but America—an Indian in war paint—is escaping from slavery: he has broken the yoke on his shoulders and tramples on the Stamp Act; beside him are discarded wooden shoes, fetters, and a scourge. A symbolical procession approaches the throne in which Liberty is personified by Wilkes and Fortitude by Alderman Beckford. In *The City Carriers* [4296] on the same petition, an Alderman shouts, 'I feel for the wrongs of America.'

A Wilkite print, *Political Electricity; or, An Historical & Prophetical Print, in the Year 1770* [4422], is an emblematical design that in scope, complications, explanations, and size (22¾ by 15¾ in.) approaches more nearly to *Magna Britannia Divisa*[2] than to contemporary prints—a last flare-up it would seem of an obsolescent manner. Description is impossible. There are thirty-one little designs, most of them linked by an 'electric chain' which issues from Bute, who stands on the French coast and is

---

[1] Douglas Adair, 'The Stamp Act in Contemporary British Cartoons', *William and Mary Quarterly*, Williamsburg, x. 539 (Oct. 1953).   [2] See pp. 26–28.

described as an 'electrical machine in ye Character of Dr Franklin'. The chain crosses the Channel to the Princess Dowager beside whom stands the King as a button-maker, with a book beside him—'History of Charles, A Dissolution dangerous to the Crown.' Ministers dine off the British Lion. There are mobs protesting against wages at 5s. a week, beef 8d. a pound, corn 8s. a bushel. There is also a Wilkes and Liberty mob after the third Middlesex election. London is in flames and in ruins, 'alluding to ye furious Distress and Anger of ye Inhabitants occasioned by ye late unconstitutional Proceedings of ye Ministers'. Scene 24 is 'The City of London transferred to Boston' and described as 'the Coasts of America where ye Inhabitants are Industrious in every Art to provide themselves with ye Manufactures that Great Britain used to furnish them with, being constrained & drove as it were to Industry by ye late Mi—l harsh Proceedings, in forcing ye Stamp & other Acts of Internal Taxes upon them contrary to ye true Spirit of British policy, & which sooner or later this Country will rue ye Imprudence of'.

In this 'Electrical Print' Chatham is still a lapsed Patriot, clogged by his pension and condemned for his attitude to Wilkes. The prints show little appreciation of his return in 1770 to violent opposition, but the *Political Register* published a tribute to the short-lived co-operation between Opposition groups: *The Hydra* [4370] is an eight-headed beast (Bute, Mansfield, and others) attacking Britannia and itself attacked by Chatham (with his crutch), Temple, and Rockingham.

Two unfortunate happenings, skilfully exploited, inflamed the anti-Bute element in Wilkite emotion. During the riots outside the King's Bench prison (10 May, 1768) the troops were mobbed and stoned. A young man, one William Allen, was chased by three soldiers and eventually shot. In some form or other this incident appears in almost every Wilkite print —and all political prints were Wilkite. The soldiers happened to be Scottish, and the affair was represented as an attempt on British liberties, planned and directed by Bute, and carried out by Scots. The magistrate who read the riot act and gave the order to fire was execrated and tried for murder (which largely explains the supine conduct of the magistrates in the Gordon Riots). Again, during an election affray at Brentford, a Wilkite was killed in a quarrel with an Irish chairman; medical evidence that death was not due to the blow was not believed, and the incident was represented as a second deliberate murder followed by a royal pardon. Only the prints can give an idea of the way in which these things were inflated. Among very many cartoons are two called *The Scotch Triumph* [4195, 4228]. The second was announced as 'A Satiric Scratch, in the Stile of Rembrandt, . . . with the Representation of their amazing Exploits in St. George's Fields, the Murder of the Innocent, and the Sacrifice of Liberty, by Moloch; with some curious anecdotes'.[1] There are also two called *The Scotch Victory* [4196–7]. The second [Pl. 42] is barbed by an unusual realism, and is inscribed, 'To the E—l of [Bute, represented by a boot under a petticoat], Protector of our Liberties . . . by L Junius Brutus.' *Scotch Amusements* [4237] include the shooting of Allen and the *amours* of Bute and the Princess.

In these prints there are frequent appeals to history. Cromwell's portrait is used as a threat of deposition or regicide. In *The Triumverate* . . . of 1769 already mentioned, there are medallions of Cromwell, Charles II, and James II; there is also a picture: Henry III 'forced by his Parliament and People' to 'renew the Charters', while the Archbishop is 'denouncing a terrible curse against all those who should violate the laws and alter the Constitution of the Kingdom'. In *The Times. Pl. 2* [4243], the design is headed by a medallion of Cromwell and on contrasted columns are the names of Patriots and anti-Patriots: Hampden, Andrew Marvell, Algernon Sidney, and Lord Russell (the last two executed for the Rye House Plot) are contrasted with Carr (Somerset, favourite of James I), Buckingham, Laud, and Macclesfield (the Chancellor impeached for corruption in 1725). In *The Funeral of Freedom* [4288] are the tombs of those 'murdered' in Wilkite riots; the gravedigger has thrown up the skulls of Charles I and Cromwell. Such allusions were characteristic: Junius, in his *Letter to the King*, warned him to profit by the fate of the Stuarts. The Address of the City Livery presented by Beckford in March 1770 declared that the exclusion of Wilkes from Parliament was an illegality 'more ruinous in its consequences than the levying of Ship Money by Charles I or the dispensing power exercised by James II'.

With all these menacing comparisons the Whig thesis of the King's attempt to recover the powers of the Crown finds little if any countenance; he is the victim of evil counsellors—Ministers of course, but pre-eminently his mother and Bute. 'A New Song' for Wilkes's birthday in 1769 begins, 'Here's a Health to our King, lets rejoice drink and Sing, and may he grow wiser and wiser; and may he grow wiser and wiser; and wise he'd now be, were it not for a she, and a Damnable Scottish adviser.'[2] George III is persistently attacked for neglecting the business of government when he was in fact attending to the details of administration with industry and

---

[1] *Public Advertiser*, 13 June 1768.   [2] *Freeholder's Magazine*, 1769, p. 168.

tenacity. He neglects State affairs for his hobbies—button-making repeatedly—and farming, as in *Farmer G—e, Studying Wind and Weather* [4883], in 1771, through the wrong end of a telescope.

1771 was a turning-point in cartoon history—a change of mood, a change of scene, and a change in technique, which, as often seems to happen, coincides with other changes. Two new targets and the disappearance of an old one contributed to the change. Lord North, 'Boreas' (who had succeeded Grafton in 1770), and Charles Fox, whose fortunes were to be so dramatically linked, were discovered by the caricaturists in 1771. Early in 1772 the Princess Dowager died. Prints had been largely responsible for the hate that literally followed her to the grave in the insults of the mob. 'Satirical prints generally dispersed throughout the Kingdom in which her Highness was not at all spared, inflamed the public mind.'[1] Legacies from the past were Bute—completely outside politics for years—and the blasted reputations of Sandwich (Jemmy Twitcher), Mansfield (Judge Jeffreys for condemning Wilkes), and Germain (Minden),—all contributing to the animosities that bedevilled the conflict with America.

The Wilkite turmoil was over. 'After a noted fermentation in the nation', Burke wrote in July 1771, 'as remarkable a deadness and vapidity has followed it.' The deadness withstood two crises that might have revived the fermentation. One was the quarrel of the Commons with Wilkes and the City over the publication of Debates. Despite the importance of the issue and the imprisonment in the Tower of the Lord Mayor and a Wilkite Alderman and consequent riots, the public were more interested in the quarrel between Wilkes and his friend Horne (afterwards Horne-Tooke), carried on in the newspapers with reciprocal insults. In the prints Horne is accused of being instigated by the Devil, by the Pope, by Ministers (as he was by Junius), but the affair was clearly discreditable to Wilkes, who was involved in other damaging quarrels. The situation was correctly summed up in *Patriotic Meteors* [4887], a *London Magazine* plate in October. Three heads with civic chains round their necks are being drawn into gaping hippopotamus jaws—'The Gulf of Oblivion'. They are Wilkes, Lord Mayor Crosby (the Patriot recently in the Tower), and Alderman Bull, Wilkes's co-Sheriff. 'Wilkes is almost as dead as Sacheverell, though Sheriff,' wrote Walpole in December.[2]

The other crisis was the Falkland Islands affair. The Opposition violently attacked the Ministry for corrupt subservience to Spain after the

---

[1] Walpole, *Last Journals*, 1910, 17 and n.
[2] *Letters*, ed. Toynbee, Oxford, viii. 122.

seizure of Port Egmont by the Governor of Buenos Ayres. Chatham led an attempt to rouse war fever against Spain and France, and indignation against the Ministry, in the way that had succeeded against Walpole. But Port Egmont was restored and the aggressor disavowed after successful diplomacy and naval preparations. All the prints were violently Oppositionist—it might be more true to say that they violently express memories of Walpole and 'the Ear' as they did again in 1790. Islands are 'to be given away—French Mistresses paid for conveying them.' In *Admiral Rodney before Carthagena* [4940] Glover's ballad, *Hosier's Ghost*, was quoted again, as in 1740 [2422]; he stands with his hands tied behind him: 'Nothing has its wealth defended / But my Orders—Not to Fight.' Another print demands notice because, after the Boston Tea-Party, it was copied by Paul Revere for an American magazine to show England humiliated by Spain: *Spanish Treatment at Carthagena* [4934] in the *London Magazine* for December 1771 is a purely imaginary scene of English sailors forced to labour on Spanish fortifications.

The old manner was strongly entrenched in the magazines. *The Young Heir among bad Councellors or the Lion betray'd* [4859], a December plate in the *Oxford Magazine*, recalls prints of 1762. The King is a lion, blindfolded and in chains; North, a dog with one leg in a jackboot (for Bute), gashes him with a barbed paw. In the foreground is a foppish and Frenchified fox-cub (Charles Fox) with one foot in a dice box, holding a muff and the ace of clubs, and looking through a single eyeglass. Two prints in a rather more modern manner reflect the change of scene. *The Politician* [Pl. 44] by S. H. Grimm is a caricature portrait of Lord North as a flabby and repulsive degenerate, sitting draped in a sheet, in the hands of a French hairdresser who whispers in his ear. He is dismayed at reminders of the Falkland Islands and menaced by a bust of Cromwell. There is a picture on the wall of Don Quixote tilting at a windmill. The other is *The Young Politician* [Pl. 45]. An elegant young man, with the head and brush of a fox, sits between two French hairdressers and tears up Magna Charta for curl-papers, looking with cynical langour in the glass held by a sinister-looking valet. He is the embodiment of the man of pleasure and the reckless enemy of Liberty, and it is easy to forget that this was Fox's reputation on his first astonishing impact on society and politics —when he was a Lord of the Treasury and an uncompromising enemy of Wilkes. He was also pre-eminently the man of fashion and the Macaroni as in *Charles James Cub Esq* [4811], a satirical portrait in the *Oxford Magazine* for May.

The transition that outmoded the emblematical print and prepared the way for Gillray and Rowlandson was due chiefly to Matthew Darly and his wife. From 1770 to 1777 or 1778 they dominate the print-selling world with caricatures in the newer manner, largely from the drawings of amateurs etched by themselves. (Bunbury was now the leading amateur, but he was soon lost to Darly.) In 1771–3 he published six sets (twenty-four in each) of single (occasionally double) satirical portraits, commonly known as Macaronies, which he reissued in volumes as *Caricatures, Macaronies and Characters* (the order of the words changed for different volumes). Macaroni was a new coterie word in 1764 for ultra-fashionable travelled young men, Italianate and Frenchified—the macaroni super-seded the beau and anticipated the dandy. From about 1770 for a few years the word was used widely and facetiously. It also connoted a new fashion in men's dress which succeeded the full-skirted coat and flapped waistcoat of the mid-eighteenth century and prepared the way for the plainer dress of the '80's, usually attributed to French Revolution fashions, but which had been introduced into France by the *Anglomanes* before the Revolution. Darly's Macaronies were personalities of the town in all classes: for in-stance the Duke of Grafton was 'The Turf Macaroni', Cosway the minia-ture painter, who was very small, was 'The Miniature Macaroni', Darly's shop was *The Macaroni Print Shop* [Pl. 43].[1] Darly followed these up with other series, larger and more elaborate, decorative and attractive, suitable for colour but usually found uncoloured. Their chief subjects were the follies of fashion—extravagant hairdressing and the like. But into these from 1777 political prints (pro-American) occasionally intruded. After 1781 his imprint disappears.

About 1773 Darly held an exhibition of caricatures (seemingly of original drawings), forerunner of the caricature exhibitions of London print-sellers. A catalogue has survived[2] and each entry (all are anonymous) is specified as by a Gentleman, a Lady, or an Artist: out of 233 exhibits 106 are by gentlemen, 74 by ladies, 27 by artists, 26 unspecified.

Darly thus prefaced his Macaroni volumes:

Comic Humour, Caricatures, &c In a Series of Drol Prints, consisting of Heads, Figures, Conversations and Satires upon the follies of the Age Design'd by several Ladies, Gentlemen and the most Humorous Artists &c. Pub^d by M Darly Engraver and Printseller at No. 39 . . . Strand, London, where Gentle-

---

[1] The window displays recognizable prints, including *The Fly-Catching Macaroni* [4695], Joseph Banks catching a butterfly, striding from the 'Arctick Circle' to the 'Antarctick Circle' (on his expedition with Solander).   [2] In the British Museum Print Room.

men and Ladies may have Copper plates prepared and Varnished for etching. Ladies to whom the fumes of the Aqua Fortis are Noxious may have their Plates carefully Bit, and proved, and may be attended to their own Houses, and have ev'ry necessary instruction in any part of Engraving, Etching . . . &c,—Ladies and Gentlemen sending their Designs may have them neatly etch'd and printed for their own private amusement at the most reasonable rates, or if for publication, shall have ev'ry grateful return and acknowledgement for any Comic Design. Descriptive hints in writing (not political) shall have due Honor shewn 'em & be immediately Drawn and Executed. . . .

The exclusion of politics is significant and altogether exceptional. (From 1756 to 1766 Darly had been the chief publisher of political prints—first against Fox and Newcastle then against Bute.) The link between social and political caricature is Charles Fox, the fox-cub, the Macaroni *par excellence*, leader of fashion, and extravagant gambler. In the Darly series he is *The Original Macaroni* [5010] dressed for a masquerade, and inscribed 'Tom Fool the First'—not a political gibe—'Tom Fools' with cap and bells were conspicuous characters in the fashionable masquerades of 1772. But he is the macaroni-politician of *The Senators*, a verse satire of 1772:

> By turns solicited by different plans
> Yet fix'd to none, Fox dresses, games, harangues:
> Where varying fashion leads the sportive band,
> And whim and folly bound it hand in hand,
> Behold him ambling through these flow'ry ways
> A model Macaroni, *A l'Anglaise*.

During the calm before the storm raised by the Boston Tea Party the prints are anti-ministerial in a rather tired way, with George III still asleep or blindfolded. The unpredictable transformations of Charles Fox from reactionary to Patriot, and thence to insubordinate placeman (junior Lord of the Treasury) are the context of *A Peep in the Garden at Hayes* [Pl. 46] dated 1 May 1773, an imaginary but significant scene. Chatham (who was not at Hayes), a gouty invalid, just risen from his wheeled chair, listens with wary friendliness to Fox, who stands before him as if making terms for a political alliance. This is by William Austin, a drawing-master rival of Darly, and is a cartoon in the newer manner, without explanation. Not so a print of 1774 on the deflation of Wilkes when he had become Lord Mayor. In *The Two Jacks* [5245] he is 'Jack Minor', the bottle imp, emerging from a bottle—that is, he is an impudent impostor.[1] 'Jack

---

[1] The bottle imp hoax contrived by the Duke of Montagu in 1749, the subject of several prints [3022–7]. Cf. p. 99.

Major' is a diabolic Bute standing in a jackboot; there is a Wilkite mob of tiny labouring men, 'Waking dreamers', who have dreamed of fabulously cheap porter and bread and cry, 'down with the rates and taxes'. There are verses ending, 'Firm to his int'rest each with Zeal Abides / The Secret Motive gain on both their Sides.'

IX

FROM THE AMERICAN REVOLUTION TO THE COALITION

WITH the news of the Boston Tea Party, which reached London in January 1774, America absorbs the caricaturists. The prints not only reflect opinion but were weapons of war. In England as in America 'the Revolution was in the hearts and minds of the people'.[1] The struggle in England was against the minority in Parliament who identified the Colonial cause with their own opposition to the authority of the Crown. Being almost entirely anti-ministerial, the prints are naturally, though not exclusively, pro-American. Two contentions were highly comforting to the enemy: one, that it was impossible for Britain to win and the war would end not only in defeat but ruin. The other, that victory, if achieved, would mean the end of British liberty. These contentions are lavishly illustrated—explicitly and implicitly. There is also a recurring strain of No-Popery and anti-Episcopacy, under the combined influence of dissent and of the attitude of the bench of bishops to the war: the bigotry that exploded in the Gordon Riots had flourished on allegations against Bute (whose name was unfortunately Stuart) and attacks on the Quebec Act.

The prints of 1774–5 attack Bute, Mansfield, and Ministers for the 'Intolerable Acts' passed to punish (to quote the King's message to Parliament) 'the outrageous proceedings at Boston'. *The Able Doctor, or America Swallowing the Bitter Draught* [Pl. 47 a] was at once copied by Paul Revere for an American magazine, and often passes as the American print which it might well be. Mansfield holds down America, while Bute stands behind with a drawn sword, watched by the deeply interested Kings of France and Spain: North forces her to drink from a teapot, and Sandwich twitches up her skirts to peer; Britannia weeps. This attack on the Boston Port Bill was in the *London Magazine* (April 1774). *The Mitred Minuet* [5228], also in the *London Magazine*, attacks the Quebec Act; bishops, approving 'The Roman Religion', dance to the bagpipe music of Bute

---

[1] John Adams (President U.S.A. 1796–1800), quoted Schlesinger, *New Viewpoints in American History*, 1922, p. 162.

and are directed by North who is instigated by the Devil. This measure, 'dictated by an enlightened liberalism . . . to secure the loyalty of the French Canadians',[1] was classed with the 'Intolerable Acts' against Massachusetts, and, in England as in America, singled out for special condemnation, provoking a stream of No Popery propaganda. Chatham denounced it as 'a most cruel, oppressive and odious measure, tearing up justice and every good principle by the roots'.[2]

Two pleas for conciliation strike a quite exceptional note; both are mezzotints in the grand manner by John Dixon. In *The Oracle . . . Dedicated to Concord* [5225],[3] Time shows a magic-lantern view of the future to Britannia, Hibernia, Scotia, and America: they see Concord putting Discord to flight while Liberty and Plenty, Truth and Justice, walk together. The unprophetic scene was the basis of a well-known satirical engraving published in Paris in 1778 with English, German, and French titles: *The Tea-Tax-Tempest, or the Anglo-American Revolution* [5490].[4] The four women now personify the four quarters of the world; Time shows them a vision of an exploding teapot bringing defeat and ruin to Britain. In its turn this was adapted (in March 1783) in an English print [6190] with the painful allusions made more explicit. The lesson of Dixon's second print is that punitive measures will bring disaster: in *A Political Lesson* [5230], published in September, a horse, America, rears violently and has thrown its rider, whose head has broken a milestone: 'To Boston VI Miles'; a signpost points to Salem. (Owing to the Boston Port Act seaborne trade was transferred to Salem.)

Two prints followed attacking the coercion of Massachusetts, published just before news of the outbreak of hostilities at Lexington on 19 April. In *Virtual Representation. 1775* [5286], dated 1 April, Bute is a highwayman who aims a blunderbuss at America (by exception a man), while the Speaker of the House of Commons says, 'I give you that man's money for my use'; America retorts, 'I will not be robbed', and an English sailor hurries to his defence. Bute and the Speaker are egged on by a Frenchman and a monk with a cross and gibbet. Britannia, blinded, rushes towards 'the Pit prepared for others'. On the horizon are two contrasted towns, one in flames, the other flying a Union flag: 'The English Protestant Town

---

[1] Morison and Commager, *Growth of the American Republic*, New York, 1930, p. 21.
[2] *Parl. Hist.* xviii. 1402.
[3] Exhibited, Society of Arts, 1774.
[4] By Carl Guttenberg of Nuremberg. Described, *Mémoires secrets* (xii. 172–3), 27 Nov. 1778 (known in France as *Lettres de Bachaumont*, the first scribe being Louis Petit de Bachaumont).

of Boston', and 'The French Roman Catholick Town of Quebec'. The title of this fantastic attack on the Quebec Act derides the theory that the Colonists, like Britons without the franchise, were virtually represented in Parliament. In *The Scotch Butchery, Boston. 1775* [5287], advertised and described in the *London Chronicle* for 18 April, Boston is bombarded by 'English Ships with Scotch Commanders' to the satisfaction of Bute and Mansfield, 'Superintendants of the Butchery from the two great Slaughter Houses'. Scottish soldiers attack unarmed fugitives with bayonets, but English ones are 'Struck with horror and are dropping their arms'. Both prints are typical of the more violent pro-American propaganda, as, for instance, that of Wilkes's ex-friend Horne who advertised for subscriptions for the dependants of Americans killed at Lexington, who 'preferring death to slavery, were for that reason only inhumanly murdered'.[1] His manifesto has a pictorial counterpart in one of the very few prints on specific military operations, *The Retreat from Concord to Lexington of the Army of Wild Irish Asses Defeated by the Brave American Militia*,[2] a realistic view of houses burning and soldiers fighting and plundering. In *Bunkers Hill or the Blessed Effects of Family Quarrels* [5289] America, a Red Indian woman with tomahawk and scalping knife, is seized and threatened by Britannia, who is mortally stabbed in the back by France; Spain, striding across two hemispheres, slashes Britannia's shield.

Till the disasters of Saratoga and Trenton, 1776–7 were years of success for the British. The first of the few anti-American prints is *The Yankie Doodles Intrenchments near Boston 1776* [5329], ill drawn, badly produced, and without imprint; the 'Death or Liberty' men are ridiculed as unsoldierly incompetents and canting Puritans, devoted to 'Old Oliver's Cause / No Monarch or Laws'. The artist is under the impression that Israel Putnam (not Washington) was the Commander-in-Chief. This was in a vein never repeated: Washington, with one post-war exception, is a hero, Benedict Arnold an arch-traitor; the exploits of Paul Jones are celebrated in popular prints without a trace of condemnation.

In this civil strife the hate which war engenders and needs was not for the Americans, not even for continental enemies—Holland scarcely excepted. It found its targets chiefly at home. From 1775 to a peak in 1779–80 the prints register a crescendo of anti-ministerial violence, with a developing counter-trickle of resentment against the Patriots. *The Parricide.*

[1] For this he was sentenced (1777) to a year's imprisonment and £100 fine.
[2] In the John Carter Brown Library, Brown University, Providence, U.S.A.

A Sketch of Modern Patriotism [Pl. 47 *b*] in the *Westminster Magazine* (previously pro-American) was altogether exceptional in 1776. America, an Indian woman with tomahawk and dagger, attacks Britannia, directed by Wilkes and watched by members of the Opposition, including Chatham and a fox—Charles Fox—his first appearance as a Patriot. 'With an effrontery beyond example in any other age or nation, these men assume the name of Patriots . . . they bind the hands of the mother while they plant a dagger in the hands of the daughter.'

Many things combined to make North's Conciliatory Propositions (with which Commissioners were sent to America in April 1778) a crisis of opinion. They gave up all the original points at issue, stipulating only for political union, and, but for the French alliance, still ostensibly secret, would probably have been accepted.[1] They dismayed the extreme Patriots in America: 'more dangerous to our cause than ten thousand of their best troops'—so Governor Johnson of Maryland was warned when the terms were distributed from Howe's headquarters. The French, dreading a reconciliation above all things, impugned their good faith and represented them as England's recognition of defeat.[2] Their reception in England was all that her enemies could desire. The Opposition, who preached surrender, were dismayed at the possibility of conciliation achieved by North and Co. and in a way which—so they persuaded themselves—would increase the power of the Crown. They denounced the terms as specious and deceitful and poured scorn on the choice of Commissioners. Even some Whigs traduced the terms as humiliating, and, though there were those who welcomed them as 'the only means of getting out of the scrape we are in',[3] the prints are violently hostile. Any one of them might have served as enemy propaganda; at least two did, one of them to a sensational degree. Paradoxically, this was a plea for the more active conduct of the war and a traditional attack on Holland as a profiteering neutral.[4] It exactly illustrated the motives and hopes of France and Holland: the destruction of British trade leading (on mercantilist principles) to the crippling of Britain. This was the first of the prints on the Propositions, a plate to the *Westminster Magazine* for March, *A Picturesque View of the State of the Nation for February 1778* [Pl. 48]. British Commerce is 'a poor tame cow'; an American—'the American Congress'—saws off her horns 'which are her

---

[1] Morison and Commager, *op. cit.*, p. 96.

[2] P. G. Davidson, 'Whig Propagandists of the American Revolution', *American Hist. Rev.* Apr. 1934.

[3] *Lord Fife and his Factor*, ed. A. and H. Taylor, 1925, p. 105.

[4] Cf. p. 98.

natural defence and strength'; a Dutchman milks, a Frenchman and a Spaniard walk off, each with a bowl of milk. The sleeping British Lion is trampled on by a pug dog (Holland) and 'A Free Englishman in mourning' bewails his inability to rouse him. In the background the Howe brothers—the admiral and the general—sleep over their wine and punch in Philadelphia (evacuated in June 1778), 'out of sight of fleet and army, the flagship laid up and all the rest of the fleet invisible, nobody knows where'. The Howes (who are attacked in a number of prints) were much condemned at home and despised in America for inactivity. The points are stressed in an 'Explanation' which concludes that the 'proof' of the deplorable state of things is the abject character of the Propositions. Darly published an enlarged version:[1] *Poor Old England: Or the Bl–ss–d Fruits of a Wise Administration*, one of three which he advertised[2] as 'Impolitical Prints'—its use by the enemy shows how very impolitic it was. The design was also copied on Staffordshire pottery—a sure sign of popularity. Foreign copies[3] use the original explanation in the magazine, but omit all reference to the Propositions. A copy was published in America in 1778 'taken from an English copy'. A second American copy, attributed to Paul Revere, appeared in 1780 with the Howes transferred to New York—a correction not made in continental versions. Three French versions are extant (one the subject of a paragraph in the *Mémoires secrets* for 13 August 1778), besides an adaptation for a fan and another adaptation where the Frenchman tramples on a peacock, symbol of British pride. Five Dutch versions were exhibited in the New York Public Library in November 1939; in the British Museum there are four, besides a small copy in a composite sheet of 'Political Fables'. Two sequels, in 1781, carry on the story. First, in February, a naïve English print: *Mynheer Nic Frog's Lamentation: Or Dutch Milk a Fine Relish to British Sailors* [5830]: the Hollander, no longer neutral, mourns the loss of his ships. *York Town* [5859] is the triumphant Dutch retort: the cow is now moribund and feeds on thorns; the Dutchman carries off a heavy pail of milk, the Frenchman and the Spaniard have their smaller shares; the Englishman kneels in abject despair; the wounded Lion howls, hurt by the exploding 'American Tea Pot'. Obsequiously, the British approach America, who has thrown off her yoke and shackles; on the shore an American prepares exports for European ports; the British flagship is wrecked, the French fleet is near

[1] John Carter Brown Library.
[2] *Public Advertiser*, 1–3 May.
[3] See *B.M. Satires*, v. 285, 449–51; R. T. H. Halsey, 'Impolitical Prints', *Bulletin of the New York Public Library*, Nov. 1939.

the horizon. There could hardly be a better example of the international importance of pictorial propaganda than this sequence of prints, with its illustration of the deep concern for seaborne trade.

Darly's two other 'Impolitical Prints' were attacks on the Commissioners. In the first, *The Commissioners* [5473], each of the five makes a speech in character to a triumphant America, irradiated and enthroned on barrels and bales of tobacco, rice, and indigo destined for continental ports. Admiral Lord Howe: 'We have block'd up your ports, obstructed your trade, with the hope of starving ye & contrary to the Law of Nations compelld your sons to war against their Bretheren.' His brother the General says, 'We have ravaged your Lands, burnt your Towns, and caus'd your captive Heroes to perish, by Cold, pestilence & famine.' (Both Howes had refused to act as Commissioners.) And there is much more of the same sort.

A pair of pictograph letters (rebuses) published by Darly and dated 6 and 11 May sum up the situation facetiously: In *Britannia to America* the former holds out an olive branch and signs herself 'your Friend and Mother'. The answer, *America to her Mistaken Mother* [Pl. 49], is headed by a print of America as a Red Indian woman with flag and shield of stripes and stars, holding a fleur-de-lis for the French alliance. She begins,'you silly old woman that you have sent a lure to us is very plane', and ends, 'take home your ships [and] soldiers . . . leave me to myself as I am at age to know my own interests without your foolish advice & know that I shall always regard you & my Brothers as relations but not as friends. I am your grately injured Daughter America.'

Another Darly plate, *Folly on Both Sides or a View of the Political State of the Nation* (11 May),[1] has a quite exceptional lesson—that both the Ins and the Outs were contributing to disaster. The overladen State Car, driven by an outsize diabolical Bute, is bogged down by its burden of 'Pensions, Needless Expenditure, Civil List, National Debt, Placemen'; placemen, bishops, and King's Friends try to push it from the mire, since 'no work, no play'. The team of ministerial asses are assailed by ferocious Opposition curs; most only bark, but two bite savagely: Fox attacks Germain, Richmond tears at Sandwich; the barkers are an emaciated Wilkes with a fool's cap on his 'pole of Liberty', Burke, and four peers including Shelburne but not Rockingham. The Commissioners are flying to America with 'Sureties for Intreaties, Contrition, Reparations, Concessions'—bladders embodying 'The Hope or England's Last Shift'. There are small inset

[1] In the John Carter Brown Library. Photostat in the British Museum.

designs; in one the Devil superintends a seesaw with France and America safely uppermost and England about to fall into his net. Verses in a showman's patter point the moral—Ministers deceive the King with tales of victories—and so on. There is a French copy with a prose translation of the verses. The discomfiture of the Commissioners in America, where they were ridiculed and obstructed in every way, is the subject of a French print with an English title and a fictitious and ante-dated publication line but with French inscriptions, including 'le Lord Burthe couronné sur un ane.' 'Infortunez Anglois, à quoi vos Bills Conciliatoire [*sic*] ont-ils servis?' The mysterious Burthe is seemingly Lord North. This is *The Olive Reject^d or the Yankees Revenge.*[1]

A typical misrepresentation of the Stamp Act characterizes the last belated print on the Commissioners, *The Curious Zebra* [Pl. 50] on 3 September. The names of the thirteen colonies are inscribed on the creature's stripes; four men compete for it, while the three Commissioners find their oats and hay rejected. Grenville (died 1770) saddles it with the Stamp Act: 'I say Saddle the Beast, She will be able to bear great burdens for plac—n and Pensioners.' 'Boreas' says, '. . . I hold the Reins and will never quit them till the Beast is Subdued' (an odd comment on his Propositions). Washington and a Frenchman pull at the tail: '. . . dis Zebra Vill look very pretty in my Menagerie.'

Moderation at last—and quite exceptionally—breaks in with a Darly plate in November: *The English and American Discovery, Brother, Brother We are Both in the Wrong.*[2] John Bull and Brother Jonathan sit together over pipe and glass in serious meditation; a picture on the wall of clasped hands points the moral.

Attacks on recruiting were effective anti-war propaganda. There are several. First, in 1775, when trade was booming, *Six-Pence A Day* [Pl. 51]: the calamities of a soldier and his family are contrasted with the prosperity of 'the lowest trades' (a chairman and a waggoner) who 'earn sufficient to enjoy the Comforts of life'. Even a little chimney-sweep's boy gets a shilling a day, and mocks the starving family. A personification of Famine and Death, ragged and skeleton-like, beckons to 'The Target' a tall, emaciated melancholy soldier, who is flanked by his protesting family—pregnant wife and hungry children; and the subscriptions for soldiers' comforts are bitterly derided. In 1779, when invasion seemed imminent and so-called loyalty regiments were being hurriedly raised, these were ridiculed and disparaged. The 85th regiment, raised in London, was de-

[1] *Collection de Vinck*, no. 1215.   [2] In the John Carter Brown Library.

rided in *The Terror of France or the Westminster Volunteers* [5552]; four extremely unsoldierly pairs with fixed bayonets are guyed in a quatrain, beginning, 'Can we Invasion dread, when Volunteers / Like these, propose to Fight the Gay Mounseers.' At this moment—26 August—the country was in danger: the combined French and Spanish fleets were in the Channel; 30,000 French troops were on the coast between Havre and St. Malo. Defeat is prophesied in *The Horse America, throwing his Master* [Pl. 52], dated 1 August 1779. George III is about to fall head-first from the plunging animal which he has maddened by a cruel scourge, to each lash of which is tied a sword, sabre, bayonet, scalping knife, or axe. A French officer walks towards the riderless horse.

In 1779–80 there is violent and increasing animosity to George III—a tyrant—'Sultan'—an oriental despot—through whose obstinacy the country is in danger of ruin. Commercial and industrial distress darkened the gloom; the agitation against the Catholic Relief Bill aggravated the hostility to the King. A savagely ironical *Birth-Day Ode* [5540] for 1779 is sophisticated; North is first violin, Sandwich performs with great vigour on kettle-drums, Germain on the oboe. The 'Full Chorus' ends: 'His Worth's the same in Jove's impartial Eyes / Who saves a sinking Empire, or destroys.'

Mr. Trade & Family or ye State of the Nation [5574] is dedicated by 'Thomas Tradeless' to 'his Excel^y. Genl Washington Pat. Pat^æ': A destitute man, with his starving wife and children, holds out his hat for alms: 'I was once a Capital Dealer but thro ye Obstinacy of ONE MAN & ye Villainy of many More—am reduced to Beggary.' Two owls on a dead tree say, 'Long live Sultan—as long as he lives, We shall never want ruin'd Towns & Villages.' (About this time several versions of a mezzotint bust portrait of George III in Turkish dress were published with ironical titles—*The Patriot*, or *Behold the Man*.) In another print with the same date, December 1779, *The Botching Taylor cutting his Cloth to cover a Button* [5573], the King (the button maker) sits crosslegged in a tailor's workroom, slashing his cloth—the United Kingdom—to pieces. Guided by Bute he is about to cut off Ireland; North holds 'North America'—already cut off; Sandwich has a 'Scheme for ruining the Navy'. Discarded scraps lie under the table, the 'Bill of Rights, Magna Charta, Remonstrances, Petitions', and so on. The Pope embraces the Pretender and both watch the besotted King with deep interest. There is a picture of the 'Flight to Egypt', the King and his family are on their way to Hanover; among the broadsides on the wall is one headed by crossed axes: 'Dr. Cromwell's effectual and only remedy for the King's evil', a gibe that verges on treason. The spirit of this print is that of a famous speech by Fox (24 November) with its menacing allusions to the fate of the Stuarts: 'When a nation was reduced to such a state of wretchedness . . . the people would inevitably take up arms and the first characters in the kingdom would be seen in their ranks' —a speech which the *Morning Post* stigmatized as a 'parliamentary invocation to rebellion'.[1] The publisher's name on the *Botching Taylor* may be fictitious, but another savage attack on the King was openly published by John Almon; in *The Allies—Par nobile Fratrûm*! [Pl. 53], 3 February 1780, George III shares a cannibal feast (on his American subjects) with an Indian brave. A very fat bishop hastens up to them followed by a sailor laden with 'Scalping Knives, Crucifixes, Tomahawks, Presents to Indians 96,000': 'The Party of Savages went out with orders not to spare Man Woman or Child. . . .' (Almon cites his own propagandist annual *The Remembrancer*.) The bishop is clearly Markham, much attacked for his attitude to the war, 'Archbishop Turpin' as Walpole called him; *General Sanguinaire Mark-ham* [5400] in a print of 1777, where he is the third Archbishop of York to be part-bishop, part-soldier, but he is treated more harshly than Williams or Herring. In *Review of the York Regiment* [Pl. 55] he leads a troop of soldier-clerics against Britannia (who wears a cap of Liberty): 'Please you Madam, for Mitres, Deaneries and Prebendaries, we will wade through an Ocean of Yanky Blood.'

In one of his earliest political plates, dated 10 February 1780, Gillray expressed the general contempt for the Ministry at the peak of the pressure against it. North, Sandwich, and Germain are *The State Tinkers* [Pl. 54], who break up a giant bowl, 'The National Kettle', under pretence of mending it. The King, in his oriental turban, looks on with a fatuous smile, directed by the delighted Bute.

Such prints reflect the spirit of near-revolution expressed in the vast movement of Associations and Petitions early in 1780 when the people were 'mad from virtue, and were bent on reforming and amending the Constitution on erroneous principles . . .'.[2] First came the famous Yorkshire meeting of 30 December with its project for radical parliamentary Reform, then Burke's Plan of Economical Reform to eliminate jobs and so curb the power of the Crown. These are the subject of approving prints, for instance, *Association or Public Virtue Displayed in a Contrasted View* [5638]

---

[1] *Parl. Hist.* xx. 1123–5. See Butterfield, *George III, Lord North and the People 1779–1780*, 1949, 166–7.

[2] Lord Hillsborough, debate of 14 Apr. 1780, quoted Butterfield, op. cit., pp. 327–8.

on 15 February, a complicated allegorical design. Britannia, robbed by Bute of her staff and cap of Liberty, turns to the marching processions of petitioners: 'Tis you alone my Friends who can revive my drooping Hopes & save me from Distruction.' The ghost of Chatham, saying 'O Cleanse yon Augean Stable', points to the House of Commons which is 'Ruled by Powerful Influence' and placed near the King's Closet.

The success of Dunning's famous motion on the increasing power of the Crown (6 April) is acclaimed in *Prerogative's Defeat or Liberty's Triumph* [5659] on 20 April, anticipating a change of Ministry, peace with America, understanding with Ireland. Aided by Fox, Dunning treads down Bute and North, saying, 'I'll trample on Corruption's favourite Minions.' America, a feathered Amazon, stands beside an armed Irish Volunteer; one says, 'now we will treat with them'; the other, 'We are loyal but we will be free.'

Nevertheless, supported by successes in America, North held on for nearly two more years. The prints register a change of political climate; Ministers of course are attacked, but the King is no longer a tyrant—there are even indications of a return of popularity. The most obvious cause of the reaction against the Opposition was the object lesson of the Gordon Riots on the dangers of Associations and mass petitioning. But this is not to be deduced from the prints which with one exception are pro-Protestant Association. There were other reasons for the reaction. It is remarkable that the Catholic Relief Act of 1778, the only measure on which the Ministry and Opposition were agreed, should have been popularly regarded as an outrage. That cartoons were part of the adroit propaganda of Lord George Gordon's Protestant Association cannot be doubted. Highly significant is *Sawney's Defence against the Beast, Whore, Pope, and Devil* [Pl. 56], dated 1 April 1779, in which the organized and successful rioting in Scotland against Catholic Relief is applauded in the familiar imagery of the seventeenth century. John Bull is urged to imitate a Scottish soldier—not now an emissary of Bute but a hero with a shield inscribed 'Begone Judas'. But John is helpless, tied hand and foot, and trampled on by the Beast, led by George III, whose 'Plot' is resisted by Sawney. The Pope absolves the King from his Coronation Oath,[1] of which so much was to be heard—not quite its first appearance, it had been invoked

---

[1] Cf. *An Heroic Epistle to an Unfortunate Monarch*, 1779, pp. 195–8.

> Proceed, great Sir! and breaking all restraint,
> Embrace the *scarlet whore* and be a *Saint.*
> *Sworn* to maintain the establish'd Church advance
> The cross of Rome, the miracles of France.

against the Quebec Act. In *The Invisible Junto Dedicated to the Truly Honourable Lord George Gordon* [5671, n.d.] the King is compared with the wicked and idolatrous King Manasseh and is outweighed, in a pair of divinely held scales, by the Bible, 'Sidney on Government',[1] and the cap of Liberty. As *The Royal Ass* [5669] on 20 May 1780 he is led to Rome by Bute and Archbishop Markham, and as *The Mangy Whelp* [5670] he is taken there by 'Father Peters'—an echo of 1688 which probably points also to Lord Petre, head of the English Catholics. *The Ecclesiastical and Political State of the Nation* [5678] was timed to appear on the day of the mass meeting and march to Westminster (2 June) which started the Riots: urged on by the Pope and a swarm of devils, George III and North attack Protestantism and the Constitution. In other cartoons 'Protestant' themes infiltrate prints on the constitutional issues and vice versa.

After the Riots, as before, Gordon is the Protestant Hero; the stream of propaganda does not stop but is diverted to showing that the Protestant Association was blameless. (One print only, *Fanatacism Revived* [5685], impugns it.) The culprits are the underworld [5679], George III, the Papists; the Government are accused of using the riots to foster a military despotism [5683]; the Lord Mayor is ridiculed for what he called his 'temerity' (meaning his lamentable cowardice). On 10 June, the first day the shops ventured to open, appeared *A Priest at his Private Devotion* [5680]; George III is a monk, kneeling at an altar, having dishonoured both the Protestant Petition and the County petitions for Reform. Finally, Gordon and the Protestant Association were eulogized in a plate [5841] to a new edition of *Foxe's Martyrs*, attributing the riots to 'the mischievous Emissaries of the Papists', a view of Palace Yard and the Petitioners utterly unlike the disorderly scene on 2 June. It is emphatically not in Gordon Riots prints that the reaction—still slight—against the Opposition is to be traced.

In 1780 popular preoccupations—besides Constitutional Reform—were naval victories and swelling indignation against the Dutch as profiteering neutrals, both unfavourable to Opposition. A significant—though exceptional—print dated 27 February is *Opposition Defeated* [Pl. 57]; North, riding a bull—John Bull—damages enemies at home and abroad. The bull, trampling on France, Spain, and America, has fatally wounded

---

[1] This republican work was influential in America; cf. Caroline Robbins, 'Algernon Sidney's *Discourses concerning Government*: Textbook of Revolution', *William and Mary Quarterly* Williamsburg, 1947, pp. 267–96. See pp. 68, 165.

Shelburne—'Malagrida'—who sinks back into the arms of his protégés, Price and Priestley, both disparaged as materialists and pro-Americans. Burke leads Lord Rockingham by the nose, and Fox carries the Prince of Wales on his shoulders; the young man tries to grab the crown (on a sign-board) but North—Boreas—blows it out of his reach and Fox exclaims, 'Here end the hopes of me and the Jews.' Very faintly sketched in the background is a man blowing the 'Horn of Rebellion'. The early recognition of the political association of Fox and the Prince (usually attributed to 1782) is remarkable. Or was it anticipation, based on the usual attitude of Hanoverian heirs apparent?[1]

Nevertheless, in 1780 Charles Fox was at the peak of his popularity, established as the 'Man of the People'. One of the landmarks of this year of landmarks was the founding of the Westminster Committee and the invitation to Fox in February to stand for Westminster (without expense), followed by his return at the general election after a heated contest—an event celebrated by the founding of the Whig Club. It is true he was second to Rodney, elected in his absence. An interesting print of the scene in Covent Garden is one of a long line; Rodney is supported by Neptune, Fox by a band of butchers with marrow-bones and cleavers; the second Court candidate is denigrated for bribery. Another foretaste of the future was *Florizel and Perdita* [5767], a Green Room scene at Drury Lane between the Prince and 'Perdita' Robinson—a prelude to the prolonged obsession with the *amours* of the future George IV.

Faction had raged disastrously in the Navy—mainly owing to hatred of Sandwich; it had exploded over Keppel's court martial for inaction at Ushant (27 July 1778), and on his acquittal he became a popular hero. But he had justified himself by pleading the dangers of a lee shore; this was long remembered against him, especially when (after January 1780) he was brought into rivalry with the more daring and successful Rodney. Already in December 1779 Keppel was satirized in *Who's in Fault?* (*Nobody*). *A View of Ushant* [Pl. 58]. (Since Palliser had also been acquitted nobody was in fault.) Keppel stands on the shore pointing to a naval engagement: his legs are joined to his shoulders to show that he is Nobody—an old folk-print device:[2] '. . . if *it* has a Heart it must lay in its Breeches.' In January 1780 there was national rejoicing, vividly illustrated, at Rodney's victories: two Spanish squadrons defeated, prizes taken,

---

[1] In the Windsor election, Sept. 1780, George III actively and openly opposed Keppel and secured his defeat: the Prince 'took great part for Keppel'. See *The Stable Voters of Beer Lane Windsor* [5700]; Ian Christie, *The End of North's Ministry*, 1958, pp. 86–87.

[2] Cf. C. Mitchell, *Hogarth's Peregrination*, Oxford, 1952, pp. xxiv–xxviii.

Gibraltar relieved. Popular sentiment was expressed in a rebus, *An Herio-glyphical Epistle from Britannia to Admiral Rodney* [5658]:

> To you my darling Child I deign to write
> Who dared the haughty Spanish Dons to Fight
> The Cause like others you did not betray
> Who faintly Fought and almost Ran away
> Like a Bold Man you us'd Britannia's Power
> And scorned that dreaded Circumstance—LEE SHORE . . .
> Go on Brave Rodney in thy Bold career
> And let thy Vengeance, Burst on False Mounseer
> Then lost America no more shall Roam
> But find with me true Greatness is at Home . . .

Though a Tory, Rodney had the merit of being on bad terms with Sandwich; it was understood that he got a command only through the King's intervention. Hence *The Appointment of the Brave Admiral Rodney and Jemmy Twitcher in the Dumps* [5673] in May 1780. The King says to the kneeling Rodney, 'do all in your power for the honour of my Crown & ye good of ye Nation.' Rodney: 'May it please your Majesty I will never fear a Lee Shore but conquer or Die.' His action off St. Vincent had in fact been 'regardless of a blowy night, lee shore and dangerous shoals'. Two years later the politics implied in this rivalry became crucial.

In this war the perennial resentment against Holland reached its climax. It was forcibly expressed in the much-copied *Picturesque View . . . of* 1778, so gratifying to the Dutch. *The European Diligence* [5557] in October 1779 is a wheelbarrow containing Britain's enemies; a boorish Dutchman, charged with 'Ingratitude & Duplicity', trundles it over the prostrate Britannia, saying, 'What's treaties to gelt?' Despite three treaties of alliance between Britain and the United Netherlands, Dutch merchants were carrying on an immense trade with her enemies; Dutch papers were freely given to American privateers; Paul Jones was allowed to refit his ships in Holland and acclaimed as a hero; the Dutch West India island of St. Eustatius was a vast storehouse of munitions of war for America and her allies, without which, it was contended, they must have been defeated. All this can be followed in the prints. As an enemy Holland would be far less dangerous than as an unfriendly neutral, and the King's manifesto of 20 December 1780, a virtual declaration of war, nicely timed to forestall Dutch adherence to the Armed Neutrality, was highly popular though denounced by the Opposition. This was a moment when Horace Walpole could reflect despondingly that the Government were more popular than the Opposition.[1]

[1] *Last Journals*, 1910, under date 31 Dec. 1780.

Rodney's capture of St. Eustatius was a blow to the enemy. It was also, as Selwyn wrote to Lady Rodney, 'a thunderbolt to the Opposition'. Reactions are illustrated in Gillray's *The Dutchman in the Dumps* [5837] in April 1781. An English sailor rejoices, the enemy are horror-struck; 'St. Eustatia by gar / Vas de Storehouse of War', says a foppish Frenchman. America, an unimpressive youth, adds, 'America now, / To Old England must Bow.' It was otherwise, and faction raged round Rodney's high-handed disposal of captured stores, satirically depicted in *The Late Auction at St. Eustatia* [5842]. It was found that many British subjects had been using the island for enemy trading. Rodney was violently attacked by Burke in Parliament; charges and counter-charges filled the newspapers, and he was involved in lengthy lawsuits—claims being made that exceeded the whole value of the captured property. The loss of the command of the sea that led to the surrender at Yorktown has been attributed in part to his prolonged stay on the island. But the dismay with which British Patriots (enemy traders) heard the news of the capture was illustrated by Bunbury in October in a realistic coffee-house interior: *The Coffee-House Patriots: or News from St. Eustatia* [Pl. 59].

From 1780 it is possible to trace the beginnings of the revolutionary change of opinion that accompanied and sanctioned Pitt's triumph in 1784. Never were prints more potent, more revealing. They forcibly suggest that behind the change was a basic patriotism and a basic loyalty to the Crown, both offended by the attitude of the Rockingham Whigs to the war and the monarchy. We all know how Fox had 'grieved at the terrible news from New York' and rejoiced at Saratoga and Yorktown. The Duke of Richmond when Lord Lieutenant of Sussex sailed his yacht through the fleet when the King was there, with the American colours at his mast-head.[1] The Opposition, in their blue and buff, called Washington's army 'our army'. 'It is strange that they should never learn', wrote Lord Loughborough after Yorktown, 'that to show rejoicing at a public calamity makes them odious and aids those they are attacking.'[2] This is one of the occasions when the prints throw light on a change in popular opinion—a striking change indeed from the anti-monarchical peak of 1779–80 to enthusiasm for prerogative in 1784. The check given by Yorktown was surprisingly slight.

But bad news from the West Indies had revived the declining hopes of Opposition and after Yorktown Ministers were clearly doomed, though

[1] Greville, *Memoirs*, under date 5 Sept. 1834 (information from Lord Holland).
[2] *Hist. MSS. Comm., Carlisle MSS.*, p. 539.

they held on for nearly four months. At last North's long, disastrous Ministry came to an end. He resigned on 20 March 1783; on the 25th Fox took office as Foreign Secretary under Rockingham. *The Royal Hunt, or a Prospect of the Year 1782* [5961], dated 16 February, anticipated the change and yet more disasters, exaggerating those already known. The print is noteworthy for the first appearance of Pitt the Younger: aligned with the Patriots, Fox, Burke, and Richmond (the omission of the nominal First Minister is characteristic), he says to North, 'shake off this indolence'. On 22 March Gillray produced *Changing Places,—alias; Fox Stinking the Badger out of his Nest* [5964]; the badger (North) runs off from his little cave towards 'Tower Hill', snarled at by a fox which excretes a stream of 'Eloquence'. In the distance is the royal hunt; the King leaps a gate and falls on his head, losing his crown; North's attributes are his budget and taxes; Fox's are emblems of gaming—a 'faro bank', discharging guineas. Fox's faro bank at Brooks's had been extremely profitable, and is the scene of Gillray's *Banco to the Knave* [5972] in April, where North and Co. have lost everything to the new Ministers, and Fox (with a fox's head) has acquired a heap of coin and notes. It was his fate to be disparaged both as a ruined and a fortunate gambler.

The *Morning Herald* (30 March) acclaimed the change as 'the end of the Butean system' and prophesied that a popular Ministry would bring ruin to the print-shops. But the new Ministers soon ceased to be popular and the print-shops went on from strength to strength. One of the relatively few pro-ministerial prints is *The War of Posts* [5984] by Colley on 1 May: the Devil drives ex-Ministers into the jaws of Hell; their successors are astride on 'posts' (small columns), and beside them stands Pitt, who had refused a post; he holds a sheaf of thunderbolts with darts inscribed 'Vox Populi', and says, 'The Lightining of my Father.' Though the antagonists are Fox and North, the rivalry of Fox and Pitt is latent. Another print which by exception is ministerial appeared in May, *Anticipation, or, the Contrast to the Royal Hunt* [5988], a complicated condemnation of the old Ministry and eulogy of the new one. Rockingham is an oculist removing a film from the King's eyes; North, an old washerwoman (he had taxed soap), says, 'My Northstrums had almost totally blinded him.'

But increasingly Ministers are attacked for their attitude to the Crown. The caricaturists, Gillray especially, make the most of damaging allegations of Republicanism. 'Every Devil is at work to divide us', wrote Walpole on 2 April, 'and half Styx at work to calumniate our party and represent us as worse levellers than John of Leyden and his Anabaptists.'[1] Fox's indiscreet talk at Brooks's was retailed by Selwyn to Carlisle: 'He talked of the King under the description of Satan . . .' He said, 'That this Revolution which he brought about was the greatest for England that ever was; that excepting in the mere person of a King, it was a complete change in the constitution. . . .'[2]

In *The Captive Prince—or—Liberty run Mad* [Pl. 60] George III exclaims, 'Oh! My misguided People', but stands passively while his new Ministers fit shackles to wrists and ankles—Fox kneels to adjust a fetter, saying, 'I command the Mob'; Lord John Cavendish silently attends to the other ankle. Keppel and Richmond chain his wrists; Rockingham walks off with the crown, saying, 'Dispose of these jewels for the Publick use'; other ministers speak in character; Burke eulogizes the king. One of Gillray's double-edged thrusts is *Guy Vaux* [6007, n.d.]: the King, with an ass's head, sleeps on the throne above a cask of gunpowder, with the crown and sceptre in a sack, ready for departure—presumably to Hanover; Fox, with a fox's head and holding a dark lantern, leads in his band of conspirators. On 10 May Gillray produced *Britania's Assassination—or—The Republican Amusement* [Pl. 61]. Ministers try to break up and pull down a sadly mutilated statue of Britannia seated on a globe, while two judges, Thurlow and Mansfield, try to protect her. A fox (Charles) bites her leg; Wilkes threatens her with the 'North Briton' and 'Libel', Dunning with 'Sydney on Government', Richmond with a musket. Keppel hauls down the flag, quoting 'He that Fights and runs away . . .'. America (an Indian) runs off with Britannia's head, and is pursued by the empty-handed France; Spain has got a leg, Holland the shield. Here is a complete reversal (anticipated in *The Parricide*) of the old attitude to North's Ministry, and an attack on Whig factiousness: 'Sydney on Government' is no longer an emblem of Liberty[3] but of sedition, and approval for Mansfield and Thurlow is unprecedented.

The Ministry were further discredited by Rodney's resounding victory over de Grasse at the battle of The Saints, removing the threat to the West Indies. News reached London on 18 May: in the moment of victory Rodney was recalled to be replaced by the inadequate Pigot; it was freely said that the appointment was made to enable him to pay his notorious gaming debts to Fox. Exultation at the victory was combined with resentment at Pigot's appointment, which was 'loudly and generally expressed in every

[1] *Letters*, ed. Toynbee, Oxford, xii. 216.
[2] *Hist. MSS. Comm., Carlisle MSS.*, pp. 599, 604 (19, 23 Mar. 1782).
[3] See pp. 68, 160 and n.

part of London'.[1] Gillray exploited the situation in a set of four cartoons. The first was a plate already 'worn out' and reprinted by 31 May: *Rodney Triumphant.—or—Admiral Lee Shore in the Dumps* [5992]. Keppel, now a viscount and First Lord, gloomily watches de Grasse's surrender to Rodney and the long procession of prizes: 'This is more than we expected more than we wished.' Fox: 'Dam the French for coming in his way say I.' Rodney's triumph, Pigot's appointment, are the subjects of the second and third. In the third, *Rodney Introducing de Grasse* [5997], Fox and Keppel stand by the King while Rodney kneels to present the captured Admiral; 'This fellow must be recalled,' says Fox, 'he fights too well for us—& I have obligations to Pigot, for he has lost 17000 at my Faro Bank.' Keppel reads a list of prizes: 'Ville' [de Paris]: 'This is the very Ship I ought to have taken on the 27th July.' In the fourth, *St. George and the Dragon* [Pl. 62], Rodney slays the dragon—the naval power of France—while Fox runs towards him, saying, 'Hold my dear Rodney, you have done enough, I will now make a Lord of you, and you shall have the happiness of never being heard of again.' This is an early example of Gillray's penetrating comments: he could not have known that on news of the victory Keppel told the King, 'He thought it absolutely necessary that some ostensible reward should be bestowed . . . the more so that he did not wish this event should stop Admiral Pigot's being sent to relieve him.'[2] Rodney's barony and recall were contrasted with Keppel's viscountcy and appointment as First Lord.

When Rockingham died on 1 July, and the King appointed Shelburne, and Fox resigned five days later, the fatal coalition with North was foreshadowed. The prints spoke with hardly a dissentient voice: 'The man of the people is snouted and foxed in the tap room of every porter house.'[3] Sayers's first cartoon, a famous one, was *Paradise Lost* [6011] in which Fox and Burke stand arm in arm, gazing disconsolately at the gates of Eden—that is—of the Treasury. Milton's poem was also the setting for a classic print by Gillray: *Gloria Mundi—or—The Devil addressing the Sun* [Pl. 63]. Fox, a ruined gambler with empty pockets, stands arrogantly on an E.O. (roulette) table poised on the globe, looking up at the sun which contains the head of Shelburne, looking down in cynical triumph:

> 'To thee I call,
> But with no friendly voice, & add thy name
> Sh—ne! [O Sun] to tell thee how I hate thy beams . . .'

[1] Wraxall, *Memoirs*, 1884, iii. 127.
[2] *Correspondence of George III*, ed. Fortescue, 1928, vi. 33, George III to Shelburne.
[3] *Morning Herald*, 3 Aug. 1782.

(The design was adapted for the vanquished Napoleon *vis-à-vis* the Regent, for George IV *vis-à-vis* his wife, for Queen Caroline *vis-à-vis* her husband.) Six months later, in another Miltonic plate by Gillray, Fox is Satan watching Adam and Eve: 'Aside he turn'd for Envy, yet with jealous leer malign, ey'd them askance' [6044]. In a woodland glade Shelburne sits with Pitt, his Chancellor of the Exchequer, at a table covered with money-bags and coin, the Treasury-Eden they enjoy with sly complacency; Fox stands aloof, scowling towards them. The near unanimity of the condemnation of Fox is remarkable, in view of the extreme unpopularity of Shelburne (Malagrida, the Jesuit). Burke shared the discredit of the resignations and was treated by Gillray as a secret Papist (educated at St. Omer)—a Jesuit, and as a Jesuit (in a biretta) he is depicted for many years. *Cincinnatus in Retirement* [6026], in which Burke is 'driven back to his native Potatoes', is noteworthy as the first of the prints in which he is an Irish Jesuit or a crypto-Papist, and is an example of Gillray's bad manners where emblems of Popery are concerned.

Meantime the peace was the prevailing topic. There is none of the un-mixed execration for the peace-makers there had been in 1762–3. An early reaction to the Preliminaries with France, on the eve of the Coalition, was *Peace Porridge all Hot | The Best to be Got* [6172], by Colley, 11 February 1783, the heading to a song: '. . . Yet a Blow or two more might have made them all Stoop . . | Tho things have gone Cross for a long time Confest | Yet now to lament is no more than a Jest | But as well as we can out of Bad, make the best.' As so often in future John Bull and George III agree: 'When I reflect on the Want of Soldiers and Sailors . . .', he wrote in January, 'the more I thank Providence for having through so many diffi-culties, among which the want of Union and Zeal at home is not to be omitted, enabled so good a peace with France, Spain, and I trust soon the Dutch to be concluded.'[1]

Fox's attack on Shelburne for the Preliminaries revealed unmistakably his 'infamous' coalition with North. A sequel to the *Fox Stinking the Badger out of his Nest* of less than a year before was *Shelb—n Badgered & Foxed* [6176]—on 20 February—the two animals combine to tear at Shel-burne and the Preliminaries. Moreover, the chief ground of attack was the treatment of the Loyalists for whom Fox had shown a marked lack of sym-pathy during the war. It was realized at once that the attack was an excuse for the junction with North. Condemnation was instant, emphatic, and prolonged. 'If satiric prints could despatch them', Walpole wrote before

---

[1] *Correspondence of George III*, vi. 222.

they had been in office a month, 'they would be dead in their cradle.'[1] There is no doubt that satiric prints were potent. Gillray summed up the position in a pair of prints dated 9 March, *War* and *Neither War nor Peace* [6187–8]. The first is a cloud-borne vision of past debates, Fox and Burke make one of their virulent attacks on North—'deserves the ax! disgrace! infamy! . . .', &c., &c. North defends himself, '. . . our Misfortunes entirely owing to Opposition'. In the other, Fox, Burke, and North combine against 'The Preliminary Articles of Peace'. Prints of 1782 had shown Fox and North in conflict for the fruits of office; now they are displayed in a shameless compact to enjoy them. For instance, in Gillray's *The Lord of the Vineyard* [6204] they reach up for an enormous bunch of grapes which Portland, nominal head of the Ministry, hands down to them. According to Lecky, North was more blamed than Fox—but not by the caricaturists: Fox is sly and triumphant, North bewildered and anxious, as in Sayers's famous *A Coalition Medal Struck in Brass* [6183], and in *The Mask* [Pl. 72], also by Sayers. Fox is Catiline (repeatedly), North the Vicar of Bray [6179].

The other lines of attack beside brazen self-interest were the Rockinghams' attitude to America and the Crown. In *The Ass-headed and Cowhearted Ministry making the British Lion Give up the Pull* [6229] on 8 May, the American rattlesnake says, 'The harangues of the British Patriots help me more to Independancy than 40000 Men'; the Ministry is denounced as 'a set of frantic sophistical Patriots'. Only once in 1782–3 is George III blamed for the disasters of the war and the losses of the peace, and that is in one of the very few apologies for the Coalition—an attack on the King for their dismissal when their speedy restoration was expected, *Today Disliked, and Yet Perhaps Tomorrow again in Favour, so Fickle is the Mind of R–y–l–ty!!!* [6291]. In this George II is 'The Father of his People' while George III is 'The Father of his—Children!' This print is the sole exception to unqualified condemnation of the Peace of 1763, which here, by contrast with 1783, becomes 'glorious, honourable & advantageous'. More characteristic is the verdict on Fox and North of Rowlandson's *The Times . . .* [6384] in January 1784: 'The cursed 10 Years American War, fomented by Opposition and misconducted by a timid Minister.'

With reprobation for Fox's attitude to the King went blame for his relations with the Prince—foreshadowed in 1780. On the eve of the Coalition Walpole recorded: 'The Prince of Wales had of late thrown himself into the arms of Charles Fox, and this in the most indecent and undisguised

[1] *Letters*, ed. Toynbee, xii. 436 (25 Apr. 1783).

manner . . . Fox's followers were strangely licentious in their conversation about the King. At Brookes's they proposed wagers on the duration of his reign.'[1] This is the context of *Out of the Frying Pan into the Fire* [6237] in which a fox executes a crowned goose, while North and the Prince caper delightedly.

A new phase opens for Cromwell—he no longer stresses a threat to the monarchy—he has become—*quâ* dictator—a reproach to Charles Fox, who is more repeatedly Cromwell than he is Catiline, or Guy Vaux or Milton's Satan, or even Carlo Khan, extravagances to be explained by accumulated resentments and Foxite indiscretions. *Falstaff & his Prince* [Pl. 64] by John Boyne, in May, with Fox as the misleader of youth, is the first of a number of prints over many years in which the pair are Falstaff and Prince Hal; eventually the Prince succeeds to the Falstaff role.

These and many other satires prepared the way for Fox's two India Bills and the King's dismissal of the Coalition, when the influence of the prints was all-important, as Fox and North both complained in Parliament. The Bills were brought in on the 20th and 26th of November; on the 25th Sayers struck his first blow, *A Transfer of East India Stock* [Pl. 65]. Fox runs off in triumph with the India House on his shoulders, transferring patronage and sovereignty from the Company and the Crown to himself and the Coalition. It is a brilliant summary of the attacks on the Bill, though less striking than the more famous *Carlo Khan's Triumphal Entry into Leadenhall Street* [Pl. 66] on 5 December: Fox, as an oriental prince, rides an elephant with the face of North. Burke—inspirer of Fox's Indian policy—leads the animal towards the India House. Fox has a triumphant smile, North registers pained anxiety; a raven croaks a prophetic warning. The effect of the print was multiplied by sequels, piracies, and imitations, and the name 'Carlo Khan' stuck. 'It is difficult to conceive the moral operation and wide diffusion of these caricatures through every part of the country,' wrote Wraxall.[2] And Lord Eldon records that, 'Fox said that *Sayers's caricatures* had done him more mischief than the debates in Parliament or the works of the press. . . . These and many other of these publications, had certainly a vast effect upon the public mind.'[3] An almost equally impressive testimony to their effect is that Pitt rewarded Sayers with the sinecure office of Marshal of the Court of Exchequer; this must have been a return for his services, not the hire of his pencil: Sayers turned more and more to social subjects, though he did some effective political prints. The

[1] *Last Journals*, 1910, ii. 496 ff. (Mar. 1783).   [2] *Memoirs*, 1884, iii. 254.
[3] Twiss, *Life of Lord Eldon*, 1844, i. 162.

political impact of caricature is spotlighted by the extraordinary conduct of Lord Abingdon: in the course of a violent speech on 2 December, he laid on the Table of the Lords one of the most savage (and unpleasant) attacks on the Coalition. This was Dent's *The Coalition Dissected* [6257], published in August; a composite figure of Fox and North, each bisected, and with their organs laid bare and covered with insults. The plate was thereupon reprinted, with more insults, and the whole text of Abingdon's speech.

The defeat of the India Bill in the Lords on 17 December by the King's intervention, followed by his dismissal of the Ministry and the appointment of Pitt, was acclaimed in two sequels to *Carlo Khan* (not by Sayers), both published on the 24th. In *The Retreat of Carlo Khan from Leadenhall Street* [6285] by Boyne, Fox sits on an ass with North's face, facing its tail, and vomiting into his feathered turban; the City, a woman wearing a mural crown and a brooch with the City arms, leads the ass, and scourges it with the whip of 'Public Resentment'; Burke, dressed as a Jesuit, follows in deep dejection. George III leans from a window of the India House, which is inscribed 'Business done as usual,' flourishing a cap of Liberty. In *The Fall of Carlo Khan* [6286] Fox, crying 'Secret Influence', falls head-first from his elephant which is being chased by peers among whom the King is active and aggressive; Burke runs away, having dropped his 'Plans of Œconomy'; Pitt shores up the India House with large beams.

Soon after the experiments of the Montgolfier brothers in 1783, a new symbol appeared, the balloon.[1] In a double-edged satire, *The Political Balloon or, the Fall of East India Stock* [6275], on 4 December Fox ascends on a terrestrial globe, from which he has hurled three men, whose pockets empty as they fall; his aims are 'the gold and silver mines' of India; one of the falling Directors says, 'If the Nation knew his treacherous heart as well as me, the directors wou'd be prefer'd.' It was soon clear that they were preferred. The balloon is used as a symbol for sudden rise and sudden fall in Rowlandson's sequence of ten little designs on the Coalition on 29 December, *Two New Sliders for the State Magic Lantern* [6287]: in 'Political Montgolfier' a balloon ascends with a fox's head projecting from its summit; in the next, 'His Fall into a Pitt', Fox falls from the balloon into a round hole (like his father in a print of 1757).

[1] The earliest satirical balloon print in the national collection is *The Montgolsier* [sic] *A First Rate of the French Aerial Navy* [6333], 25 Oct. 1783, a burlesque, with emblems of folly.

X

THE CLASSIC AGE OF ENGLISH CARICATURE

THE Christmas holidays were a breathing space before the issue between Fox and Pitt could be joined in Parliament. Something must be said of the changes which were transforming caricature under the impact of Gillray's early work and the political tensions of the early 1780's. Gillray, who had pursued Fox so unrelentingly, contributed almost nothing to the post-India Bill phases of the war against the Coalition. The field was left to Sayers and a number of new caricaturists and of artists and amateurs who, under the stress of politics, became caricaturists. The classic age of English caricature which was beginning depended also on Rowlandson, whose political satires begin effectively with attacks on the Coalition and the India Bill, and though he was primarily a water-colour artist, and his most characteristic prints are social comedy, his cartoons are an important contribution to graphic satire. These two had many followers, and at first both owed much to J. H. Mortimer, with his burlesques of the grand manner. The new look was a product both of changing techniques and of a more realistic approach to politics. The old school had been based on the technique of the engraver, modified by the use of etching. The new school was influenced by the water-colour and the pen drawing as well as the etching needle.

By the old school people had been depicted conventionally—often identified only by attributes or inscriptions. Gillray's people were human beings, with personalities and passions—studies in character. His portraiture was based on sketches from life, drawn on little pieces of card, sometimes from the gallery of the House of Commons. At first, it is true, North may be a badger, and Fox is often a fox or has a fox's head (like his father a generation earlier). But the fox has a sly rapacity and the animals have a strong individuality that was new (and reappears in the caricatures of F. C. Gould in the later nineteenth century). Soon Fox's 'gunpowder jowl', heavy eyebrows, and slovenly dress were to be charged with meaning and character. Though Hogarth has been styled the father of English caricature, and artists—for instance Paul Sandby and Benjamin Wilson—had occasionally done political satires, Gillray can perhaps be called the first professional English caricaturist. Most of the old prints were the work of professional engravers and book-illustrators, notably George Bickham the younger who specialized in satirical prints; they turned out emblematical designs on conventional lines or worked on ideas suggested to them.

The change of course was gradual. Gillray had forerunners: Hogarth's *John Wilkes Esq* was a classic hard to equal. The old school had been associated with the conventions of 'Corruption' versus 'Opposition'—'Court' against 'Country'. In 1782–3 these conventions died, and 'Patriot' acquired an ironical Johnsonian sense, though the bias against the executive remained and 'Corruption' (with varying implications) was recurrently a main theme of satire. But in the past simple-minded print-gazers had learned that Ministers were nearly always wrong and often wicked. Anything to the contrary could be attributed to hirelings. The new lesson might well be that there is more than one side to most questions. Gillray delighted in irony and in disrespect for the highly placed; his prints were not more savage in intention than those of his predecessors, but they were more effectively cruel, and the savagery was blended with wit and humour. Till late in 1797 (when Canning's influence got him a pension), he was scarcely a political partisan, and he was never a mere hireling. Though it is seldom safe to deduce a cartoonist's politics from his work, it is impossible to study Gillray without concluding that his political penetration went with some strong prejudices. From first to last he was a bigoted anti-Papist and a patriotic John Bullish anti-Gallican. From 1782 he showed consistent hostility to Charles Fox and progressively to Burke and Sheridan. He was fond of mystification; all his early prints are anonymous or pseudonymous; he would occasionally hide his own style under an assumed incompetence —either as part of the joke or to cover his tracks. In 1787 he adopted Sayers' signature and imitated his manner, probably more to tease than to deceive—his own hand is unmistakable.

It is impossible to study Rowlandson without concluding that he was indifferent to politics but excelled at illustrating the ideas of other people. The uprush of political excitement, the stimulus of a developing art, competing print-sellers, brought new caricaturists into the field round about 1783–4. John Boyne, a water-colourist and engraver, and like Darly a drawing-master, did effective Pittite prints. Isaac Cruikshank's caricatures begin tentatively and imitatively in January 1784 when he seems to have left Edinburgh for London, but his work does not become characteristic and assured till about 1789. Other clever artists are concealed by anonymity, particularly the elusive Henry Kingsbury, a painter and engraver and a follower of Rowlandson.

More important than these was Richard Newton, whose work does not begin till 1791 when he was only fourteen. His death at the age of twenty-one may have robbed England of a great caricaturist. He had a rollicking boyish humour and a gift for bold design and the grotesque. He was also a miniaturist, and had an alternative manner, realistic, charming, almost graceful. His short career illustrates the talent for caricature so often remarkable in the young. Newton's prints are youthful—to their advantage —but they also have political bite. James Hook (Dean of Worcester and brother of Theodore) did some striking cartoons as a Westminster schoolboy, and a gifted caricaturist may have been lost in a pillar of the Church. William Heath's career belongs to the last phase of the Gillray tradition, and he regarded himself as primarily a 'straight' artist, but he was a prolific and much-admired caricaturist whose published work begins when he was about fourteen. The obvious instance of the youthful caricaturist is George Cruikshank; he began to work on his father's plates at a very early age, adding details and lettering, but his own original cartoons hardly begin before he was seventeen or eighteen when he helped to fill the gap left by Gillray. We know tantalizingly little about such beginnings, but there is an illuminating modern instance in the career of David Low.[1]

The influence of the amateur has been noted. It increased as caricature gained in status and became a modish hobby. At first an Italianate art form practised by virtuosi, it was now an affair of infinite variety. Many well-known people have left examples of their work. But besides fashionable practitioners such as Lady Burlington, Lady Di Beauclerk, Lady Craven, Lord Bolton, and the more important Bunbury (whose work rarely touches politics), there were the semi-amateurs whose work was published by themselves or print-shops and who made a serious contribution to political caricature. The chief of these were James Sayers, John Nixon (of the Bank of England), whose political designs were infrequent but sometimes striking, and William Dent. Sayers, a Yarmouth attorney, was also a writer of political squibs in prose and verse; he contributed a famous song against Coke of Norfolk to the Norfolk election squibs of 1784,[2] and he was occasionally paid by the Treasury for 'writing in the newspapers'.[3] His best-known prints, those of 1783, are the least competent; he afterwards adopted soft-ground etching and aquatint to his great advantage; his work is in black and white, without colour, but otherwise belongs to the

---

[1] *Low's Autobiography*, 1956, pp. 25–36.
[2] Sarah Sophia Banks MSS., Print Room, British Museum. The verses are printed, A. M. W. Stirling, *Coke of Norfolk*.
[3] A. Aspinall, *Politics and the Press, c. 1780–1850*, 1949, p. 165.

new school. Dent's prints begin in 1782 and end in 1793—at first little scratchy etchings without merit, but as he learnt to exploit his own short-comings and adapt his work to colour, they greatly improved. He had a gift for burlesque portraiture, uninhibited personalities, and ribald com-ment which made his prints very popular.[1] There was also Thomas Colley of whom nothing is known beyond his prints which are found only from 1780 to 1783, admirable burlesques, with a crude attractive *naïveté*. He takes a special pleasure in naval victories and his ships are drawn in a way that suggests he had been in the Navy. His style lent itself to imitation, and there is, I think, a pseudo-Colley using his signature, but with a more skil-ful touch and in a very different spirit, whom I believe to be Gillray.[2] George Murgatroyd Woodward worked professionally for the print-sellers, but was an amateur in that he was an untrained artist who never etched his own designs, the son of a William Woodward of Stanton Hall, Derby, a large house still standing in 1940. His work does not begin effectively before about 1790 and his political prints belong mainly to the time of the French wars. He was original, prolific, varied, humorous, and good-humoured. His designs were etched by Isaac Cruikshank and Rowlandson (and others), and the Woodward–Rowlandson collaboration was fruitful. He was the inventor of the sailor ashore—typical of Nelson's day—generous, reckless, pugnacious, tough but tender-hearted, simple-minded and shrewd—belonging to a race apart, and to the world of Charles Dibdin's songs. It was a loss to caricature when he died suddenly in 1809.[3]

Among the countless amateurs, usually anonymous, who supplied the print-sellers with occasional sketches to be etched by professionals, two demand attention. One is Colonel Braddyll who designed among other things the two famous plates of George III inspecting a Gulliver-Napoleon through his spy-glass. Water-colour originals of one of these and of other prints show how closely Gillray followed his designs, though improving the drawing and adding touches of his own. The other is Gillray's friend and patron the Rev. John Sneyd who designed, among other things, Gill-ray's very elaborate *Apotheosis of Hoche* [9156] and the set of plates on the weather, one of which is the familiar *Very Slippy-Weather*, with its view of Humphrey's shop window in St. James's Street.

[1] Angelo, *Reminiscences*, 1904, p. 334.

[2] I believe *Out of the Frying Pan into the Fire* (mentioned above) signed 'Colley' to be one of these crypto-Gillrays; the motive for concealment is obvious; the true Colley prints are without rancour.

[3] After his death many plates were reissued with the 'Woodward del' erased and they have been attributed to Rowlandson: the social comedy of the two men was essentially different.

The newspapers and the print-shops had a great share in the changes which were giving political caricature so much more realism and penetration. Particularly the day-to-day publication of debates, by which for instance Fox's former tirades against North were put into his mouth with devastating effect. The development of the satirical newspaper paragraph, often with quotations from speeches, was a boon to the caricaturist. Sheridan attacked Dundas for a speech which 'might fairly be deemed hints for paragraphs and sketches for prints'.[1] And print-shops multiplied. The old-fashioned window-displays of the two Bowles's, one in Cornhill, the other in St. Paul's Churchyard, were long established. They chiefly exhibited humorous mezzotints into which politics intruded only by exception. Prints were sold by booksellers and in pamphlet-shops as well as in print-shops and many engravers sold prints, as Hogarth did from the Golden Head in Leicester Fields and George Bickham from the Blackmoor's Head in the Strand. For many years Darly's at the Acorn (afterwards 39) in the Strand was the leading caricature shop [Pl. 43]. With his disappearance after 1778 the two Humphreys came to the front, William in the Strand, Hannah in Bond Street, both with early associations with Gillray. Fores was established in Piccadilly by January 1784 and at once took the lead, a rival of Miss Humphrey who surpassed him only when (about 1794) she had monopolized Gillray's output. In 1797 she moved from Bond Street to St. James's Street and her fame was secure. She and Fores were both personalities, and so was Holland whose shop (at first in Drury Lane and then in Oxford Street) was opened by January 1784. He was a caricaturist and a publisher of books as well as of prints, with Radical views which landed him in Newgate in 1793 for a seditious publication, after which Radicalism gradually disappears from his prints. When he died in 1816 he achieved an obituary in the *Gentleman's Magazine* which throws light on the role of a print-seller: '. . . an eminent publisher of caricatures and a patron of Woodward, Rowlandson, Newton, Buck and other artists, was himself a man of genius and wrote many popular songs and a volume of poetry, besides being the author of the pointed and epigrammatic words which accompanied most of his caricatures.'

The print-shops were an institution. The exhibitions—entrance a shilling—belong to the early years of the French Revolution, when French caricatures were an additional attraction. But the fashionable shops always provided what was then called a lounge, and their windows were the picture galleries of the public. Like a visit to Tattersall's, a visit to the cari-

[1] *Parl. Hist.* xxiv. 295 (12 Jan. 1784).

cature shops to see the new caricatures, was an incident in the daily round of a man of fashion according to a German visitor in 1802.[1] Fores, like some other print-sellers, advertised 'Folios of Caricatures lent out for the evening'.[2] The rate was 2s. 6d. a day, with a pound deposit to secure return in good condition. He also lent individual prints by the year or less 'for copying'; he arranged prints for screens and scrapbooks and sold large collections of caricatures bound in many folio volumes, and he advertised 'Prints and Caricatures wholesale and for exportation'.

From late in the century Rudolph Ackermann's 'Repository of Arts' in the Strand was more than a print-shop, and he advertised it as 'the best morning's lounge'. Caricatures were the last of many items in his advertisements, but he published some notable ones, including copies of German prints (1814–15) as part of a campaign against Napoleon. In his way Thomas Tegg was also a man of note, a bookseller in Cheapside who specialized in cheap reprints and abridgements for a wide public. From January 1807 he applied similar methods to print-selling, advertising prints at a shilling coloured—half the usual rates—but the paper was poor, the colouring crude, and with repeated reissues the plates were worn. His first titles were reissues of invasion prints by Roberts, an engraver-publisher who had gone out of business. In 1807 he also began what he called a 'Caricature Magazine'—eventually five volumes of it with a total of 499 plates originally published separately or in pairs. It was not a magazine in the usual sense: Darly had done something similar in his six volumes of 'Characters, Caricatures and Macaronies', and these have more coherence. Tegg's innovation was to apply—so far as was possible—the methods of mass production to the hand-coloured etching, and to cultivate a wider public than that of the fashionable print-shops. Others followed his lead, especially three Radical ones with shops in the City who were active in the post-war period—Marks (a caricaturist), Fairburn, and Johnstone. As a rule print-sellers rather than caricaturists seems to have influenced the political bias of their prints, though a majority were concerned to give the public what it wanted.

Besides the influence of caricaturists and print-sellers, there was inevitably that of events. Not only do prints multiply in times of crisis, but their forcefulness varies with the intensity of convictions and passions. Something was lost, for instance, with the deaths of Pitt and Fox. The evolution

[1] C. A. G. Goede, *The Stranger in England*, 1807.
[2] A usual inscription on his prints. The further details are from an advertisement of *c.* 1819 in the Windsor Archives.

of John Bull was conditioned by ideas and situations as well as by artists. In the days of the separately published cartoon there is no standardized Bull, but much variety. Beginning in the 1750's as a symbol for England, he gradually becomes also both the typical Englishman (the bearer of burdens who grumbles and pays) and the mouthpiece of collective opinion. He is perennially the victim of doctors and quacks—official and unofficial —but under the stresses of war and politics he criticizes, admonishes, judges, condemns, even dictates. In fact his development corresponds to the subtle process of democratization which was going on despite appearances of political reaction.[1] In 1803 (both as Britain and Briton) he is the sole obstacle to Boney's 'Stride over the Globe'.[2] Gillray invented, and others imitated, the uncouth yokel, probably because this was a character in which a seeming *naïveté* could be a cover for shrewdness blended with malice. At the opposite extreme, nearly forty years later, was HB.'s dignified and portly gentleman farmer or squire. But John Bull was as often citizen or merchant as countryman; he was also, less often, an artisan, or a sailor, or a soldier—but when a soldier essentially a civilian. Despite his double role and his occasional identity with the King, when a typical Englishman he was outside the governing classes. Something was lost when John Bull became stereotyped—in these prints he is a splendid personification of changing mental climates and shifting currents of opinion. But there is already something of the traditional Bull of the mid-nineteenth century and after, especially *vis-à-vis* France, and this is mixed up with the Roast Beef of Old England mystique (still 'Hogarth's Roast Beef' in 1810), and contempt for frogs and *soupe maigre*.

[1] Cf. Mackintosh on newspapers in his defence of Peltier (Feb. 1803): '. . . it is very certain that the multiplication of these channels of popular information has produced a great change in our domestic and foreign politics. At home, it has, in truth, produced a gradual revolution in our Government. By increasing the number of those who exercise some sort of judgement on public affairs, it has created a substantial democracy infinitely more important than those democratical forms which have been the subject of so much contest.' *Trial* (for criminal libel on Napoleon at the instance of the French Ambassador), 1803, pp. 160-1.

[2] See *E.P.C. 1793-1832*, Pl. 26.

XI

FOX VERSUS PITT

THE prints do not reflect the Foxite confidence that Pitt's ministry would not survive the Christmas holiday. For the first five months of 1784 the temperature chart of polemical print production registered an unprecedented peak with over 260 surviving prints in the national collection. The battle raged in the print-shops as well as in the Commons. While Pitt gained rapidly in the country and in the House, the number of Foxite prints—small at first—tended to increase, as (presumably) propaganda came into play.

This supreme crisis began with one of the recurrent waves of popular indignation fomented by the Opposition against the Ministry—Excise in 1733 being a classic example. But the outcry against the Coalition and the India Bill was exceptional—the Crown was ranged against the Ministry. In the second phase of the crisis, after Pitt's appointment, the situation was more exceptional still—the clamour was against the Opposition. Besides the basic constitutional issues involved there was the drama of the contest between Pitt and Fox which was to influence politics to the end of their joint lives. One of the central threads of political caricature for the next twenty-two years—the relations of Pitt, Fox, and the King—was manifest.

In 1783–4 the themes were, on one side, Fox as a would-be dictator, trying to usurp the patronage and prerogatives of the Crown by a corrupt alliance with North which gave him a majority in the Commons against 'the sense of the People'. On the other was 'Master Billy', a presumptuous youth, the creature of 'secret influence', achieving office by the back stairs, and attacking the House of Commons, the palladium of British liberties. This line of attack broke on the popularity of the King's action and belief in Pitt's integrity and public spirit. 'Prerogative' is a parrot cry in Foxite prints while Addresses were pouring in (first, according to precedent from the City) thanking the King for the salutary use of his prerogative in the overthrow of 'a corrupt oligarchy' or 'a desperate faction'. And 'secret influence' had been so much the cry against North that it was doubly ineffective against Pitt.[1] It is significant that in the 'secret influence' prints a sinister but totally irrelevant Bute is nearly always introduced.

[1] At the great Yorkshire meeting on 25 Mar. Spencer Stanhope declared: 'Secret influence

To return to January 1784. In this contest for power in which popularity was a factor the antecedents and reputations of the rivals were important, and the advantages were overwhelmingly with the son of Chatham against the son of the hated 'public defaulter of unaccounted millions' who had been depicted repeatedly as a ruined gambler devoured by ambition. In a print on the first day of the year by Collings (sometimes attributed to Gillray), *Hudibrass and his Squire* [6361], Fox and Burke sit in the pillory guarded by Pitt; behind Fox hangs a scourge with two lashes, 'Prerogative' and 'Vox Populi'.

Even more persistent than the Carlo Khan theme was the comparison with Cromwell. Fox's truculent tactics in January and February laid him wide open to this line of attack—his attempts to stop the issue of money from the Treasury, contending against law and precedent that the King had not the prerogative of dissolution. This was the context of a famous print by Sayers, *The Mirror of Patriotism* [Pl. 67], dated 20 January. Fox, as if rehearsing a speech, looks in a glass and sees himself as Cromwell scowling back. 'Je sais de bonne part', wrote the French Ambassador, 'que M. Fox a été sensible a cette caricature.'[1] And in Rowlandson's *His Highness the Protector* [6379] on the 19th, Fox guards the Treasury door, dagger in hand. In *The Historical Painter* [6408] on 10 February, by Dent, Fox, as Cromwell, paints a picture of Charles I's execution, putting his brush, a sceptre, against the King's head; on the wall hangs a picture of a fox holding a cap of Liberty, and presenting 'Independence' to an Indian warrior, America.

At a meeting of Westminster electors on 14 February Fox was shouted down and insulted with cries of 'No Grand Mogul!, No India Tyrant!, No Usurper!, No Turncoat!, No Traitor!, No Dictator!, No Catiline!'. This occasion, an important one, was the subject of several prints; in Sayers' contribution [6426] Fox was charged with (among other things) 'Cromwell's Ambition, Cataline's Abilities, Damiens Loyalty, Machiavels Politics'. How does Fox resemble Cromwell? asked a Westminster Election squib, and answers, 'A Republican who is in his heart so attached to monarchy as to despise every other form of government—a tyrant, a hypocrite, a notorious enemy to the constitution of his Country.'[2]

Fox's relations with the Prince encouraged the Cromwellian allegations. Even in January, in *An Harangue about the Goose* [6377], when he and Pitt

has been the cry since Lord Bute's time ... yet all his sons vote with the Coalition, Lord North too has been called the creature of secret influence.' *Wyvill Papers*, ii. 340.

[1] Britsch, *La Jeunesse de Philippe Égalité*, 1926, p. 406.

[2] *History of the Westminster Election*, 1784, p. 355.

compete for the goose that lays the golden eggs, Pitt concludes: 'You say you'll have the Goose again / Not surely Fox in this King's reign, / But be not over much perplext / You have a prospect in the next.' In *Political Sculpters* [6401] Fox kneels to carve a bust of the Prince, complacently using a mallet inscribed 'Distruction' on a chisel inscribed 'Vice'. North sharpens a chisel with an expression of angry distress. The pedestal is inscribed 'extremely docile, easy moddel'd into Vice and exceedingly soft about the head'.

The inevitable hydra allegory was used on both sides. One celebrates the defeat of the India Bill: in *In Memory of Decemb^r the 17th, 1783* [6443] a hydra with the heads of Fox, Portland, and Co. attacks the 'British Constitution', a column topped by a bust of the King which is defended by Pitt supported by Britannia and her Lion. In the other, by Rowlandson, three days later, Fox is *The Champion of the People* [6444] wielding the sword of 'Justice'; eight fanged mouths spit out 'Tyranny, Assumed Prerogative, Despotism, Oppression, Secret Influence, Scotch Politics, Corruption'. Fox's supporters are East Indians (naked and prostrate), Englishmen with the standard of Britannia and 'Universal Liberty', and a band of Irish Volunteers. The Indian and Irish allusions are altogether exceptional.

For the first time—in *George and the Dragon* [6405]—the King is Saint George (highest of praise in these prints); he strikes down a monster with the heads of Fox, North, and Burke which is under the hooves of his rearing horse. He is also Jove holding thunderbolts and hurling the Coalition 'down to their native Hell', in *The British Titans* [6419]; his crown is inscribed Prerogative, and he is surrounded by the other gods—Pitt and his supporters.

A characteristic of the new look was a lighter touch, both in conception and draughtsmanship. Rowlandson's burlesque of Pitt's triumphal progress to receive the Freedom of the City is an example: *Master Billy's Procession to Grocer's Hall* [6642]. So is his second set of lantern slides, in nine little scenes, *The Loves of the Fox and the Badger—or the Coalition Wedding* [Pl. 68]; beginning with the Fox savaging the badger in the Commons—'Ye Bear Garden'—the two come together, each compelled by a menacing dream: the ruined gambler sees himself as a highwayman in jail; the badger sees a vision of impeachment and the scaffold. So, 'from necessity', Satan unites them, and they have a 'mopstick majority' in the House.

Fox's dwindling majority was attributed to the activities of John

Robinson, North's Treasury Secretary, who had put his knowledge of borough patronage, so acquired, at the service of Pitt. Those who changed sides were known as 'Robinson's Rats'. On 10 February the *Morning Post* printed a woodcut of six rats above a list of twenty-three names, given in full and headed 'Jack Robinson'. Three cartoons followed, one a famous print of Rowlandson, *The Apostate Jack R— The Political Rat Catcher— N.B., Rats Taken Alive!* [6431, n.d.]. Robinson kneels to trap rats with human heads—the bait being place or peerage; the rats are identified by the list from the *Morning Post*, the names being ostensibly hidden by the use of initial and final letters only. This was an ancient theme and long survived. Robinson's rats were a trickle which Pitt's popularity out of doors soon turned into a landslide that left the Opposition with a majority of one on 8 March. 'So strong was the tide without doors against Mr Fox and his majority, that they thought proper to pass the Mutiny Bill in compliance with the wish of the public.'[1] No further obstruction was possible, and the long-awaited dissolution followed on 25 March.

Pitt's popularity, shared by the King, was manifested in Addresses and was denounced in Foxite prints as 'Popular Frenzy' [6438] or 'The Breath of Popularity' [6445]. In the first, on 4 March, the title explains itself: *Popular Frenzy; or, the Destruction of St. Stephen's Chapel* (by a rabble of Addressers). In *Solomon in the Clouds!!* [6486] on 1 April the King excretes a 'Proclamation for Dissolution' while he is supported by Pitt and Thurlow, who are themselves held up by 'Air Balloons' inscribed 'Wishes of the People'. The Pittite version of the 'breath of Popularity' was national indignation with the Coalition, repeatedly illustrated, and nowhere better than in Rowlandson's *Brittannia Roused, or the Coalition Monsters Destroyed* [Pl. 69]; the massive giantess with her cap of Liberty beside her has seized two little manikins, Fox and North, and hurls them into space.

There is a set of three prints etched by Rowlandson which demands attention (the feeble drawing for one of them survives in the British Museum). It is difficult not to believe that they were devised in the highest Foxite circles: here, if anywhere, is Fox's answer to the Carlo Khan prints whose effect he so deplored. *A Peep into Friar Bacon's Study* [6436] on 3 March shows George III as the Bacon of chapbook legend, a magician consulting his 'brazen head'. He evokes three visions of the Constitution, each in a circle: in the remote past, unlimited monarchy with bubble appendages to the throne to indicate embryo Houses of Parliament. In

---

[1] *Pol. Memoranda of the Duke of Leeds*, ed. O. Browning, 1884, p. 95.

the recent past, that is, till the dismissal of the Coalition, King, Lords, and Commons are equal. In the present, the King dominates the Lords, the Lords the Commons; but he is far from satisfied and points to the ancient Constitution, saying, 'What is this to this?', showing that he aims at despotism; the new Ministry, led by a demon, hurry down the 'back stairs', expressing contempt for the resolutions of the House, while Fox, saying 'Beware', watches the scene with Burke and North. In *The State Auction* [6469], dated 26 March, the auctioneer—'licensed by Royal Authority'— is Pitt, with Dundas as his porter; raising the hammer of 'Prerogative', he orders 'Harry' to hold up 'Lot 1', a huge pile of books, 'Rights of the People in 558 Volumes' (the 558 M.P.s). There are other lots, with 'Magna Charta' as Lot 2. The members are leaving the House, but Fox confronts Pitt, saying, 'I am determined to bid with Spirit for Lot 1. he shall pay dear for it that outbid's me.' In the third, five days later, *The Hanoverian Horse and British Lion* [Pl. 70], the scene is again the House of Commons, and again the Dissolution. Pitt rides the horse (the King) which snorts 'Pre-ro-ro-ro-ro-ro-ro-ro-tive', kicks at Fox (who rides the British Lion), and drives away the M.P.s with his heels and a blast of 'My faithful Commons'. Its forefeet are planted on 'Magna Charta', 'Bill of Rights', and 'Constitution'. The Lion, which has descended from the Royal Arms above the Speaker's Chair, says, 'If this Horse is not tamed he will soon be absolute King of our Forest.' Fox invites Pitt to dismount and 'let some abler jockey' take his place. More than any of the other prints these three by the same hand embody Foxite doctrine and Fox's obsession with the power of the Crown. The weak point in such protests against the Dissolution was that this was a Parliament returned in 1780 to strengthen North, which had supported four Ministries in turn. And that in 1780 Fox had denounced the House as corrupt, maintaining that 'the sense of the People' was in the Addresses—the exact opposite of his contention in 1784.

With the Dissolution the cartoonists switched their energies to the Westminster Election, the most sensational of all English elections. The momentous contest from 1 April to 17 May is displayed in all its aspects. The aim of one side was to discredit Sir Cecil Wray (Admiral Lord Hood the senior ministerial candidate was unassailable); a chief aim on the other side was to neutralize the canvassing of the Duchess of Devonshire—indeed the grosser prints can be interpreted only as an attempt to stop her canvass. The election was fought on personalities—an attempt to make an issue of Reform failed. For the first twenty days Fox despaired, though on the eleventh day the tide had turned against Wray; on the twenty-third

day Fox passed Wray but the struggle was bitter to the end, with a satur-
nalia of rival mobs (sailors for Hood and Wray, Irish chairmen for Fox),
flags, mottoes, and uproar. The wild scene is the subject of a Pittite print,
The Humours of Covent Garden or Freedom of Election [6511]. Throughout
the forty days there was an orgy of squibs, lampoons, songs, bill-posting,
newspaper paragraphs, and caricatures, unprecedented, and unsurpassed
until the greater excitement and 'boundless rage of the Press' during
Queen Caroline's affair in 1820. That the Duchess turned the scale was
agreed: Walpole even says, 'she certainly got the greater part of Mr Fox's
votes for him, though the Court party endeavoured to deter her by the
most illiberal and indecent abuse'.[1]

Wray was vulnerable because he had been brought in by Fox—as a
Reformer—for Westminster in 1782; as a Reformer he now supported
Pitt and could therefore be traduced as Judas. He was even more vulnerable from a reputation for parsimony and addiction to small beer. And he
had made two unlucky financial proposals which were misrepresented
with deadly effect. One was for the abolition of Chelsea Hospital (to have
a greater number of out-pensioners), the other for a tax on maidservants
(actually on their employers). Thus he was called in the prints and squibs
'Sir Judas Iscariot', Lord High Keeper of the Small Beer Cellar', 'Sir
Chelsea Tax Girl', 'Woman Hater', 'Knight of the Back Stairs', 'Knight
of the Key'. In Isaac Cruikshank's *Plumpers for Sir Judas or the Chealsea
Pensioners Revenge* [6502] he is assailed by maids with mops and old soldiers with crutches and peg legs.

The first election print, on 29 March, was probably intended to push
aside the Reform issue. It was Rowlandson's *Drum Major of Sedition*
[6374]: Wray's supporter, Major John Cartwright, advocate of manhood
suffrage and annual Parliaments, speaks from the hustings, inviting
electors to help to pull down the House of Commons and so gain the favour
of Bute and Jenkinson (the so-called King's Friend); in Foxite prints Fox
stands for Liberty, Wray for slavery and wooden shoes.

Prints on the Duchess's canvassing begin on 1 April with *Election Tate
à Tate* [6487] in which she and Sam House (who appears in many prints)
hob-nob over tankards of porter. Sam was a Westminster character, a
publican who canvassed and kept open house for Fox at his own expense,
though 'when political reasons made it necessary for Mr Fox to unite with
Lord North, Sam's confidence in Mr Fox was shook to the centre'.[2] This
and other prints show that the Duchess's canvass began at once, not, as is

---

[1] *Letters*, xiii. 41 n.   [2] *Life and Opinions of Sam House*, 1785, p. 24.

often said, when the tide turned. The gross abuse heaped on her, though 'all the world, young and old, male and female' was 'employed on canvassing on either side',[1] is a measure of her achievement. When she left London, ostensibly for her mother's health, she was urgently recalled by the Duchess of Portland, another canvassing lady: 'I am almost worn out ...', she wrote on 13 April, 'if we should lose it is owing to your absence.' And Georgiana wrote later to her mother who was imploring her to give up canvassing: 'I am unhappy here beyond measure and abus'd for nothing. Yet as it is begun I must go on with it. . . . My sister and Lady (name illegible) were both kiss'd, so it's very hard I who was not should have the reputation of it.'[2]

The *Morning Post* specialized in spiteful paragraphs, but the prints must have been the most offensive part of the campaign, not only on their demerits, but because they were posted up in ginshops, alehouses, and taverns. Since they failed to stop the Duchess they can only (one supposes) have damaged Wray. A Foxite squib gives among the items of a 'Secret Service Ledger', 'To several Print Shops £2000', 'To Mr — for his indecent engravings £500':[3] the blank can safely be filled with Dent's name. One of the advertisements for Hood and Wray began, 'To be hired for the day, several pairs of ruby pouting lips of the first quality . . .', &c., &c. Time has made many of the prints—by no means all—innocuous. Prints of kisses bestowed on butchers have a distinct attraction, and some even convey something of Georgiana's dazzling charm.

The balance of youth, beauty, and fashion was heavily for Fox, who had, among others, Mrs. Crewe, Lady Duncannon, the Ladies Waldegrave. On the other side, Lady Salisbury was praised for her 'correct' canvassing, and Mrs. Hobart was perhaps a liability. She was 45, very fat and very lively, and was to become a target of caricature for her social activities. 'Where ye agents and observers can you find one fitter to be placed in *contrast* to the fair *Duchess*?' asked a newspaper wit. She was derided in prints and newspapers as 'Madam Blubber'. In *The Poll* [Pl. 71] by Rowlandson, a see-saw represents the state of the poll while still favourable to Wray—Mrs. Hobart sits on one end, held down by Hood, and completely outweighing the Duchess, though Fox tries to pull down her end of the plank; the ladies face each other, astride and with bosoms bare; Wray watches with an enigmatical expression. Behind are the hustings.

---

[1] Malmesbury, *Diaries and Correspondence*, 1844, ii. 65 (letter from Sir Gilbert Elliot, n.d.).
[2] *Georgiana . . .*, ed. Earl of Bessborough, 1955, p. 79.
[3] *History of the Westminster Election*, 1784, p. 352; cf. pp. 194, 324, 327, 376.

Like the Duchess, Mrs. Hobart took voters to the poll in her coach; a ribald drawing attributed to Townshend (now Viscount) was etched by Rowlandson as *Madam Blubber's Last Shift or the Aerostatic Dilly* [6561] with an offensive explanation and a song. Enclosed by a balloon from the waist downwards—her inflated petticoats—she carries voters towards Covent Garden. The print, dated 29 April, had been prepared for by a poster adjuring the friends of Hood and Wray not to despair: 'A much distinguished lady has found a way. . . .' A newspaper afterwards announced that 'Mrs H—t has not ballooned a single vote since she was caricatured by the unmerciful Viscount . . .'. Here, seemingly, was an elaborate device to stop Mrs. Hobart from collecting outlying voters—a counter-thrust to attacks on the Duchess.

Among the allegations of Pittite prints was the polling of unqualified voters—lodgers, or those who had not paid poor rates and so on. This, and wholesale bribery, was associated with the Duchess's canvass in the poorest parts of Westminster. Such was the context of *Wits' Last Stake or the Cobling Voters and Abject Canvassers* [6548] by Rowlandson in which the Duchess, supported on Fox's knee, lavishly pays a cobbler for imaginary repairs to her shoe. The result was the unfortunate demand for a scrutiny which kept Fox out of his Westminster seat till March 1785.

The Prince's electioneering for Fox was the subject of a few savage prints. Gillray, under cover of assumed incompetence, produced *Returning from Brooks's* [6528]. The Prince, wearing the usual election badges of a 'Fox' favour and his own plume of feathers, staggers along very drunk, held up by Fox and Sam House. With one doubtful exception this is Gillray's only political print for 1784.

In this struggle, where personal popularity was all important, two of Pitt's supporters emerge as liabilities—Thurlow and Wilkes (this is seen also in pre-election prints). Thurlow is natural enough with his reactionary views, overbearing ways, and blackbrowed scowl. Wilkes's reconciliation with the King (which followed his wholehearted support of Pitt) was a godsend to the caricaturists, and this 'new coalition' was the subject of prints and newspaper squibs: 'When Piety and Blasphemy agree, / Can there a stranger Coalition be! / O best of Kings! cries W—kes, for ever live, / Subjects like W—kes, says G—, kind of fortune give!'[1] This is the theme of *The New Coalition* [6568] on 1 May, in which the pair, exchanging compliments, stand with arms round each other's shoulders. Sayers' *Coalition Medal Struck in Brass* was parodied in *The Grand Coalition*

---

[1] *Asylum for Fugitive Pieces*, 1785, i. 264.

Medal, Struck in Base Metal Gilt [6571] on 3 May. Instead of Fox and North are busts in relief of the King and Thurlow facing each other, with Wilkes squeezed between and squinting violently; emblems of slavery decorate the background. In *A New Coalition Mask* [6584] on 17 May, Sayers' famous composite of Fox and North [Pl. 72] is imitated by a mask of George III and Wilkes. The notion had already been applied to Fox and the Duchess in *Cheek by Joul or the Mask* [Pl. 73] on 3 May.

The Ministry were ill served by caricaturists during the election. Fox's chief enemy, Gillray, and Pitt's chief supporter, Sayers, left the field to others (Sayers was using his pen in Norfolk). Rowlandson, active against both sides, was the chief artist of the election. One of his prints stands out in cartoon history. *The Covent Garden Night Mare* [Pl. 75] is a parody of Fuseli's *The Nightmare* exhibited at the Royal Academy in 1782 and familiar from engravings [Pl. 74]. Fuseli's arrangement is closely followed but, instead of the elegant female in classical draperies, Fox lies in burly nudity, dreaming of defeat; dice box and dice replace the toilet bottles on the little table. As in the picture, a demon sits on his chest and the horse with starting eyeballs puts its head through the curtain. This is the first of a long series of burlesques of Fuseli's picture. Like the Laocoon (parodied first by Titian and many times since then) it has shown itself peculiarly attractive to travesty. And though Hogarth had burlesqued the old masters in *Paul before Felix*, this is the first English example of the travesty of the picture as a political satire—a genre developed by Gillray.

As the end drew near gibes at the female canvassers gave way to praise for the 'female patriotism' that had turned the scale. On 3 May Fox is *Wisdom led by Virtue and Prudence to the Temple of Fame* [6573], there to be welcomed by Britannia. The Duchess, of course, is Virtue; her sister Lady Duncannon is Prudence. *Vox Populi Vox Dei* [6594] on 23 May is 'Dedicated to the Ladies who so conspicuously exerted themselves in the Cause of Freedom'. Fox, armed with the staff of Liberty, stands besides the Duchess who holds a 'Shield of Virtue' which protects her from the arrows of 'Woman Hater', 'Morning Post', 'Malice', and 'Envy'. Wray walks off, bending under a massive burden of 'Deceit, Ingratitude, Perjury', and acknowledging his 'Transgressions'. In *The Apotheosis of the Dutchess* [6597] on 25 May, supported by Truth and Virtue, she tramples on Scandal and the *Morning Post. Carlo Khan's Entry into St. Stephen's* [6588, n.d.] by Collings is less respectful: followed by a rabble of butchers she enters the House of Commons with Fox on her shoulders.

In these surviving election prints there are, at a rough estimate (a few

undated ones may fall outside the election), 95 Pittite (for Wray) to 44 for
Fox, with four that are double-edged. Yet, in studying them, the impres-
sion remains that Fox has the best of it (reversing the pre-election position).
The advantage of Fox over Wray, of the Duchess over Madam Blubber, is
unmistakable. Scurrilous attacks on the Duchess are an asset to her side.
If Fox is Satan—Milton's Satan—Wray is Judas. There is not a single
defence of Wray, who, quite unjustly, is depicted as a saturnine conspirator.
In a Foxite election print of 1782 [5998] he had been 'a Wray of Honesty'.
The Admiral hardly appears, Pitt and North seldom do. The election
ended only because polling could not legally last more than forty days.
Fox beat Wray by 236 votes,[1] as Pittites believed through the polling of
unqualified voters—a scrutiny was demanded. Westminster, in the full
flood of Pitt's victory, was a triumph for Fox—and he was henceforth im-
pregnable there. In the words of a Foxite election song,

> Our Westminster, Norwich, and London successes
> Are a glorious comment on your boasted addresses.[2]

In each 'success' the single Coalition candidate just managed to beat
the *second* Pittite (in the City Foxites scraped into the third and fourth
seats). In general, Foxites were thrown back on close boroughs.[3]

The election over, the temperature at once dropped, the prints become
fewer and the trend is strongly anti-Foxite. The bankruptcy of the party
and their desperate resolves are the theme of Dent's *The Whig Club, or the
State of the Blue and Buff Council* [6671]: Fox revengefully presides under
a bust of Cromwell. This is noteworthy as the first of the Whig Club
prints. In 1785 Pitt's Irish Propositions, defeated by Fox, are the principal
topic. There are prints on both sides—blame for Fox's factious and dis-
ingenuous tactics (one voice for England, a contrary one for Ireland),
condemnation of the Propositions as damaging to British interests—
combined with condemnation of Pitt's taxes—especially the very unpopular Shop Tax.

The weight of taxes on John Bull was a perennial theme, expressed
especially in two classic forms that went through many adaptations: the
cruelly overburdened man and the even more savagely maltreated bull.
Both were introduced by Dent in 1786. The *Free-Born Briton or a Per-*

---

[1] Hood 6,694, Fox 6,234, Wray 5,998. After the Scrutiny was stopped as an expensive and
unsavoury nuisance: Hood 6,588, Fox 6,126, Wray 5,895 (High Bailiff's return 4 Mar. 1785).

[2] *History of the Westminster Election*, 1784, p. 501.

[3] M. D. George, 'Fox's Martyrs; the General Election of 1784', *Trans. Royal Hist. Soc.*,
1939, pp. 133–68.

spective of Taxation [Pl. 76] is more comprehensive than even Sydney Smith's famous squib in which the schoolboy whips his taxed top; John, who 'Pays shillings fourteen in the pound', stamps with rage at the double yoke of debt and taxes on his shoulders—a good survey of the complications of Pitt's budgets in pre-income-tax days. In *The End of Parliament* [6962] taxes are combined with that other standard grievance—politicians enjoying their loaves and fishes. A snorting bull lies down under a monstrous load of taxes new and old, while Pitt, Dundas, and Pepper Arden (the Attorney General) tug at a long chain of alternate loaves and fishes which they drag from the animal's rump: 'Pensions, Annuities, Gratuities &c., &c.'

In the space between Pitt's installation and the mighty impact of the French Revolution three things gave opportunities on which the art of caricature throve and developed, comedy and fantasy gaining still further upon invective and allegory. There was the marriage of the Prince and Mrs. Fitzherbert—a print-shop obsession in 1786; the affair of Warren Hastings which began in 1786, but belongs chiefly to 1788 when the impeachment opened. After the alarming crisis in Holland with its happy ending in 1787, came the King's illness and the Regency crisis in 1788–9, preceded by a sensational by-election at Westminster with a special interest for students of Gillray.

Mrs. Fitzherbert's marriage (in December 1785) was the talk of the town. 'Oh but the hubbub you are to hear and talk of', wrote Walpole (10 February), 'and except which you are to hear and talk of nothing else, for they tell me the passengers in the streets of all ranks talk of it.' The print-shops embroidered on the rumours with a spate of prints, chiefly from March to May. The prevailing genre of the 'marriage' prints, and an innovation, was the conversation piece charged with innuendo and sometimes with burlesque and ribaldry. Kingsbury seems to have been the anonymous author of the most characteristic of these prints which were published by Fores. The Piccadilly shop-window is the background to a coarse attack on the Prince, *The Cock of the Walk Distributing his Favours* [6961], in which Fores seems to declare himself an enemy of the Opposition: his shop-front is decorated with the heads of Fox, Burke, and North on spikes arranged like a pawnbroker's sign.

The marriage was mixed up with the Prince's debts, with his relations with his parents and the Opposition, and with reports of riot and dissipation at Carlton House. This is the beginning of satires on the Prince's boon companions—especially represented by George Hanger—who like Louis

Weltje (Controller of the kitchens and cellars at Carlton House and a factotum of the Prince), figures repeatedly in prints of the wedding. The Prince is not as a rule personally caricatured, indeed some justice is done to his youthful elegance, and he is occasionally the artless victim of a designing widow as in *An Extravaganza, or Young Solomon Besieging Fitzhubbub* [6949]. Fox and the Opposition often abet the marriage (which Fox tried to prevent). Gillray's contribution was the invention of a runaway match promoted by the Foxites. *Wife & No Wife—or—A Trip to the Continent* [6932], 'Design'd by Carlo Khan', is a characteristic blend of fantasy and realism. The scene is a French or Flemish cathedral; Burke, a Jesuit, marries the pair, Fox gives the bride away, with Hanger and Weltje in attendance. North, the coachman, sits against the altar-wall characteristically fast asleep. Pictures on the wall of Susanna and Eve imply seduction by Mrs. Fitzberbert abetted by Fox (Judas). Conversation piece and theatre—another growing influence on caricature—are effectively combined in *A Scene from the School for Scandal* [Pl. 77], a satire on the Prince's relations with the King and his ostentatious retrenchments at Carlton House (much ridiculed by the caricaturists). The Prince is Charles Surface in the auction scene, ordering the auctioneer, George Hanger, to 'knock down the Farmer', that is, 'Lot 1', *Farmer George & his Wife*, a caricature of the King and Queen [6934] which Sheridan holds up. Portraits of Mrs. Fitz and (?) Perdita Robinson are still on the wall.

A theme often elaborated was the supposed miserliness of the King and (especially) the Queen. This was peculiarly the topic of Peter Pindar (John Wolcot) in his vastly popular verse satires, and he may well be the begetter of the long campaign of detraction and ridicule, carried on when the King was popular. Gillray broached the subject on 21 April in connexion with the Prince's debts, in *A New Way to pay the National Debt* [6945], noteworthy as the first attack on Queen Charlotte (but not her first appearance). Pitt wheels a barrow-load of coin from the Treasury, handing a moneybag to the overladen King, while the Queen takes snuff with a smile of greedy and satisfied cunning, her apron heaped with guineas. The henchmen of the Treasury bench, drawn up in military subservience to Pitt, are also handsomely paid, but a disabled and penniless sailor sits on the ground. The Prince of Wales, in rags, hesitates to take money offered him by the Duc d'Orléans (who had in fact offered a loan). Placards on the wall add to the insults of this large striking cartoon, which is 'Dedicated to Mon^r Necker' (an interesting indication of Necker's inflated reputation as a financial wizard). They include reflections on the King's farming activities in Windsor Great Park. Though the King had been 'Farmer George' in a print of 1771, this topic properly begins in 1786 with *The Constant Couple* [6918] in which the Queen rides pillion on a sorry horse behind her farmer-husband. Other farming scenes followed, notably *The Farm Yard* [6947] in which the King feeds pigs and the Queen feeds chickens. To quote Peter Pindar, 'Let Great George his porkers bilk / And give his maids the sour skim-milk.'

Another facet to the royal greed *cum* miserliness theme belongs to a far more important affair, the impeachment of Warren Hastings. Public opinion on Hastings had been violently at issue since his return to England in June 1785. Sayers made the subject his own by clever attacks on the Opposition campaign, particularly on Burke as its leading spirit. Gillray produced two outstanding prints, a brilliant defence of Hastings in 1786, a bitter attack in 1788 (when the earlier plate was reprinted). In *The Political-Banditti assailing the Saviour of India* [Pl. 78], Hastings, in oriental dress, rides a camel, which like its rider looks down with proud contempt at the antics of Burke, Fox, and North, who wear armour. Burke, like a malignant insect or a burlesqued Don Quixote, carrying a wallet of 'Charges', fires a blunderbuss at the 'Shield of Honour' on Hastings's arm. Fox, frenzied with rage, lifts a conspiratorial dagger. North grabs at one of the money-bags on the camel—'Rupees added to the Revenue'; his damaged (but sheathed) sabre is inscribed 'American Subjugation'.

The early prints (in 1786) were favourable to Hastings. In March both Sayers and Dent contrast Burke's intemperate violence against Hastings with his screening and reinstatement (when Paymaster) of a defaulting cashier. The trend altered through an accident. At an unlucky moment— the day after the debate (on 13 June) that made impeachment inevitable— Hastings presented a large diamond in a packet (bulse) sent from India for the King by the Nizam of the Deccan. Though Hastings was merely handing over a sealed parcel this was 'as any other possible subject would be, taken hold of to insinuate connection between the Court and Mr Hastings by means of corruption'.[1] Presents from Hastings to the King and Queen (an ivory bed) had already been seized upon by the authors of those famous satires, the *Rolliad* and the *Probationary Odes*. 'Newspapers and print shops formed the channels through which the enemies of Hastings generally transmitted their accusations or insinuations throughout the kingdom.'[2] The print-shops opened fire on 11 July with a set of prints

---

[1] *Hist. MSS. Comm., Rutland Papers*, iii. 323 (14 July 1786).
[2] *Memoirs of Wraxall*, 1884, iv. 342–5.

using the court cards of the suit of diamonds. Hastings (in his own person) is *Knave of Diamonds* [6966] with packages for the King and a book lettered Bribery. George III is *The King of Diamonds* [6969] in a pack of cards. A portrait of the Queen, bejewelled and taking snuff, is *The Queen of Hearts Covered with Diamonds* [6978]; in this the Nizam's diamond figures as a big heart-shaped jewel surmounted by a crown and embedded in diamonds in a box or 'bulse'. In a companion print George III is *Cheyt Sing in his Eastern Dress* [6979] with the diamond in his turban. Hastings's treatment of Chait Sing, Raja of Benares, was the subject of the crucial debate when Pitt and Dundas voted against Hastings and impeachment became certain. Pitt's motives for the vote are still controversial: the prints suggest that if he had not done so the outcry against 'corruption' would have been noisy indeed.

Tension slackened in 1787. A Foxite attack on Pitt's commercial treaty with France, an attempt to repeat their Irish success, miscarried; the terms were too obviously favourable to British trade. The attempt and failure are the subject of a number of prints, notably two by Sayers [7140–1] in which the importance of Josiah Wedgwood as spokesman of the industrialists is illustrated. Violent but futile attempts to storm the massive door of the Treasury by the Prince and his friends are the subject of *A Convention of the Not-Ables* [7158] (the French Assembly of Notables met in February). Fox bites the padlock, Burke's weapon is 'Impeachment'; North, passive as usual, has an axe inscribed 'To subjugate America'. Their programme is on a placard: '. . . attack the Treasury with all proper Weapons, Get into Place, Humble the Pride of Master Billy, Kick out the Treaty of Commerce, Convict Hastings, Remove the Sceptre, Repeal the Shop Tax, Pass Fox's India Bill. Keep their places & do many more things if they are able.' But inside the gate the crown is 'safe', and Pitt's words float out: 'I have Gain'd the affections of my Sovereign, and they must cut keener than a *Diamond* to affect me.'

One cause of slackened tension was a quasi-reconciliation of the Prince and the King after a quasi-repudiation of Mrs. Fitzherbert by Fox's denial in Parliament: 'a miserable calumny . . . a tale only fit to impose on the lowest order of persons in the streets'; he asserted—under pressure—that the marriage 'not only could never have happened legally but never did happen in any way whatsoever'.[1]

---

[1] Though illegal by the Royal Marriage Act and the Act of Settlement, the ceremony was regular; it salved Mrs. Fitzherbert's conscience and in some degree was accepted by the royal family.

Gillray's *Dido Forsaken, Sic transit gloriae Reginæ* [7165], is a mordant comment on Fox's denial in the context of the arrangements of Pitt and Dundas with the Prince for reconciliation with the King and the payment of his debts. Mrs. Fitzherbert—Dido—is seated on her funeral pyre, surrounded by emblems of Popery; with a tragic gesture she watches the Prince sail away in a small boat—the 'Honour'—towards Windsor Castle. A blast from the mouths of Pitt and Dundas—two winds—inflates the ragged sail and blows away Dido's crown, sceptre, and coronet. The Prince sits between Fox, who steers, and Burke who wears a biretta and says, 'I never saw her in my life, Never': Fox echoes, 'No never in all his life'; North, seemingly asleep, adds, 'No, never.'

The Dutch affair was another factor in the abatement of party rancour. A state of civil war had developed between the Orangists and the Patriots, supported by France. The United Provinces seemed about to become a French dependency when the joint intervention of Prussia and England caused the complete collapse of the anti-British Patriots and the restoration of the Stadtholder. It was a triumph for Pitt and the only occasion when Fox praised a Pittite achievement—this followed from his recent anti-Gallican outburst against the Commercial Treaty. There are some ten prints on the crisis which ended with the surrender of Amsterdam. Gillray then produced *Amsterdam in a Dam'd Predicament—or—the Last Scene of the Republican Pantomime* [7181]. The sovereigns who had been concerned watch from the boxes the antics on the stage of the Stadtholder —William V—and his frog-subjects. These bring emblems of submission and kneel abjectly to the notoriously inert Stadtholder who is burlesqued as a ferocious soldier slashing and decapitating his frogs, some of whom escape by leaping into the orchestra—otherwise Hell, with its demon-musicians who are dominated by the late Frederick of Prussia blowing his flute. Suppliant frogs fawn on the Princess of Orange, who smiles coquettishly—her energy and courage had contrasted with her husband's apathy. In the boxes George III looks belligerently at the horrified Louis XVI; Catherine of Russia and Joseph II (in a fool's cap) threaten the Sultan. A grotesque figure of Fame dominates the stage background. This is the first of some striking cartoons in which a complicated European situation (notably the peace-treaties of 1814–15) is given a theatre setting.

Excitement seethed and bubbled in 1788. First, over the Hastings impeachment which began as a superb spectacle and a social and political sensation, and thereafter dragged out its weary seven years, little regarded by the public. The prints are predominantly anti-Hastings—it could hardly be otherwise: 'All the world against poor Mr Hastings,' recorded Fanny Burney, 'though without knowing what his materials may be for clearing away these aspersions.'[1] The rhetoric of Burke, Fox, and Sheridan absorbed attention: the evidence was a bore—the barely audible quibbling of lawyers. The most savage attack was Gillray's *Blood on Thunder Fording the Red Sea* [Pl. 79], impressive, though less so than the larger *Political Banditti* which Holland reprinted in 1788. Was one, or both, commissioned? Or is the contradiction Gillray's ironic contempt (which he shows repeatedly) for the extremes of propaganda? Or had he simply changed his opinion? Thurlow, scowling, wades waist-deep in a sea of blood in which float the mutilated corpses of Indian victims. On his shoulders sits Hastings, serenely content, with a huge money-bag marked £4,000,000 crooked in each arm. Thurlow, who as Chancellor presided, was openly opposed to the impeachment, but, to quote the *D.N.B.*, 'by the consent of all contemporaries he nobly sustained the dignity of British justice'. This is one of the comparatively few prints to reflect the main contentions of the orators—the rapine alleged against Hastings. The cartoonists' favourite theme was bribery and the venal protection of Hastings by Thurlow and George III. A mild example—said to have amused the King—is *H–st–gs Ho, Rare H–st—ngs!* [7267]; Hastings, as always in oriental dress, wheels King and Chancellor in a barrow with the motto 'what a man buys he may sell. Blackstone's Commentaries . . .'. ('Hastings', early green peas, was a London street cry.)

In Dent's *The Raree Show* [7273] the splendid spectacle in Westminster Hall is burlesqued as a display of booths at a fair, with their big pictorial placards advertising the show within (an early example of a cartoonist's device which may owe something to Hogarth's *Southwark Fair* but more probably illustrates the familiar fair ground display). Among the placards are 'Alexander the Great' (Hastings); 'Alexander the Little' (the King); 'A Tragi-comi-Exhibition called the Nabob in Purgatory'; 'The Prodigious Monster arrived from the East' (Hastings devouring an Indian woman). Spectators fight for access to the fair (as they did to get into Westminster Hall—when fifty guineas was paid for a seat) and in the foreground the King, with a big 'Bulse' hanging from his ribbon, carries Thurlow on his shoulders; the Chancellor has a demon's body with a barbed tail inscribed 'Defence'. Burke, Sheridan, and Fox are the clown and zanies who proclaim the attractions of their booths. Burke, standing

---

[1] *Diary of Mme d'Arblay*, 1854, iv. 87.

in water, harangues seven ladies and a man, who are all spouting tears and are submerged to the neck. 'Burke exceeded all his former excesses . . .', wrote Sir Gilbert Elliot, 'and in one of his excesses he did not, I believe, leave a dry eye in the whole assembly.'[1]

The defender of Hastings was pre-eminently Sayers; the others were Ramberg the Hanoverian artist, a protégé of George III, and James Hook (brother of Theodore), a Westminster schoolboy. Their themes are the rhetorical exaggerations and the vindictive animosity of the orators, the conspiratorial spite of Francis, the unworthy insults to a great man. *The Trial* [7321] (from *The Merchant of Venice*) is a remarkable achievement for a boy. Fox is Shylock; Hastings, Antonio; Law, his leading Counsel, is Portia; Thurlow presides and the Managers are in their box. Fox, looking extremely Jewish, theatrically clasps a knife. The plate is inscribed:

> *Shylock.* My deeds upon my head, I crave the Law.
> *Anthonio.* He seeks my Life, his reason well I know.

This represents Fox's anger at Thurlow's opinion (accepted by the peers) that the rules of evidence in courts of law should be followed, and not the *Lex Parliamenti* used at Strafford's impeachment. Sayers did two prints on the same subject [7276, 7289]. Francis is the instigator in *The Princess's Bow alias the Bow Begum* [7309] by Sayers; he emerges from the ground with a conspiratorial stare to say (correctly), 'I am at the bottom of it.'

Rhetorical extravagance is the subject of several prints by Sayers; one attracted a counter-print by Gillray in an imitation of Sayers' manner. *Galante Show* [Pl. 80] is a small design; Burke is a showman with a magic lantern; he has thrown on a sheet four objects, grossly distorted and enlarged as their titles show: 'A Benares Flea' becomes an elephant; 'A Begum Wart' appears as three piled-up mountains, Ossa, Pelion, and Olympus; four large eyes floating half submerged in their own tears are 'Begum's Tears'; 'An Ouzle' (weasel) becomes a spouting whale. The Managers applaud: 'Finely imagined'; 'Poor Ladies they have cried their eyes out.' Polonius's words when fooling Hamlet to the top of his bent are quoted: 'Very like an Ouzle.' Three days later Gillray produced *Camera-Obscura* [Pl. 81], using Sayers' signature. Hastings displays objects in the diminishing rays of his camera obscura to Thurlow, the King and the Queen. An elephant devouring Indians is reduced to 'a Flea'; Mount Ossa becomes 'a Wart'; a British officer murdering women and an infant while a waggon-load of 'plunder' is driven off is called 'skin'd mice'; a spouting whale is 'An Ouzle'.

---

[1] *Life and Letters*, i. 195.

The impeachment was in the hands of the Opposition, represented by the Managers, and it was supposed that they were anxious 'to work it up into a flame against Government'. They failed, and only one print credits them (perhaps) with public spirit. This is Gillray's *Opposition—Coaches* [7323-4], two plates making one design. The 'Opposition', 'Licensed by Act of Parliament' and driven by Burke, is plunging into the 'Slough of Despond'; in the boot are Magna Charta and the Bill of Rights; the crest is a bull (John Bull) with the motto (commonly used ironically by Gillray) 'Pro Bono Publico'. Thurlow drives the other in the opposite direction, uphill towards 'the Temple of Honour'. The passengers are Hastings and his bejewelled wife, the guard is George III with a blunderbuss, and on the roof sits an old market woman—the Queen—with a basket of 'Golden Eggs'. A quotation about 'very gorgeous harlotry' implies a censure on her favour to a divorcée.

Here chronology must be dropped as the impeachment disappears from the political foreground. In 1789 and 1790 there are still one or two allusions to Hastings, chiefly by some reference to a diamond, and after that a silence reflecting public unconcern. Only Sayers produced a print on the final (majority) verdict in 1795—a tribute to Hastings. *The Last Scene of the Managers Farce* [8647] takes place in 'an old Hall (formerly a Court of Justice)'. On the stage a big cauldron filled with the different 'Charges', and inscribed 'Exit in Fumo', sinks through an aperture in the boards sending up a dense mass of smoke which fails to dim a brightly irradiated bust of Hastings. The contents are 'Ingredients mixed up by the Managers to blacken a character out of their reach'. About to sink through another hole in the floor stands Burke, gesticulating furiously with a paintbrush and with a document inscribed 'More Arguments'. He is 'one of the Managers & a principal Performer, who having "Out-heroded Herod" retires from the Stage in a passion at seeing the farce likely to be Dam'd'.[1] Other Managers are in their box, the outside of which is patterned by the meandering slime of a snail, which, starting from '1787', has passed every intermediate year till its head touches '1795'. Just outside the box appears the head of Francis, his eyes fixed balefully on the Hastings bust.

To return to 1788 and the Westminster by-election. When Hood was made First Lord his re-election was not expected to be opposed. Suddenly

---

[1] Burke's closing speech (reprinted as a pamphlet) lasted for nine days between 28 May and 16 June 1794 and was censured in the debate on the vote of thanks to the Managers. Between 13 Feb. 1788 and 23 Apr. 1795 there had been 148 sittings; only 29 peers voted. Thurlow had been succeeded by Loughborough who voted against Hastings on all the charges except the two on which the Not Guilty verdict was unanimous.

the Foxites challenged the Government by putting up Lord John Cavendish—a far-from-strong candidate. The Treasury financed Hood[1] and the Opposition are said to have raised £50,000 for the disorderly contest which lasted the full fifteen days to which elections had been limited after the experience of forty days of riot in 1784. It is the only election in which the Ministry is known to have paid for caricatures. Charles Stuart, a journalist, organized propaganda for Hood and his account to the Treasury of disbursements contains (besides payments for newspapers, bill-stickers, hand-bill distributors, and cockades) the items of £15 each 'for paper' to an engraver (probably Gillray) and a printer. A few days later there was a further sum of £20 to 'Mr Gilwray engraver'.[2] During July Gillray produced seven of the twenty-seven extant election prints (nine of which are Foxite), all anti-Cavendish, ineffective as propaganda and with claims to be his worst political plates. The interesting thing is that in August he published his first signed caricature ('J^s Gillray inv^t and fec^t') and that this was a violent attack on the recent official electioneering. In *Election-Troops, Bringing in their Accounts, To the Pay-Table* [7369] Pitt stands at the Treasury Gate dismissing ministerial hacks and hirelings: 'I know nothing of you my Friends, Lord H—d pays all the expences himself—Hush! Hush! go to the back door in Great George Street under the Rose!' (apply to George Rose, the Treasury Secretary). The leading applicant is Topham, editor of the *World*, who proffers an account 'For Puffs, & Squibs and for abusing Opposition', and has a claim also 'For changing Sides; for hiring of Ballad Singers & Grub Street Writers'. Gillray followed up this onslaught by another (with an obliterated signature), *Charons Boat; or—Topham's Trip with Hood to Hell* [7371], a savage attack on Hood's electioneering. The terrified Hood, approaching Hades in a boat propelled by Topham, is gnawed by a serpent, 'Worm of Conscience'. Here, seemingly, is an explosion of resentment at having been one of Hood's election troopers.

The election was so closely fought and so ruinously expensive that both sides agreed to support one candidate only at the next election; this very usual compromise was to have important consequences. Meanwhile the sensation of Cavendish's victory (by 6,382 against 5,569) was followed by Fox's departure for Switzerland with Mrs. Armistead (afterwards Mrs. Fox) and soon gave way to the far greater sensation of the King's illness.

From November to May the illness, the Regency crisis, and its after-

[1] By a levy on the great offices of State and leading ministerial peers; the balance was paid by the Treasury: *Proceedings in an Action for Debt by C. J. Fox against J. Horne Tooke*, 1792; Buckingham, *Courts and Cabinets of George III*, ii. 16.

[2] Aspinall, *Politics and the Press, c. 1780–1850*, 1949, pp. 420–1.

math monopolized the caricaturists. In the national collection there is not a single political print unconnected with the absorbing drama till mid-May. Some eighty caricatures reflect more of propaganda than of opinion, which, outside Carlton House and Foxite circles, was overwhelmingly for the King and Pitt against the Prince and Fox—for those who wished to keep the crown on the King's head against those who wished to remove it for ever—that being the issue at its simplest. Starting from 5 November the first six prints are anti-Foxite; on 12 December the tide turned and till the King's recovery they are mainly anti-Pitt. Though over the whole period there are 36 Foxite prints against 35 that can be classed as Pittite, with nine neutral or doubtful, during the crucial weeks from 12 December to 17 February the score is Fox 33, Pitt 15, and the Foxite ones are more violently explicit.

The Regency prints illustrate a propaganda campaign of passionate ferocity. Some papers were 'veering towards the rising sun'. Newspapers— 'such as had not virtue to resist temptation'—were bought up; some control of others was acquired by the purchase of shares—this *The Times* (in June) denounced as a conspiracy against the Liberty of the Press.[1] William Combe described a Foxite committee which sat daily, perhaps nightly, in a well-known tavern in Covent Garden, 'to shape paragraphs, frame handbills, and propagate falsehoods: in short to do their utmost, by any and every means, to inflame the people against the *King's* friends, and to influence the public mind in favour of their own masters. . . . Inflammatory handbills seem to have been blown through the air to our market towns, in order (as one of my farmers expressed himself) to make people as glad as the writers of them that the *king* was out of his mind.'[2] Pitt was urged by a pamphleteer 'to be cautious and in manly contempt of Print Shops, Pamphlets, and Prostitute Publications to keep the reins till the King and People are secure'.[3] Owing to the King's timely recovery and the mistaken tactics of the Whigs in obstructing the Regency Bill, he succeeded.

On 29 December the *Morning Post* revealed that a parcel of papers entitled 'Prince Pitt or the Patriot Minister' was dispatched on 27 December to a Bristol stationer (and doubtless elsewhere) by 'C. W.' (? Charles Weltje) with promises to refund the expenses of distribution. On 2 January the *Post* was bought up by Carlton House at an inflated price, Louis Weltje being the negotiator.[4] 'Prince Pitt' is the main theme

---

[1] Aspinall, *Politics and the Press, c. 1780–1850*, 1949, pp. 271–2.   [2] Ibid., p. 283.
[3] *Alfred* [B.M., T. 1120/5].   [4] Aspinall, op. cit., p. 274.

of a set of caricatures (perhaps crypto-Gillrays) violently attacking him
between 29 December and 19 January. The Opposition saw power within
their grasp, and refused to believe in the possibility of the King's recovery.
As early as 16 November Thurlow turns his coat in *Dead. Positively Dead*
[7377] in which the Prince feigns grief and Mrs. Fitzherbert is crowned
queen. And in *Filial Piety!* [Pl. 82] by Rowlandson on 16 November the
Prince enters the King's room in a drunken frolic, followed by Hanger and
Sheridan. 'Damme, come along,' he says, 'I'll see if the Old Fellow's —
or not —'; on the wall is a picture of the Prodigal Son, and a bishop is
interrupted in a prayer for the King's recovery. Such disrespect to the
Prince is exceptional: was he not the rising sun?

Fox's return post-haste from Bologna is satirized in Gillray's *King
Henry IVth The last Scene* [7380] on 29 November; Fox is Falstaff,
Sheridan is Bardolph (with a fiery face), and Hanger is Pistol, telling Fox
'thy tender lambkin now is King'. Falstaff's words, quoted on the print,
are remarkably apt to Fox's nine days of exhausting travel: '. . . to ride day
and night . . . to stand stained with travel and sweating with desire to see
him. . . .' The terms on which the Prince should be Regent were the subject of the famous debate on 10 December, when Fox laid down that 'the
Prince of Wales had as clear a right to exercise the power of sovereignty as
if the King were actually dead', and Pitt maintained that, 'except by
decision of Parliament the Prince had no more right—speaking of strict
right—to assume the Government than any other individual subject', and
that 'to assert a right in the Prince to the Regency independent of . . .
Parliament was little less than treason to the Constitution . . .'. Fox retalia-
ted with charging Parliament with treason if they 'arrogated a power to
which they had no right'. This is the famous occasion when Pitt said he
would 'Unwhig' Fox, and Burke called Pitt 'one of the Prince's competitors'. Two days later Dent produced *The Competitors* [7382] in which
they fight for the crown, and the Prince treads on a bag, displacing a squal-
ling cat labelled 'King William fourth'. (In the Prince's circle Pitt was
called 'Prince William, William IV, and William the Conqueror'.[1])

In some form or other the thesis that Pitt was arrogating to himself
the powers of the Crown by a Regency Bill imposing restrictions on the
Regent's powers (although he was known to be preparing to return to the
bar when the Bill came into force) appears in all the Foxite prints. *Prince
Pitt* [7389], with another version of the same design called *King Pitt* [7388],
on 29 December, is a key print; it embodies the main contentions of the

---

[1] *Auckland Correspondence*, ii. 280.

Foxites, except the attacks on the Queen which came later, and has the rather laboured character of concerted propaganda. Hamlet's words on Claudius are quoted, 'A cut purse of the empire and the rule that from a shelf the precious diadem stole, and put it in his pocket.' The Prince lies prostrate, trampled on by the Dukes of Grafton and Richmond; Pitt stands on their shoulders to reach the crown on its shelf. Insults and accusations are heaped on all three. The Prince says, 'I appeal to the People of England to defend their own rights and those of the House of Brunswick against this Banditti of Plunderers.' Verses elaborate the attack:

> See here Prince George! our Sovereign's darling Son,
> Old England's Hope, & Heir to Britain's Throne:
> Trod under Foot the Royal Victim lies:
> The while Prince Pitt above him dares to rise. . . .
> Two base-born Dukes of the curs'd Stuart Breed
> Bend their vile necks to help him to the deed . . .
> Rouse Britons, rouse!—hands hearts in chorus join
> To guard your laws and save the Brunswick line . . .

In his own unmistakable manner, Gillray expressed a similar idea much more graphically in *The Vulture of the Constitution* [Pl. 83] on 3 January. Gorged with 'Treasury' gold, the monstrous bird with Pitt's head crushes crown, sceptre, Magna Charta and the Prince's coronet, from which he tears the feathers.

Attacks on the Queen multiplied after the debate on the fifth restriction (carried 19 January). This gave her the care of the King's person and his household with the assistance of a council, and was attacked as a plot to obtain patronage and money. She was thereupon accused of secretly sending money to Germany (by Mrs. Schwellenberg, Fanny Burney's enemy and a butt of the caricaturists), and charged with concealing the state of the King's health and compelling the doctors to alter their bulletins. In *The Q.A.* [Queen's Ass] *Loaded with the Spoils of India and Britain* [7384] she is a zebra (her own zebra) with a large jewel—'Bulse'—hanging from its neck: 'What are Children's rights to Ambition,' it asks, 'I will rule in spite of them if I can conceal things at Q' (Kew). Pitt rides the animal, which is laden with paniers of jewels, and says, 'I have thrown off the Mask. I can blind the People no longer and must now carry every thing by my bought Majority.' In Dent's *Point-Blank at the Constitution* [7488] on 20 January Pitt fires a blunderbuss at a bull (John Bull), using the zebra as a stalking horse—the saddle cloth with a big crown and the word 'Avarice' proclaims its identity. His bullets are 'Council, Household', and so on, and he tramples on 'Parental Affection'. This is evidently a counter-thrust to Sayers' *A Mis-Fire at the Constitution* [7483] on 12 January; Fox fires at the British Lion, which holds a scroll, 'The Rights of the People'; he takes deliberate aim, resting his gun on a blinkered pony with the Prince's feathers in the *Ich Dien* headband. Sheridan holds the animal's head (to signify his favour at Carlton House) and papers flutter from his pockets: 'Paragraph against the Minister', 'Puffs direct for the P—e'; 'Puffs oblique for the P—e'; 'Abuse of the Minister'. He tramples on 'The Oath of Allegiance' and the pony treads on 'Addresses' and 'Vote of thanks to Pitt'. The management of the Press campaign was attributed to Sheridan and in *Joseph Surface Posted* [7510, n.d.] by Dent he is castiga-ted for the newspaper attacks on the Queen; he writes lies for the *Morning Post* and the *Morning Herald* and gives them to winged demons who fly off with them: 'Vienna Bank Millions' (the Queen's) and 'Settled Melan-choly'. His paper rests on the back of a demon who leans against a turn-about pivoting on a post and inscribed 'Wits last Stake' and 'Literary Corruption'. For the *Morning Post* he writes, 'her political interference', but another demon flies towards him to say, 'Recovery complete'. This print is 'Designed by Misrepresentation Executed by Purchase'—the purchase of the *Morning Post*. The *Morning Herald* was to be publicly burnt with 'universal execration' in March[1] and to incur a libel action for a savage attack on the Queen.

The confident Whigs had been cabinet-making when their hopes were suddenly dashed. How suddenly appears vividly in two prints by Sayers, dated 18 and 19 February. In the first, *The Comet* [Pl. 84], the Prince's friends (their heads) fill the tail of the downward slanting star in which the Prince's head is enclosed. They include two of the 'rats' and Sheridan has first place, Fox second with Portland next to him. Burke's angry spectacled face is near the end of the tail. The Prince's comet is expected to be 'within our horizon from Oct[r] 1788 to Augt 1789 but is expected to be most visible (if it forces itself upon our Notice) in . . . February and March'. In the second, *The Regency Cake not cut up* [7509], the final distribution of the portions of a Twelfth Cake decorated by the Prince's coronet and feathers and already allotted to the new Ministers, is interrupted by a broad ray of light and the words 'The King shall enjoy his own again'. Weltje drops his knife and the others register varying shades of anger and disappointment. The motto is, 'And all the People rejoiced and said Long Live the King.'

[1] For saying (7 Mar.) that the King was incapable of reigning: Aspinall, op. cit., pp. 271, 283.

They did. On news of the King's recovery London was immediately and spontaneously illuminated. Propaganda can seldom have boomeranged more completely.

In the Pittite prints there is no corresponding evidence of a concerted campaign, but presumably Pitt had his propagandists. After the December debate Piccadilly was placarded 'Fox for the Prince's Prerogative, Pitt for Privileges of Parliament and the Liberties of the Nation'.[1] Pitt's chief support was that the popularity which the King had acquired by dismissing the Coalition had deepened into affection which was outraged by Foxite fears of recovery. This is the background of several prints. In Rowlandson's *Blue and Buf Loyalty* [7394, 31 December] Sheridan and Dr. Willis face each other in two pairs of half-length portraits, one inscribed 'Saturday' the other 'Sunday'. Twice the doctor answers an unseen inquirer: 'Doctor how is your Patient to Day.' On Saturday, registering melancholy, he answers, 'Rather Worse—Sir'; Sheridan exclaims with a cunning and satisfied smile, 'Ha-ha—rare news.' On Sunday the contented answer is 'Better thank God', and Sheridan angrily shouts 'Damnation'. Having convinced themselves that recovery was impossible the Opposition cross-questioned and browbeat the doctors and attacked the Queen on reports of improvement. In *A Peep behind the Curtain at Drury Lane* [7484] by Sayers on 14 January the pit are shouting 'Play God Save the King' (not then generally played in the theatre); Sheridan, with a conspiratorial scowl, speaks to the orchestra through a small gap in the curtain: 'Damn'em dont play God Save the King.' On 26 December the Drury Lane audience had called loudly for 'God save the King, when the huzzaing at ". . . Scatter his enemies" exceeded all imagination',[2] an anti-Foxite demonstration that must have galled Sheridan.

The extravagance and unseemliness of Burke's Regency speeches are illustrated. On one occasion he blamed Pitt for not having sent his letter to the Prince in a black box, protested against the decision that the House should not sit on 30 January—'of all days most fit for taking that step which was to annihilate the constitution . . .', went on to attack the Lords of the Household for 'sticking to the King's loaf', while protesting (he said) that 'they did not value the money three skips of a louse'. Rowlandson ridiculed this in *Neddy's Black Box* [7499]: urgently abetted by Sheridan, Burke kneels before the throne, presenting to the Prince the head of Charles I in a 'Treasury Box'; 'My Liege I told them in the House no day

[1] Feiling, *The Second Tory Party*, p. 180.
[2] *Harcourt Papers*, ed. E. W. Harcourt, iv. 97.

so proper to settle the Regency as Charles's Martyrdom' (with a quotation from his speech on the plate). These speeches were long remembered against him, especially one on 5 February, when he said that the King had been 'hurled by Providence from the throne'. A handbill on Burke was stuck up in Whitehall imitating the bulletins on the King, 'calmer this morning but tending towards unquietness'.[1] His wild words became a recurrent theme in connexion both with Hastings and the French Revolution, with flames or smoke rising from his over-heated brain. In May Gillray depicted him [7529] as a lunatic in a cell, screaming accusations against Hastings as he sees a vision of his *bête noire* being welcomed into St. James's.

The crisis ended in laughter with the arrival 'a day after the Fair!' [7511] of a deputation from Ireland headed by the Duke of Leinster to offer the unrestricted Regency to the Prince. The expected mission had been the subject of *Irish Wolf Hounds putting English Blood Hounds to Flight!* [7512]. Their arrival, 'just soon enough to be too late', on 27 February, the day the King was declared 'free from complaint', was ridiculed in six prints. 'It is impossible to describe how much and how universally their Excellencies are laughed at', wrote Grenville.[2]

Rejoicing at the King's recovery was unbounded. His thanksgiving procession to St. Paul's could hardly be directly attacked (though the Prince and the Duke of York did their best to mar the occasion). Opposition rancour found an outlet in representing that seats on the route were too dear and were unsaleable, and ridiculing the clumsy horsemanship and unsoldierly appearance of the 'cits'. Such was the theme of two striking prints, one by Dent [7524]. The other, *The Grand Procession to St. Paul's on St. George's Day 1789* [7525], is a large strip design, starting at Temple Bar with the King's coach (burlesqued and with Pitt as sole postilion). On placards in windows 'Seats two guineas' are scored through and replaced by 'Seats 5 Shill^{gs}'. There are 'Seats in the Gutter one shilling'. This is probably by Wigstead, an imitator of Rowlandson who was Pitt's most persistent (pictorial) enemy during the Regency crisis.[3]

Gillray produced an epilogue to the Regency in one of the recurrent funerals of Whig expectations, *The Funeral Procession of Miss Regency*

[1] *Harcourt Papers*, ed. E. W. Harcourt, iv. 195.
[2] Buckingham, *Courts and Cabinets of George III*, ii. 124.
[3] Twelve drawings by Wigstead in pen and wash were exhibited at the Léger Galleries, New Bond Street, in Nov.–Dec. 1951, one of them endorsed, 'Mr Weltje with Mr Wigstead's compliments.' Seven are not known to have been engraved—they were probably overtaken by the King's recovery. The other five have been attributed to Rowlandson, whose authentic Regency prints are Pittite.

[7526], an important processional design. The coffin is carried by the six 'Irish Ambassadors' with bulls' heads, hooves, and tails; on it are dice and an empty purse. Burke is a Jesuit, 'Ignatius Loyola'—Mrs. Fitzherbert chief mourner, followed by Sheridan and Fox as 'second mourners' exchanging reproaches (many rancours were left behind by the crisis, notably as between Fox, Sheridan, and Burke). Of course Weltje is there, so, among others, is Loughborough—Chancellor-elect to the Regent. It is remarkable that, apart from one or two allusions to Sheridan's impecuniousness, this is the only reference in the prints to the fact that the Prince, Fox, Sheridan, and Burke were in financial straits that a Regency would have removed.

The King's restoration probably marks the peak of Pitt's popularity though there is no obvious sign of this in the prints. Startling events in France could now demand attention, but Cowper's *Annus Mirabilis 1789* celebrates, not the opening of the Revolution, but 'His Majesty's happy recovery': 'A theme for poetry divine/A theme to ennoble even mine/In memorable eighty-nine.' In this time of calm after storm the most vocal grievance was Pitt's transference of the tobacco duties from customs to excise, and there was an attempt to revive the clamour that had been so effective against Walpole and Bute. It failed, but in 1789 and 1790 it inspired some nine surviving prints. One is to be noted as the first print on the French Revolution: on 28 July Gillray produced two designs on one plate with the captions *France|Freedom* and *Britain|Slavery* [7546]. One is the triumph of Necker in a land of freedom (restored to office after the attack on the Bastille), the other that of Pitt in a land of slavery. Necker, stout, bland, beneficent, sits in a chair carried by Orléans and Lafayette. He holds a royal crown and the staff and cap of Liberty; an irradiated laurel-wreath floats halo-wise above his head, giving a touch of absurdity; behind are the ruins of the Bastille. Pitt, lean and arrogant, stands on a crown, holding implements of death and torture and also chains attached to the King and others who kneel at his feet. Behind are gibbets and an executioner standing on a scaffold. The application is shown by a big tobacco pipe marked 'Excise' in his pocket. Is this ironical? One supposes so—a satire on both the excise agitation and the 'Prince Pitt' propaganda (and characteristic of Gillray that he should satirize what he had himself taken part in). However that may be, the print was copied in France with deadly seriousness, without acknowledgement, and as two separate prints. The print of Pitt, 'foulant au pied la couronne d'Angleterre', was again copied, probably during the war, with an addition to the title: 'D'une main il tient une hache et les chaines dont il a su charger la Nation et le Roi, de l'autre il porte le Drapeau de l'Esclavage, les impôts et les Echafauds sont les moyens qu'il employe pour soutenir son pouvoir chancelant' [8364]. An excellent example of the way in which English irony or faction could be used by the enemy.

XII

THE FRENCH REVOLUTION

ENGLISH impressions of the French Revolution must have been largely coloured by the print-shops. The caricatures—French as well as English—were almost the only rapid pictorial reactions to events in France. This was the time when more or less permanent exhibitions were being advertised by Holland and Fores. Holland's exhibition began in 1788 and may have lapsed after 1794. Fores's lasted from 1789 to 1794 at least; both charged a shilling entrance. By September 1789 Holland was advertising, besides 'all the French caricatures', 'the largest collection in Europe of Humourous Prints' [7554]. From February 1790 the formula was 'In Holland's Caricature Exhibition Rooms may be seen the largest Collection in Europe of Political and other Humorous Prints with those published in Paris on the French Revolution' (an early use of the new phrase).[1] Fores began with 'Fores's Museum is now Opened . . . the largest Collection in the Kingdom', but in 1793 this became 'The largest Collection of Caratures [sic] in the World . . .' [8332]. He expanded his advertisements in his own *New Guide for Foreigners* (c. 1790): 'To the works of Hogarth, Bunbury, Sayre, and Rowlandson, is added every other Caricature Print executed by other hands that has been published during many years, the whole forming an entire Caricature History, political and domestic of past and present Times. . . .' In 1790 Fores added the attraction of 'the head and hand of Count Struenzee'[2] and in March 1793 'a correct model of the Guillotine, 6 feet high'. For many years—even into the 1830's—the guillotine continued to be the emblem of horrific revolutionary ruthlessness.

The two events in France that attracted the cartoonists in 1789 were—naturally—the fall of the Bastille in July and the march of the women to Versailles in October. Isaac Cruickshank, who was specializing in French subjects—probably commissioned in France—produced *Les Sacrefices*

---

[1] Holland's exhibition (c. 1794) is the subject of a water-colour by Richard Newton [Pl. 85]; many exhibits are recognizable versions of his own caricatures (seemingly original drawings) and there is a self portrait of the artist—a boy in fashionable riding dress.

[2] From casts taken after the execution (1772) of the lover of the Queen of Denmark (George III's sister) by order of Christian VII.

forces [7553] on the surrender of feudal privileges on 4 August. It is hostile to the King and Queen and to the first *émigrés*. Gillray followed up his Necker-Pitt plate with *The Offering to Liberty* [7548] on 3 August, a processional design. Liberty, irradiated, and enthroned on the ruins of the Bastille, receives the acclamations of the French people, headed by Louis XVI, 'a repentant Monarch'; he proffers his crown to her, she returns it graciously. Orléans and Necker, as 'Honor & Virtue', walk behind the King, Orléans proffers his sword and a chain of five prisoners, the first is 'Messalina', a hideous travesty of Marie Antoinette.[1] Lafayette as 'General of a Free People' heads the National Guard who are followed by a cheering crowd. *La Chute du Despotisme* [7550] on 14 August, a large elaborate design with inscriptions in (incorrect) French and English, shows the fall of the Bastille as a symbol of the iniquities of the *ancien régime* and the aspirations of the Revolution. D'Artois and Marie Antoinette are enclosed in a setting sun of tyranny which is encircled with instruments of torture. On 31 October Isaac Cruikshank produced *Le Roi Esclave ou les Sujets Rois* [7560], a long processional design with all the inscriptions in French except for a sub-title, 'Female Patriotism'. The women are driving the King, Queen, and Dauphin from Versailles to Paris; a woman carrying a head on a pike threatens Lafayette: 'si vous êtes traitre on vous traitera ainsi'; five bodies hang from a lamp-post and in the foreground a little demon blows a trumpet: 'chacun y trouve son avantage'. The royal family are depicted without sympathy.

In the next few years there is a rapid change from sympathy or tolerance for the Revolution to horror. The chief factor in this is the revolutionary enthusiasm of the dissenters, especially the Unitarians. Here was the irreligion which had had such dire results in France; here was the old antagonism to Church and King. Anti-dissent is the dominating emotion, with Priestley and Price as arch-villains. The attitude to the Church is usually symptomatic of opinion. The motions for relief of dissenters by the repeal of the Test Act in 1787 and 1789 had been ignored by the caricaturists. In 1790 relief became a party question and an organized agitation by dissenters for a pressure campaign at the general election (they agreed to support 'those well affected to civil and religious liberty') roused a storm of protest and a pamphlet war which recalls the days of Hoadley and Sacheverell. Indeed they were recalled in a popular ballad satirizing

[1] It is to be suspected that the harsh treatment of Marie Antoinette derives from cruel French caricatures of *l'Autrichienne*.

the Church and the Universities, *Now or Never; or, a Reveillée to the Church:*

> Oh who shall blow the brazen trump
> By famed Sacheverell sounded,
> That spread confusion to the Rump,
> And silenced every Roundhead.
>
> The Sects they prate of rights and stuff
> And brawl in fierce Committees
> And soon will put on blue and buff
> While Price sings *Nunc Dimittis.*[1]

In the prints the dissenters are compared with the Republican sectaries of the seventeenth century. A sudden upsurge of 'the Church in danger' cry was inflamed by events in France and by Price's famous sermon (*Nunc Dimittis*) to the Revolution Society (which was celebrating the centenary of the Glorious Revolution) and by a pamphlet[2] by Priestley in which he anticipated grains of gunpowder which would blow up orthodoxy and hierarchy 'perhaps as suddenly, as unexpectedly, as completely, as the overthrow of the late arbitrary government in France'. Hence Priestley's firebrands and the explosion which blows up St. Paul's in *Puritanical Amusements Revived!* [7632], 'Designed by Oliver Cromwell, etch'd by William Holland'; in a composition crowded with separate incidents, dissenters renew the reputed excesses of Puritans in England and New England—savage punishments are inflicted for such offences as 'being detected in the abominable Sin of Kissing his Wife on the Sabbath Day'. This burlesque may not be wholly serious. But an elaborate print by Sayers is in deadly earnest; 'the most forcible stroke of satire', said the *St. James's Chronicle*, 'that, since the time of Hudibras, has been aimed at the cause of fanaticism.' This is a key print, the first general indictment of the French Revolution, and in its crude way an anticipation of Burke's attack on Price in his *Reflections*. In the *Repeal of the Test Act A Vision* [7628], 16 February 1790, the point of departure is Price's sermon on 4 November (widely circulated as a pamphlet) and the Address he then moved to the National Assembly (signed by Stanhope as chairman), congratulating them on the Revolution. The scene is a church; Price stands in the pulpit between Priestley and Dr. Lindsey (who is tearing up the 39 Articles). The clerk has passed up a paper to Price: 'The Prayers of this Congregation are desired for the Patriot Members of the National Assembly now sitting in France.'

[1] Quoted, Wright, *Caricature History of the Georges*, n.d., p. 449.
[2] *Letters to the Rev. Edward Burn.*

With a sanctimonious gesture Price responds, 'And now let us fervently pray for the Abolition of all unlimited and limited Monarchy, for the Annihilation of all ecclesiastical Revenues and Endowments, for the Extinction of all Orders of Nobility and all rank and Subordination in civil Society and that Anarchy and Disorder may by our pious endeavours prevail through the Universe—See my Sermon on the Revolution.' Flames from his mouth expand into four columns of smoke, 'Atheism, Deism, Socinianism, Arianism', which drive a cross-bearing angel out of a window. The details are too complicated for description here. Fox sits in the front pew; his 'Hear hear hear' ascends in smoke. The American flag hangs from the roof and on the sounding board over the pulpit are two books: 'Priestley on civil Government' and 'Price on civil Liberty' (his propaganda for American independence in 1776). Among the many characters are Lord Stanhope and Tom Paine (a first appearance); as an excise man he is gauging a Communion cup. Through a doorway leading to the 'Sanctum Sanctorum' is seen a portrait of Cromwell. Lines are quoted from Samuel Butler: '. . . Fanatics, Hypocrites, Dissenters/Cruel in power and restless out/And when most factious most devout/. . . .'

Other preoccupations of the caricaturists in 1790 were the Nootka Sound crisis and a Westminster election which though uneventful was important. The first began in the usual way with Spanish attacks on British ships and on a trading station on what is now Vancouver Island. The interesting thing about this is that the cartoonists saw it in terms of past slogans (against Walpole and North) and accused Pitt of truckling to Spain [7662]; Admiral Howe is reluctant to fight [7769]; the Navy is not intended to fight [7674]. Fox on the contrary attacked him for bullying Spain, and despite these twofold attacks the outcome was deservedly popular and a triumph for Pitt. But one print (probably by young James Hook) was startlingly new, the first pacifist print in the national collection. It reflects Opposition complaints of the financial burden of the armament. In *Arming John Bull to Fight the Bugaboos!!!* [7666] John is a stout, heavily armed, very unmilitary soldier, looking up in angry dismay at the irradiated helmet of 'Glory' which Pitt is about to place on his head. A paper hangs from his pocket: 'List of Ships £5000000.' 'O D—n the Glory,' he says, 'I shall never be able to bear it all!' The Convention in October was a victory for skilled diplomacy and the armament: the demands for reparation were accepted, Spain abandoned her claim to monopoly in the Pacific (with vast but not yet apparent opportunities for Canada). Yet the Opposition denounced it as the unmeaning conclusion to unprovoked bullying—Fox called it loss rather than gain. Cartoonists on the other hand embroidered the Walpolean tradition that a Convention with Spain was a face-saving humbug.

The Westminster election was a foregone conclusion through the agreement that each side would support one candidate. The very usual arrangement was denounced as a coalition. An election on strictly economical lines, without mobs, free beer or favours, was bound to be unpopular. For instance, Fox is *The Man of the People attempting another Coalition to creep in for Westminster*, with Hood as *The Modern Judas* [7641]. Horne Tooke intervened, demanded a poll and stood as an independent Reformer. Seeing that he was unsupported against the candidates of the Treasury and of the Westminster Committee and the Whig Club the results were surprising, a portent of reviving Radicalism and of events that made Westminster the pre-Reform Radical stronghold.[1]

Home politics gave way in November to the sensation of Burke's *Reflections on the Revolution in France* which is vividly illustrated. Prints emphatically do not support the French Ambassador's opinion that the book had united the whole nation against changes in France. The reaction was instant: the book was a favourite subject from November to May, when it merged with the equally attractive topic of the quarrel between Burke and Fox. All but three of the prints are hostile, and range from raillery through derision to reprobation. The caricaturists anticipated Tom Paine by depicting Burke as Don Quixote (for whom the age of chivalry was dead) and by seizing on the famous passage about Marie Antoinette. But one phrase in the book which became a democratic watchword went unnoticed (in the prints) till 1793—this was 'swinish multitude'. Immediately on publication there was a burlesque *Frontispiece to Reflections . . .* [7675], dated 2 November (publication date was 1 November). This was one of a set published, perhaps designed and etched, by Holland. Burke kneels, gazing ecstatically on a crowned and irradiated vision of Marie Antoinette standing upon clouds, and the famous passage is quoted, beginning, 'It is now sixteen or seventeen years since I saw the Queen of France.' A cherub holds a firebrand to Burke's head, drawing sparks from his heated brain. Next came the same artist's *The Knight of the woeful Countenance going to extirpate the National Assembly* [Pl. 86]. Burke as a Jesuit-Don Quixote, wearing armour, a miniature of Marie Antoinette, and a biretta expanded into the hat of a Death's-head hussar, rides out of his publisher's shop on an ass (the Pope). On his 'Shield of Aristocracy and Despotism' are scenes

---

[1] Fox 3,561, Hood 3,217, Horne Tooke 1,779.

of imprisonment and torture. In a third print Burke is *Don Dismallo*, *after an absence of sixteen years embracing his beautiful Vision* [7679]. Watched by the weeping Mrs. Burke, who is dressed like a farmer's wife, he embraces the Queen who pays him extravagant compliments.

The first pamphlet attacks on the book—there were at least thirty-nine—are the subject of *Don Dismallo running the Literary Gantlet* [7685] dated 1 December. Burke, in a fool's cap and stripped to the waist, is scourged by his active enemies: Mrs. Barbauld, Sheridan (with whom he had quarrelled), Mrs. Macaulay (the Republican historian), and Horne Tooke. These are urged on by Dr. Price and Helen Maria Williams. Liberty walks off arm in arm with the aged prisoner from the Bastille (actually transferred to a lunatic asylum) who carries a banner quartered with scenes relating to the fall of the fortress, including heads on pikes and the anniversary fête. Burke's 'foes show how deeply they are wounded by their abusive pamphlets', wrote Walpole on 20 December. 'Their amazonian allies headed by Kate Macaulay and the virago Barbauld spit poison at eighteen pence a head....'[1]

Dent attacks Burke for exaggerations and inconsistencies in *Sublime and Beautiful Reflections . . . or the Man in the Moon at large* [7689] with the motto 'Reason to Madness is near allied'. The passionate defence of monarchy in France is contrasted with his pronouncements (in 1780) on the influence of the crown, and with quotations from Regency speeches, including 'hurled by Providence from the Throne'. The Radical viewpoint appears more emphatically in *The Aristocratic Crusade or Chivalry revived by Don Quixote de St. Omer . . .* [7824], 31 January 1791, an elaborate design by Isaac Cruikshank in which labels from Burke's mouth contrast his attitudes to the French monarchy and to the *Tiers État* ('low bred illiterate Traders, Lawyers & Country Clowns'). Bishops and peers are denounced and so are members for close boroughs—Old Sarum makes a first appearance. This is very different from the old Wilkite prints, or the usual tributes to Liberty. Here, perhaps for the first time, is class consciousness (to which 'swinish multitude' made a contribution). Burke stands on the back of a monster with five heads (four wearing coronets) which tramples on the backs of 'base born plebeans'.

The exceptions to the chorus of dispraise are three attacks on Price for the sermon in the Old Jewry to the Revolution Society. In *The Doctor indulged with his favourite Scene* [7690] by Cruikshank, Price, kneeling on a royal crown, looks through a peep-hole into the Queen's bedroom at Versailles, where murderous ruffians are searching for her. A devil clutches

---

[1] *Letters*, ed. Toynbee, Oxford, xiv. 345.

him round the waist as he utters his *nunc dimittis*: 'Lord now lettest thou thy Servant depart in peace for mine Eyes have Seen . . .'. Below is Burke's passage on the sermon, ending, 'These Theban & Thracian Orgies, acted in France, and applauded only in the Old Jewry. . . .' Another pro-Burke print is less serious and tinged with irony, Gillray's *Smelling out a Rat; —or—the Atheistical—Revolutionist disturbed in his Midnight " Calculations" owing to a Troubled—Conscience* [7686]. Dropping his pen, Price turns from his table in horror at a cloud-supported vision of his enemy's enormous and spectacled nose resting on the back of his chair and framed by two great hands holding up an irradiated crown and cross, with his open book poised above his spectacles. Beside Price are his 'Sermon . . .' and two imaginary works with revolutionary titles. On the wall is a picture, '. . . the Glory of Great Britain'—the execution of Charles I.

The third, by Sayers, on 6 May 1791, is one of many prints on the famous quarrel between Fox and Burke in the debate on the constitution for French Canada. It is the first in which the Foxites are Jacobins and it foreshadows the split in the party. In *Mr Burke's Pair of Spectacles for short sighted Politicians* [7858] a hand from the margin holds out spectacles enclosing bust portraits of Fox and Sheridan. The vision displayed to them is of a Cromwellian Fox cutting down a tree on which are symbols of monarchy, religion, and aristocracy, with an axe: 'Rights of Man'. He is aided by Sheridan and Priestley, and in the foreground the skeleton of Price (who had recently died) rises from the tomb to utter his *nunc dimittis*. A demon holds out to the horrified Portland 'A Plan of the new Constitution of France, the Perfection of human Wisdom recommended as a Model for Canada by the Rt. [Hon. C. J. Fox]'; the plan is a picture of a tree in a pot of 'Republicanism' whose leaves are 'Atheists', 'Demagogues', and 'The Mob'.

After the quarrel with Fox attacks on Burke's book were combined with charges of self-seeking apostasy. Fox's tears were derided, but Burke was more savagely treated. His wild eloquence and quotations from his book or his speeches were treated as the ravings of a madman as in *The Volcano of Opposition* [7863]. This recalls Fanny Burney's comment in her diary (18 June 1791) on Burke's otherwise delightful conversation: 'politics, even on his own side, must always be excluded; his irritability is so terrible on that theme, that it gives immediately to his face the expression of a man who is going to defend himself from murderers.' In *The Wrangling Friends or Opposition in Disorder* [7855] Fox's tears are baled up in a bucket, and a demon applies bellows to Burke's steaming head.

Burke was attacked by both sides—in the Opposition papers for caballing against Fox: 'the Ministerial papers held up Mr Burke . . . in the character of a king's evidence who had impeached his accomplices. The pencil was called in to the aid of the pen, and paragraphs were embodied in caricatures.'[1] The leading print on this theme was Gillray's *The Impeachment,—or—"The Father of the Gang, turnd Kings Evidence* [7861]. Fox and Sheridan (Joseph Surface) are two jail-birds, prisoners at the bar; Burke towers over them with a stern frown, seizing them by the hair. Sheridan curses, Fox weeps, grieving that his 'Chum in all infamy, for Twenty five years, should now turn Snitch at last! . . .' Despite their persistent hostility to Burke the prints are increasingly anti-Jacobin and reflect the emotions that produced the deplorable riots in Birmingham on 14 July. Disparaging allusions to Paine's *Rights of Man* (the principal attack on Burke's *Reflections*) recur, and Gillray gave the book a print to itself: "*The Rights of Man—or—Tommy Paine the little American Taylor, taking the Measure of the Crown, for a new pair of Revolution-Breeches* [7867]. He is a ragged fellow wearing a French cocked hat with a 'Vive la Liberte' cockade, using his inadequate tape-measure on a gigantic crown, and delivering one of those satirical monologues in which Gillray specialized.

His *Alecto and her Train, at the Gate of Pandæmonium,—or—The Recruiting Sarjeant enlisting John-Bull, into the Revolution Service* [7889] on 4 July is a satire on the coming dinner of the Revolution Society on the second anniversary of the fall of the Bastille, and in it Gillray's John Bull as an uncouth countryman in a smock makes a first appearance. The serjeant is Alecto, a ragged fantastic hag with snaky locks, wearing a French cocked hat and tricolour cockade, and holding a pike with the cap of Liberty. Her fifer and drummer are Sheridan and Fox, offering John Bull *assignats* as 'bounty money', and making specious promises: '. . . the glorious 14th of July is approaching when Monarchs are to be crushed like maggots, and brave men like yourself are to be put in their places . . .'. John hesitates between the lure of the drum and the fine prospects, and reluctance to leave 'the Varmer': '. . . Ah Varmer George has been a rare good Measter to I. . . .' Sheridan, small and deprecating, pipes, 'Though I am but a very silly Lad. . . .' Fox is burly and persuasive: 'Then come my Lad, our Glory share. . . .' They stand outside the Crown and Anchor in the Strand (where the dinner was to be held). Stanhope runs off, holding a warning letter from Pitt. He resigned from the Society on 12 August. None of the three attended the dinner.

[1] *Annual Register*, 1791, p. 119.

The passions and fears that raged round the Revolution Society and its anniversary celebrations are illustrated also in two prints by Gillray published on 19 and 23 July—after the Birmingham riots. In *The Hopes of the Party prior to July 14th*—"*From such wicked Crown & Anchor-Dreams Good Lord deliver us*" [7892] Fox—masked—is about to strike off George III's head, while Pitt and Queen Charlotte (cruelly caricatured) swing from the same lamp-post. Sheridan and Horne Tooke hold the King down, while Priestley proffers consolation: '. . . a man ought to be glad of the opportunity of dying, if by that means he can serve his Country, and bring about a glorious Revolution—& as for your Soul, or anything after death don't trouble yourself about that. . . .' Sir Cecil Wray, a steward at the recent dinner, is introduced to be again derided as a small-beer addict. The other print is directed mainly against the Unitarians: in *A Birmingham Toast, as given on the 14th of July by the —— Revolution Society* [7894] the same revolutionaries and Dr. Lindsey drink the toast which Priestley gives, holding up an empty Communion dish and a brimming chalice: 'The —— Head, here!' The other guests applaud and a group of subordinate lankhaired zealots add their prayers: 'Preserve us from Kings & Whores of Babylon!!! . . .' Their sanctimoniousness contrasts with the stern fanaticism of the principals. On the wall is a picture of St. Paul's: 'A Pig's Sty. . . .' The Unitarians were chiefly suspect, but the Birmingham mob which burnt dissenters' houses and chapels and destroyed Priestley's valuable scientific collections shouted, 'damned Presbyterians, Long live the King, No Olivers, down with the Rump, Church and State, No false Rights of Man.' In fact they harked back to the days of Sacheverell at least. In *Self Murder . . .* [7899], a print by Cruikshank, in which Priestley is a wolf in sheep's clothing, a parson answers a bishop: 'Yes Sir, Under the Denomination of Dissenters they P—y, P—e and L—y have brought a stigma on all Dissenters in General. . . .'

In English politics the outstanding event of 1791 was the Russian Armament in which Pitt hoped to repeat the success of his Spanish Armament (still under attack from the Opposition). Pitt's plan was to compel Russia to make peace with Turkey on the basis of the *status quo ante*—that is, to return Oczakof (where Odessa now stands) to the Porte. This was to be done by sending a fleet to the Baltic with support from Prussia and Holland. The stakes were the balance of power, the Russian stride southwards, and the protection of Poland from the pending absorption by Russia. The affair was and remains controversial, involving a whole sequence of might-have-beens. It was one of the occasions when the

Opposition, mobilizing public opinion, forced the Government to abandon its policy—a crisis in the Fox versus Pitt drama in which Fox avenged his failure over the Spanish Armament—not to speak of the Regency fiasco. The prints are almost all Oppositionist with one or two that are merely ribald—Catherine's morals were irresistible. The dominant motives are fear of taxation and the loss of Russian trade. J. H. Rose calls Pitt's policy 'playing the part of Petruchio to Catherine', and that had been Gillray's idea in *Taming of the Shrew:—Katharine & Petruchio:—The Modern Quixotte, or what you will* [7845]. Pitt, an arrogant Petruchio dressed as the Don, rides a Rosinante, the White Horse of Hanover—George III; seated behind him are Prussia and Holland (Sancho) with the Sultan crouching obsequiously behind the horse. He orders the kneeling Katharine to remove her cap—a Turkish crescent—but his words are altered to show that he has usurped sovereign power: "off with that bauble 'tis my royal will. The moribund animal weeps: 'Heigho! to have myself thus rid to death by a Boy and his playmates, merely to frighten an Old woman. . . .'

The affair dragged on with an epilogue: the Empress ordered a bust of Fox, to be placed between those of Cicero and Demosthenes, in gratitude for his opposition to the Armament. The inscription: 'il a délivré, par son éloquence, sa patrie et la Russie, d'une guerre, a laquelle il n'y avoit ni justice ni raison.' Pitt's aim had been, not war, but irresistible pressure. The Opposition taunted him with having been publicly flouted by Catherine (whom they had encouraged); resentments were bitter indeed. Pitt referred to the bust in answering an attack by Fox: he did not reveal what he knew of Opposition relations with the Russian ambassador in London and their intrigues in Moscow against the British Embassy: 'to do so would have covered the Opposition with obloquy but the Cabinet with ridicule.'[1] But there is reason to believe that his answer to Fox was in verses engraved below a print by Gillray which he probably 'invented'. His nephew ascribes the verses to him.[2] *Design for the new Gallery of Busts and Pictures* [Pl. 87], 17 March 1792, shows the three busts on their pedestals, with Fox between 'Demosthenes against Æschines' and 'Cicero against Cataline'. The two pictures—attacks on Catherine—are typical of Gillray—

[1] J. H. Rose, *Pitt and National Revival*, 1912, p. 624.

[2] James Boswell junior said on the authority of Pitt's nephew that the verses were written by Pitt (*Poetry of the Anti-Jacobin*, ed. C. Edmonds, 1890, p. xxxi). They were reprinted in Canning's *Anti-Jacobin* as 'written by a Traveller at Czarco-zelo under the bust of a certain Orator, once placed between those of Demosthenes and Cicero', with slight alterations to adapt them to 1798: the 'tool confessed . . .' becomes 'the advocate of foreign power'.

not so the busts. The first three verses are praise for Demosthenes and Cicero, the last two dispraise for Fox:

> Who then in this presumptuous hour
> Aspires to share th' Athenian's praise?
> The tool confessed of foreign pow'r
> The Æschines of modern days,
>
> What chosen names to Tully's join'd
> Is now announced to distant climes?
> Behold to lasting shame consign'd
> The Cataline of later times.

Here, probably, is one of the rare prints 'invented' at the very highest levels.

Seldom did the prints reflect ideas in greater conflict than in 1791–2. The prevailing Church and King climate is seen in violent attacks on dissenters and on the Republican Tom Paine, and in a vogue for militant adaptations of 'God save great George our King'. The democrats were to retaliate with parodies to the treasonous tune of 'Bob shave a King'. Prints on the royal family were never more cruel, though there can be no doubt of the King's popularity. Pitt is an arrogant upstart, usurping the powers of the Crown or presuming on royal favour. Events in France increasingly darkened the scene in 1792. In 1791 the most startling news was the escape and capture of the royal family; this is said to have roused universal sympathy in England, but the caricaturists are far from sympathetic; their prints are rapid reactions to the first reports before details were known, and the flight and capture are treated as comic. One print goes farther; it is the earliest print by Richard Newton in the national collection, remarkable for a boy of fourteen or fifteen—broad burlesque with a serious core. In *An Escape a la Francois!* [7886] the fugitives are escorted by Pope and Devil, 'Ma chere amie, le Diable', asks the King (of the Queen and the Devil), 'what will become of My Oath?' (to the Constitution). But both look complacent and the Devil points to the Pope, 'O never fear that—here is Absolution.' Below the design are two couplets:

> Lo here is the King of France, a
> Going to lead a War Dance a . . . .

The leading motif in satires on the royal family was parsimony at Windsor. *From the Originals* [altered to 'Original'] *at Windsor* [Pl. 92] is a close parody of 'The Misers' by Quintin Matsys in the royal collection.

George III counts his coins and writes in his ledger, the Queen leans on his shoulder. Gillray's pair of prints are maliciously amusing: *Frying Sprats* [7922] for the 'Royal Supper' and *Toasting Muffins* [7923] for 'the Royal Breakfast'; the Queen with her gridiron, then called a save-all, is much caricatured, her pocket bulging with guineas, but patched. The King is homely and eccentric. In a famous pair of plates by Gillray in July 1792 insults are carried farther. In *A Voluptuary under the Horrors of Digestion* [8112] the Prince, languid with repletion and dissipation, leans back from a table covered with the remains of a meal. The room is crowded with objects reflecting, it would seem, the artist's hatred and contempt for his subject. Books and papers imply (among other things) that the Prince was a gambler (which he was not) with a share in the profits of the faro tables which women of fashion kept as a source of income. In *Temperance enjoying a frugal Meal* [8117] the King eats a boiled egg, the Queen stuffs sauerkraut into her mouth. Everything in the room denotes miserliness; there is no fire, though holly and mistletoe in the grate show that it is winter. Behind the Queen is the heavily bolted door of a strong room, with a 'Table of Interest' from her vast (and mythical) hoard of savings. These are only indirectly political, but in May Gillray related his imputations to politics in a print which is more cruel because less fantastic: *Vices overlook'd in the new Proclamation* [8095] on 24 May satirizes the Royal Proclamation of 21 May, 'for the preventing of tumultuous meetings and seditious writings' (aimed chiefly at Paine's works) which the Prince approved in his maiden speech in the Lords. Scenes of 'Avarice', 'Drunkenness', 'Gambling', and 'Debauchery' are four designs on one plate. In the first the King and Queen face each other across a table, hugging huge money-bags. Next, the Prince, very drunk, is supported by two watchmen from the door of a brothel. In the third the Duke of York throws dice in a gambling hell, and in the last the Duke of Clarence and Mrs. Jordan embrace.

In 1791–2 it was a Foxite–Carlton House tenet that the King and Queen had separate interests, the Queen's preponderating and more favourable to Pitt. That is the context of a brilliant parody by Gillray of Fuseli's picture of Macbeth's witches. In *Wierd-Sisters; Ministers of Darkness; Minions of the Moon* [Pl. 89] on 31 December 1791, Dundas, Pitt, and Thurlow gaze with apprehensive intensity at Queen Charlotte's smiling profile which encloses the old moon, the darkened head of George III. Instead of the outstretched arms and pointing fingers of Fuseli's picture [Pl. 88], each presses his fingers on his lips, intent on seeking knowledge, not foretelling it. Pitt had been shaken by the Oczakov affair and there were rumours that the King wanted to get rid of him. But the strength of his position was shown by the way in which he got rid of Thurlow—who had flouted him in the Lords, counting on the King's favour. He wrote to the King asking him to choose between himself and the Chancellor. Cartoonists treated the affair as a fight between them, one supported by the Queen, the other by the King as in *The Fall of the Wolsey of the Wool Sack* [8096] on 24 May 1792, by Gillray. Out of some six prints the outstanding one is Gillray's *Sin, Death, and the Devil* [Pl. 91] on 9 June, with quotations from Milton, in which disrespect to the Queen reached a climax. I do not think it has been noticed that this is a travesty of an engraved version [Pl. 90] of Hogarth's picture, 'Satan, Sin and Death', now lost. Pitt is Death, emaciated and corpse-like, wearing a crown and with an ermine-bordered mantle hanging from his shoulders. He uses a sceptre as his weapon against the more formidable Thurlow, Satan, whose (broken) weapon is the mace, and whose shield is emblazoned with a tiny Woolsack and the Purse of the Great Seal. The Queen as Sin intervenes with outstretched arms to protect Pitt (thus reversing Milton). She is a hideous hag, with pendent breasts (Milton's Sin is 'woman to the waste and fair'), two massive serpents for legs, and writhing serpents for hair. The large key at her waist, 'The Instrument of all our Woe', is clearly not only the key of Hell Gate but of the back stairs, that is, of secret influence. Cerberus has the heads of Dundas, Grenville, and Richmond, Pitt's chief supporters. The artist recommends 'these portraits of the Devil & his Relations, drawn from the Life . . .' to Messrs. Boydell and Fuzelli, showing that this is not only a political satire but a jibe at the Shakespeare Gallery of Boydell (a *bête noire* of Gillray's) and at Fuseli's projected Milton Gallery. Behind these rancours one guesses personal frustrations—that Gillray would have liked to practise 'high art' as well as burlesque it.[1]

French topics in 1792 begin with *émigrés*—as usual they are ridiculed. In *A German Howl or the Emigrant Princes mourning the loss of their dearest Friend* [8068] by Isaac Cruikshank on 15 March, d'Artois and others surround the coffin of Leopold II, ankle deep in their own tears (but though the Emperor's death was a blow to the cause of monarchy in France, the *émigrés* at Coblentz rejoiced). The French declaration of war

---

[1] Cf. his large engravings, e.g. *The Wreck of the Nancy Packet*. This is signed 'Drawn & Engraved by James Gillray 1784', when all his satirical work was anonymous or pseudonymous. The art criticism expressed and implied in *Shakespeare Sacrificed;—or—The Offering to Avarice* [7584], 1789, on the Boydell Gallery, and in *Titianus Redivivus . . .* [9085], 1797, is highly significant. The former also expresses resentment at the exclusion of engravers from the Royal Academy.

on Austria was followed by the panic flight from Tournai, when the French murdered their officer, General Dillon: this occasioned two contemptuous anti-Gallican, anti-revolutionary prints [8085–6], one by Isaac Cruikshank, one by Gillray. The invasion of the Tuileries on 20 June and the 'baiser Lamourette' on 7 July, when Republicans and monarchists embraced, swearing 'immortal union' in the face of the enemy, were satirized by Dent in companion designs on one plate: *Limited Monarchy: Unlimited Democracy*[1] on 23 July. Louis XVI in a *bonnet rouge* is assailed by frantic men and women with pikes, who shout, '. . . No Veto.' This is 'The negative Power of France surrounded by the Patriotic Furies . . .'. In the other, 'the Active power of France Reconciling contending Parties by a General Hug . . .', the Devil puts his arms round fourteen Frenchmen.

Then came the September massacres. Gillray produced the most unrestrained and macabre of all his caricatures of French Jacobins: *Petit Souper a la Parisienne;—or—A Family of Sans-culotts refreshing, after the fatigues of the Day* [8122]. A heraldic print, *Democratic Arms, or Emblems of Gallic Liberty*, attacks 'The horrid Massacres that lately happened at Paris'. The supporters are a Jacobin executioner and a sansculotte streetmurderer.[2]

Brunswick's manifesto, his defeat at Valmy, and disease-stricken retreat to the frontier are the subjects of six prints. All but one (a disorderly procession of savage unsoldierly sansculottes marching 'to the Frontiers' [8123] by Newton) are anti-Brunswick: he is a braggart, his misfortunes are derided, his soldiers are *Prussian Bobadils, returning to Berlin! ! ! ! ! ! ! !* [8126], another print by Newton. But always the French pursuers are unsoldierly ragamuffins (actually they were a remnant of the old royal army).

French military successes, and the famous decree of the Convention on 16 November, offering 'fraternity and assistance to all peoples who wish to recover their liberty', are the subject of a Cruikshank print favourable to the French Republic on 21 December: *The Genius of France Extirpating Despotism Tyranny & Oppression from the Face of the Earth or the Royal Warriors defeated* [8143]. In English prints the genius of Republican France is commonly a monstrosity. Here—uniquely—she is a comely young woman, wearing a Phrygian cap. She threatens the sovereigns of Europe, who are riding an ass, saying, 'I am determin'd to inflict Death on all Despots and Oppressors'; she plies a scourge with lashes for 'Religious

[1] Not in the British Museum: *Collection de Vinck*, no. 4880.
[2] Not in the British Museum; see Broadley, *Napoleon in Caricature*, ii. 232–3.

Bigots, Aristocrats, Monopolizers of Provisions to distress the Poor', &c., &c. This, published by Fores at such a moment, might have seemed ominous.[1] Dent took a different view in *French Liberality, or an Attempt to conquer the World by being too civil by half* [8136] on 8 December. General Dumouriez, holding an order from the Convention to 'Give Freedom to all the World', proffers this to three men, 'having more Liberty den we vos know vat to do wid . . .', but asks them for 'von little bit of a Contribution'. All reject his gift: the German is content with 'the Liberty of being governed by Religion and Law', the Dutchman wants only 'the right of making money where we can and a fig for your Ideal Goddess'; a very corpulent John Bull is more articulate: 'Why we are fat and free! and live under a Glorious Constitution, its old and I venerate it—to be sure Time may have made a few flaws and cracks in it—but Dam it, it can never be mended with Plaister of Paris—so you can keep your Freedom and Your Fricassee to yourself!' Gillray, using the title of his Necker–Pitt plate of 1789, expressed a similar idea with characteristic irony on 21 December; in *French Liberty v. British Slavery* [Pl. 93] a ragged and famished sansculotte in a poverty-stricken room is contrasted with an obese and gouty 'cit', surrounded with luxury, carving a great joint of beef, and with a decanter of hock on the table. The Frenchman ravenously devours raw onions and has *assignats* for a few sous in his pocket: '. . . vat blessing be de Liberté. . .', he exclaims, '—no more Tax! no more slavery!—all free citizen . . . ve svim in de Milk & Honey'. The Briton: 'Ah! this cursed Ministry! they'll ruin us with their damn'd Taxes! why! Zounds!—they're making Slaves of us all, & Starving us to Death!' A statuette of Britannia has a big sack of 'Sterling' in place of a shield.

The burning question in 1792 was how far was the country in danger from Jacobins at home. There was a bad season, with dearth and bread riots; alarm was caused by the organization of a 'National Convention' in Scotland, by the astonishing circulation of cheap editions of Paine's (Republican) *Rights of Man Part II* (translated into Gaelic, Erse, and Welsh), and by the fraternal messages of the London Corresponding Society to the French Republic. An address delivered by a deputation on 28 November by John Frost and Joel Barlow[2] gave the impression that the

---

[1] The Prussian defeat was a great encouragement to malcontents: at a celebration of Dumouriez' victory (Jemappes, 6 Nov.) near Lewes an ox was roasted whole and a procession was formed, reputedly 10,000 strong, headed by the French tricolour and a picture of Dundas stabbing Liberty and Burke trampling on 'the swinish multitude'. J. H. Rose, *Pitt and the Great War*, 1911, p. 70. Cf. *E.P.C. 1793–1832*, p. 9 and n..

[2] An American; associate in England of Horne Tooke, Price, Priestley, Paine, and others;

country was honeycombed by seditious clubs. It assured the Convention that innumerable clubs and societies were springing up in England: 'After the example given by France Revolution will become easy . . . and it would not be extraordinary if in a much less space of time than can be imagined, the French should send addresses of congratulation to a National Convention in England.' A deputation from English and Irish residents in Paris assured the Convention that a majority of the British wished to copy the French example and that the old Government would soon exist only in memory.[1] If the Ministry at home were unduly alarmed, the French were completely deceived, and believed Britain on the verge of revolution; English caricatures of British Jacobins may well have contributed to their illusions.

The prints reflect a main trend of anti-Jacobinism, qualified by a few protests against scaremongering. In which category Gillray's *Patriots amusing themselves or Swedes firing at a Post* [8082] in April should be put is open to doubt—though scaremongering had scarcely shown itself. This is a burlesque suggested by the assassination of Gustavus III; the patriots are Fox, sinister and conspiratorial, firing a blunderbuss, Sheridan loading a pistol, and Priestley providing him with wadding: 'here's plenty of Wadding for to ram down the charge with, to give it force, & to make a loud Report.' He holds out two books 'on the Glory of Revolution' and 'on the Folly of Religion & Order'. Their target is a post roughly carved into a grotesque semblance of George III in a hunting cap, the bull's eye being on the object's posterior.

Priestley and Paine were the main objects of attack. Isaac Cruikshank's *The Friends of the People* [8131], though the title is that of the Reform society of the advanced Whigs, is a violent diatribe against these two *bêtes noires* as murderous and conspiratorial revolutionaries in which the guillotine makes a first appearance. With an altered title, *Sedition, Levelling and Murdering; or, the Pretended Friends of the People in Council*, it was used as an illustration to 'God save the King' with six interpolated verses attacking Paine, Priestley, and the Unitarians:

> Tom Paine and Priestley are
> More base and desp'rate far,
> Than vile Jack Cade

author of *Song of the Guillotine*, a parody of *God save the King* exulting at the death of Louis XVI and looking forward to that of George III: 'And when great George's Poll / Shall in the basket roll . . .': P. A. Scholes, *God save the Queen!*, 1954, p. 164.
[1] J. H. Rose, *Pitt and the Great War*, 1911, pp. 70–71.

He for reform did cry;
They for equality
Wou'd stain true liberty
With British blood.

Two comprehensive attacks on Paine by Gillray followed, on 26 November and 10 December [8132, 8137], the second an elaboration of the first, both called *Tom Paine's Nightly Pest*. Paine lies asleep in a wretched room (in France). He dreams of his treasons and libels and of punishments: a prison wall, a gibbet, a pillory. The 'Guardian Angels' at the head of his bed are Fox and Priestley; a torn American flag covers the straw which makes his pillow. Both prints anticipate his trial for *Rights of Man, Part II*, as a 'scandalous libel on the Constitution Laws and Government of England', for which he had sent the Attorney General a defiant letter with a sneer at 'Mr Guelph and his profligate sons'. Cruikshank's *Wha Wants Me* [8146], on 26 December, is a vicious attack on Paine, who stands, pen in one hand, dagger in the other, with a bundle of weapons on his back: his 'Letter to the Convention' (on 25 September, three days after the proclamation of the Republic) is quoted, in which he offered his services, 'Convinced that the cause of France is the cause of all mankind . . . having borne a share in the commencement and complete establishment of one Revolution. . . .' The title is from the street cry of an Edinburgh character and was first applied to Dundas [8103]. Paine was burnt in effigy by the troops in various places in December.

On 11 December came the split in the Whig Party owing to the attitude of the left wing to France, when a majority decided to support the Government. Dent produced *Jacobine Wigs, or, Good Night to the Party* [8140] on 18 December, a meeting of the Whig Club, with a remnant of three members, Fox, Sheridan, and Grey, sound asleep, with French caps drawn over their eyes. On the same day Dent published an amusing caricature of Fox as a partisan of the French Republic, *French Ambassador* [Pl. 94], oddly suggesting the famous scene in the Tuileries in 1802. Isaac Cruikshank used the split personality device for an indictment of Fox, *A Right Honorarle* [sic] *alias a Sans Culotte* [8142].

In the meantime the Association for preserving Liberty and Property against Republicans and Levellers—Anti-levelling Society—had been founded on 20 November to discourage seditious publications and produce counter-propaganda. It was known as the Crown and Anchor Society, its headquarters being in the famous tavern. Among its tracts and leaflets it published at the turn of the year a few subsidized satirical prints. Gillray derided it—in terms that suggest that he had worked for it or had been asked to do so.

The first of his two explicitly anti-scaremongering prints of 1792 is *John Bull Bother'd:—or—The Geese alarming the Capitol* [Pl. 95] on 19 December, with a gibe at the new Association: 'Price 3 shill[s]—the engraving not having been Paid for, by the Association for vending two'penny Scurrilities.' The subject is the proclamation on 1 December for calling out the militia—partly to repress riots—on alarming news from Scotland and Ireland. Pitt and John Bull (again a yokel but in a militiaman's coat in place of a smock) stand together on a fortified tower; Pitt looks through a telescope at a flock of geese, his hair rising, his knees bending in terror. John, bewildered and almost equally frightened, holds an old musket with a broken bayonet; there are two favours in his hat: 'Vive la Liberte' and 'God save the King'; in one pocket is 'The Rights of Man', in the other 'One Pennyworth of Truth' (an anti-Jacobin tract 'from Thomas Bull to Brother John' denounced in the Commons by Grey as a libel). He is 'bothered', or 'botheared', that is, bemused by being 'talked to at both ears by different persons'.[1] The point of the satire is elaborated in the very Gillrayesque speeches engraved on the plate. Pitt begins by warning John to get his arms ready: '. . . they're Rising & coming upon us from all parts . . . theres Ten Thousand sans-Culottes . . . there's Five Hundred Disputing Clubs with Bloody Mouths; & twenty Thousand Bill-stickers with *Ca Ira* pasted on the front of their Red-Caps! . . . ' John sees only a few wild geese, but adds, 'I dont know what reason for I to see at all, for that matter;—why Measter does all that for I,—my business is only to Fire when & where Measter orders, & to pay for the Gunpowder. . . .' Here, one supposes, is an echo of Fox's irony: 'An Insurrection! Where is it? . . . Good God! an insurrection in Great Britain, no wonder that the militia were called out. . . .'[2]

The other Gillray protest against scares, dated 30 December, is *The Dagger Scene;—or—the Plot discovered* [8147], a caricature of the famous scene in the Commons on 28 December. Burke has just thrown down the dagger and looks with a contemptuous frown at Pitt and Dundas on the Treasury Bench, though a bag-wig and a new corpulence suggest that he now draws funds from the Treasury. He makes a speech which parodies his own: 'There! . . . Three Thousand such Daggers are now manufacturing for this Country!—for where French principles are introduced, you must

---

[1] Grose, *Dictionary of the Vulgar Tongue*, 1796.
[2] *Parl. Hist.* xxx. 14 (13 Dec.).

prepare your hearts for French Daggers!—Nineteen Assassins are already here. . . .' Fox and Sheridan clutch each other in terror. Fox: 'Confusion! —one of Our daggers, by all that's bloody! . . . —' (&c., &c.) Cruikshank effectively satirized the same scene in *Reflections on the French Revolution* [Pl. 96], dated 1 January.

Gillray's ironic double-edged satires reflect the problems of the day. How great was the danger from revolutionaries at home? Did the Foxite attitude not only mislead France and so encourage the Republic to declare war, but lead to provocative and regrettable precautions? By the end of the year it was evident that war could hardly be averted, though negotiations went on. For the next eight years the prints directly or indirectly relate to war with the French Republic. The old contest between Pitt and Fox, with all its accumulated rancours, became the contest between Ministers and a small but vocal and socially powerful Opposition, refusing to recognize the aggressive character of the Republic, and bitterly opposed to the war; between anti-Jacobins and Jacobins, between those who thought the war 'just and necessary' and those who derided Pitt's phrase to pillory its whole policy and conduct, to whom Foxite protests were the defence of British liberties.

Q

buted to him; other attributions from 1775. His principal plates reissued by McLean as *The Genuine Works of Mr James Gillray*, 2 vols., 1830, with a key, *Illustrative Description*. . . . In 1851 the plates, worn and retouched, were again reissued by Bohn, with a key, *Historical and Descriptive Account* . . ., by T. Wright and R. H. Evans. *The Works of James Gillray . . . with the History of his Life and Times*, ed. T. Wright, 1873 but by J. Grego, is useful. 2, 21, 116, 147, 158, 163, 164, 165, 166, 167, 168, 171–2, 174 & n., 175, 177, 179, 185, 186, 188, 189, 190, 192, 193, 194, 195, 196, 198, 199, 202, 203, 206, 211, 212, 213, 214–15, 216, 217 & n., 218, 219, 220, 221, 222–3; Pls. 54, 60(?), 61, 62, 63, 78, 79, 81, 83, 87, 89, 91, 93, 95.

Gould, Sir Francis Carruthers (1841–1 Jan. 1925). Stockbroker, caricaturist, and journalist. Political cartoonist of strong Liberal sympathies, notably in the *Westminster Gazette* (to 1901). An amateur draughtsman but a professional cartoonist. 171.

Gravelot, Hubert-François (1699–1773, in England from 1732). Engraver. 90.

Grimm, Samuel Hieronymus (1734–94). Born in Switzerland. Watercolour painter and occasional caricaturist. Exhibited R.A. See R. M. Clay, *Samuel Hieronymus Grimm of Burgdorf, Switzerland*, 1941. 146; Pl. 44.

Guttenberg, Carl (b. 1743 Nuremberg, d. 1790 Paris). Engraver and illustrator. Worked in Paris. 151 & n.

HB = John Doyle (1797–1868). Lithographer, portraitist, and caricaturist. 177.

Heath, William (1795?–1840). Watercolourist, military painter, etcher, and caricaturist. 173.

Hogarth, William (1697–1764). Painter, engraver, and publisher of his own prints. His engravings catalogued by Austin Dobson, *Hogarth*, 1907; his paintings by R. B. Beckett, *Hogarth*, 1949. See A. P. Oppé, *The Drawings of William Hogarth*, 1948; P. Quennell, *Hogarth's Progress*, 1955. 7, 11, 73, 75–77, 80, 83, 85, 105 n., 107–8, 111–15, 117, 118, 121, 122 & n., 125, 128–31, 171, 172, 175, 177, 186, 193, 205; Pls. 20 (*a*), 21, 31, 35, 36, 90. *See* Pl. 32.

Holland, William (d. 1816). London printseller and occasional caricaturist. 175, 205 & n., 207, 209–10; Pl. 86(?).

Hollar, Wenceslaus (1607–77). Bohemian etcher and engraver. Worked in England 1637–44 (a Royalist) and 1652–77. Catalogue, by Parthey, *Wenzel Hollar*, Berlin,

1853–8. 7, 12, 21, 22, 25, 28, 44; Frontispiece, Pls. 4, 5.

Hooghe, Romeyn de (1648–1708). Painter, engraver, sculptor, medallist, and goldsmith. Ennobled by the King of Poland 1675. Worked for William III from 1689. Dutch political cartoonist in the grand manner, many anonymous and pseudonymous plates. 62.

Hook, James (1771–1828). Chaplain to the Prince of Wales. Dean of Worcester 1825–8. While at Westminster edited the *Trifler* and did caricatures. Published novels (pseudonymous), pamphlets, and sermons. 173, 194, 208.

Kingsbury, Henry. Portrait and landscape painter and engraver in London, *c.* 1775–98. Exhibited R.A. 1787–91. Occasional caricaturist. 172, 188.

Laroon, Marcellus, the younger (1679–1772). Painter and engraver. 12 n.

Loggan, David (1635–93). Born Danzig of Scottish extraction. Engraver. 'Public Sculptor to the University of Oxford' from 1669; afterwards also to Cambridge. 57 n.

Marshall, William (worked 1630–50). Engraver. The most prolific of contemporary illustrators, chiefly from his own designs. 7, 12, 19, 34–35 & n., 37; Pl. 12.

Metsys, Quentin (1466–1530). Painter, Flemish school. 215–16; cf. Pl. 92.

Mortimer, John Hamilton (1741–79). Historical painter. Designed caricatures, some of which were etched after his death. 171.

Newton, Richard (1777–98). Caricaturist and miniaturist. 173, 175, 215; Pl. 85.

Nixon, John (d. 1818). Merchant and officer of the Bank of England. Watercolourist, exhibited R.A. 1784–1815. Occasional caricaturist. Secretary to the Beefsteak Club. 173.

Ogborne, John (1755–1837). Engraver. Pl. 91.

Picart, Bernard (b. Paris 1673, d. Amsterdam 1733). Engraver and miniaturist. A leading engraver in Holland. Pl. 20*b* signed 'Picart'.

Pine, John (1690–1756). Engraver. The friar in Hogarth's *Calais Gate*. 74.

Pond, Arthur (1705?–58). Painter, etcher, and art-dealer. From 1736 to 1747 produced 25 plates in imitation of chalk and

GENERAL INDEX

PLATES

PLATE 1

The Image of Antichrift exalting himfelfe in the Temple of God.   771.

The end of the firft Volume of the Booke of Martyrs.

¶A liuely picture defcribyng the weight and fubftaunce of
Gods moft bleffed word, agaynft the doctrines and
vanities of mans traditions.

¶AT LONDON
Printed by Iohn Daye, dwellyng ouer
Alderfgate beneath Saint Martins.

Anno. 1576.

¶Cum gratia & Priuilegio Regiæ Maieftatis.

Page in *Fox's Martyrs*   *p.* 4

PLATE 2

a. Copy of *Gorgoneum Caput*   *p.* 6

b. Copy of Reformation token   *p.* 6

PLATE 3

The Double Deliveraunce

pp. 15–16, 63–64, 88. Cf. Pl. 29 a

PLATE 4

Who am I, who am I like, what nobody.
Sure I'me the Picture of a Patenty

Loe' here is he, whose Hogs=head now doth vent
Naught but Peccavies, since the Parliament,
Wolse like devourer of the Common wealth
That robs by Patent, worse then any stealth
Alls Fish, comes to his hooke, Tobaco wine & raggs
Make full his Cofers, with his numbred baggs

Coales, Salt, & Butter, pipes, Cards, Pynns, and Soape
Are free to buy, and sell, leaue him the Roape!
Hee feares no damning, this doth make him start,
That Patents damned are, this breakes his hart;
Strong serues, support him that hath seru'd vs all
And now we liue, to see this strong man fall.

B.M. 264   The Patenty. Hollar   pp. 7, 21

PLATE 5

This Burden backe to *Rome*, I'le beare againe;
From thence it came, there let it still remaine.

When Times Great Maker (the most high Eternall)   He to his daughter Truth gaue straight Command   This trunke of trash & Romish Trumperies
In mercy loked from his Throne supernall: That shee those dang'rous Errors should withstand   Deluding showes infernall forgeries
And saw the Euils which began to grow   Then vp I tooke vpon my aged backe,   And therefore am I hence in post thus riding
In his deare Vine here Militant below,   This load of vaniti, this Pedlers packe   To Rome againe, for here is no abiding

Time and the Pope. Hollar

PLATE 6

PLATE 7

Much meate doth gluttony produce. Hee needes no napkin for his handes
And makes a man a swine——— His fingers for to wipe
But hees a temperate man indeed Hee hath his kitchin in a box
That with a leafe can dine——— His Roast meate in a pipe

B.M. 268   *The Sucklington Faction*   *p.* 24

PLATE 8

PLATE 9

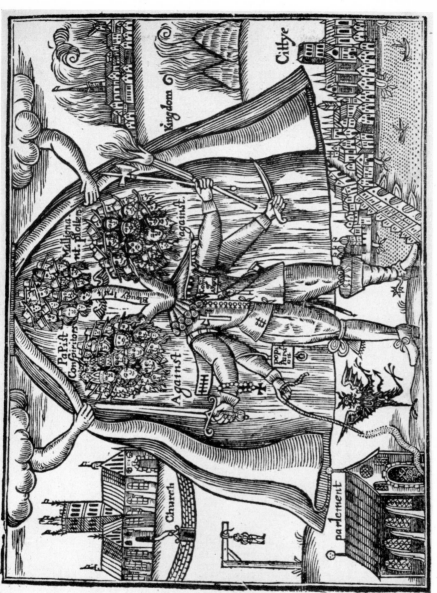

pp. 28-29

The Kingdomes Monster Uncloaked from Heaven

B.M. 375

PLATE 10

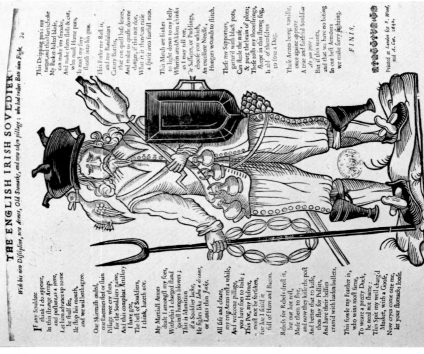

B.M. 305   Broadside   *p.* 20   B.M. 1714   Robert Knight   *p.* 79

PLATE 11

Englands Wolfe with Eagles Clawes *pp.* 12, 30

PLATE 12

Bodleian   *Eikon Basilike*   *pp.* 34–36

PLATE 13

pp. 49–50

Copy of a Dutch print

B.M. 1044

PLATE 14

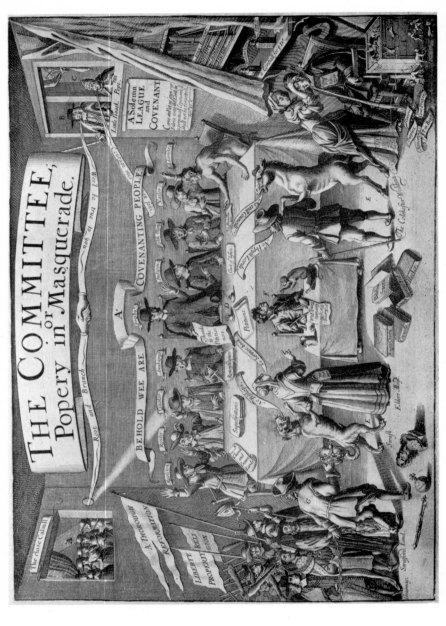

pp. 54–55

Heading to verse broadside

PLATE 15

Heading to verse broadside

B.M. 1683

PLATE 16

pp. 56-57

A RA-REE SHOW.

To the Tune of I am a Senceless Thing.

Heading to a verse broadside

PLATE 17

The happy INSTRUMENTS of ENGLANDS Preservation.

Come and behold ȳ salvation of ȳ Lord

HEAVEN SHALL TURN THY WEAPONS AGAINST

THE INFERNALL CONCLAVE

Behold th'Infernall Conclave, mett in state. / Pardons were streight prepar'd, and men made free / But he that sitts enthron'd, in mercy chose:
Contriving Englands, and its Monarchs Fate. / Of Heaven, to perpetrate their Villany. / Those instruments, that did the whole disclose.
Affaſsinate the King Subvert his Laws. / And thus secure, their Plotts went briskly on, / And thus to Oates and all the rest wee owe
They cry'd, and on their Ruin build our Cause. / Against our fixed Laws, and settl'd Throne. / The Kingdoms Peace; if wee can keep it so.

London Printed for Ben Combe at the ball and Anchor in Lombard street. 27. April 1681.

PLATE 18

A British Janus
Anglicè a Timeserver.

Since Moderation is so much in vogue,
And few can tell a Trimmer from a R——;
I am perswaded such a Print as this,
Thus modell'd and contriv'd can't be amiſs,
At such a juncture, such a time as this,
When to be loyal is eſteem'd a fault,
Obedience hiſt at, Scripture ſett at nought,
And ỹ reverse for pure sound doctrine taught,
I mean by them this picture doth resemble,
Who preach not half so fine as they diſsemble.
Of Heterogeneous parts as opposite
Compos'd, as darkneſs to Meridian light,
Made up of halves that can no more agree,
Than Regal pow'r and Independency.
A British Janus with a double face,
A Monſter of a strange Gigantick Race:
His head half Mitre, and half hat doth bear;
His looks are ſainted, and refin'd his air.
Not more prepoſterous in his black & white,

Than the true ſemblance of an Hypocrite.
Always Conformist to the ſtrongeſt Party,
Always deceitful, Ever more unhearty.
The Moderate Man ne'er yet a Martyr dy'd,
But tack'd about, & chose the ſtrongeſt side
Always recanted in the time of trial:
Is ever best extempore at denial.
Scorne to be moderate then in any thing,
But where to be immoderate is a sin.
In eating, drinking, and such things as these
Be moderate as moderate as you please.
But in Religion there's no Medium. No
Who is not truly zealous, is not so.
Glory to be eſteem'd an High-c—h Man:
Let them prove Low-c—h true c—h, if they can
Zeal for the c—h's Cauſe aCrown will gain;
And Martyrdom for Heven's an eaſy pain.
Dare to be true, tho' in a ſuffring time.
A Bare Denial then's a Double Crime.

PLATE 19

MEMENTO

MORI

B. Hoadly D.D.

THE
Living Man's
ELEGIE
OR
Doctor Sacheverell's
much lamented silence. *March ý 23 1710.*

A'lack, and a well a day! the Noise of late
Is silenc'd how, Sacheverell's mett his fate.
From Judges who were most compasionate:
Then mourn you Jacks, and all the factious crue,
Of High Church vermin who wou'd Church undoe:
Lament your Tool that did defend your Cause,
Against the Queen and our most wholesome Laws:
Weep for the Man that did so boldly prate,
That Brethren false were in our Church & State:
For now He's silenc'd and disgra'd most just;
His Sermons burnt and turned into Dust,
And may such haughty Priests for ever lie,
Obscure from Truth whilst moderate Hoadly high
Shall mount with Fame & Angels to the Sky.

HIS EPITAPH
Here lies Sacheverell, who would have thought it
Jacks and High Byerrs did not tho; they wrought it
From Fiercely Preaching in a railing way
He's now debar'd, then laugh and go your way.

1710

PLATE 20

B.M. 1722   The South Sea Bubble. Hogarth   *pp.* 73, 75–76

B.M. 1710   The Skreen. Picart   *pp.* 78, 92

PLATE 21

Some of the Principal Inhabitants of yͤ MOON, as they Were Perfectly Discoverd by a Telescope brought to yͤ Greatest Perfection since yͤ last Eclipse, Exactly Engraved from the Objects. whereby yͤ Curious may Guess at their Religion, Manners, &c.

1725.

Price Six Pence

B.M. 1734   Hieroglyphic Print. Hogarth   pp. 7, 77–78

PLATE 22

EXCISE IN TRIUMPH

PLATE 23

pp. 24, 84

PLATE 24

PLATE 25

The Stature of a
Great Man   or the English   Colossus.

Why Man, he doth bestride ŷ narrow World   Men at some times are Masters of their fates,
like a Colossus, and we petty Men   The fault, dear P——y is not in our Stars,
Walk under his huge Legs, & peep about   But in our Selves, that we are Underlings.
To find our Selves, dishonourable Graves.   Shakespear.

Description.

The Colossus at Rhodes, a Statue of ŷ SUN 70 Cubits high, placed at ŷ Mouth of ŷ Harbour; one Man could not grasp its
Thumb with both his Arms. Its thighs were stretch'd out to such a Distance, that a large Ship Sailing might easily pass
into ŷ Port betwixt them. It was Twelve Years a makeing, & cost 300 Talents (a Rhodian Talent is worth 322 Pounds, 18
Shillings & 4 Pence in English Money). It stood 50 Years, & at last was thrown down in an Earth-quake. And from this
Coloss ŷ People of Rhodes were named Colossenses, & every Statue since of an unusal Magnitude is call'd Colossus.

PLATE 26

B.M. 2479

The Motion

pp. 89–90

PLATE 27

The Butcher,

Taken from ye Sign of a Butcher in ye Butcher Row.

Old Æsop who in Morals did surpass,
Wrapt in a Lion's Skin produc'd an Ass,
And sure as fit a Cloathing we provide,
Who dress a Butcher in an Oxe's Hide,
Ye Candle serves his Foe-men to disclose,

The Tray's a Breast-Plate to ward off their Blows,
His Axe, Knives, Cleaver is prepar'd for fight,
And Death & Slaughter are his sole delight,
Thus arm'd he Terror o'er ye ——
Has he not terror'd from
a Calf his Head.

Decem.r 19 . 1746

PLATE 28

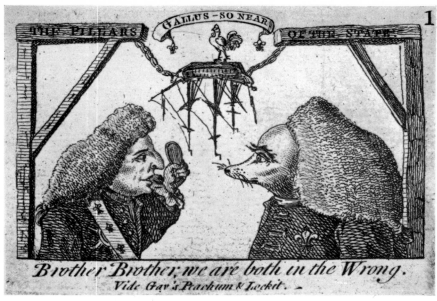

THE PILLARS · GALLUS -SO NEAR · OF THE STATE

Brother Brother, we are both in the Wrong.
Vide Gay's Peachum & Lockit.

B.M. 3371   Newcastle and Fox   *pp.* 102, 116

111   1761

Believe not evry flattering Knaves Report,
theres many a Reynard lurking in the Court;

The Fox beguiles
the Goose.

Vide Dry's Cock & Fox

B.M.   Fox and Newcastle   *pp.* 6, 102

PLATE 29

Henry Fox

Bubb Dodington, Fox and his sons

PLATE 30

PLATE 31

The Invasion. England Plate 2ᵈ. Hogarth

pp. 114-15

PLATE 32

The Hungry Mob of Scriblers and Etchers

p. 122 and n.

PLATE 33

The Loaded Boot

PLATE 34

PLATE 35

The Times
Plate I

Designed & Engraved by W. Hogarth

Published at the Act Directs Sep.r 7 1762

Hogarth

pp. 128–30

PLATE 36

John Wilkes Esq.r
Drawn from the Life and Etch'd in Aquafortis by Will.m Hogarth.
Price 1.Shilling.   Publish'd according to Act of Parliament. May y.e 16. 1763.

PLATE 37

pp. 133-4

The Great Financier

B.M. 4128

PLATE 38

B. Wilson

PLATE 39

B. Wilson

pp. 135–6

PLATE 40

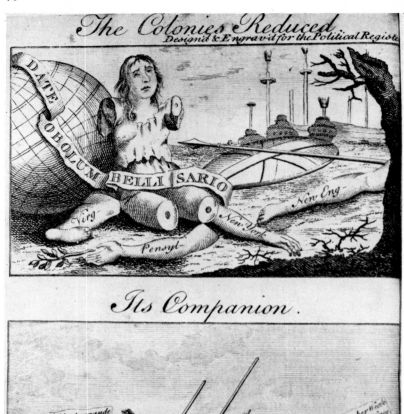

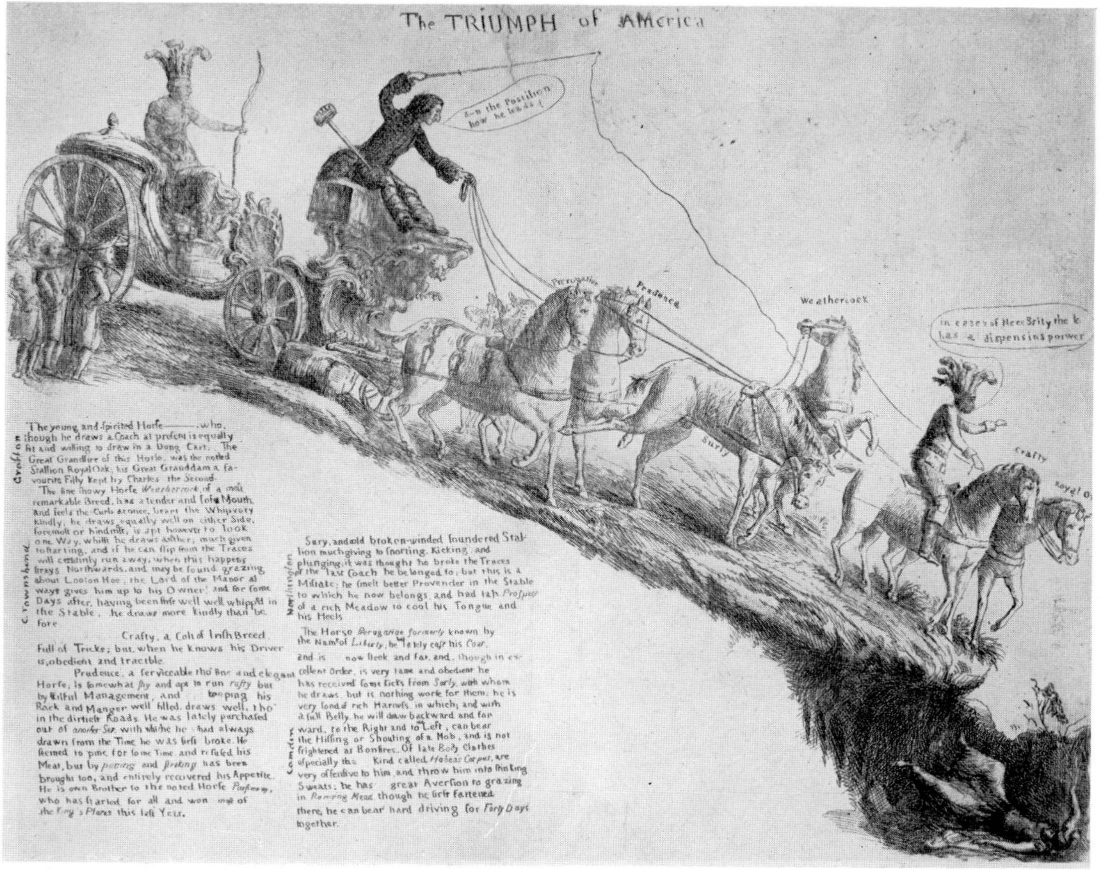

PLATE 41

The TRIUMPH of America

PLATE 42

THE SCOTCH VICTORY

Allen

To the Earl of ——— Protector of our Liberties
this Plate is Humbly Inscribed by &c
L. Junius Brutus

PLATE 43

THE MACARONI PRINT SHOP.

PLATE 44

The POLITICIAN.

Done from the ORIGINAL DRAWING by S. H. GRIMM.

Printed for S. Sledge Printseller, in Henrietta Street Covent Garden. Publish'd as the Act directs 4 May 1771.

PLATE 45

C.J.Fox.

THE YOUNG POLITICIAN

Publish'd accor.g to Act by H. Bryer London.

PLATE 46

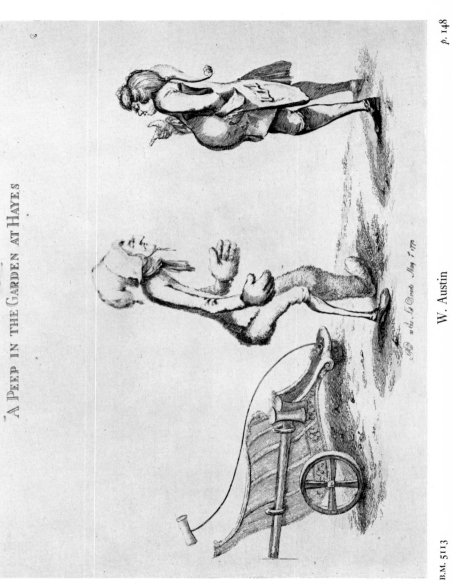

A Peep in the Garden at Hayes

W. Austin

PLATE 47

The able Doctor, or America Swallowing the Bitter Draught.

The Parricide.
A Sketch of Modern Patriotism.

PLATE 48

Westm. Mag. Feb. 1778.

PHILADELPHIA

A Picturesque View of the State of the Nation for February 1778.

PLATE 49

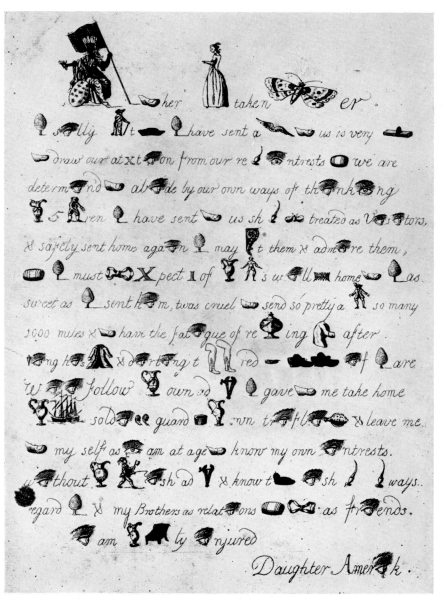

America to her mistaken Mother

PLATE 50

PLATE 51

PLATE 52

THE HORSE AMERICA, throwing his Master.

PLATE 53

PLATE 54

THE STATE TINKERS.

The National Kettle, which once was a good one, | *The Master he thinks, they are wonderful Clever,*
For boiling of Mutton, of Beef, & of Pudding, | *And cries out in raptures, 'tis done! now or never!*
By the fault of the Cook, was quite out of repair, | *Yet sneering the Tinkers their old Trade pursue,*
When the Tinkers were sent for, —— Behold them & Stare. | *In stopping of one Hole—— they're sure to make Two.*

Publish'd Feb.r 10th 1780, by W.Humphrey N.o 227 Strand.

10 Feb. 1780

PLATE 55

p. 158

Review of the York Regiment.

B.M. 5492

PLATE 56

PLATE 57

OPPOSITION DEFEATED

27. Feb. 1780

pp. 160–1

PLATE 58

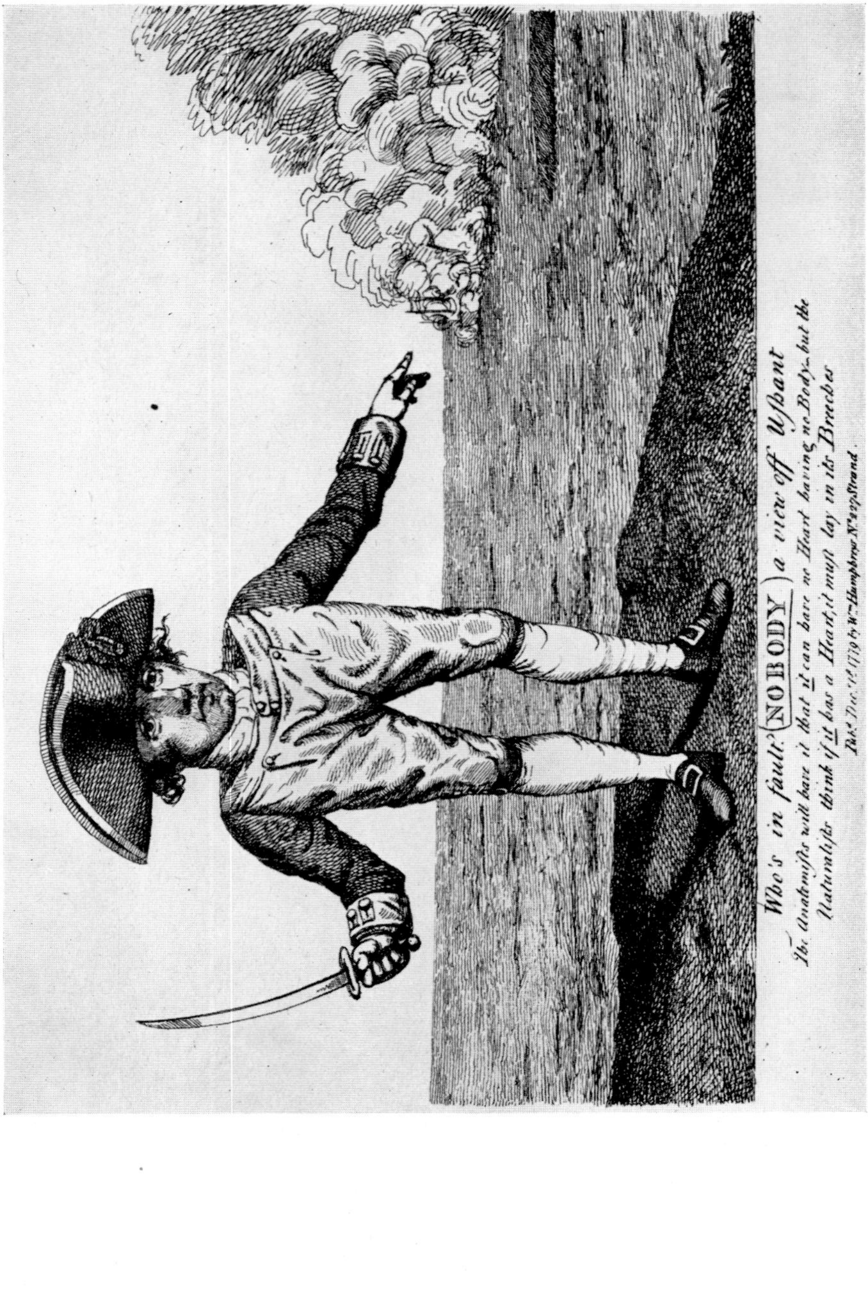
Who's in fault? (NOBODY) a view off Ushant
The Anatomists will have it that it can have no Heart having no Body – but the
Naturalists think if it has a Heart, it must lay in its Breeches
Pub.d Dec.r 1st 1779 by Wm Humphreys No 227 Strand.

B.M. 5570

p. 161

PLATE 59

After Bunbury

PLATE 60

? Gillray

B.M. 5079

PLATE 61

Gillray

PLATE 62

ST GEORGE & the Dragon.

Gillray

PLATE 63

GLORIA MUNDI,

or — The Devil addressing the Sun. Par.ˢ Loſt Book IV.

C. J. Fox   L.ᴰ Shelburn.

PLATE 64

London Published as the Act Directs May 16 1783 by J Boyne N.º 2 Shoe Lane Fleet S.ᵗ

PRI There is a Gentlewoman in this Town her name is —— FALSTAFF & HIS PRINCE FAL. Master George I will first make bold with your Money next give me your hand & last as I am a Gent.ᵐᵃⁿ you shall if you will Enjoy —— Wife

B.M. 6231   Boyne   p. 169

PLATE 65

A Transfer of East India Stock.

Sayers

PLATE 66

Carlo Khan's triumphal Entry into Leadenhall Street.

PLATE 67

The Mirror of Patriotism.

C. J. FOX

PLATE 68

Rowlandson

PLATE 69

BRITTANNIA ROUSED,
OR THE COALITION MONSTERS DESTROYED

B.M. 6403   Rowlandson   *p.* 181

PLATE 70

THE HANOVERIAN HORSE AND BRITISH LION.
A Scene in a New Play lately acted in Westminster with distinguished applause. Act 2 Scene last.

Pub March 10 1794 by H. Humphrey 27 Strand

Rowlandson

PLATE 71

p. 184

Rowlandson

PLATE 72

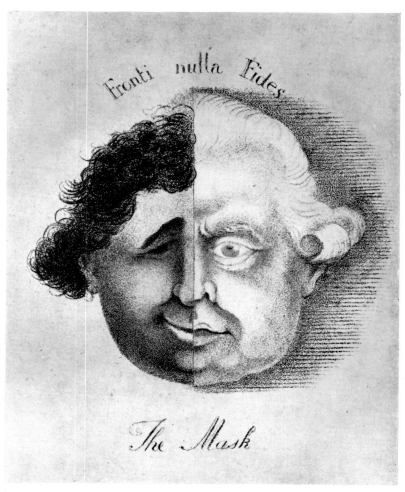

PLATE 73

Cheek by Joul or the MASK

Dſs. Devonshire   C. J. Fox.

Two faces here in one you see defign'd, | One rough & virulent, th' other fair & free,
Each ſtrongly mark'd declares the inward mind, | with looks that promiſe ſenſibility.
One ſeems ambitious of a daring ſoul, | When ſuch as theſe in harmony unite,
The other ſoft the paſsions to controul. | The contraſt ſurely muſt amize the ſight.

Publiſh'd by E. Hedges Nº 9 2 Cornhill May 3ᵈ 1784

PLATE 74

The Nightmare. After Fuseli

PLATE 75

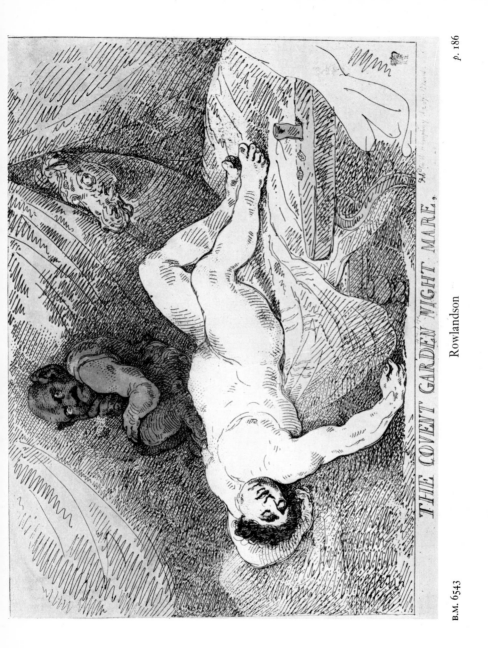

THE COVENT GARDEN NIGHT MARE.

Rowlandson

PLATE 76

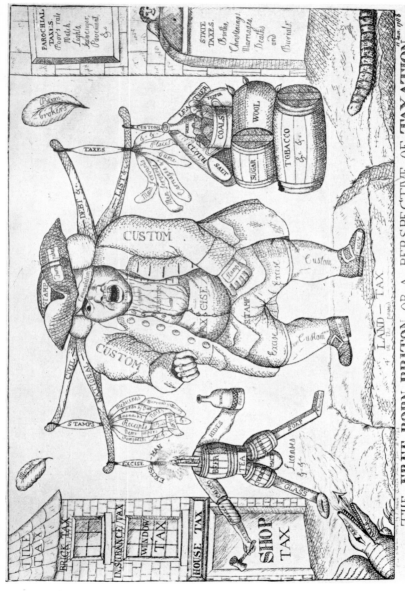

THE FREE-BORN BRITON OR A PERSPECTIVE OF TAXATION.

PLATE 77

PLATE 78

Gillray

PLATE 79

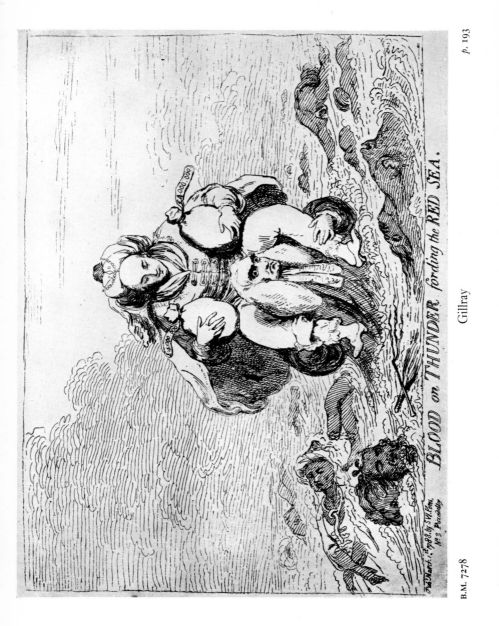

BLOOD on THUNDER *fording the* REID SEA.

Gillray

p. 193

PLATE 80

PLATE 81

PLATE 82

Rowlandson

PLATE 83

The VULTURE of the CONSTITUTION.

Gillray

B.M. 7478

p. 199

PLATE 84

The Comet. Sayers

PLATE 85

p. 205 n.

Watercolour by R. Newton

PLATE 86

THE KNIGHT OF THE WOFUL COUNTENANCE
GOING TO EXTIRPATE THE NATIONAL ASSEMBLY.

London Pub.ᵈ Nov.ʳ 15. 1790 by Wᵐ Holland Nᵒ 50 Oxford Street.

It is undoubtedly true, though it may seem paradoxical; but in general, those who are habitually employed in finding and displaying faults, are unqualified for the work of reformation; because their minds are not only unfurnished with patterns of the fair and good, but by habit they come to take no delight in the contemplation of those things. By hating vices too much, they come to love men too little. It is therefore not wonderful, that they should be indisposed and unable to serve them. From hence arises the complexional disposition of some of your guides to pull every thing in pieces. — Burke on the French Revolution. Page 250.

15. NOV. 1790

In Holland's Exhibition Rooms may be seen the largest collection in Europe of caricatures admittance one shilling.

PLATE 87

B.M. 8072

Gillray

pp. 214–15

PLATE 88

p. 216

The Three Witches. After Fuseli

PLATE 89

To H.Fuzelli Esq.r this attempt in the Caricatura-Sublime, is respectfully dedicated.

WIERD-SISTERS; MINISTERS of DARKNESS; MINIONS of the MOON"

―― 'They should be Women! ― and yet their beards forbid us to interpret.― that they are so ―

Gillray

pp. 216–17

PLATE 90

p. 217

Satan, Sin, and Death. After Hogarth

PLATE 91

SIN, DEATH, and the DEVIL. *Vide Milton.*

Gillray

PLATE 92

From the Originals at Windsor.
—L—C—town's Dreams
London Pub.d by Jack Dense, near Turnstile, Holborn, March. 20. 1791.

PLATE 93

FRENCH LIBERTY.

BRITISH SLAVERY.

Gillray

PLATE 94

FRENCH AMBASSADOR.

Executed by Citizen.

PLATE 95

Gillray

PLATE 96

Reflections on the French Revolution.

I. Cruikshank

pp. 222-3

Tan Lines

Prologue

Page Six sizzled with hot items about a grisly murder, a premature birth, and a public meltdown.

Faye Hudson of North Bay Lane in East Hampton devoured the main gossip headlines, amazed that all of them involved the three girls who signed last year's summer share lease on the very property she called home nine months of the year.

Liza Pike, Kellyanne Downey, and Billie Shelton.

Faye rarely remembered the young singles who made their invasion of the Hamptons a summer ritual, hitting the streets and beaches like locusts on crops. Year after year, a new set would come and go. The names and faces were sketchy, as the previous season's residents often blurred into the next. Usually, they were just cash to her, a way to finance her decadent summers in the south of France. But this last group had been different. Sin by sin, their sordid lives were played out in the traditional columns and online gossip sites. Scandal. It seemed to be the new generation's proof of life.

Tossing the *New York Post* aside, Faye pushed through the French doors and stepped out onto the balcony. She would read the rest later. The sun shone a bright, mellow glow, every Hollywood lighting director's dream. Eastern Long Island was magical that way.

The clatter of men at work boomed louder and louder from the living room. They were replacing the hardwood floors, stripping the walls, carting away the furniture. Thank God. She could not look at those ghastly bloodstains one more day.

But it would take more than an extreme home makeover to get the place in proper shape for the rental season. Once upon a time, her house had been Pottery Barn perfect. Now she wondered if anyone would show an interest in occupying it this year, even at a drastically cut rate.

These days, her home radiated a certain Amityville quality. People cruised by slowly in their cars, windows down, fingers pointing, no doubt re-creating the brutal scene in their voyeuristic minds. Fifteen stab wounds. And they said she had put up a ferocious fight.

Faye banished the image from her mind as a slight mist began to form in her eyes. The newspaper beckoned. She stepped back inside to consume all the details. It was a heady realization to vividly recall the way those girls had been in the beginning, before everything had gone so wrong. No one ever could have imagined that it would all come down to this.

Suddenly, last summer . . .

Billie

ONE

There are eight thousand nerve endings in the clitoris, and this son of a bitch couldn't find any of them. Billie Shelton had definitely picked the wrong guy tonight.

It was almost over. She could tell by the rapid breathing and the slight body shudder. Anyone who thought nineteen-year-old boys possessed serious stamina should be introduced to Robbie Shamblin.

"Oh, fuck!"

Billie rolled her eyes. Is that what this was? At least he had the optimism of youth.

Robbie shot a look at the computer monitor, where two cheap blondes with implants and multiple body piercings were getting it on. "Shit, that was awesome." He jumped up and carelessly flung his condom to the floor. Then he sat down and started up a street racing game on Xbox 360.

Billie had been with her share of lame assholes, but this guy was a shoo-in to make her greatest hits list. "Well, I guess we're done here."

Robbie glanced back at her for a fraction of a second, causing his digital Shelby GT500 to skid onto the make-believe sidewalk. "Motherfucker!" He focused on the screen for several long, obsessed seconds. Finally, he spoke. "I could eat you out, if you want. But most girls say I suck at that."

Billie began to search for her clothes. She'd gone for the lean, funny guy on the main stage, the one who'd brought down the house at the Comic Strip. Big mistake.

And right now the choice was slowly killing her. To think she'd opted for this idiot over the hot marine. God, what a waste. The military man would've fucked her all night. And he wouldn't have needed to diddle around with his computer to get hard, either.

That insult bugged her more than the bad sex. Jesus Christ. She was Billie Fucking Shelton, a goddamn indie rock star. But that wasn't enough anymore. Not in the age of Internet porn. Guys had become desensitized by streaming smut on demand. Women today had to compete with super-sluts like Jenna Jameson. And for what? Fifteen minutes of awkward groping followed by a jizz spill? Men were lazy shits.

Billie sat on the edge of the futon and slipped on her shoes. From the TV, engines roared. From the computer, XXX whores moaned. Whatever. Chalk it up to another lost night. It wasn't the first. It wouldn't be the last.

"You heading out?" Robbie asked without so much as a look in her direction.

"Yeah."

"Do me a favor. Knock on the door across the hall and tell my roommate he can come back in."

Billie laughed. At least this loser could make her do that much. "I haven't heard that kind of shit since college. Is this your apartment or your dorm room?"

"Huh?"

"Forget it," Billie said. Starting out, she went straight for the

4

stairwell, then doubled back to grant Robbie his little favor. Hell, maybe she'd get lucky and end up doing herself one instead. After all, the last place she wanted to go was home. It was still too early. She was still too horny.

A hot guy answered the door. Better face than Robbie's. Better body, too. In the background, another man with a nasty bruise under his eye smoked a joint. He looked like a young Al Pacino from the first *Godfather*.

Without exactly being invited, Billie walked inside. "Your roommate doesn't know how to fuck . . ."

When the telephone blasted her awake hours later, Billie groped for it, if only to stop the shrill ringing from its relentless attack on her brain. "Hello?"

"You sound like shit." It was Amy Dando, her manager.

"I feel like shit. Call me later. I need to sleep."

"There is no later," Amy barked. "We're supposed to be in Todd Bana's office at eleven."

Billie groaned, craning her neck to get a look at the alarm clock. It was almost ten. "I can't. I'm all fucked out. Reschedule."

"No way."

"Come on. Today's not the day. Trust me."

"This is bullshit, Billie. You *need* this meeting. Todd is close to dropping your ass altogether. Just get in the goddamn shower. I'm coming over there." And then Amy hung up.

Billie was dripping wet and staring at herself under the harsh bathroom light when she heard Amy let herself inside her apartment. "I'm up," Billie called out. The reflection in the mirror had startled her. She looked shockingly bad.

Amy appeared in the doorway, very glamour-puss in a jewel-tone satin/chiffon number, a bulky Christian Dior ID bracelet blinging on her slim wrist. "If I had to guess right now, I'd swear you were thirty-eight."

"Fuck you." Billie puckered her lips, dramatically emphasizing her cheekbones. "I don't look that old." She peered closer. "But maybe I should get some injections. You know, Botox. And maybe laser resurfacing for the sun damage. I hear Dr. Parikh at the Tribeca Skin Center is a miracle worker."

"Maybe you should just get some sleep and stop drinking and smoking so much."

Billie rolled her eyes. "Why don't you save the speech and just leave the pamphlet on the coffee table?"

Amy opened up her snakeskin Gucci bag and pulled out a makeup case. "I've got my tools. I'll do what I can. But that hair is your problem."

Billie gave her an up-and-down glance. "You must've seen *Nick* last night."

Amy's face revealed nothing, which revealed a lot. "Why do you say that?"

"Because you always dress extra pretty the day after." Billie started to giggle. "So . . . did he use the strap-on?"

Amy had it bad for a twenty-two-year-old named Nicole. In lesbian culture, Nicole was what they called a *boi*—young, masculine, and ready to party. She worked as a Federal Express courier, took testosterone supplements, and recently spent $7,500 on surgery to remove her breasts.

Billie couldn't keep up. The dyke world was so much more than bad haircuts and box-shaped asses these days. Nicole dressed in NBA jerseys, oversize jeans, and baseball caps flipped to the back, while insisting that everyone call her Nick. And here stood Amy, ridiculously girly and runway stylish, every straight man's fantasy lesbian.

"Your situation with Nicole is so fucked up," Billie said. "Don't ever try to talk about my life."

"Nick," Amy corrected. "And FYI—as your manager, it's my job to talk about your life, especially when it interferes with your work." She sighed and began using a small white sponge to apply

6

foundation to Billie's face. "In a perfect world, this would be a shade lighter."

Billie grinned. "I bet you used to say that to all the girls."

Amy cracked a smile. "It *was* a great way to meet women."

A few years ago, Amy had spent her days as a makeup artist, working the Chanel counter at Bergdorf Goodman on Fifth Avenue. By night, she hit the Manhattan bar scene, trolling for musicians who just might be eager enough to sign a management contract with a novice. Billie was the first to take the leap. Every good firm in the city had already turned her down flat, and Amy was promising to manage Billie's career away from after-midnight acoustic sets in crappy bars.

"So how did you meet this freak anyway?" Billie asked.

"Craigslist," Amy said. "And Nick's not a freak. She's just different."

Billie couldn't believe that classy Amy frequented the online meat market. "*Craigslist?* Seriously?"

"I think her headline read, BOI SEEKS GIRL." Sifting through the makeup bag, Amy smiled at the thought. "There was a photo." She shrugged. "What can I say? I was hooked."

"I don't get it. She had her tits removed, she dresses like a guy, and she uses a strap-on. Why not save yourself the trouble and just find a man?"

"It's not the same," Amy insisted, making two quick sweeps over Billie's eyelids.

"I guess everybody's got their kinks."

"Your skin looks awful," Amy said. "You should go in for one of those lunch-hour chemical peels. I'll set up something with my dermatologist." Amy glanced around the bathroom. "I don't see any skin-care products. What are you using these days?"

"Hot white cum," Billie said, trying to keep a straight face but losing the fight. "You should try it sometime."

Amy's mouth tightened. "You've been blessed with beauty and talent, Billie. But you have to nurture those gifts. Otherwise, you'll fuck it all away." As she made her speech, she carefully lined Billie's eyes and lips. "Your hair's a mess, your skin's a wreck, and your body's seen better days." She reached for the underside of Billie's upper arm. "Look at that jiggle. When's the last time you saw the inside of a gym?"

Billie's first internal impulse was to lash out, but something deep inside told her to resist. Amy dished out the tough love for good reasons. At the end of the day, Billie Shelton was a corporation, and Amy Dando owned 20 percent of it. The relationship between artist and manager was intense. It ranked up there with husband, boyfriend, and parents, none of which Billie had presently. Amy was the only person in Billie's life truly looking out for her best interests.

"I've been working," Billie murmured, finally.

"On what?" Amy demanded. "You haven't done any shows. You haven't written any new music."

"I've got some great songs in my head. I just have to get them down on paper."

Amy dipped a skinny brush into a glossy pot and began to paint Billie's lips. "You make me crazy. If you had the killer drive of a Madonna, there's no telling where you'd be today."

"What about my third CD? I worked my ass off to finish it, and Todd's been sitting on those tracks for months."

"The label wants a hit single," Amy said matter-of-factly. "Can you blame them?"

"There were at least—"

"Billie, that album was shit, and you know it. I don't think you spent one sober moment in the studio. Now shut up, so I can finish."

Billie stole a glance in the mirror. Amy was applying an explosive Mardi Gras red, making her lips pop with inevitable sin. They were Billie's best feature. Especially her lower lip. It was naturally, impossibly, decadently plump, with a deep gully carved down the center.

Men loved her mouth. Sometimes she could hear the horny

gears churning in their stupid heads as they wondered what it would feel like to have her lips wrapped around their cocks. Onstage she took full advantage of this, practically fellating the microphone. Her fans went wild for it every time. *Christ.* The fucking fans. They conjured up alternate feelings of gratitude and rage.

Billie had left Dartmouth with a degree in government and a six-song demo recorded in the bathroom of her college apartment. The last thing she wanted to do was enroll in law school or work for some tight-ass politician. So she moved to New York and began making the rounds with her music.

In the beginning, she was a walking cliché. Girl with guitar. A Michelle Branch wannabe. A poor man's Jewel. All the rejection had been slow murder on her soul. And she made quite a spectacle of herself at management firms and record labels, telling bitchy receptionists to fuck off and refusing to leave until someone who made decisions turned up to give her a chance.

Luckily, she found Amy before causing this scene at Olympic Records. BMG Entertainment had just acquired it, and the buzz on its founder, Todd Bana, was deafening. He'd gone from producing concerts on his college campus to launching his own independent label with an all-girl punk band called Menstrual Cramps. The group had gone on to sell over a million copies of their first release, *That Time of the Month.* Now Todd was a multimillionaire and the president of a major label. And the bastard wasn't even thirty yet.

The first meeting Amy set up for Billie had been with Todd. He signed her right away, even though he thought her demo was weak. He told her to write songs that would grab listeners by the throat and squeeze hard. She dug deep, and the result was *Dick Magnet,* a crude collection of sexually charged antilove songs that spoke to men and women of her generation. The breakout track was "Make Me Laugh and Make Me Come and I'll Fucking Marry You." College radio went ballistic. Rock critics went apeshit. They said that she had more to say than Sheryl Crow, that her vocal chops outranked Alanis Morissette.

Sales were so-so. The CD got halfway to gold, about a quarter of a million copies. But her first tour did boffo business. She sold out small venues and wowed the fans. Word of mouth began to build that Billie Shelton could deliver a live show that kicked ass. A fifteen-date trek became thirty, then sixty. Ultimately, she stayed on the road for more than a year. It was exhilarating. It was exhausting, too.

Touring life could be a real bitch. It was boring, monotonous, and lonely. Musicians put up with so much shit just for that ninety-minute orgiastic rush of performing before a crowd. And it was easy to be seduced into the never-ending rock-and-roll cycle. Getting drunk, getting laid, getting to the next gig.

Billie turned the old double standard upside down. Male rockers who banged every groupie in sight were studs. Well, what was she supposed to do after a show—sit around doing a BLESS THIS HOME cross-stitch? Fuck that. She had groupies, too. College guys. They were young, they were hot, and they made up for a lot of lost time.

In high school, Billie had been the depressed ugly girl with bad skin. Mommy died of ovarian cancer. Daddy killed himself over the loss. She got shipped off to live with a bitchy aunt. But a few years later, Billie blossomed. The acne went away. Once awkward features chiseled into exotic good looks. A new confidence to explore her artistic side materialized. It sounded like a bad Lifetime movie, but it was her fucking life story.

Before the whole rock chick thing, she'd only slept with two guys in her entire life. Now she couldn't even begin to count how many men there'd been. Online message boards crackled with I-Fucked-Billie-Shelton stories. Of course, most of them were far from the truth. "She gave me a blow job after her show in Birmingham!" But she'd never once set foot in Alabama.

Billie hated the hypocrisy. The way people worried about a woman who went out there and fucked like a man. Nobody speculated that Adam Levine of Maroon 5 had been molested by his

Uncle Charlie. A guy who enjoyed sex and balled his way across the country was a cocksman, but a woman who did the same had to be damaged goods, acting out some past violation. What bullshit.

Still, the dick parade was growing tiresome. For every mind-blowing session that made her toes curl (a rugby player from Trinity College came to mind), there were always several encounters that did nothing at all for her. Like last night's interlude with Robbie, the comedian. Maybe one day he'd figure out that his funniest joke was dangling between his legs.

When would the boy train stop and let her off? All the college dudes. And other musicians. Oh, God, the musicians. Even if they were twenty years older, they were still boys. Where were the real men? Not listening to her music and showing up at her concerts. That's for goddamn sure.

Billie's core base of support skewed younger—primarily eighteen- to twenty-four-year-old males, but some females, too. And here she was inching closer and closer to twenty-nine. The thought was sickening. Her true die-hard fan boys called themselves Billie Goats. They waged online wars to see who could build the most lavish Internet shrine dedicated to the worship of Billie Shelton. Depending on the day, this could make her feel grateful, dismayed, or just creeped out.

It didn't help that her first album had been so fucking awesome. *Dick Magnet* was widely regarded as a masterpiece. And nobody let her forget it, least of all the Billie Goats. They wanted another one just like the first.

Pussy Power sure as hell wasn't. That had been her follow-up, or, as the industry commonly referred to it, her sophomore slump. Sales on the set dropped 30 percent from her debut. It contained no buzz tracks, either. The only silver lining was the concert revenue for her second tour. That remained strong. But it was the old music that triggered passionate crowd responses. The new songs just didn't excite them.

Billie could see the writing on the wall, and it terrified her. She didn't want to be one of those new artists whose best work was already behind them. Maybe that's why she'd stayed drunk throughout the recording of her third CD. After all, alcohol dulled fear. And if worse came to worst, it was something to blame failure on, too.

Suddenly, Amy broke her free of the reverie, guiding Billie's head to face the mirror directly. "See . . . you're almost pretty again."

Billie stared at her own image as if at an X-ray. "Almost" was right. A journalist had once described her ripely round yet sharply angular face as an aesthetic wonder. But none of that seemed to be working for Billie now. Had the slow rot from years of raunchy living suddenly become visible?

Amy reached for the blow-dryer and began fluffing out Billie's long black hair.

"Make me an appointment with that dermatologist you were talking about," Billie shouted above the hot air flow. "And a good hairstylist. I want a personal trainer, too. I need to put this package back together."

Amy nodded blankly to the beat of each request.

Billie eyed the pack of Marlboro Lights near the sink. Oh, God, how she wanted one. And in all honesty, she deserved it. Usually, a cigarette was in her mouth before she opened her eyes in the morning. Amy had screwed up her routine today, so one smoke right now would still be cutting back.

Amy shut off the dryer. All of a sudden, she seemed pissed off. "You know, I shouldn't have to do this, Billie. I've got other clients. Having to wipe your ass all the time is getting old."

Billie lit up, dragging deep. Right away she felt better. She didn't understand why Amy was talking shit. "Yeah? Well, get over it. I'm your biggest act."

"Not anymore." The comeuppance in Amy's tone was bracing. "Internal Bleeding is."

For a second, Billie just looked at her. "Those losers you found at that bar mitzvah?"

Amy nodded. "One of their songs just got tapped for the next Ben Stiller movie. And they're going to be opening for the Killers. A lot of press is coming their way, too. There's a *Blender* interview scheduled for later today."

Each bit of news hit Billie like a punch in the gut. One of *her* songs should be in a movie. Why hadn't Amy landed *her* a gig as an opener for a major act? And speaking of *Blender*, *she* should not only be featured in the magazine, but on the fucking cover. This made Billie wonder if Amy was doing enough for her. Maybe she needed to start thinking about a new manager.

"I know what's going through your head," Amy said. "You're wondering why all of this isn't happening for your career."

Billie stared, taking another drag on her cigarette before answering. "Yeah, that thought crossed my mind."

"It's because these guys actually give a fuck. And they work their asses off."

Billie stomped out of the bathroom and began pillaging through her closet, searching for something to wear, practically setting herself on fire with her own cigarette in the process. She chose a schoolgirl's uniform skirt and a distressed T-shirt emblazoned with Minnie Mouse grabbing her crotch and flipping her middle finger.

Amy turned up in the doorway of the cluttered bedroom. "I'm sorry, but that's the truth."

Billie turned on her hotly. "You know what the real truth is? I signed up when you were just a lipstick girl. But you had some success with me and got inside the system. That's how you're making things happen for your new clients. Some fucking loyalty would be nice. I took a chance on you. Make something happen for me!"

"What do you think I'm trying to do? Without me, you would've slept through today's meeting or shown up looking like a road whore. By the way, take off that hideous shirt."

"I thought you didn't want to wipe my ass anymore. Now you're picking out my clothes."

Amy sighed, shutting her eyes for a moment. "Jesus, Billie, you're exhausting. Sometimes I wonder if it's worth it anymore. Are you happy with me? Do you want to end this?"

Billie experienced a minor sense of alarm.

"Maybe you should find a new manager."

Billie couldn't believe it. The bitch was looking for an out. And this scared the hell out of her. Shopping for new management when her career was in a slump could be risky. She might easily end up with someone lower on the food chain than Amy. "I can't believe you just said that. We fight all the time. Now all of a sudden you think I want to call it quits?"

Wearily, Amy leaned against the door. "I don't know what you want anymore. I just know that you're high maintenance and not worth the trouble. It's May, Billie, and you haven't earned a dime of new income this year. You made some nice money on your tours, but not enough to keep living the way you do."

"Am I broke?" Billie had no idea about her personal finances. She just relied on ATMs, charged up credit cards, and wrote out checks, assuming there would always be plenty of money to cover the damage.

"No, you're not broke," Amy said. "*Yet.* But you don't listen. I told you that Hamptons house was a bad idea. Keep spending fifty grand on a summer share, and you *will* be broke."

Billie had to admit the price tag on the East Hampton digs was high—$150,000 for the full season. Even split three ways, the figure stung. But Billie and two girlfriends, Liza Pike and Kellyanne Downey, would be living like stars in a spacious palace with ample privacy.

Liza had secured all the arrangements, obviously thinking money was no object. From her vantage point, why should it be? Her first book, *Whore,* had been a bestseller. It was basically a four-hundred-page bitch session about the way American culture sexualizes young women too soon. Billie never got through the first chapter. Beyond that, Liza wrote a syndicated newspaper column and appeared on an issues-oriented cable talk show every week. As for Kellyanne, she had no money worries, either. Some married real estate developer in Miami bankrolled her every move. So how could Billie poor-mouth and balk at her share of the summer house? After all, *she* was the fucking rock star.

The idea of spending an entire summer with the girls made her nervous, though. Back in college, this was a group that had forged a bond during a spring break trip to Cancún. To Billie's amazement, they still kept in touch. Once a year, they plotted a weekend getaway—shopping in Los Angeles, a spa retreat in Arizona. But a whole summer together?

Now Billie was smiling at Amy, hoping for an instant truce. In all honesty, she needed her. Amy didn't blow smoke up her ass. If something was fucked up, she said so. Billie could trust her. And Amy kept her eye on the big picture all the time. These were critical qualities in a good manager. "I know this summer share thing is a splurge—"

"*A splurge?*" Amy cut in. "Paying retail for a Gucci bag is a splurge. This is completely irresponsible."

"Even if you have a standing invitation to come any weekend you want?"

Amy didn't appear to be sold. "I hate the Hamptons."

"Why? It's beautiful—the sun, the beach, the fresh air. What are you going to do? Stay in the city all summer? Aren't you sick of the same crappy dyke bars night after night? I bet Nick would get really turned on by the sight of tan lines on you."

A faint smile found its way onto Amy's lips. "I'll think about it."

Billie gave her a look of contrition. "Are we cool now?"

"We're cool," Amy said. "But please change your shirt. I don't want Todd to mistake you for Courtney Love's little sister."

Todd Bana inhabited so much cocksure macho swagger that Billie swore she could hear his balls clang when he walked. It was uncanny how closely he resembled Scott Caan, the actor with the Hollywood pedigree. They shared the same good looks, muscled physique, and height challenges. Both men stood five foot five, providing they had on boots with a generous heel.

But Todd Bana would do nicely. He was just as hot as his more famous look-alike, if not more so. Even better, he was right in front of her, sitting behind his massive desk as if he ruled a small country.

Billie and Amy had been forced to cool their heels in his outer office for almost an hour. Had he really been busy? Or was it just a sick opportunity to make an artist sweat the outcome of her future?

She glanced over to see Todd's assistant—a sleek, efficient-looking fag in regulation Prada—discreetly off to the side, headset microphone in place, pen poised for quick note-taking.

Billie knew that she should be feeling anxious right now. Her career at Olympic could already be over. This meeting might just be the formal good-bye. But deep down, she sensed otherwise. Most companies were motherfuckers about such things. If they were dumping her, she'd likely read about it on the entertainment newswire, along with everybody else. Plus, Todd couldn't take his eyes off her mouth. Those famous Billie Shelton lips. She knew exactly what he wanted them to do.

"What do you feel like hearing first?" Todd asked. "The good news or the bad?"

Amy spoke up. "The bad. We assume it has something to do with your sitting on the third CD."

Todd propped up his feet. The soles of his expensive Italian shoes were unblemished, as if he'd just taken them out of the box. "Sitting on it implies that we're waiting on the right time for release. There is no right time to release absolute shit."

Billie stared at him impassively, even though she was seething inside. What a smug son of a bitch. She waited for Amy to rise to her defense. Playing bad cop was the manager's job at business meetings. But Amy just sat there like a dumb-ass while Todd went on.

"Instead of releasing Billie from the label, I'm willing to try something else." He zeroed in on her now. "I liked what you had to say with your first CD, but your second one was weak, and this third effort was a disaster. Maybe you've hit a dry well when it comes to writing your own songs. Nothing wrong with that. Happens to artists all the time."

Amy leaned forward, finally showing signs of life. "I think you're rushing to judgment, Todd. Billie's toured extensively. But she's had some time to recharge creatively. I think her next batch of—"

Todd cut her off. "Plenty of artists tour extensively. You record, you promote, and you hit the road. That's the gauntlet for everybody."

"Give Billie a chance to—"

"That's exactly what I'm doing," Todd snapped. "I'm giving Billie a chance that most labels wouldn't." Then he threaded his fingers behind his head and smiled.

Billie noticed Todd's biceps straining the fabric of his shirt. As much as she hated him right now, she found him insanely sexy, too. "And what chance would that be?" she asked.

"To go back into the studio and record again," Todd explained. "But not on your own, this time. You'll just be a singer working with outside producers and writers on material that I preselect."

Billie shot a look to Amy, who didn't seem happy at all. But Billie wanted to hear more. Just showing up to sing? It sounded like a vacation. Writing and producing her own stuff had always been a real grind. Maybe Todd was right. What if creating the kind of music that made up *Dick Magnet* was all part of her past?

"I want to mainstream your image," Todd went on. "Glam you up a bit." He gave her a quick, assessing once-over. "You should lose at least ten pounds. Do something with your hair, too. The goal is to take things in more of a pop direction but still keep that rock edge. I just had a meeting with White Tiger. They've got three new songs that would be perfect for you. And they're interested in hooking up."

Billie just sat there, humiliated by the makeover bit, stunned by the proposal, but mostly shocked by the mention of White Tiger. They were a writing/production team that had generated radio hits for scores of bubblegum acts with factory-like regularity.

Amy lengthened her spine. "*White Tiger?* Todd, what the fuck are you thinking? They've worked with Hilary Duff and Britney Spears. You're talking to Billie Shelton."

"I know that," Todd said. "They worked on the last Hannah Montana record, too. That went platinum. Meanwhile, I can't scrape together gold adding up sales on all my Billie Shelton albums put together."

Amy shook her head. "I don't like this. The shift is too extreme. It alienates her fan base. And if it bombs, what then? She's back at zero. An alternative rocker who sold out."

Billie just sat there. What scared her more than the idea of failing at something big was the thought of just scraping along. She didn't owe the Billie Goats a goddamn thing. How could Amy sit there and worry about a fan base that didn't have the numbers to push her to gold? Fuck them! What was so wrong about going pop? Hell, she'd go polka if it meant a platinum record. Why should that fake punk bitch Avril Lavigne squeeze all the cash from those Hello Kitty purses?

Billie looked at Amy. Then she turned back to Todd. "I'm in." By peripheral glance, she could see the surprise on Amy's face.

"Good," Todd said, winking at her. "Because I'm going to make you the baddest bitch in pop music."

Billie smiled. She liked the sound of that. It might mean selling out. But it also meant trading up.

Todd swung his feet to the floor and rested his forearms on his desk, shifting to serious business mode. "Amy, we'll need to work out a new deal. I'll want a piece of the action on Billie's touring and merchandising to offset the investment in a launch like this."

Billie saw the immediate flush of anger hit Amy's cheeks. Traditionally, those pieces of the artist's pie were off limits. But the business was changing. Every possible revenue stream was up for grabs. The Internet and the iPod revolution had turned the old music industry economic model upside down.

When Billie nodded her agreement, Amy stood abruptly. "Call me later, Todd," she said tightly. "We'll hammer out the details. I'm late for another meeting." And then she glared at Billie and walked out.

Todd gestured for his assistant to exit, then got up to shut the door behind him. He turned the lock. "I'm going to make you rich, Billie. Famous, too." His gaze never left her mouth as he unhooked his belt and started toward her. "I'm going to get your next single all over the radio. Do you want the cover of *Rolling Stone*?"

Billie moistened her lips with her tongue and nodded.

"I'll get you that, too." He stopped directly in front of her and dropped his pants. "So what are you going to do for me?"

Billie went to work, determined to suck Todd Bana until his eyeballs fell out if that's what it took to get the Olympic machine behind her. She thought about his platinum promises. She thought about the Hamptons getaway, too.

"Goddamn, you've got a hot mouth," Todd moaned.

Billie gazed up. The idea of this man becoming a beach boyfriend had a certain appeal. Todd could spend his weekdays making her a star and spend his weekends making her come. The fantasy was almost as delicious as he was. And she no longer had to wonder why Todd was such an overachiever. He was a short man with a big cock. Those kind of guys were unstoppable. They wanted to conquer *everything*.

Billie thought about Liza and Kellyanne, the way they always laughed at her for attracting stoners and skater boys. But this time she might have a major music mogul on her arm. That easily trumped their men. Liza's husband was a fireman, and Kellyanne's benefactor was old enough to be her grandfather. Game over.

As she snaked her tongue up and down Todd's long and thick shaft, a certain feeling struck her. Even with Memorial Day still more than a week away, Billie knew that this would be the most un-forgettable summer of her life.

"Come on, baby, show me how deep you can take it," Todd whispered thickly.

Billie laughed to herself. The bastard had no idea . . .

Liza

TWO

"It used to be that any girl in a horror movie caught sleeping around—or even losing her virginity to a guy she loved—was guaranteed a slashed throat," Liza Pike said.

Slyly, she checked her appearance on the monitor. The flirty, banana-print Chloe dress rocked; the freshly blown-out hair went on forever. She was a twenty-first-century fashionista feminist. Hated by the old guard, but loved by the new. *Feminism* had become a dirty word. Her goal: to make the next generation *own* the label. *Glamour* had recently voted her one of their Women of the Year. It was a step in the right direction.

"Classic misogyny," she went on. "The slut has served her purpose, so let's kill her. Now, thanks to movies like *Watch Her Bleed*, she just needs to be smart and accomplished to deserve an ugly death."

Tom Shapiro, host of CNBC's *The Roundtable*, raised his brow and gestured to Liza's on-air sparring partner, March Donaldson. "*Watch Her Bleed* just spent a second week at the top of the box office, March. Should we be concerned?"

March shook his head. "I don't see the big deal here. This is an R-rated thrills-and-chills popcorn flick. Besides, I get to see Jenny Barlow take a shower. You won't hear me complaining."

Liza pounced. "So you'll rail against Paris Hilton and *Sex and the City* reruns for being cultural poison, but garbage like *Watch Her Bleed* is okay?" She regarded him closely. "I'm impressed, March. For a man so young, you have the Republican double-talk down to a fine art."

He brushed off the political dig, flashing a smile that would make Tom Cruise insecure about his dental work. A halting arm went up. "There's a difference. When we've got middle school girls identifying themselves as Carries and Samanthas, society has a problem on its hands. But this is a movie for grown-ups. Relax. Have a Junior Mint."

Liza laughed at him. "Come on! Do you actually believe that this film is being marketed to adults? They're going after fourteen-year-old boys!"

March gave the host a deadpan look. "Tom, I think she's suggesting that I'm an adolescent."

Liza smiled. "If the shoe fits . . ."

A few crew members chuckled.

But March Donaldson was a good sport who knew how to laugh at himself. "Actually, my fiancée might say that it does."

Tom shifted his attention. "In all seriousness, Liza, you're deeply offended by this film, aren't you?"

She gave him a serious nod. "The women in this movie have one thing in common—they're assertive, opinionated, high achievers who, one by one, are stalked, terrorized, humiliated, and brutally murdered. This reflects a trend of sexualized cruelty prevalent in mainstream pornography."

Wearily, March groaned in protest, then opened his mouth to speak.

But Liza thundered on. "And I'm not talking about the extreme material that exists on the fringe. I'm talking about the mainstream product that neighbors, bosses, husbands, and boyfriends are watching on DVD and the Internet. This movie is an extension of that. Tonally, it's the eroticization of pushing women to the edge. The larger question is why are men getting off on this?"

Tom Shapiro leaned forward. "I should tell our viewers that Harrison Beck, the writer and director of *Watch Her Bleed,* declined our request to be here."

"Lucky for him," March cracked.

"Oh, I don't think he's lucky at all," Liza said. "Any man who uses his creative gifts to display that much anger toward women must have a very small penis."

The crew exploded into guffaws.

Tom shrugged helplessly, as if to say, "I can't control what comes out of her mouth."

March tried to fight off laughter but lost the battle.

"That will have to be the last word for this week's Culture Wars segment," Tom said. "Liza, March—a spirited discussion as always." He turned slightly to address another camera. "Until next week, thank you for visiting *The Roundtable.*"

"And we're out!" the producer shouted.

"You just had to go for the crotch shot," March muttered under his breath.

Liza cut a glance to the blond, buff, tanned, and hazel-eyed Texan. She widened her thumb and index finger apart to measure about four inches. "And I'm probably being generous."

March shook his head. "Poor guy. He won't get a date all summer."

Liza smiled, knowing an insult like that would be played up and often in the press, extending the life of the debate, solidifying her position as the go-to It Girl for topical feminist spin.

The building blocks for a brilliant career were stacking up nicely. She had a bestselling book on her résumé with *Whore,* a weekly stint on *The Roundtable,* a syndicated newspaper column, a regular blog on *The Huffington Post,* and a new deal in the works to join Sirius as a satellite radio talk-jock. Total media saturation. Politically, it was the only way to be heard in today's culture.

She rose and extended a hand to March. "Thanks. It's always a pleasure to wipe the floor with guys like you."

His shake was firm, his look flirtatious. "Well, one of these days you're going to have to let me be on top."

It drove Liza crazy that she found March Donaldson so attractive because she found conservatism so repulsive. March was a young Republican mover, the kind of man who grew up watching *Crossfire* and reading Peggy Noonan's *What I Saw at the Revolution*. He finished a law degree at the University of Texas, then joined George W. Bush's health-care policy pod in Washington. It didn't take long for his youth and sex appeal to generate fierce attention. The party needed some hot guy mediagenic bombast. Now he ran his own right-wing think tank, Our America, and played pundit hopscotch on network and cable news outlets.

She breezed past his double entendre. "Republicans are outnumbered five to one in the city. Manhattan dinner parties must be a real bitch for you."

March winked. "Not so much. Being on television gets me laid all the time. What can I say? I'm family values and rock and roll."

Liza wondered about his fiancée, Amaryllis Hartman. She worked in PR for fashion designer Stella McCartney and hailed from an impressive lineage of old money Connecticut Democrats. Beyond the obvious, what did a woman like that see in a man like March? His brand of contemporary narcissism hardly called for long-term commitment.

"Family values and rock and roll?" Tom Shapiro repeated this as he laughed. "If you ever run for office, use that for your campaign slogan. You'll own the young male swing vote."

Liza managed a wry smile. "Don't encourage him, Tom." She started out. "I'll see you next week."

"Hey, you up for a drink?" Tom called after her.

"Next time," Liza promised. "I'm heading back for a book party."

Tom pulled a disappointed face. He was astonishingly handsome—fine features, beautiful teeth, a smattering of sun freckles, slightly rumpled brown hair. With his easy speaking style and cool gesticulations, he gave off intellectual frat boy vibrations. The cable brass saw him as their great hope to attract young viewers, a demographic that got most of their news from Jon Stewart and Stephen Colbert.

But Tom Shapiro was the real thing, having endured a short tour of duty in the White House press corps. At daily briefings, he shrewdly hogged the mic with long what's-your-question questions. This ensured that the superimposed video ID would hit the screen and identify to 40 million people his name and affiliation. The exposure got him an agent, and a few months later, his own cable show.

As Liza picked up her pace, March fell into step beside her. "I'm guessing this book party isn't for Ann Coulter."

Liza grinned in spite of herself. She hated that cunt for the radical right. March knew it, too. "And they say you're not inclined to big think."

"Who says?"

She played coy. "No one in particular."

"Is Tucker Carlson bashing me again?"

Her smile was teasing.

"He says I'm more like a guy in a sports bar who won't shut up than a political analyst." One beat. "Dick. He's just jealous because I get more face time on TV."

Liza started to laugh and pushed open the exit door, bracing herself for the shock of going from meat locker air-conditioning to sticky summer heat.

A Town Car and driver were waiting, ready to whisk her from the Englewood Cliffs, New Jersey, studio back to New York.

"So, tell me, how does a feminist like you spend the summer?" March asked. "Will you slip into a swimsuit at some point, or does that represent man's evil plot to reduce you to a sexual object?"

"See? You *are* that guy in a sports bar."

March shrugged. "I've been called worse." He gestured for Liza's driver to remain seated and opened the rear passenger door.

"Believe it or not, I'm renting a house in the Hamptons for the season with a few girlfriends," she announced, slipping into the roomy cabin. "How's that for girly?"

March kept his hand on the door and leaned inside. "My fiancée's parents own a house in Watermill. I'll be there every weekend." He grinned, practically dripping with sexual heat.

With a pang of guilt, Liza thought of Justin. "Good. I'd love to watch my husband kick your ass in beach volleyball."

March rose up to his full height and gave her a cocky nod. "You're on." He shut the door, then just as quickly knocked on the tinted window.

Liza zipped it down.

"Don't get me wrong. I have great respect for firemen. But that pussy is going down."

She laughed as the driver coasted away, her body tingling with the animated energy that flirtation brings. And then came the shame. But Liza convinced herself that she harbored no desire for this to turn into something else. It was nothing more than the charming suggestion that, in another life, without her husband in the equation, without March's fiancée in the wings, they might have a fantastic time together. Her anxiety eased, Liza reached for her cellular to call Justin.

He picked up on the first ring. "Hey."

"How was your day?"

"Long and boring."

She breathed a quiet sigh. It was relief to her, misery to him. Justin was a truckee, a distinction that made him responsible for finding the fires and getting the survivors to safety. He worked Engine 40, Ladder 35 on Amsterdam and Sixty-sixth, a station house that had lost twelve men on September 11. "I'm on my way back," Liza announced. "The party starts at seven. If nothing else, the food will be good. Have you eaten?"

Justin hesitated. "What party?"

"Pila Anderson's book party. She gave me an advance quote for *Whore*. We've talked about this half a dozen times."

"I forgot," Justin said lamely. "Right now I'm heading to the gym with a buddy. Will you be pissed if I skip it?"

"I'm pissed that I even had to remind you," Liza spat. "Get your ass home, get a suit on, and get to the party. Details are on the fridge." She slammed the phone shut. "My fucking husband!"

The driver adjusted his rearview mirror, seeking eye contact, hoping for conversation.

But Liza didn't have the energy for chatter. She turned away, gazing blankly out the window in an effort to pinpoint the root cause of her annoyance. It couldn't be Justin exclusively. From time to time she had to get parental, all part of the currency of marrying a man-child.

Maybe it was her gnawing hunger. In the days that led up to a television appearance, she went on a punishing calorie restriction diet. Nothing but flaxseed, rice bran, brewer's yeast, sprouts, green tea, and sugar-free gum. This not only kept her model-thin but the preoccupation of always thinking about what she ate crowded out other worries. Of course, it didn't help that a strange ravenousness hit her after every taping of a show.

As she dug into her purse for a piece of Trident, she noticed the syringe. A wave of dread spread across her abdomen. Better to just do the deed fast before she had a chance to get anxious. She pulled up the skirt of her dress and jammed the needle into her hip.

It was a hormone cocktail—Perganol, Gonal-f, and Lupron—designed to stimulate her ovaries to mature multiple eggs for freezing. This would be her second round at fifteen grand a pop. But it meant she could put off having a baby until forty. At twenty-nine, her eggs were still young, brilliant, and beautiful, not the old, dark, and grainy things they'd be if she waited.

At moments like this, she felt like a fraud, as if her public persona didn't represent a true ideology but a mercenary career move. Liza Pike, tough-talking feminist. Yeah, right. What would people think if they knew the real truth? That she had married a big, strong, stupid guy out of fear of being alone, that she starved herself even though she was already thin, that she had succumbed to baby panic propaganda and had thrown herself onto the guillotine of high-tech science.

Everything changed when the first plane hit the World Trade Center's north tower. Liza had been outside her TriBeCa apartment, close enough to feel the heat of the explosion on her face. From that moment on, nothing seemed the same. A garbage truck hitting a grate could scare the breath out of her lungs. For a long time she stopped taking elevators, refused to drive over the George Washington Bridge, and avoided the subway altogether. She also bypassed major airlines, thinking small carriers would be safer and likely under the radar of terrorists.

Relationships were altered, too. Tony Grant, a victims'-rights lawyer based in London, had been her boyfriend for two years. After a few days of consoling her about the attacks, he wanted to move on to other things—phone sex, politics, his tennis game, anything but her paralyzing fears. Playing the emotional caretaker was beyond him and, as the weeks went on, bad conversations got worse. She ended up dumping him the night he tried to argue that U.S. foreign policy had justifiably provoked the jihad.

For a few months, Liza did fine alone, but then CBS aired the six-month anniversary special with graphic new footage of the towers falling, images that simply reactivated her traumatic symptoms. Feeling vulnerable again, she reached out to Tony, though his week-long visit failed to repair the relationship. There was nothing quite like those long, silent minutes—after disconnected sex and before sleep—to trigger deep reflections on how absolutely wrong Tony was for her. When he returned to London, Liza knew it was over for good, only to discover weeks later that she was pregnant.

Tony had announced over drinks on their first date that he didn't want children. The last thing she needed to hear was some crude offer to pick up the tab for an abortion, so she never told him. Liza volunteered at a Planned Parenthood location near her apartment, but it had recently been destroyed by arson. She went to another clinic but knew no one on staff. The nurse was aloof, helping to guide Liza's hips to the edge of the table but offering little else. The doctor never said a word. He just stepped into the room and roughly pushed in the speculum. She remembered the cramping, the painful tugging sensation, the daze of the relaxant. And then it was over.

Liza thought about her decision every day. She even noted the anniversary to herself, a morbid birthday for a baby never born. But she didn't regret it. There'd been so much she wanted to accomplish career-wise. And the idea of being linked to Tony Grant by way of a child seemed unbearably wrong. So Liza mourned, she gave her body time to heal, and then she swore off self-absorbed urban types by trespassing into bars where real men hung out.

It was time for an action-figure guy. After all, you couldn't find a toy based on a lawyer or a stockbroker. Liza wanted a cop, a cowboy, a fireman, someone who'd make love like an animal and lug a sofa bed up five flights of stairs without complaint.

When Liza saw Justin Beal for the first time at a casual bar near Ground Zero, he stood out like neon. Nicknames were big deals in firehouses, and all the men referred to Justin as Calvin Klein. Knocking back his beer in distressed jeans and a white tank, he did look more like a male model than a rescue worker.

But he was no high-maintenance pretty boy. There was hair on his chest. His hands were large and rough looking. And the corded musculature of his arms looked like the natural result of years of sports and physical work, not slavish dedication to a Bowflex machine. That night, he'd been the object of both ridicule and celebration for being cover boy of the new FDNY hunk calendar.

But Liza had managed to cause a minor commotion of her own. She knew how to take elements of elegance and mix them with nonchalance—a killer dress, wash-and-go hair, makeup so light you couldn't tell she was wearing any, and flats. This set her apart from the other huntresses who stalked the man jungle with their peekaboo cleavage and hooker heels.

Justin had responded to the novelty and approached her right away. She found him so desirable that the air seemed to leave the room. Shallow banter turned more shallow, and they ended up at her apartment. After the best sex of her life, he unloaded his survivor's guilt for breathing, eating, and fucking while the bodies of some of his firefighter brothers remained unaccounted for. Liza held him. For a first-night hookup, it was off the charts for intensity. Six weeks later, they were married. And more often than not, she still wondered why.

Zipping open her Celine clutch, Liza inspected her face. In the grind of the traffic halt, she carefully reapplied her Nars Hot Voodoo lipstick. *Shit.* They hadn't moved an inch in five minutes. Goddamn New Jersey. She huffed and shoved the tube back into her purse. More time to reflect on her darling husband.

Liza knew that saying those vows to Justin had been more of a response to circumstances than to love. The sky had already fallen once. She didn't want to be alone if it happened again. Plus, a new husband represented her post–September 11/post-Tony view on men: *simple guys only.* And that, Justin was. His interests were limited to work, sex, food, and the gym. Talk was scarce. He didn't read or keep up with the news enough to offer cognitive volley on anything.

But this gave Liza private space to think, a cerebral sanctuary all her own. She could do intellectual sparring at the office. At home, she thought she wanted something else—to feel safe and protected. Six years in, it wasn't working. But what else could she expect? The paradox of fearing loneliness and craving solitude was hardly the first building block for wedded bliss.

Liza had come to learn that simple men were just self-absorbed in their own way. Justin was no different. His needs were primitive, and they rarely involved her now. Even physically. In that first blush of togetherness, the sex had rocked her world. In fact, she could honestly admit that their relationship had been purely based on it. But now the act took on no greater or less a role than it would have with a Tony clone or some other man who in his lifetime had actually read a novel from beginning to end.

She tried not to think about Justin as a freeloader. The salary for a fireman would never catch up with the exalted status of being one. There were men at his firehouse—with children and stay-at-home wives—who were eligible for food stamps. But Justin was content. His ambition chromosome seemed to be missing. Even taking the exam to become an officer was beyond him. But he definitely lived better than his station buddies. After the wedding, he moved out of his dinky apartment in one of the outer boroughs and into the TriBeCa loft that she owned.

Liza felt like a bitch for thinking this way, but knowing that she could provide for herself financially conjured up a crazy lust to live off her husband. As if that could ever happen. The last wire transfer from her literary agency for a foreign sale of *Whore* was more than Justin's take-home pay for the year. And that money had been a surprise. Adding up American royalties, the contract with CNBC, the new Sirius deal, revenue from her Web site, newspaper syndicate income, and speaking fees, Liza easily brought in eighty dollars for every one that Justin earned.

Not that it bothered him. Why worry about how much money he made when he could just spend hers on expensive guy toys—the plasma TV, the top-of-the-line stereo equipment, the motorcycle. And it's not as if he even attempted to make up for his lack of income by overcompensating in other areas. Being responsible for a single goddamn meal was too much to expect.

Once, on his day off, with Liza on a schedule gauntlet from hell, Justin had promised to take care of dinner. She came home to find on the table a pot of overcooked pasta and a room-temperature jar of Prego. No wine, no salad, no bread. His excuse? "I never cook. I didn't know." Yet the man had been eating his whole fucking life. Even worse, meals were the social center of firehouse living. The men usually took turns putting on feasts. He knew what to do. The son of a bitch just didn't care enough to make the effort.

Moments like that were hardly a turn-on. Liza never rejected Justin sexually, but then she didn't exactly transmit seductive signals, either. They morphed into—at best—a once-a-month couple.

Sometimes she regarded him as an overgrown boy with an undeserved allowance. So she really had no desire to pay the American Express bill and then suck his dick to make him feel like a king.

Maybe Pila Anderson's book party would be a shot in the arm. Her new tome was called *The Sex Factor,* a manifesto on the epidemic of passion-deprived marriages, complete with tips on reigniting the erotic fire. But time apart could help ease Liza's hostility, too. Liza was looking forward to weekends in the Hamptons with the girls. Hearing about Billie's dead-end romances and Kellyanne's geriatric sugar daddy just might make her stop and appreciate what she had with Justin.

As often as that little voice told her to put an end to their union, Liza ignored it, knowing instinctively that seeing a fading tan line on her ring finger would dial up feelings of failure and regret. She didn't want to be one of those starter-marriage women, the kind who emerge from what should be a lifetime commitment with all the emotional despair of a college party girl bidding adieu to a spring break fuck buddy.

The Town Car stopped in front of the Rem Koolhaas–designed Prada store in SoHo. Liza stepped out, feeling sexy in her towering Cesare Paciotti sandals. No wonder March Donaldson had followed her out of the studio like a stray dog.

She adored the sensation of knowing that she looked fabulous, a character trait which earned her the wrath of feminist colleagues. They labeled her a lightweight, argued that she was just in it for the media attention, and openly resented her rapid rise and high-profile position. Even among the intelligentsia set, it was still high school all over again. Three cheers for sisterhood.

Liza spotted Justin right away. It was amazing what a beautifully cut jacket and a great pair of shoes could do for a man with ramrod-straight posture. She felt the urge to just drag him home right then and there. Stopping a strutting waiter, she relieved him of his last champagne flute with a smile and drank deeply to prepare herself for the night. A gazillion familiar faces. The place was a total ratfuck.

A stressed publicist moved the mouthpiece of her headset out of the way and approached. "Are you from *The Apprentice*?"

Liza shook her head. "Sorry."

A copy of *The Sex Factor* got shoved into her hands anyway. "Hold this up when you pose with Pila." Then the flak grimaced, scanning the area for her reality-show PR prize.

Liza pressed onward, waving across the room to one acquaintance, then another, finally closing in on Justin.

Her husband kissed her lightly on the lips and tasted of crab cakes. "You were right. The food's good."

Liza fidgeted with the hem on her short dress. Suddenly, she didn't want to be here. But she loved Justin for following her bitch rant orders to the letter. His reward would be an early exit and a smashing blow job the moment they got home. "Give me a minute to say a few hellos, and we're out of here."

Locating Pila among a crowd of well-wishers, she started over.

"Liza!" The shriek came from a rotund man in funny glasses. K.K. Vermorel. He was a freelance fashion stylist who recently outfitted Liza for a "New Manhattan Braintrust" pictorial in *Bazaar.* "You didn't tell me you were renting Faye Hudson's house for the season! You'll love it!" K.K. kissed her on both cheeks and gave her an approving once-over. Then he scoffed at the book in her hand as his gaze danced around the room. "You don't need that book, you lucky bitch. Where's that hunky husband of yours?"

Liza merely laughed. If he only knew. "Maybe I'll see you at some parties this summer. I'm thinking about hosting one with my friends."

"That sounds delicious," K.K. gushed. "And speaking of parties, I can't wait for Harrison Beck's Memorial Day bash. It's shaping up to be quite the event, what with all the success of *Watch Her Bleed.* Have you seen it? God, I had to look away. It was awful. Not the violence—that I could handle. Did you notice Jenny Barlow's breast implants? One is bigger than the other!"

Liza decided to let the subject pass. What could she possibly say to someone who left the multiplex with that mindless thought?

"Of course, you'll be there," K.K. went on.

"Actually, I didn't get an invitation."

K.K. swatted away this potential obstacle like a gnat. "You and your friends can be my plus one. A fat queen with a harem. It'll be a scream."

Liza instantly accepted. Today's taping of *The Roundtable* would air on Sunday. By Monday, Page Six would plant a snarky item about Liza's speculation on the size of Harrison Beck's dick. But instead of hiding out, she'd be drinking his Krug champagne with no remorse. That son of a bitch was about to find out that women were not just tits and ass.

Some girls have balls.

Kellyanne

THREE

The first time Kellyanne Downey kissed a woman, she was in college. A fraternity party at the University of Alabama. On a dare from a group of guys who were probably still masturbating to the memory today, she made out with a drunk cheerleader for the Crimson Tide.

Now it was happening again. No dare this time. Just some naughty encouragement from Jab, the sexy bartender at Silk Electric, a new Miami restaurant/bar/place-to-be-seen.

Midnight ticked past. It was Kellyanne's last shift. Beyoncé and Jay-Z had just left her a monster tip. The only other waitress still on duty, Pommie, had been flirting with her all night, shooting seductive glances across the crowded floor, instructing Jab to sneak them raspberry Bellinis in celebration of Kellyanne's final hours on the job.

Pommie was gorgeous—a tall, leggy Italian with dark olive skin and wild, jet black curls that cascaded down the small of her back. Her lips were full and pliant, her mouth exquisitely yielding.

35

Kellyanne felt a jolt in the stomach as Pommie's tongue swirled around her own. Their knees were touching. Oh, God, this is how she remembered it—the softness, the sweetness, the same rhythm. But when Pommie's hands began easing up her torso and toward her breasts, Kellyanne pulled back.

Pommie's dark eyes flashed with frustration.

"Shit, don't stop," Jab hissed. "I smuggled six drinks your way. At least let her suck some nip."

Pommie scowled at him. "You're a pig."

They were in a dimly lit corner near the bar. The three Bellinis had gone to Kellyanne's head. But she still knew the truth. Jab was a harmless straight guy obsessed with girl-on-girl action. The real pigs were in the last party holding up the restaurant's closing. "I better get back to my table." She started off.

Pommie reached for her arm. "Come home with me," she whispered.

"Now we're talking," Jab said.

Kellyanne shot a sharp glance in his direction. "How are those four Ketel Ones coming?"

All of a sudden, Jab got busy.

Pommie nuzzled closer. "Just one night—you'll never look back."

Kellyanne started to giggle. Maybe it was the alcohol. Maybe it was the fact that she was actually warming up to the idea. Sort of. "I can't . . . Pommie, this isn't me. Not really. I'm just goofing off. Don't read anything into it."

Pommie sighed in defeat. "I can't believe you're blowing *me* off, but you let that old man put his shriveled old dick—"

"Walter's a decent guy," Kellyanne cut in.

Pommie rolled her eyes. "Yeah, well, if it wasn't for that liver-spotted sugar daddy, you wouldn't be leaving."

"Bless your heart, you're going to miss me." Kellyanne thickened her already thick Southern drawl.

Pommie cracked a smile.

"It's just for the summer. I'll be back in the fall." Her voice was breathy, almost singsong.

"No, you won't," Pommie said. "You'll find a richer guy in the Hamptons and become a kept woman there."

"I'm not kept," Kellyanne insisted lightly. "I'm just not opposed to generosity, that's all." She grinned. "Anyway, you can visit. Most of the time my friends will be going back to the city during the week. You should fly out for a few days." She glanced over at the bar. "You, too, Jab."

"Is this Bellini talk?" Jab asked. "Because I'll definitely take you up on a free place to crash."

Kellyanne laughed. "Y'all should come together. We'd have a blast."

Pommie traded a high five with Jab. "You're on, bitch."

Jab gestured to Silk Electric's last remaining customers, a raucous group of four. "Are those assholes giving you any trouble? Because I'll happily whip out my special straw for these cocktails."

Kellyanne shook her head, laughing. Jab was famous for using his penis to stir the drinks of particularly rude patrons. "Keep it zipped. They're just a little loud. Nothing I can't handle." She took the tray and off she went, praying that this would be the last round. Maybe if she suggested the perfect strip club to keep the party going, they'd get the hell out.

"Hold on a minute, dude! All I'm saying is we could do better. We've got some hot girls lined up, but we could do better." The leader of the pack was talking—late thirties, buzz cut, about six foot four, dressed down in a T-shirt, board shorts, and flip-flops. "Take this chick." He robbed a Ketel One from Kellyanne's tray and raised the glass to salute her. "She's fucking beautiful. I mean, come on, dude! Nobody we signed up has anything on this girl."

Kellyanne pretended not to hear and simply distributed the drinks as each guy zeroed in on her with a laser intensity. "Can I put this on one check?" She knew how to ignore men even as she was talking to them. Always being the hottest girl—on campus, at the party, in the room—had taught her such skills.

The obnoxious one continued staring. Even behind the sunglasses at night, she could see his eyes swirling kaleidoscopically. Typical male reaction.

Kellyanne knew the drill. Since blossoming almost overnight at fifteen, guys would take one look at her and all brain activity would revert from their head to their crotch. She was a dewy drop of California nectar by way of the Deep South—an object study in blond superiority. People didn't bother talking about her beauty. Why struggle to articulate the obvious? It was like pointing out the sun.

She was tiny, just five foot one, but not built like a little girl. Kellyanne's body screamed, *And God Created Woman*, only in miniature—hips so slim and narrow that some internal organs appeared to be missing, breasts that were pert and shapely, and, despite her slight height, limbs that seemed long and languid. No matter the season, there was an impossible golden glow to her skin and hair, a perpetual just-walked-off-the-beach look. Exercise bored her to death. Luckily, she possessed a metabolism that didn't require it. Her secret was to just take vitamins and echinacea until her body rattled. That kept everything together.

It wasn't all perfection, though. Kellyanne's nails were hideous. From the age of eight, she'd been a chronic biter. And no amount of behavior modification sessions could roll back the nasty habit. Walter had spent a fortune on hypnosis therapy, and that'd been a bust, too. Even the foul-smelling lotions designed to make her fingers taste bad failed miserably. After chewing down the first nail, she stopped noticing the yucky flavor. The overall act was familiar routine now, almost pleasurable.

"So what did you do today, baby? How come you weren't at the Palms auditioning for my show?"

Kellyanne gave him a look she usually reserved for roadkill. She knew this type. In high school, he was the parking lot stoner, the kind of guy who spent his weekend hours earning money for pot at some loser job behind a Smoothie King counter. Now he had a lame gig in entertainment that pulled girls who would show him their boobs for as little pay as a free beer. And he thought he was a junior Hugh Hefner.

The asshole tilted up his shades to reveal bloodshot eyes. "I'm Brad Lucas, by the way. But call me Bonzi." Going clockwise around the table, he introduced his cronies. They all had grandiose, meaningless titles preceded by the qualifying classification of "assistant." They all had names, too.

But Kellyanne was barely listening. If somebody held her at gunpoint, then she might be able to recall that one of the idiots was Jeff. Maybe John. She couldn't be sure.

"So what's your name?" Bonzi asked.

She told him.

"*Kellyanne.*" There was a lewd timbre to his voice. "Sweet, Southern Kellyanne. That is *hot.*"

She sighed impatiently. "I'll be right back with your check."

"Hold on a minute!" Bonzi cried. "You never answered my question. How come you didn't audition for my show?"

"And what show is that?" Kellyanne asked. "*Girls Gone Wild South Beach*?"

Bonzi looked genuinely offended. "I don't produce shit like that. I'm in reality television. I've got a development deal at Fox. Ever watch *The Cul-de-Sac*?"

Kellyanne nodded vaguely. She remembered people at the restaurant talking about it. Some trash involving a group of sexy singles who move into a neighborhood to tempt the married residents.

"That was my show," Bonzi said proudly.

"Congratulations," Kellyanne sniffed. Please. As if the shit were *Masterpiece Theatre.*

"The bank already has," Bonzi shot back. "Congratulated me, that is. Last year it was Fox's second-highest rated show among the eighteen-to-forty-nines."

"I don't watch much TV."

"What are you doing for the next two weeks?" he asked.

"Actually, I'm leaving tomorrow for the whole summer."

Bonzi shrugged diffidently. "So delay that. I can put you up in a mansion on Star Island."

Kellyanne started to leave. "No thanks."

"At least let me tell you about my new show."

She glanced at her Cartier tank watch—a gift from Walter—and saw Jab closing down the bar and Pommie knocking back another Bellini. "Okay," she relented. "Give me a thirty-second pitch. But then you guys have to take off."

His face lit up, and he began speaking in a stream of exclamations. "Okay! It's called *Soul Mates*. Fox has us locked in this summer. *Everybody*'s gonna be watching. No joke. This show is gonna be fucking *huge*! At first, you think it's a rip-off of *The Bachelor*. We've got thirty smoking fine girls going after this one dude. And this guy's hot—former pro athlete, did some modeling, now he makes seven figures running the family consulting business. I'm telling you—this dude's the shit. There's not an ounce of fag in me, and *I'd* fuck him." Bonzi laughed as his posse practically convulsed under the table. He turned back to Kellyanne. "You like Brad Pitt?"

A half-smile curled onto her lips and threatened to stay there. "Who doesn't?"

"This man is like a Brad Pitt. No lie. His name's Vlad Branigan. So my man Vlad has thirty beauty queens on his jock. He's trying to decide which one he digs the most. By the way, when you introduce yourself, it'll be fucking over. He loves blondes. He'll fall for you big time. I swear to that. But just when he narrows it down and is about to choose between two of the original thirty, we've got a twist that'll knock him on his ass." He paused for dramatic effect. "A blast from the past. The one that got away. It took some serious background research to find a guy this perfect with a lost love, but we did it. Are you with me?"

Kellyanne nodded. His thirty seconds were up a minute ago, but she actually found this doofus mildly entertaining.

"So Vlad's heart is fucking bleeding on camera. Does he go for his new soul mate or the soul mate from his past? But the gag is this—no matter which girl he chooses, dude goes home alone. The new girl and the old girl split a million bucks and leave his ass high and dry on national television!"

At first, Kellyanne just laughed. "You're joking, right?"

"No, I'm fucking serious!"

"But that's so mean," Kellyanne said.

"That's the point! People are sick of these fucking bachelor types having their pick of the litter like some Saudi prince. This dude will get humiliated. It'll be awesome!"

"If you say so." She started off again.

"Does that mean you're in?" Bonzi asked.

Kellyanne stopped and gave him a quizzical look. "In what?"

"The show," Bonzi said. "You'll be on it, right? He stood up and turned to his boys. "Can you believe I just told this bitch the big reveal? I'm fucking trashed, man. Which one of you has a clean copy of the boilerplate?"

One of the men dug through a worn leather satchel and pulled out a document at least one hundred pages thick.

Bonzi passed it to Kellyanne. "Sign this and you're on the show. It's usually not this easy, but I've got a feeling about you." He retrieved a silver case from his back pocket and handed over a business card.

She fingered the embossed lettering. BRAD "BONZI" LUCAS, THREE KEGS ENTERTAINMENT.

"Call my cell when you decide," he said. "But don't wait too long. I'll need an answer by noon tomorrow."

When Kellyanne walked through the door of her condo and saw Walter Isherwood passed out on the couch, she experienced a moment's pure dread. The last thing she ever wanted him to do was tell his wife that he wanted a divorce. Kellyanne saw him too much as it was.

Rushing over to nudge him awake, she halted all of a sudden, admiring the peaceful image of him sleeping. Even at sixty-four, he still possessed an undeniable appeal and virility. Walter had the sort of timeless charisma that made men like Jack Nicholson so sexy to younger women. He swam a mile every day and lifted weights three times a week, which made for a body more taut and firm than could be found on many men half his age.

A late-night infomercial for Proactiv Solution was blaring from the plasma television that floated on the wall like a prop from a sci-fi movie set.

Kellyanne dug out the remote control from underneath Walter's hip and zapped the power off, noticing the empty highballer on the Noguchi coffee table. He loved his Scotch. A little too much at times. Gently, she shook his shoulder. "Walter . . ."

He stirred slightly, slowly opened his eyes, and gave her a groggy smile. "What time is it?"

"It's almost two," she whispered. "What are you doing here?"

"You're not happy to see me?" There was an instant edge to his voice.

She kissed him. "Don't be stupid. I had no idea you were coming tonight. You should've told me. I wouldn't have stayed behind to have a drink with Pommie and Jab."

He gestured to the bulging *Soul Mates* contract under her arm. "What's that?"

Kellyanne tossed the thick packet onto the Noguchi. It landed with an almighty thud. "It's too late to get into that. I'll tell you about it later. Shouldn't you be getting home? I can make some coffee."

"There's no rush. Connie's on a cruise with her sisters."

Connie was Walter's wife of thirty-two years. They had three children, each close in age to Kellyanne. For the past few years, she'd heard about all of them in bits and pieces. To deal with the guilt, she began to think of herself as some sort of family friend and inquired about them often. How was Connie's museum benefit? Did Allison get that promotion? Has Brock set a wedding date yet? And so on. Now she found herself genuinely curious about this cruise. "Where'd they go?"

"Alaska . . . Bermuda . . . who knows?" Walter's uncertainty on the subject matched his lack of interest. Slowly, he ran his hands down Kellyanne's slender arms, a faraway look of lust in his intelligent green eyes. "I took a Levitra a few hours ago . . ."

It was the same routine. He studied her as she went through the rituals of getting ready for bed. For Walter, this constituted foreplay. He watched her take a bath. He watched her shave her legs. He watched her pee. He watched her apply all the expensive La Prairie skincare products that his credit card paid for.

Walter always insisted that Kellyanne tell him everything about her day, too, and he was a good listener, even as his arousal heightened and he began to touch himself. On this night, she relayed stories about her near car accident on the way to Silk Electric, the three-hundred-dollar tip that Beyoncé and Jay-Z left behind, her silly makeout session with Pommie, and the standing offer from Brad "Bonzi" Lucas.

It'd been three or four hours since he popped the Levitra, but that little pill remained on call in the body for up to six. By the time they slid into bed, he was as rigid and randy as a soldier on weekend furlough. But his skills as a lover were average at best.

Walter loved going down on her but lacked the know-how. Forget the G-spot. He could never stimulate her clitoris properly, either. And he never applied pressure or used his fingers. He just lapped like a baby kitten taking in a saucer of milk. But Kellyanne writhed and moaned appropriately. No need to make him feel insecure at sixty-four.

Just one night—you'll never look back.

Pommie's bold assertion played back in Kellyanne's mind as she lay there, bored as hell and ready for sleep. Thank God she was going away for the summer. Of course, she owed that indulgence to the very man she wanted to get away from. When she told Walter about Liza's idea, he'd scratched out a fifty-thousand-dollar check the moment the details came through. He told her that she deserved a break and waxed lyrical about rendezvousing in New York a few times each month. Secretly, Kellyanne hoped that it'd be less than that.

Walter ran the Isherwood Group, a residential real estate development company. There were definite perks to being the president's girl on the side. For instance, he put her up in the Jade building, a forty-eight-story waterfront condominium property on Brickell Bay. Her unit was a one bedroom/two bath with amazing views, a stainless-steel kitchen with built-in wine cooler and cappuccino maker, and an in-home touch-screen monitor in every room for security and personal services. The spoiling went on with a silver Mercedes SL600 Roadster, too. Kellyanne had to admit that the Isherwood Group was *very* good to her.

"You're nice and wet," Walter announced. "I think you're ready now." He turned Kellyanne onto her side, slid into her, and began pumping in his typical rhythm-challenged manner. When he came, there was a loud cry and a violent shudder. Levitra orgasms were deliciously forceful. They left Walter's face so hot and flushed that each time Kellyanne swore she might have to call 911.

He was still breathing hard when he reached into the night-stand drawer, pulled out two Wrist Rockets from the London-based erotica shop Coco de Mer, and passed them over with a dirty grin. "My favorite part." And then he settled back for the show.

Kellyanne slipped her hands through the straps and twisted the tips of the pink, bullet-shaped devices. The single-speed motors revved up. She rested one against her anus and positioned the other on her clitoris. It didn't take long for the vibrating power-tool toys to work their magic. Her satisfaction was quick and intense.

"You're beautiful when you come," Walter said, stroking the inside of her thigh.

Kellyanne smiled. "I thought I was beautiful when I slept."

"That, too." Sighing heavily, he rolled over to stare up at the vaulted ceiling.

She brushed a tendril of hair away from his eyes. "What's wrong?"

"You leave tomorrow, right?"

"I'm supposed to."

"We've got some problems with the Indian Creek project. I might not make it to New York as often as I thought this summer."

Kellyanne fought to conceal her relief. It was precisely what she'd wished for. The Indian Creek high-rise was the most ambitious construction of Walter's career. Its Atlantic, intracoastal, and city views would be unparalleled. "Then I'll just come back home to see you," she said, practically holding her breath for his response.

"No . . ." he began softly.

Thank God!

"This is your time away with your girlfriends. I'll get there. It just won't be as often as I planned."

Kellyanne spooned into him and began playing with the light hairs on his chest. "Maybe the problems won't be as bad as you think. Besides, if anyone can set things right, you can." A few beats of silence passed. "You never said anything about the reality show. What do you think?"

Walter yawned. "I don't know. What does Adam say?"

Adam Griffie worked out of the William Morris Agency office on Miami Beach. Another mistress benefit. Walter had called in a favor to get Kellyanne representation. The idea had been to lift her acting career off the ground. But sometimes she wondered if it was all just a ruse to keep her distracted. So far, Adam had only served to get her one lousy commercial and a walk-on in some rap video for an artist she'd never heard of.

"I'm going to show him the contract tomorrow," Kellyanne said. "I never thought about a reality show before. It always seemed so stupid. But it'd give me some great exposure. Don't you think?"

Walter was silent.

Kellyanne glanced over to find him asleep. He didn't give a fuck about her career. And suddenly, it struck her. What career? It was more like a delusion than anything else. She'd been at this for eight years. Shit! That was almost an entire decade. And with nothing to show for it. Miami was her third crack at a new city, too.

The first campaign happened in Los Angeles. She was fresh out of college with a degree in theater. As if anyone in Hollywood cared. Most casting agents told Kellyanne she was *too* beautiful— appealing to men but threatening to women. Back then, the executives wanted the next Julia Roberts. Today they wanted the next Katherine Heigl.

A few times, she got lucky. A producer or director or actor with connections would take her out and make vague promises of helping her get work. Always code for "if you sleep with me." Often, she did. But only with the ones she found attractive. It sure beat the rejection battering ram at audition after audition. And it usually included a fabulous dinner and drinks. Still, whatever job materialized turned into nothing. Once she showed up for a two-line party scene, but the lead actress took one look at her and said, "I'm not sharing the screen with her. Fire that bitch." L.A. was hell. In fact, she got out just in time.

She moved to New York to try her luck there. Things were no better, though. People complained about her thick Southern accent. One casting director said, "If we ever decide to do a revival of *Hee-Haw,* we'll give you a call, honey." Bitchy queen.

Kellyanne ended up killing a few years with service-oriented jobs. Like being a greeter at Abercrombie & Fitch. All she had to do was wear bottom-skimming shorts with a tight tank top and flash a smile as people walked inside. She also waited tables at the Coffee Shop on Union Square, thinking it might bring her good karma. After all, Taye Diggs and Jennifer Esposito had once worked there doing the same thing. But nobody ever discovered her.

Except Walter. He sat in her section one morning and flirted outrageously. And it wasn't I'm-an-old-man-and-I'm-just-lonely flirting. It was clearly of the I'm-an-old-man-and-I-want-to-take-you-to-bed variety. She found his cockiness sexy. Plus, he seemed kind, handsome, and easy to talk to. The ultimate seduction was that he appeared genuinely interested in what she had to say. When he asked her back to his hotel, Kellyanne said yes right away. He was sweet, she was bored, and a night at the Four Seasons sounded better than the dump she shared with two sloppy roommates she could barely stand the sight of.

The sex left something to be desired, but he was gentle and tender, almost worshipful. All the kinkier stuff came later—the toys, the let-me-watch-you-pee bit, the dirty talk. But it was basically harmless. Whatever turned him on. There was no pain or humiliation involved.

Convincing her to move to Miami proved easy. Nothing was happening for her in New York, and she missed the sun and the water. So eight years after college, here she was, pushing thirty, schlepping expensive meals, and playing sex kitten to a man older than her father.

Walter had set things up in the way that only a shrewd bastard could. No assets were in her name. Not the condo, not the car. Her entire way of living was on loan. At the snap of his fingers, Kellyanne could be homeless and without transportation. That's why she insisted on working, even if it was just waiting tables at Silk Electric. Having her own source of cash made her feel more in control. And the staff camaraderie was good balm for her soul. Otherwise, she might just waste away hours until Walter decided to walk through the door.

Finally, Kellyanne drifted off to sleep, and the next morning, she woke up to find Walter still there, sipping coffee on the balcony. Her unit was on the forty-first floor, and the sensation of being up so high always made her stomach do somersaults.

"You better be careful," Kellyanne teased, kissing the back of his neck. "Spending the night, hanging around for breakfast. I just might start calling myself *Mrs.* Isherwood."

Walter smiled and took in the view—of her—as the breeze lifted Kellyanne's silk robe and exposed white lace briefs by La Perla, a pair that fit low enough to expose her tan line. He stared silently for a long time and then reached down to adjust himself.

"Did you take another—"

"Yes, I did," he cut in thickly. "It's been a half-hour already, so your breakfast should be ready anytime now."

Kellyanne refused to think of this as a scientific miracle. Those goddamn pills caused more problems than they solved. "I want Adam to look over that contract. Do you think he'll see me without an appointment?"

"Why wouldn't he?"

Kellyanne shrugged. "I don't know. Sometimes it takes him a week to return my calls. I'm not exactly a priority client."

Walter grimaced, reached for his cell phone, scrolled through his stored numbers, and made a selection. "Adam, Walter Isherwood . . . I'm fine, can't complain. Listen, Kellyanne wants to stop by this morning and get your advice on some reality show she's up for . . . I'd consider it a personal favor if you rescheduled that appointment and made time for her . . . Expect her in about an hour or two . . . Thanks, Adam."

Kellyanne shook her head. "I can't even get that man on the phone!"

"That should change," Walter said. "Remind him that he wants a good deal on one of the Indian Creek apartments."

Kellyanne giggled. "I can tell him that?"

"If you're not getting what you need, then absolutely," Walter said. "But I don't think you'll have a problem. Adam understands that one good turn deserves another." He loosened the tie on his robe and let it fall open, exposing another rigid hard-on. "Do you?"

Kellyanne reached for his hand, hoping to pull him inside.

Walter resisted. "Right here," he said. "On the balcony. Show Miami what you do best."

She grabbed a cushion from one of the chairs and threw it down to protect her knees.

Adam Griffie kept her waiting. Big shock. But he let go with an impressive stream of so-glad-to-see-you bullshit the moment his Eva Longoria–look-alike assistant ushered her inside his inner sanctum.

William Morris was the largest and oldest talent agency in the world with offices in Los Angeles, New York, London, and Nashville. That a branch had opened on Miami Beach was a major event. But not, so far, for Kellyanne. Maybe they handled so much Latin talent that they didn't know what to do with a blond girl from Tuscaloosa, Alabama.

Adam sat perched on the edge of his desk—impeccably groomed, well dressed, and very tan. Probably gay, too. Because he didn't seem even remotely affected by her beauty. Instead, he regarded her with something close to annoyance, as if she were yet another bimbo-with-a-dream that some rich bastard had twisted his arm into dealing with. "Walter tells me you're thinking about doing a reality show."

Kellyanne handed over the contract and told Adam about meeting Brad Lucas.

Her reluctant agent's head bobbed knowingly. "*Bonzi*. He's hit the ratings jackpot with his last few projects. Fox has him locked in to an exclusive deal."

"Do you think a show like this could help my career?"

Adam gave her a look that translated, "What career, bitch?" Then he began to casually thumb through the contract. "If the show takes off, you could end up with some celebrity magazine coverage, maybe get an offer from *Playboy*."

"I've *had* an offer from *Playboy*," Kellyanne shot back. "A long time ago. I'm not interested in that." She remembered how close she'd come to posing, though. It was during the L.A. years, and she'd called home to discuss the opportunity with her father, who owned a machine shop.

"Baby, I'd be a hypocritical son of a bitch if I told you not to do it. I've been getting that magazine for years, and those Playmates are somebody's daughters."

It was the closest thing she could expect for a parental endorsement. But she still said no.

"Put it this way, if the show's a hit—reality's tricky but Bonzi's on a hot streak—opportunities will surface," Adam said. "No doubt about that." He continued going through the contract.

"How does it look?" Kellyanne asked.

"Standard. They basically own you for up to a year after the show airs. Until then, any publicity or creative activity has to be approved in advance by the producers."

"But you're my agent. Can't you do better than that?"

Adam shook his head. "Reality's a different animal. Nobody negotiates. You don't want to sign—fine. In five minutes, they can find ten girls on the beach who will." With a shrug, he passed back the bundle of slave pages. "My advice—go for it. What do you have to lose?"

Quite a bit—her anonymity, the control of her image, and her dignity, for starters. She thought about Liza. Oh, God, she'd hate the idea. First, doing the show would mean missing the first few weeks of their vacation, leaving Liza alone to contend with Billie. And even worse, Liza believed reality television was rolling back the progress of the feminist movement.

Kellyanne experienced a pang of shame as she realized that her own life was hardly a step forward for the cause. By signing this contract, she'd simply be trading Walter's rule of law for Bonzi's. Wasn't it time she started living life on her own terms?

But she found herself reaching for a pen and signing on the dotted line.

Billie

FOUR

"I think it's a mistake," Liza said. "Kellyanne's going to regret this. *A reality dating series?* Come on! All the women on those shows are depicted as vulnerable, desperate, or manipulative. One look at the prince, and they're ready to slit their wrists if they don't get chosen. It's disgusting, misogynistic crap."

Billie downed the last of the Angelo Gaja and signaled the waiter for a second bottle. It might be rude to casually add another two hundred and fifty bucks to a bill she had no intention of paying, but if she had to sit here and listen to this shit, then at least she deserved the most expensive wine on the menu.

They were at Savanna's on Elm Street in Southampton. It'd been Liza's idea. And a fucked-up one at that. The restaurant sat right across from the train stop and, on Friday nights, every bitch and bastard migrating from Manhattan mobbed the place. At least the atmosphere was pleasant. Votive candles lined the windowsills and beautiful Grecian columns supported the structure. But the next time she walked through the door, Todd Bana better be her date, not Liza.

"You know what? I'm glad she's doing it," Billie said. "Maybe it'll lead to something. What do you want her to do? Suck that old fuck's cock for condo squatter's rights the rest of her life?"

Embarrassed, Liza glanced around to see if any other patrons had overheard. "*Billie,*" she admonished in a low hiss. "This isn't a tour bus."

Billie rolled her eyes. She didn't care what people thought. "All I'm saying is at least she's doing *something.* Think about it. What has Kellyanne really accomplished in the last ten years?"

Liza was silent.

"Exactly. She's moved from city to city waiting tables, and now she's a private whore for some rich guy in Miami." Billie took a stab at her Chilean sea bass. "Oh, I forgot. She had a nonspeaking part in a tampon commercial and was bikini girl number six in a rap video." With a whoop-dee-doo twirl of her fork, Billie went on. "Shit, maybe the problem is that she doesn't have any talent. I've never seen her act. Have you?"

Liza lengthened her spine defensively. "Of course, she's talented. She has a degree in theater."

Billie cackled just as the waiter returned to go through the ceremony of opening the second bottle. As far as she was concerned, he couldn't pour it fast enough. The first gulp gave her the incentive to continue. "That doesn't mean anything. I have a degree in government, but I'm nobody's mayor. Personally, I think Kellyanne's lazy. She doesn't try that hard, and she's never taken any real acting classes that I know of. All she does is trade on her looks."

Liza mulled this over as she tore off a piece of focaccia bread, brought it to her lips, and then returned it to her plate.

Billie noted the sly maneuver. No wonder she was so skinny. The bitch didn't eat. She just pretended to.

"We shouldn't talk about her this way," Liza said. "It's not fair."

"Why not?" Billie countered. "Whenever the third Musketeer is out of the picture, the other two always talk about her like a dog. It's called friendship."

Liza laughed lightly. "Remind me to stick around all summer." Sipping her wine, she took in the dining room with a circular gaze. "I love to people watch. Don't you? Think of all the plots that are being hatched here tonight."

Billie glanced around and gave a little snort of derision. These status-seeking star fuckers didn't impress her. "Who cares? Anyway, I thought the Hamptons were supposed to be over. Aren't people moving up to Ulster County?"

Liza swirled her wine as if to dismiss the notion altogether. "A few. But it's not like there's a mass exodus. Besides, they've restricted the club scene somewhat. This place will never go out of style." With her fork, she played with the oven-roasted half chicken and moved around the sautéed spinach. But she never ate very much. All of a sudden, she gave Billie a studied once over. "You know, I just saw you about a week ago, and you didn't look this thin. Your hair looks great, too."

Billie finger-combed her shorter locks. Amy had booked her chair time with Paul Podlucky. The master hacked off four inches and gave her a new look with heavy bangs and face-framing layers, insisting that the style would play up her cheekbones. Then he put his color talents to work, taking her base hue a shade lighter and weaving in gold highlights.

But that was the easy secret to tell. Explaining the rapid weight loss? Not so much. Billie had considered a cleansing camp in the Adirondacks—several days of saltwater only, then a strict regimen of greens and supplements. By the end, a girl was supposed to be pounds thinner and positively glowing. It sounded too hard core, though.

Luckily, Todd Bana had turned her on to a better method. They'd been partying into the night. She was drunk. He was high. His coke supply was gone, and for a man fucked up and still going strong at two in the morning, this could be a mood killer. But Todd had a quick solution.

They ran across the street to an all-night doughnut shop. He touched his nose as he made eye contact with a black guy loiter-ing near the counter. The man approached. A discreet exchange followed. And back they went.

At first, Billie wanted no part of it. Crystal meth? That drug was for freaks and fags. But then Todd gave it the Tony Robbins pitch.

"It's not just for trailer trash," he'd said, as if reading her mind. "In Hollywood, lots of executives are into it. A buddy in L.A. gave me a hit of his stash once. It's like fucking rocket fuel. Sex is *insane* on this shit. Oh, and talk about an awesome diet boost." He snapped his fingers. "Ten pounds in a week. Gone. Just that quick. You have to be careful, though. Only use it in moderation. Like any drug, I guess." He laughed. "Or else you could end up tricking for a street fix on your way to rehab."

Todd crushed the rock into powder. For his own hit, he tapped some onto a tiny square of toilet paper and swallowed it, telling her that pro tweakers called this parachuting. For Billie, he did some-thing even more wild. He loaded up a syringe with meth powder and water and shot the mixture straight up her ass. Users referred to this as a booty bump. And it was *fanfuckingtastic.*

But what Todd told her about sex on meth was a lie. Insane? Hardly. The experience went so far beyond that. Every touch . . . every sensation . . . every erogenous pulse was heightened to the *n*th degree. The euphoria stretched on and on. It was binge fucking. Completely mad. They did it for hours. The frightening thing was that Billie craved more than even a cranked-up Todd could hu-manly offer. She felt like taking on a football team. And given the chance, probably would have. It was no wonder so many crystal addicts ended up HIV-positive.

Even after the high, she still had killer energy. And no appetite. Billie didn't eat for four days. It was ridiculous. But in a good way. Coming off the bender, she looked almost svelte. So she begged Todd for another hit. Not because she needed it. Just to get rid of the remaining weight. One more booty bump.

Todd obliged her but didn't indulge himself. His next several days were slammed with business on the West Coast. The fever rush of her second dose worked the same voodoo as the first. *Var-o-o-o-o-o-o-m!* Todd did what he could to satisfy her and then told her to go fuck a doorknob if she had to.

Instead, Billie stayed up for hours and wrote songs. The inspiration was macrocosmic, like receiving an internal telegram from the fourth dimension. Creativity flowed. Her tunes wrote themselves. The process was sublime. She opened a window. The noise from the street below took on a natural rhythm. She wrote lyrics. She crafted melodies. It was subatomic harmony. And she couldn't wait to show them to Todd. As soon as he got back from Los Angeles. Once he heard Billie's new stuff, then he'd ditch that White Tiger idea. Outside writers and producers? Bullshit. After all, she was no studio puppet like Britney. She was Billie Fucking Shelton!

The second time around also transformed her body. Oh, God, she looked fabulous. She was lean and cut. Losing more weight in her face enhanced her cheekbones. Now they were as sheer as a Mexican cliff.

A booking agent from Marilyn, Inc. stopped her on Park Avenue and wanted to know if she was already a model or interested in becoming one. Billie accepted the card and promised to call and set up an appointment.

Todd loved the idea but told her to wait. Maybe when the new album was ready to drop. He said everything had to be planned with military precision, that launching her new image would be like going to war.

It was an interesting comparison. Billie just hoped that Todd had better strategic instincts than Cheney, Rumsfeld, and the other neocon assholes who'd managed to fuck up the Middle East.

"How did you lose the weight so fast?" Liza was asking.

Before Billie could toss out a lie, a dead-sexy man approached the table and smiled intimately at Liza. "And so the season begins."

Billie knew the accent. Definitely Texas. Obviously, he'd worked hard to get rid of it, but a slight twang remained. She'd performed enough concerts in Austin to recognize it. His impossibly white teeth were glinting. And she was swooning. Literally. Like an eleven-year-old girl in the face of a Zac Efron sighting. She felt caught up in the tidal wave of his charisma. The way he filled out a simple pink Oxford and a pair of old jeans. It was sick.

Liza beamed back a knowing smile that telegraphed a certain smugness to the current population at Savanna's. *We have an inside joke. Aren't we clever?* She seemed almost lit from within.

None of this was lost on the woman accompanying the object of immediate lust. She lingered just a few steps behind—icy and perpetually pissed off—like the always-ignored wife of a rock star.

"Where's the husband I'm supposed to whip in beach volleyball?" he asked.

"Back in the city waiting for a fire to start," Liza replied. Then she gestured to Billie and made the necessary introductions. "March and I scream at each other once a week on *The Roundtable.*"

"You're Billie Shelton the singer, right?" he asked, his face bright, his tone hopeful. There was almost a fan boy quality to his expression.

Billie nodded.

"I love your stuff. I just downloaded some of my favorite tracks onto my iPhone."

Liza stared up at March in complete dismay. "*You* like Billie Shelton music?"

"What's wrong with that?" He glanced at Billie, then back to Liza.

Billie wanted an answer, too. Should it be such a fucking shock that someone appreciated her songs?

Liza seemed to pick up on the instant resentment. "Don't get me wrong, Billie. I'm only surprised because March here is a young Republican. I thought Lee Greenwood might be more his speed." The smirk on her face was intended for him.

"Now why would you think that?" March wondered easily. "I don't assume that all feminists listen to Melissa Etheridge."

"What's your favorite song of Billie's?" Liza asked. There was a challenge in her tone, as if she half expected him to be unable to name one.

March winked at Billie. "'Make Me Laugh and Make Me Come and I'll Fucking Marry You.'" He paused a beat. "That's a personal favorite." Suddenly, he reached back to clasp the forgotten girl's hand. "Forgive my rudeness." Then he proceeded to introduce as his fiancée a cold bitch named Amaryllis Hartman.

Billie hated her on principle. Because she had the impervious countenance of a girl who came from real money. Because her aloof, patrician blond beauty made for a legitimate comparison to Gwyneth Paltrow. And because March had asked her to marry him.

It surprised Billie that she was crushing so hard and so quickly. And over a man like March. God, he wasn't her type at all. Usually, she went for the guys who had a prison yard's worth of tattoos running down their arms and legs. Or a son of a bitch like Todd Bana— he was young and successful in a cutthroat industry, which required a certain amount of sleaze. Plus, he could advance her career. That made it love.

And here stood March Donaldson. A conservative Texas male. Jesus Christ, this didn't make any sense. They were polar opposites. He was a political animal. She was almost thirty and had never registered to vote. But he was without a doubt the hottest guy Billie had ever met. A stunning specimen of man.

She noticed Amaryllis discreetly pinch the palm of his hand with her perfectly manicured nails.

"We need to run," March said. "It's Amaryllis's birthday."

The luckiest whore in the room winced as he mentioned this. Probably because it only delayed their escape.

Billie merely stared back impassively.

Liza started in with predictable and meaningless best wishes.

"Her parents are hosting a party in the outdoor pavilion," March went on. "Come have a glass of champagne before you leave."

Amaryllis managed a tight, insincere smile. "It's just family and a few close friends." Her implicit message came through loud and clear: *In other words, not you two bitches.*

Liza watched them go.

Billie clocked her reaction. "Are you fucking him?"

Appalled, Liza drew back. "What? No!"

"But you want to," Billie accused.

Liza put on her best you-must-be-crazy face. *"March Donaldson?* Billie, the man stands for everything that I fight against. We've found a little corner of the earth where we can deal with each other. It may look a bit flirty, but it's completely harmless. So *no,* I don't want to."

Billie drank deeply of her wine. "Well, I do."

Liza's brow went up.

Billie grinned.

"Isn't he a little traditional for you? March actually goes to church." One beat. "And I'm pretty sure that he loves his mother."

"Okay, I have to admit—that's some scary shit."

Liza laughed.

"But he probably only goes to pray for his soul. I bet he's a secret party animal."

"Not like you're used to," Liza said. "He's a Texas fraternity boy. It's just beer kegs and yelling at the television during football games."

Billie didn't buy that. A gut feeling told her that March Donaldson was a closet freak. And her instincts were rarely wrong about such things.

"Anyway, he's engaged," Liza said dismissively. "But Amaryllis seems nice."

"A fiancée wouldn't stop a man like that. A wife wouldn't, either. And even from that brief exchange, we both know that Amaryllis is a cunt."

The waiter swooped in to take away their dinner plates and inquire about dessert.

Billie announced her intention to finish the wine.

Liza ordered coffee.

Billie noticed that Liza seemed relieved when they moved past the subject of March. She didn't quite believe her friend's denial. How could Liza be content with a man like Justin? Okay, physically, he was flawless. But Liza was such an intellectual creature. March's politics might take a hard turn to the right, but at least the man could think. When Justin wasn't pumping iron, he just sat around waiting for an alarm bell to ring.

There was real electricity between Liza and March. Billie was almost drunk, but she could still read a situation. It didn't matter, though. Not now. March was fair game. She'd given Liza every opportunity to stake a claim of interest, even on a look-but-don't-touch fantasy level. So Billie would just have to take the woman at her word.

They lingered at the table, nibbling on the peanut brittle teasers, talking about their first weekend in the summer share. They intended to spend most of the daylight hours working on their tans. With a two-week head start, they just might be able to stand next to Kellyanne without looking like a couple of ghosts.

Beyond that, the evenings were all planned out. Reservations at Nick & Toni's for Saturday night. Half a dozen cocktail parties on Sunday. Film director Harrison Beck's big Memorial Day bash in Sagaponack on Monday. Too bad they had to be escorted there by K.K., the fat queen. Billie had seen him on television leading a panel to dish red carpet fashion after an awards show. Cartoon fags were so annoying.

When the check arrived, Billie made no move to contribute. It wasn't her idea to come here. Liza didn't blanch, though. With tip, the bill had to be almost eight hundred dollars. But she just threw down her American Express Black. Must be nice. Amy lectured Billie regularly on cutting down her spending. Meanwhile, Liza was making money in her sleep. And for what—raising hell about some stupid slasher movie? Some people had all the luck.

As they made their way out of Savanna's, Billie announced, "I'm going to the ladies' room. Meet you outside, okay?"

Liza seemed to think nothing of it and ventured on.

Billie fell back, waiting for her to exit, then made a beeline for the pavilion. There was a tentlike structure. More Grecian columns. A beautiful garden. But with balloons everywhere and a table chockablock full of gifts, it looked as if Amaryllis was celebrating her sweet sixteen.

Suddenly, March appeared and offered a flute of champagne. "Where's Liza?"

Billie drank up and passed the empty glass back to him. "Waiting for me outside."

He took a step closer. "That's not very sociable."

"I can't stay, either. I just wanted to give you my number." She slipped a scrap of paper into his front pocket.

He smiled. "Is that the kind of information that could get me into trouble?"

Billie licked her lips. In her white jeans and black lace camisole top, she knew that she looked hot. "Use it. Find out for yourself."

March opened his mouth to speak.

But Billie was already gone.

From across the room, Amaryllis stood watching.

Billie matched her glare for glare. Then she silently mouthed the words, "Happy birthday, bitch," and walked out.

Liza

FIVE

Liza had forecasted the sequence of events like a gifted palm reader. On Sunday, Thursday's taping of *The Round-table* aired on CNBC. Now it was Monday, and her dig at Harrison Beck led the Page Six gossip parade in *The New York Post*.

SIZE MATTERS

Laughing about the size of a guy's . . . *ahem* . . . equipment is like Kryptonite to the male ego. Just ask that hunky morning news anchor whose wife was overheard complaining about his true measurement. Now **Harrison Beck**, director of the current blockbuster *Watch Her Bleed,* is seeing green. Fashion-able feminist spin girl **Liza Pike** recently told TV viewers that the real issue behind the high female body count in his creepy and very violent new movie is the filmmaker's tiny tool. Any ex-lovers care to confirm or deny this?

"Liza Pike, you are a witchy, witchy woman," K.K. sang. "Did the Eagles write that song about you?"

They were crammed into the stylist's Porsche 911 Carrera 4 and cruising down Parsonage Lane in Sagaponack, on their way to Harrison Beck's Memorial Day bash.

"I can't believe I'm helping you crash this party! If only I'd known you were going to insult the host's dick on national television!" K.K. squealed gleefully, no doubt adoring the fact that just by showing up with Liza, he was tangentially linking himself to the mini-scandal.

"I don't see the big deal," Billie said, folded into the backseat and still hung over from the Saturday–Sunday party gauntlet. "If it's not true, all he has to do is pull down his pants and prove it."

Liza and K.K. laughed.

Before eighties excess set in, Sagaponack had been a forgotten little hamlet of the Hamptons, home to sweeping acres of potato fields. Parsonage Lane ran through the center of what were once large tracts of agricultural land. But you could only build so much in trendier East Hampton and Southampton. So multimillion-dollar homes were now lined up and down these fields like toy soldiers.

K.K. pulled up behind a gleaming BMW and shut off the engine.

Liza admired the sight of rolling farmland and, in the distance, gorgeous beachfront. "Does he own all of this?"

"Some of that land's reserved," K.K. said. "But Harrison's house sits on about seven acres. Not a bad spread."

Liza ran the calculations. Easily $8 million, if not more. Impressive. And this property was acquired before his *Watch Her Bleed* windfall.

Liza, Billie, and K.K. tumbled out of the car and fell into step with a few others making their way up the path. Harrison Beck lived in a two-story English Country estate with an adjacent carriage house, both with wood-shingled roof and exterior. There was a sunken Har-Tru tennis court, too.

Familiar faces dotted the lawn and splashed in the pool. So far, it seemed like the same social animals attended the same parties.

Forget fresh conversation until Labor Day. What did people in the Hamptons say to each other by the Fourth of July?

K.K. offered up both arms. "Shall we, ladies?"

Just as Liza moved to accept the gesture, her BlackBerry vibrated. Scooping it out of her Hermès bag, she read JUSTIN CALLING on the screen. "Give me one minute," she said, stepping off to the side.

"Hey, baby. I miss you." His tone was overly sweet.

Right away Liza sensed a hidden agenda. "Miss you, too." A rote response. But did she actually mean it? In all truth, the weekend had been a nonstop whirlwind, and Justin had scarcely entered her mind. Or maybe she'd deliberately put him out of it.

"You having a good time?" he asked. Too solicitous. Something had to be up.

"It's been fun. We're hitting our last party right now, and then I'll be home in time for dinner."

There was a pregnant pause.

"A buddy in Brooklyn called and needs some help with his car. We're gonna get a racquetball game in first and then take care of things in his garage. I'll probably be late getting back. Don't wait up, okay?"

"A husband who's really missing his wife wouldn't make plans like that."

"Come on, baby. He needs my help." Justin laughed a little. "Carl didn't marry a rich woman like I did. They can't afford to take the car to the shop."

The sound of his voice and the content of his answer made her smile. Maybe she did miss him. Liza thought back to the big romantic plans she had in store after dragging him home from Pila Anderson's book party. But Justin pleaded a stomach upset from the food and spent the rest of the night crashed in front of the plasma screen, watching *Braveheart* for the millionth time.

A few incidents like that had now hardened into a sinister trend. Sex had practically come to a full stop. At first, Liza thought it'd been her doing, but now she believed otherwise. Justin had the uncanny ability to be absent when a husband's ardor and affection would be expected. After a few nights apart. On a lazy weekend morning unburdened by work or appointments. He always had something to do, some other place to be.

Liza wondered if her success, ambition, and earning power were part of the reason. Did Justin feel emasculated? The boys at his station house teased him about the fact that she'd kept her maiden name. How much did that really bother him?

But the more she tried to figure Justin out, the more he perplexed her. It'd be strange if the money she made caused him to feel diminished in some way. Because he sure didn't have a problem spending it. And nothing seemed to truly reach him. She could pinpoint the most emotion he'd ever expressed. It happened during those first few nights together, when he openly mourned his fallen comrades from September 11.

Oh, God, what she wouldn't give for a little bit of feeling! Here she was flooding her body with hormones to ensure the chance of one day having his baby, yet he could never conjure up so much as, "How are you doing?" Justin just blindly marched on—casual, carefree, always up for a good time with the guys. Except for work, he lived like a college boy who never went to class. Only lately, like one who rarely seemed interested in sex.

Suddenly, a male hand gently covered Liza's eyes. "Boo!"

She pulled it away, spinning around to find Tom Shapiro.

Embarrassed to discover that she was on the phone, Tom mouthed an apology and started off.

Liza reached out for his hand to make him stay. "I guess I'll see you later then," she told Justin. "Love you."

"Me, too." And then he hung up.

Leaning in to kiss Tom, she let out a half-sigh, half-groan.

"Everything okay?"

"I'm fine. It's just my fucking husband." She waved for Billie and K.K. to go inside without her.

"What is it with women in New York?" Tom wondered. "It's either the fucking husband you married or the fucking husband you can't find."

Liza grinned. "I don't think that's unique to Manhattan. It's a fairly universal complaint."

"So what's the issue? I've watched enough *Dr. Phil* to offer something."

"We live totally separate lives," Liza said matter-of-factly.

"Don't change that," Tom advised. "As I understand, it's the only thing keeping most marriages alive today."

Liza laughed and took a step back to admire *The Roundtable* host in his striped Izod shirt, weathered khakis, and battered canvas boat shoes. "I didn't expect to find you in this crowd."

"Harrison must be feeling guilty for turning down the interview. His office Fed Exed an invitation." Tom gave her a pointed look. "You're the real surprise guest. It took some balls to show up here."

Liza curled her lips mischievously. "I'm not exactly a guest. I'm crashing."

"Let me upgrade that to balls of steel. It's no wonder you're pissed off at home. You don't need a husband. You need a wife."

"Please. Sometimes I feel like I have one. I make all the money, and I can't seem to get laid. This is supposed to be progress?"

Tom chuckled. "It's the alpha woman/beta male syndrome. I can actually help with this one."

Liza folded her arms and stared back expectantly. "I'm listening, Dr. Phil."

"You might need reassurance that you're still feminine."

Liza rolled her eyes. "I've got that part covered. I need reassurance that my husband still has a dick. But thanks for trying, Tom." She began walking toward the front entrance.

Tom picked up his stride to join her. "I should probably stick to politics."

"Probably," Liza agreed. "But actually, talking about this helped. I might write about it in my next column."

"Good idea. Let his firefighter buddies read about how he can't get it up. That'll make him horny."

"They don't read. Not past the sports section anyway." Reaching the precipice of the wide-open door, Liza hesitated.

"You can't turn back now. He's already seen you," Tom whispered, cutting his eyes to a man halfway up the staircase.

Harrison Beck stared down at the latest arrivals, a big Montecristo jutting out of his mouth like an exclamation point. Going bald but not trying to hide it, he had an aura that screamed volcanic confidence. He was a middle-aged, unpolished Jewish-Italian tough guy of average height, his body hairy, taut, and compact.

One look into his blue-gray eyes and Liza knew that he didn't sleep much, that his neurotic, hyperachieving ways woke him up at three A.M. with night sweats, that his favorite pastime was riding in his Ferrari with a girlfriend born the year Internet service was invented.

The presence of Liza and Tom created a ripple of awareness in the big yet charming house—at least six thousand square feet and tastefully decorated, with large public rooms flowing easily into one another.

Harrison's guests knew she was the publicity-hungry feminist who engineered social takedowns dressed up in political drag. They knew he was the young and on-the-rise television host, rumored to be closeted but still frustratingly ambiguous about his sexual orientation.

Harrison locked a ray-gun gaze onto Liza and stepped down to the bottom of the stairs. "You've got a bad source of information." He was still chewing on the cigar that seemed to be smoking him. Then he unfastened his Gap jeans and pushed down his Burberry boxers, giving her the full monty.

Everybody in the immediate vicinity howled, causing a stampede from other areas of the house to see what was happening.

Harrison Beck was uncircumcised. And he had nothing to be ashamed about. Even without the benefit of an erection, no one could deny that the man was impressively hung.

Mortified, Liza just stood there on the French limestone floor. She was famous for always getting in the last word. Right now she was momentarily speechless. But then she regained her composure. "That's a neat trick. You unzip your pants and your brains fall out."

By this point, a standing-room-only crowd had gathered, so there was a bigger audience for Liza's punch line, which she'd actually pinched from a Jackie Collins rant about Hollywood men. Original or not, the laughter was deafening.

A flush of embarrassment started at Harrison's neck and spread all the way to his cheeks. Finally, he pulled up his jeans and gave her a conciliatory shake of the head. "Show's over!" he shouted to the masses. "Now everybody get drunk and forget this happened!"

Liza smiled. A man with a sense of humor about himself. No reason to vote him off the island . . . *yet.*

Harrison approached and boldly took her hand. "Walk with me." He started out in a rush, pulling her with him.

Liza turned back to see Tom staring at her in startled amusement. Billie and K.K. were nowhere in sight. She struggled to keep up as Harrison bounded down the porch and cut between the main house and the carriage house, heading directly into an expansive stretch of field. "Where are you taking me?"

"Someplace where's there's no audience, no camera, and no microphone," Harrison growled good naturedly. "That probably scares the shit out of you."

Liza tottered behind him, feeling like a total spasmodic, her spike-heeled Manolos doing little to help her navigate the earth like a true farm girl. "Not really. The scariest place for me is any multiplex showing your crap movie."

Harrison laughed heartily. "The studio says it'll top a hundred million within twenty-one days."

"Congratulations. Knowing Hollywood, that means a sequel's in the works. How many ways will you hack women to death next time around?"

"You're wrong about my movie. You just don't get it."

Liza stopped dead in her tracks. "What's to get about tits, ass, and gore? Besides sick to my stomach."

"I don't hate women," Harrison said, finally taking the cigar out of his mouth. "You can spout off about me having a cocktail-wiener dick. I don't care about that. But don't lay this bullshit misogynist label on me. I'm on friendly terms with both of my ex-wives. I've got three daughters. I take good care of my mother—"

"Who are you trying to convince here?" Liza cut in. "Me or yourself?"

His face broke out into a maniacal smile, and he raised his hands, shaking them as if to strangle her. "Shit! You're impossible!"

"That doesn't answer my question."

Harrison walked away, then turned around and pointed his finger at her. "You know what? You're a goddamn fraud."

Now Liza started after him, incensed with fury. "*I'm* a fraud?"

"There were great parts for women in my picture," Harrison said passionately. "It was a smart, literate script. Those characters were public intellectuals, politicians, heads of industry. I've heard you bitch about the lousy roles for actresses in film today. I do something that makes it better, and you're still busting my balls."

Liza laughed at him. "So *Watch Her Bleed* actually has a profeminist agenda? Oh, excuse me. I take everything back now."

"It's an homage to the slasher film," he began, employing a tone that implied teacher to dense pupil. "Remember those? *Halloween, Friday the 13th, Slumber Party Massacre*. The women in those movies were either getting caught naked in the woods with the high school quarterback or heading down into a dark basement in nothing but a short towel. *Watch Her Bleed* is—"

"Not much better and maybe even worse," Liza cut in savagely. "In your movie, the audience—mostly young males, mind you—*participates* with the psycho in voyeurism as he stalks these women. When he kills, they celebrate with him. Hooray! He chopped up the congresswoman fighting for equal pay in the workplace." She rolled her eyes. "So what's the message to an impressionable teenage mind? I'll tell you what it is. Women who achieve their goals and have strong opinions should be chain-sawed. Welcome to high art, Harrison Beck style."

"That's your warped point of view!" Harrison thundered. "And it's bullshit! People like you can find a crazy angle in anything. You're just as bad as that dead asshole Jerry Falwell. He thought Tinky Winky was sending gay messages to three-year-olds. Your take on my movie is just as fucked up."

Liza wanted to scream. To be compared to that fascist pig was the ultimate abuse. "Hide behind your paint-by-numbers politics all you want. Hopefully, you and your therapist will figure out the real issue one day."

"Speaking of issues, what's yours?" Harrison asked, his tone ominous.

Liza didn't answer.

"You parade around like this tough feminist with all the answers, only you dress like a *Maxim* girl. And the first thing you do after Osama and his crew attack is run out and marry a fireman. Talk about mixed messages."

Liza stood stock still and silent—a resistance to her immediate impulse to yell, "Fuck you!" and run back toward the house. Suddenly, she felt self-conscious in her Chloe number, the short white sleeveless tunic with beaded fringe, wondering if she looked like a bimbo. God, he knew how to give as good as he got. First Jerry Falwell and now her clothes. And she didn't even want to factor the damage to her psyche for the crack about Justin. "Touché," she said quietly.

Harrison made a sudden retreat inward, focusing his gaze on the sprawling land. "You know what? I moved here as a teenager," he said wistfully. "About thirty years ago. The fields used to stretch all the way to the dunes. And when you stood along the shore, you could look out as far as the eye could see and only find four or five houses, six at the most. Now look."

"It's still beautiful," Liza murmured, knowing that the words rang hollow in the actual presence of overdevelopment.

Harrison sighed. "Yeah, I guess it is." He looked at her and smiled. "So are the gloves off now?"

She averted her eyes and pretended to take in the scenery. "For the moment, I guess."

"Have dinner with me tonight."

"I can't."

"Why?"

"I came here with friends."

"That's not a reason."

Liza faced him now. "Okay, how's this for a reason—I don't want to."

"Liar."

She gave him half a smile and started back toward the house.

"Can I tell you a secret?" Harrison shouted after her. "I got a hard-on when we were arguing! You know what that means, don't you? The sex would be great! And you've seen what I have to offer!"

Liza broke out into a run, moving fast to get away from him. Almost impossible in these fucking heels, but she gave it a go. She was laughing. She was blushing. Because she knew that the son of a bitch was right.

And it scared the hell out of her.

Billie

SIX

Exactly four days.

That's how long it took March Donaldson to call. The distraction saved Billie from a murder charge. She couldn't decide who she wanted to kill more—that son-of-a-bitch label president Todd Bana or her goddamn manager Amy Dando. Hell, it was a toss-up.

Todd landed on her shit list first. He'd just returned from Los Angeles, and getting in to see him took more trouble than it was worth. All because of Van, his fiercely protective assistant, who treated Billie like some cruise ship singer angling for audition time.

"Todd's in the office but unavailable at the moment." After three calls, Van was still blowing her off.

Billie went ballistic. "Listen, pretty boy, you may kiss his ass, but I actually do what you fantasize about—I suck his cock! Now get him on the goddamn phone!"

A minute later Todd picked up the line. "Billie, why are you terrorizing my assistant?"

"This is the third time I've called. Doesn't that bitchy fag know to put me through?"

71

"He's not supposed to. I'm swamped. It's the first day after a holiday weekend, and I'm just back from L.A. Give me a chance to dig out from under. I'll—"

"Take me to lunch," Billie insisted. "You have to eat, and I'm starving. There's something I'm dying to show you."

"I'm already booked."

"So cancel. A week ago, I was swallowing your cum. Now I can't get a lousy lunch?"

"Fuck!" Todd yelled, exasperated but still in good humor. "I've got a Mariah on my hands! A royal pain in the ass!"

Billie laughed as she thought about being compared to the superdiva.

"I'll have Van get us a table at Sixty-Six. Meet me there at one."

Billie walked in at one-thirty. Why should she bust her ass to show up on time when she was the fucking talent? Todd seemed pissed off, even as he chowed down on steamed lobster claws.

Billie ignored his mood and glanced around, taking in the sumptuous details of chef-entrepreneur Jean-Georges Vongerichten's Chinese-on-acid eatery. The Eames chairs. The Saarinen tables. The waitress flitting around in a Vivienne Tam–designed uniform. It was an explosion of modernism—frosted glass, steel mesh, resin— courtesy of architect Richard Meier. Too bad it'd soon bite the dust and reopen as a sushi-and-soba restaurant. She loved this place just as it was.

Billie dreamed of the day when she could afford to buy a massive apartment, gut it, and then hire a mastermind like Meier to reinvent *her* space. It could happen. All she needed was one big record. Everything else would fall into place—the tours, the merchandising, the endorsements.

Jessica Simpson popped into her mind. That screaming bitch rang the bell with her stupid reality series first, after which the music kicked back into gear, followed by the commercial offers. The ditz was a complete joke, but she was still worth megamillions. If Kellyanne got lucky like that with *Soul Mates*, then Billie just might have to kill herself. Here she was, trying to do it the old-fashioned way—on sheer grit and talent—while someone less deserving could easily leapfrog ahead. All because of some cheesy reality show.

Billie slipped into the seat opposite Todd and grabbed a lobster claw that reeked of ginger. "Hey, thanks for waiting."

"You asked for this meeting, and I've been sitting here for thirty fucking minutes. What are you dying to show me?"

"*Relax.*"

As if on cue, the waitress appeared.

Billie asked for fried crab, squab, and scallion pancakes. By the time it arrived, she might take half a bite of each. But so what? Olympic was paying. Glancing down, she took note of Todd's water. "You're not drinking?"

"I'm jet-lagged, and I'm jammed up with meetings. Need to keep my head clear." He checked his watch—a flashy Rolex. "I squeezed you in. Let's get on with this."

"As always, impatient and not enthusiastic enough. Do you approach everything the same way you give head?" Billie smirked.

Todd surrendered a reluctant grin. "Okay. You got me to smile."

"What's your problem?"

"Just a rough day." He rubbed his eyes. "So show me this big surprise."

Billie reached for a spiral notebook and slid it across the table. On the night she had written the new songs, her lyrics ended up all over the place—on cocktail napkins, paper towels, old receipts, utility bills, any scrap of paper she could get her hands on. But she had transcribed everything into the notebook—by her own hand—to prove to Todd that her creative block was a problem of the past.

"What's this?" He stared at the offering as if it were a mess on the side of the road.

Billie leaned in meaningfully. "Some new songs. I'm still working on the melodies, but the lyrics . . . shit, Todd, I feel like I've come up with . . . *Dick Magnet: The Sequel! This* should've been the follow-up to my first album."

Todd nodded vaguely, opened the notebook, and began flipping through the pages. He scanned the words with something close to boredom. At the end, he gave her an indifferent shrug. "I thought we agreed to use outside writers and producers."

"That was before!"

"Before what?"

"Before I got my muse back!"

Todd closed the cover and pushed her handwritten heart and soul back across the table. "I know what your muse is." His tone was cold. "I'm the guy who shot it up your ass. Remember?"

For a moment, Billie believed the scene was happening outside of her own body. It felt that horrible. "This has nothing to do with the meth! These are great songs!"

Todd shook his head. "They're shit, Billie."

"But you hardly—"

He held up a hand to stop her. "I saw enough. Now listen to me. The old Billie Shelton is over. She's finished. Do you have any idea how many CDs you sold last week?"

She stared back at him.

"Less than a hundred."

The news flattened her spirit.

"Whatever force existed for *Dick Magnet* worked in that moment. But you didn't keep it going. Or maybe it was never meant to continue. Who knows?"

"But when I tour—"

"By the end of your last tour, you were selling maybe sixty percent of the house. Amy would have trouble keeping you on the road in today's market. And whatever discipline you had is gone. You'd probably cancel shows at the last minute, like that train wreck Amy Winehouse. But at least she's got the popularity to back it up. You'd have to be paired with a hotter act or start booking clubs."

Billie fingered the notebook with longing. Maybe Todd was lying. He had to be. This was just a bullshit game to rattle her confidence. That way she'd say yes to all his new ideas, like some scared little girl. The music industry was so fucking sleazy. "You know what I feel like right now?" she launched in hotly. "I feel like I'm in the porn business, and you're some producer who's brainwashing me with doomsday career talk just so I'll sign on to do a gang bang."

Todd lifted his eyebrows and sipped his water. "That's quite an analogy."

Billie's fists hit the table. "Don't fucking patronize me!"

"I don't have a chance," Todd said with a calmness that infuriated her. "You're too busy patronizing yourself. Or going psycho." He shook his head and laughed a little. "What goes on in that mind of yours? Right now, White Tiger is the most sought after production team out there. They decide who they want to work with, and they want to work with you. It's just going to take a little time. We're waiting for their schedule to open up."

Billie looked at Todd. Really looked at him. And the sexy bastard held up under the scrutiny.

"I thought you were on board with this," he continued. I thought you wanted a big radio hit."

All of a sudden, Billie's eyes welled up with tears. "I did . . . I do . . . It's just . . . I still think my songs are good."

"No one's telling you to stop writing."

She gently wiped her eyes with her fingers and wondered how fucked her makeup was. "Yeah, telling me they're shit is great encouragement. Thanks."

Todd gave her a half smile. "What can I say? I shoot straight. If you like writing songs, do it for yourself. Just don't expect me to let you record them. Not on my label anyway."

"You missed your calling," Billie said. "You should be doing motivational speeches."

This made him laugh. The expression on his handsome face was one of bemused affection. "Jesus, Billie, you're like a relic from the seventies. It's all sex, drugs, and rock and roll to you. Music used to be *it*. But you can't think that way anymore. Not in today's culture. There's so much fucking noise. You've got cell phones, video games, DVDs, iPods, high-speed Internet, reality TV. Shit, the list goes on forever. It takes so much to break through all that and create any kind of impact. These days you need a radio hit, a L'Oréal commercial, and maybe a sex tape floating around to be considered a star."

"Are you suggesting that we set up a camera in your bedroom?"

Lasciviously, Todd flickered his tongue. "Nah. That shit's over. We partied. We swung from the chandelier. But we better keep it strictly business from now on. Things will be intense enough. Don't think I won't miss it, though. You've got a magic pussy." He laughed. "And unlike your lyrics, that's not the meth talking."

Billie couldn't believe it. He was flushing her songs down the crapper and breaking up with her, too. And lunch hadn't even been served yet. What a fucking prick!

"Be glad you're a dyke, Amy, because men are shit."

Billie was still in TriBeCa, stomping down Church Street and blabbing on her cell phone. She knew Liza lived nearby but couldn't remember where. Hell, forget it. Amy would just have to listen to her bitch. She raged on.

"I don't know what the fuck they want. I'm a great broad. I'm as wild as a horse's ass. I can hold my liquor. I can handle my drugs. Think about it. I'm full of hell and always ready for sex. Yet men consistently use me like a rest stop on their way to a *real* girlfriend. Did I tell you about March, that hot guy I met in the Hamptons over the weekend? He's engaged to some frigid thing named Amaryllis. One drink and I bet you have to hold that bitch's head over the toilet. Anyway, Todd's not a serious loss. I would've dumped him in the middle of a blow job for a chance at this March guy. But it still hurts that he unloaded me first."

"Billie, I can't do this right now," Amy said tightly.

"Do what?"

"Play therapist because you did some stupid shit like screw Todd Bana. I've got a million things to do."

"If I needed a therapist, do you really think I'd call you?"

"Then what do you want?"

"What I want is for you to act like the fucking manager I pay you to be and make that asshole take my new songs seriously!"

"Let me refresh your memory since it seems those drugs you handle so well have fried your brain. The last time I tried to act like your manager, we were sitting in Todd's office. That's when you ignored my objections and agreed to this style overhaul in the first place. I haven't even heard these songs yet. But what does it matter? You'll probably jump back into bed with him and say yes to recording a Christmas album with the Wiggles."

Billie pictured Amy in her cramped little office on Broadway, hunched over the shabby desk that was always adrift in CDs, paper, pictures, and music paraphernalia. "I can bring the songs to you now."

Amy sighed. "Just wait until I get back."

"From where?"

"I leave for Japan in the morning."

"What for?"

"One of my new acts is on her first promotional tour. She's too young to handle Tokyo alone, her parents are idiots, and I don't trust the label rep."

Billie hated to hear about Amy's other clients. They always seemed to be getting deals and perks that eluded her. Olympic had never sent Billie Shelton overseas. "So you'll hold her hand across the fucking world, but you won't take a minute to look at my new songs?"

"I have to go. I'll call you when I get back."

Billie started to protest. But Amy had already hung up.

For a long moment she stood there in the middle of the sidewalk, the phone still in her hand, feeling as if everything was slipping away.

The ring startled her. At first, she assumed it was Amy calling back to say bring the songs over, but Billie didn't recognize the incoming number. "Hello?"

It was March Donaldson.

Most men punched the clock. They went down on a girl because it was the polite thing to do and usually guaranteed a blow job in return. But March ate Billie like she was his last meal on earth.

She lifted her hips to meet his mouth. She was sweating. She was clawing his back. She was crushing his skull with the pressure of her thighs.

Oh, God! It was the best ever.

He started slow, breathing hot breath onto her panties. Then he ironed out her labia with big, soft, lingering licks as she squirmed under his expert attention.

The man was a fucking Jedi master of the art. He knew how to circle up and around the clitoris and back again. He knew how to suck her magic button into his mouth and lick it at the same time.

But when he dove in face-first and nuzzled her with his nose, she wanted to have his baby. And by the time he did a simultaneous up-lick with his tongue and downward tug with his fingers, she was lost in a Richter-scale orgasm. Again. And again.

Even after March rolled over onto his back and lit up some hellacious smelling herb, Billie was still having little convulsions. "Well . . . that was certainly worth a ride on the Jitney."

He pinched the joint and puckered his lips, dragging slow and deep.

"You smoke that like a pro," Billie said.

He smiled. "It's not just rock stars and snowboarders who appreciate."

"So tell me. Are there more Republicans like you out there? I just might have to join the party."

March laughed.

They passed the joint back and forth.

Billie noticed that his upper lip was swollen. She started to giggle. "I can't believe it! You've got a fat lip from eating me out!"

"My tongue is numb, too," March said. "What can I say? I love my work."

She admired him. Sprawled across the white sheets. Naked, tan, and more gorgeous than any man had a right to be.

"Usually, I come while I'm doing it," he went on. "I don't even have to touch my cock. I just get so excited that I start shooting."

"So what happened?"

"I've already jacked off a few times today."

She gave him a curious look.

He shrugged. "I was bored. In the middle of my third round, I thought about you. That's when I decided to call."

"Perfect timing, too. I think you saved me from killing my manager."

"Glad to be of service." He finished the rest of the joint, smoking it down to his fingers.

Billie felt properly baked now. Oh, God, she was relaxed. "This is some really good shit."

"I've got a great dealer. He looks like a Wall Street guy—nice suits, expensive briefcase. People think he's a lobbyist when he shows up at my office."

"I'm jealous."

"I'll give you his number."

They stared at the ceiling in an easy silence that stretched on for a long time.

Finally, March broke it. "I hate all this propaganda about smoking pot's being a serious drug problem. The whole country's on drugs. Have you watched TV lately? Every other ad is for an antidepressant. Take Paxil: You'll have fun at the company picnic again! And now we're doing it to kids. Little Johnny's scared about the first day of school, so let's give him Prozac. What a scam. A little reefer now and then? There's nothing wrong with that. To me, it's a reward. Like a fancy after-work cocktail."

At first, Billie didn't know how to respond. It's not as if she ever watched *Hannity & Colmes*. Politics bored her. "You're right." Okay, not the most articulate thing to say, but what man didn't want to hear it?

March moistened his finger and reached down to trace the outline of her little flower tattoo. "That's sexy. Just above your pussy like that. Did it hurt?"

"Like hell."

He went sliding down to kiss it.

Bless Kellyanne for signing up to do that dumb-ass reality show. With her still in Miami and Liza back in Manhattan until Friday, Billie had the run of their East Hampton rental. Ice queen Amaryllis had returned to the city, too, and even though March had her parents' house all to himself, he didn't want to risk the staff seeing him with another woman. So Billie's summer digs made the perfect spot for an adult play date.

She stroked his hair. "You know, we can stay here all week . . ."

"I wish."

Billie held her breath for the rest.

"We're due at a fund-raiser on the Upper East Side tomorrow. I need to take off in the morning."

His choice of pronoun killed her a little bit. "What about the next day?"

"I'll be in Washington." His fingers started to encircle her delicate tangle of pubic hair. "Will you wax your bush for me?"

Billie felt a surge of delight. It meant that he wanted to see her again.

"I like the Brazilian. It's just a narrow strip in front. Smooth to the touch. Smooth to the taste."

She glanced down at him. "Is that what Amaryllis does to hers?"

"Not quite. She went through laser removal. It's completely bald down there. I prefer some hair. Not a lot. Just a little. Go to J. Sisters. They do great work. It's on West 57th."

"Instead of a landing strip, maybe I should ask them to shape your initials."

March let out a soft moan. "That'd be hot."

"Consider it done," Billie said.

With a sudden and delicious roughness, March turned Billie over onto her stomach. "I guess this means you're my summer bitch." Three masturbation sessions be damned. He slid into her from behind with a velocity and hardness that knocked the breath from her body.

"I guess so," Billie whispered, realizing with a strange mix of lust, fear, and dread that, in the space of one afternoon, March Donaldson had become her most urgent reason for living.

Kellyanne

SEVEN

Signing that contract was a horrible mistake. Kellyanne had set herself up as a willing prisoner in some tasteless mansion on Miami's Star Island. Now she desperately wished she could be anywhere else—back at her apartment waiting for Walter, on a plane heading to the Hamptons, even in a Humvee rattling down a booby-trapped road in Iraq.

Anywhere but here.

"I'm good television," real estate agent Dee Lonergan announced for what must have been the millionth time in the span of a week. She smacked her lips, swiping on another coat of gloss as she faced the smudged and splattered mirror inside the filthy bathroom.

Kellyanne cut a polar glance at her.

"I'll probably get some endorsements after this," Dee went on, never taking her eyes off her own reflection. She was pretty in that very standard, very forgettable way, the kind of girl who took first runner-up in the state beauty pageant and spent the rest of her life talking about how she should've won.

Suddenly, Kellyanne got elbowed by Bunny Corvette, a Hooters waitress rudely angling for more room to glob on her drugstore mascara. "Sorry." The apology barely made it past the girl's plump lips.

"No problem," Kellyanne sniffed. "I was sick of that rib anyway."

"Whatever," Bunny murmured under her breath. "You're just pissed because Vlad barely paid attention to you on the group date."

"Yes, it was *devastating*." Kellyanne doused a cotton square with La Prairie Cellular Refining Lotion and applied it to her face and throat in quick circular sweeps.

Dee spoke up. "The show is called *Soul Mates,* not *Slut Search.* Vlad's not going to choose the girl with the stripper name who won't stop sticking her tongue down his throat."

Bunny glared at Dee. "And you think he's going to choose you—the house bitch?"

Dee continued perfecting her lips. "Let's just say that packing up your shit before the next key ceremony wouldn't be the worst use of your time."

Bunny just stood there, stunned and hurt, though her posture seemed to indicate that she was still ready for battle.

"You're going to take that?" Rhett taunted. He was just out of college and working as a *Soul Mates* story editor. One of his jobs was to follow behind the ubiquitous camera operators and look for situations to exploit into dramatic opportunities. "Yell at her! Throw something at her!"

Kellyanne groaned and gathered up her products, slipping out just as the shrieking and clatter of flying makeup commenced.

She could hardly blame Rhett. The poor bastard was just a struggling writer desperate to get a foot in the door of the television business. But Brad "Bonzi" Lucas had slapped him with the meaningless title of story editor, a shrewd way to bypass the Writers Guild of America and enslave Rhett to a flat pay contract for what amounted to an eighty-hour workweek with no overtime, no meal periods, no health benefits, and no participation in residuals. The de facto salary turned out to be less than ten dollars per hour.

Kellyanne marched back into the master suite she shared with Dee and Bunny. During the first few days of shooting, there'd been two other roommates—a black girl named Starleana and a Japanese fitness model who called herself Asia. But Vlad Branigan—in the tradition of most white male reality stars searching for a lover on national television—had disposed of all the women of color in the first round of elimination.

A palpable sense of regret came over Kellyanne, and, as if weighed down by it, she sank onto the edge of the twin bed. What was she doing here? Why had she agreed to this? Oh, yeah, that's right. She was doing it all for her career.

In retrospect, she felt like a fool for thinking that a reality show would move her acting ambitions even one step forward. The world was littered with D-list losers who'd thought exactly the same thing.

Kellyanne tried to recall the exact selling points from Bonzi's booze-fueled marketing pitch. She should've known right away that *Soul Mates* would only be more garbage for TV's summer scrap heap. Except for the final twist, the show was a complete rip-off of ABC's *The Bachelor*.

Kellyanne was among thirty girls who'd moved into the rented Star Island mansion and instantly been denied access to newspapers, television, radio, the Internet, and phone service. One girl had been caught using a smuggled Razr V3 and was quickly jettisoned from the show.

Beyond the half-hearted attempt at assembling a diverse cast— Starleana, Asia, one plus-size girl, and an Indian belly dancer— Bonzi and his coconspirators had chosen contestants whom they could easily mold into predetermined types.

Dee Lonergan was the Antagonizer, an ice queen quick on the draw, with such bold announcements as, "I'm not here to make friends" and "You think I'm a bitch now? You haven't seen anything yet."

Bunny Corvette was the Slut. And Kellyanne had been there when Rhett fed her the line, "I prefer sex on the first date. It's like test-driving a car. If I don't like the way it rides, then I move on to another vehicle."

There was also the Disney Princess, in this case Samantha, a sweet girl from Virginia who talked in unprompted bumper-sticker speak about "finding my Prince Charming" and "meeting the man of my dreams."

Kellyanne had been recruited as the Southern Bombshell and was frequently encouraged to play up her accent and drop corn-pone regional expressions such as "ain't got enough sense to bell a cat." That was just one of the ridiculous sayings that Rhett had discovered from a half-assed online search. She refused to utter such nonsense, giving them a few y'alls but nothing more.

The program stuck to typical genre conventions. There was the meet-and-greet event, where all of the women paraded around Vlad Branigan, desperate to make an impression before the first selection ceremony, at which point he winnowed the pool to a field of twenty by presenting oversize heart-shaped keys as he offered these words: "I think you could be my soul mate. Tonight I offer this key to my heart."

There was also a series of formal dinners to ratchet up catty conflicts, a soundproof video chamber to record daily confession-als, group dates to prove Vlad Branigan's ability to attract a devoted harem, and every possible contrivance to get the women into bathing suits.

As for Vlad, he was hardly the second coming of Brad Pitt that Bonzi had promised. His hunk factor was quickly snuffed out by macho arrogance and a humorless, lunkhead personality. Every group date seemed to end in the hot tub with Vlad's directing the women to rotate positions so that he could sample them individu-ally.

Kellyanne thought she would mercifully be denied a heart

key after turning away to avoid Vlad's open-mouthed kiss in the Jacuzzi. But she was still here. Now he thought of her as a challenge. It'd come back to her through one of the production assistants—a smart girl who took a lot of shit from the other assholes on the crew—that Vlad had said, "The Alabama bitch is playing hard to get, but she'll be begging for my dick before this is over."

Kellyanne buried her face in her hands and fell backward onto the bed, feeling the full impact of all the regret, disappointment, and self-loathing that had been building throughout the week. There was a spiritual cost to signing that contract. And she was paying it right now.

Whenever she imagined the show's actually being broadcast, she experienced a suffocating sense of dread. Four letters summed up the feeling—WWLT . . . What Would Liza Think? Kellyanne knew that her opinionated friend would blast *Soul Mates* as another example of the reality TV factory stripping away women's intelligence and self-awareness to portray them as desperate sexual objects.

And she'd be right. Of course, Kellyanne had known this all along. The thought had even lanced her brain as she scratched her signature onto the contract. But a core need to have something significant of her own had propelled her forward. Oh, God, how pathetic. Her life was so empty that something like *Soul Mates* could come along and instantly qualify as significant.

She envied Liza and Billie. They had purpose. Liza's career was born out of passionate beliefs, and she'd become her own cottage industry, encompassing books, television appearances, blogging, and more. By comparison, Billie was a professional mess, but at least she possessed raw talent. It'd been harnessed before to spectacular results. No doubt it'd be harnessed again. And what did Kellyanne have? A horny old man financing her lavish lifestyle and an agent who regarded her career as an absolute joke.

"Kellyanne?"

She rose up with a start to see one of Bonzi's assistants—a guy they called Crabs for reasons she didn't want to know—standing in the doorway.

His gaze always lingered a few seconds too long. It was creepy. "Bonzi wants to see you. He's in the main production trailer."

She nodded, deciding instantly to change out of her form-fitting tank and into a regular T-shirt. The less provocative, the better. Bonzi had taken every opportunity to hit on her during the past week, and she was in no mood for his bullshit right now.

Kellyanne started down the staircase, quietly amazed at how much damage could be done to a home in such a short time. She noticed scratches on the limestone floors and fireplace mantel, broken screen doors and skylights, large holes drilled into walls to accommodate cabling, and trash strewn about everywhere—cigarette butts, personal hygiene items, beer and liquor bottles. It looked like the aftermath of a raging college party. Some misguided fools had wanted the ego boost of seeing their home as a glorious set piece for a major television program. They'd rue the day.

The production trailers crowded the mansion's circular drive, causing fatal injury to once-immaculate landscaping. Bonzi's sanctuary was a gleaming silver Airstream that hummed nonstop. The rest of his staff settled for what looked like hobbled trailers from FEMA, the kind that had been issued to Hurricane Katrina victims. Prior to the trailer invasion, footage of Vlad Branigan driving up to the mansion in his black Spyker C8 Laviolette had already been shot.

Kellyanne rapped the trailer door with three fast knocks. And then she waited. She started to try one last time when the door swung open.

Bonzi stood there, looking disheveled in an oversize NFL jersey and baggy board shorts that stopped just past his knees. Why did he feel compelled to dress like a hip-hop wannabe? Impatiently, he motioned for Kellyanne to come inside as he screamed into his BlackBerry.

"That motherfucker pitched my idea! Dude, this sucks! I've got a call in to another network. He can't edit on location. He does it after wrap in L.A. We can beat him onto the air. I'd love to see that douche bag's face when he finds out I got a green light. Call me if you hear anything else. Later." He tapped his earpiece to disconnect. "Some cocksucker stole my idea for *America's Hottest Bartenders*."

Kellyanne gave him a bored look. "And it's so original to begin with." She glanced around at the guitars, heavy metal posters, and horror film memorabilia, wondering if Bonzi would ever grow up.

"I've got something to show you." His tone was ominous.

Kellyanne braced herself for a fast exit, thinking he might drop his pants and ask for a blow job, as he'd done once before.

But this time Bonzi stepped over to an impressive bank of Macintosh computers. "Do you know what *zsuj* is?"

Kellyanne just looked at him blankly. He pronounced it *zhoodge*. She'd never heard the word.

"It's all about the *zsuj* in soaps," Bonzi explained smugly. "You know, lots of romance, candlelight, love scenes. It's a concept to make people believe they're seeing more sex than they actually are. Smoke and mirrors, you know? At the end of the day, sex rules." He raised the bushy brows canopying over his bloodshot eyes.

"Is there a point here?" Kellyanne asked impatiently.

And then Bonzi maneuvered the cordless mouse to activate an application called Avid. After a series of clicks, a night vision image filled the twenty-inch monitor. And then the scene began to play.

It was Vlad Branigan, naked in bed with an unidentifiable blonde kneeling between his legs. Over the chickachika-pow-wow music playing in the background, there were exaggerated sound effects—moaning, slurping, gulping—all being utilized to drive home the fact that oral sex was being performed. In the next scene, Kellyanne, dressed in a camisole and panties, was seen exiting a room and wiping a white substance from the corner of her mouth as she moistened her lips with her tongue.

Instantly, a sick feeling came over her. "You son of a bitch!" she screamed. "This is bullshit! I was coming out of the bathroom that

I share with the other girls! And I'd just finished brushing my teeth!"

Bonzi answered with a wicked laugh as he froze the image on the screen. "Isn't it funny how the night-vision camera makes toothpaste look like cum? And this is just a rough cut."

With a few more clicks of the mouse, another picture filled the monitor, this one of Kellyanne tipping back a glass of champagne. In the next scene, she was weaving through the bathroom doorway and retching into the commode. The vomiting went on and on.

"I looped the wettest barf sound over and over again," Bonzi said proudly. "People will think you were really hammered and puking up your guts."

Kellyanne could scarcely contain her anger. It was white-hot and rising. "You know that I got sick on the sushi that your caterer provided!"

Bonzi gave a diffident shrug. "Doesn't look that way to me. It's all in the editing, I guess."

"You can't do this," Kellyanne said. But her words lacked conviction, because she knew that she was powerless.

"Read your contract. I can do whatever I want with this footage."

Kellyanne blinked back tears as she stared Bonzi down, her eyes burning with hatred. "Why are you doing this to me?"

"Because I can." He swiveled his chair to face her full on. "You've been a disappointment. Onscreen." He paused a beat. "And off." He raked her up and down with a crude glance. "Make me feel good, and I'll make you look good."

The mere thought disgusted her. "You're a pig."

He laughed at her. "What? You've got something against sucking a pig's dick? Since when?"

Kellyanne spun fast and started out.

Bonzi reached out to grab her wrist and squeezed hard.

Kellyanne wrestled free from his grasp, adrenaline pumping as a true, cold fear consumed her. Bonzi was a big man—tall, strong, and, judging from the empty Bud Light bottles cluttering the portable editing bay, more than a little drunk. If he forced himself on her, then she'd be no match for the bastard.

Ultimately, he waved her off with a bored gesture. "Get out. If your pussy was actually worth all this trouble, you'd be a real actress by now." He turned back to the monitor, dismissing her altogether.

Kellyanne just stood there as the impact of Bonzi's words sliced into her psyche. How had she gotten here? When would she stop living this dumb life? And why did every man—her married lover included—see fit to treat her like the cheapest slab of meat in the market?

This was the tipping point. She wanted out. Right now. No matter the consequences. "I quit."

Bonzi's face registered nothing. "Fine. I've still got enough footage to paint you as the show's resident cum Dumpster. And a drunk one at that." He smirked.

Even as she was seething inside, Kellyanne did her best nonchalant act. "I'll take national humiliation over sleeping with you any day."

He cocked his head to the side, as if pondering the wonderfully cruel outcome in store for her. "Remember this moment, bitch. You'll regret it."

Suddenly, it occurred to Kellyanne that she had a card to play. *Soul Mates* was one of those metareality shows built around the gimmick that the viewing audience is in on a secret but the cast is not. A Ketel One–soaked mind made for loose lips, and Bonzi had boasted about the show's big reveal on the night she met him at Silk Electric.

"You might regret it, too," Kellyanne shot back acidly. "Especially after I tell Vlad about the trick you have planned for him at the end of the show. I'm sure the other girls would like to know about it, too."

Bonzi gave her a smug grin. "I think they just want to be on television. And I know Vlad is just in it for the pussy. It doesn't matter how fake things are. Haven't you heard? Reality is the new substitute for truth."

For a moment, Kellyanne considered a shock and awe campaign of destruction. She had the reservoir of anger to do it. And the idea of smashing up Bonzi's editing bay filled her with a certain glee. But she knew the act would be futile. No doubt the footage was stored on some unseen server. Destroying his equipment would just enrage him more.

Wordlessly, she walked out, making a beeline for the house and dashing upstairs, determined to gather up her things and leave. Before Kellyanne reached her room, a camera operator was rushing to capture her every move.

She worked fast, checking the contents of her Louis Vuitton beauty case and shoving whatever clothes she could locate into her matching keep-all.

It took no time for a gaggle of girls to form in the doorway, their faces a collage of confusion, concern, and relief.

Kellyanne ignored their questions, if only to deny Bonzi any additional footage that might be used to complete the bogus story arc he was creating.

She pushed past the throng, avoiding eye contact and jutting out her bags to force an open path.

"The girl's quitting because she knows that Vlad's not going to give her a key," Dee taunted. "I don't know how she got on the show, anyway. She must be the quota slot for Alabama white trash."

It took every cell in Kellyanne's body to fight against responding. She vaulted forward as if the bitch had never spoken.

"Did you hear what Dee just said?" Rhett asked, his voice soaked in desperation. This was a big reality-show moment. He needed a beginning, middle, and end. "Why are you leaving, Kellyanne? Is it something that Vlad did? Is it a personal crisis?"

She reached the bottom of the stairs and spun around to face him. "I need to make a call. Can I borrow your cell?"

Rhett hesitated, his expression pained. "I could get fired for that."

"I quit the goddamn show, Rhett. I just need to find someone to get me out of here," Kellyanne implored him.

Rhett shook his head. "I'm sorry."

"Whatever," Kellyanne spat. She stormed out, pushing open the front door, not bothering to close it behind her as she stalked down the drive.

It was time to get a fucking life.

Liza

EIGHT

"I don't believe in female sexuality as a zero-sum game," Liza said matter-of-factly. "This idea that you're either a *Girls Gone Wild* slut who will lift up your top for a free T-shirt or a puritan who vows virginity until marriage in exchange for a promise ring from Daddy is intellectually and emotionally dishonest."

"A classic liberal response," March Donaldson countered via satellite feed from Washington, DC. "How anyone can find fault with a teenage girl's choosing the path of abstinence is beyond me. I'm proud to see a new generation of young women embracing traditional values."

Liza shot a look at Tom Shapiro that told him she was about to annihilate her political foil. It would be another moment from *The Roundtable* destined to stir up the always intense blogosphere.

The fact that March was outside the studio sharpened Liza's instinct to not just maim but to completely destroy. "I don't think it's *traditional* for fathers to impose guilt and shame about sex onto their daughters. I think it's dysfunctional. And the double standard makes me sick. I don't hear about mothers asking their sons to remain pure until marriage."

"Maybe they should," March shot back.

Liza pounced on the lame retort. "Is that what *your* mother did?"

There was the slightest hesitation as March realized how badly he'd set himself up for the kill.

Tom shook his head ruefully.

Liza pressed on. "Are you still a virgin, March?"

"I'm taking the Fifth on that one." The Texas-born political stud flashed a sexy smile, living up to his media hype as the Matthew McConaughey of the Republican right. "I think Liza's main issue with this new modesty movement is that it's being led by young girls. I guess you could call them antirebels. But they're strong in their beliefs, and they face a great deal of social alienation in doing so. We should be applauding them."

Tom gestured to Liza. "You wrote a national best seller— *Whore*—which chronicled the flipside of this. Do you see young modesty as a true revolution?"

Liza tilted her head philosophically. "In some ways, yes. I believe there are girls who feel under attack by the oversexed media and overly permissive parents—particularly the mothers who are buying into the *Desperate Housewives* validation of being considered a MILF."

March comically feigned a malfunctioning earpiece. "Excuse me, did she just say *MILF*? Are we on HBO?"

Tom laughed a little.

Liza merely grinned. "But there's a strong component to this trend's being driven by organized religion so, at the end of the day, I think it's more of a dangerous campaign that young girls are being duped into joining."

"*Dangerous*?" March shook his head incredulously. "Well, Liza is a liberal. If Christians are involved, then it must seem dangerous to her."

"The danger is in the dishonesty," Liza went on, refusing to be rattled. "As a society, we're very undisciplined when it comes to these issues. We're more likely to debate the extremes than wrestle with the complex middle ground. A girl who acts out every horny male's stripper fantasy isn't exercising her sexual power. She's being used. And a girl who takes a vow of chastity and accepts a promise ring from her father isn't choosing purity. She's being manipulated."

Tom's brow shot up provocatively. "You view it as manipulation?"

Liza nodded severely. "The conservative position is based on a rigid set of values that don't reflect current realities. Sure, a girl can promise to Daddy that she'll save herself for marriage. But then, virginity becomes a game of semantics. There's a high percentage of girls pledging abstinence but still engaging in oral and anal sex. I don't think getting by on a technicality is the point here. But it underscores the dishonesty and avoidance at work."

"March, we're out of time," Tom said. "But I'll let you have the last word."

"If Liza's saying that even the good girls are bad, then a lot has changed since I was in high school. Wish I could go back there now." He punctuated his remark with another disarming smile.

Tom shifted to address a different camera. "And that's it for this week's Culture Wars segment. I want to thank Liza Pike and March Donaldson, as well as my earlier guests, Senator Barbara Boxer and environmental activist Laurie David. Until next week, thank you for visiting *The Roundtable*."

"And we're out!" the producer shouted.

"Did you really have to bring my mother into this?" March asked good naturedly.

"She raised you," Liza answered lightly. "I figure she bears some responsibility."

March grinned. "Tom, I'm not even there, and I can still feel the chill. Who else can we get for this gig? I know. Call Rosie O'Donnell's people."

Tom laughed.

"I'm worse than *Rosie*?" Liza pretended to be shocked but in the end couldn't hold her laughter. "When are you coming back? I don't like playing in the sandbox alone."

March winked. "Just admit it. You miss me like crazy."

Liza rolled her eyes. "Spoken like a true narcissist."

"I'll be back in Long Island this weekend. I'm just here to scare up PAC money for my think tank. Oh, and you'll love this—I'm the luncheon keynote for the College Republicans Conference at the Hilton."

"An entire ballroom of the young and the ignorant. How frightening."

March smiled, his movie-star teeth gleaming on the monitor. "I'm slammed with fund-raising meetings for the rest of the day, so drink a few shots in my honor."

"Who says we're drinking?" Tom teased, sharing a knowing look with Liza.

"It was more of a suggestion," March said. "Liza seems really uptight. Hey, instead of a couple of drinks, maybe she just needs a good—"

Suddenly, the satellite feed fizzled out.

Liza turned to Tom, a question in her eyes.

He put a finger to his earpiece. "Perry, we just lost March's signal." A few beats passed. Then an amused smile curled onto Tom's lips. "Apparently, it's nothing on our end. I think that was March's doing."

"Son of a bitch!" Liza spat. But even she had to concede that it was funny.

"You owe him big time for that one," Tom said, sliding out of his chair as a production assistant rushed over to first detach Liza's microphone, then Tom's. "Thanks, Corey." He looked at her and smiled. "You're great. Why don't you have your own show?"

"Every network turned down my pitch for the Feminazi Variety Hour."

Tom chuckled.

"I can't do what you do," Liza said. "I've been told that a little of me goes a long way on television. I'm more appealing when presented to the viewing public in smaller doses."

"Says who?"

"Agents and critics. And I'm giving you the most diplomatic version."

"Well, I've got two words for you—Nancy Grace."

Liza smirked. "But I can't cry at the drop of a dime. And I can't look in the camera and call viewers 'friend' with the same sincerity, either."

Tom laughed a little. "My interview with the deputy director of Homeland Security got canceled, so I'm finished here and heading into the city. Can I offer you a ride? The limo is fully stocked with liquor."

"Say no more. All I get is a lousy Town Car. And if I want a bar, then I better have some of those airline liquor bottles stashed in my purse."

"Well, I don't get the perks because I'm a man. It's because I'm an established CNBC *star*." He gave her an exaggerated haughty look.

"Yes, I know. I've seen the promotional ads wrapped around buses. I didn't think this was possible, but your teeth are actually whiter in person."

Tom gave her a true megawatt smile. "Let's get out of here. Traffic is going to be a bitch."

The black limousine stretched out as long as an oil spill.

While Tom busied himself as a cabin bartender, Liza obsessively checked her BlackBerry. Her addiction to the device was total. It vibrated on the nightstand when she tried to sleep. It beeped on the vanity when she took a shower. And just putting the fucking thing on silent mode for her segment on *The Roundtable* triggered a certain anxiety.

There were several missed calls—Kellyanne, Billie, her lecture agent, her literary agent, and her editor at New Woman Press. No doubt the last two wanted an answer to the same question: Where was the goddamn proposal for her second book?

She scanned through the recent e-mails, then read with interest a text message from Kellyanne sent mere minutes after her attempt to call.

I quit the reality show. LONG story. Arrive tonight at JFK. Will ride the Jitney. Can't wait 2 c u!!!

Tom proudly presented her with a crystal highballer swirling to the rim with a potent-looking dark red concoction. "Pomegranate and Absolut. With a splash of lemon juice and simple syrup. Cheers." He clinked glasses and sipped greedily.

Liza followed suit, instantly relaxed by the punch of the vodka burning down her throat. The fertility drugs were still rampaging through her body. Sometimes the pressure on her ovaries was so intense that she felt like she might explode. The smart move would be to stay away from alcohol altogether. But Liza moderated her intake. It was either a few drinks or prescription drugs. She needed something to take the edge off.

"I know this is rude, but I have to make one call. Do you mind?" Billie's number was ringing before Tom could answer.

"Hello?" A groggy voice came on the line just as Liza was about to hang up.

"Billie?"

"Christ—what time is it?" Her voice was a thick slur.

"Around five, I guess. Are you sick?"

"No, just pissed. I was waiting for some asshole to call, and he never did, so I ended up getting drunk. What do you want?"

Liza was momentarily taken aback. "I got a text message from Kellyanne."

"Yeah, she quit that stupid show, and she's coming in tonight."

Liza heard Billie light up a cigarette and take a deep drag. "Are you smoking in the house?"

Billie sighed. "Calm down. I've got the window open."

"Go out on the deck, Billie," Liza said sharply. "And take an ashtray with you. Violating that rule could cost thousands of dollars. It's in the lease."

"Okay, okay. Shit! I still can't believe I'm paying fifty grand for this joint, yet I'm forbidden to smoke a fucking cigarette."

"How did she sound?" Liza asked.

"Who?"

"*Kellyanne.* I hope everything's okay."

"She's fine. It's not like she was in a hurricane. It was just a moronic reality series. One of the producers kept trying to fuck her. That's why she bailed. She should've just let him. She fucks for rent. Why not for a TV show?"

Liza glanced over at Tom, who was nursing his drink and patiently waiting for her attention. "I have to go. I'm with a colleague. I'll see both of you sometime tomorrow."

But Billie had already hung up.

Liza gave her BlackBerry a double take, shaking her head in disbelief.

"Problem?" Tom inquired.

"One of my summer sisters is Billie Shelton, the rock singer."

Tom's eyes widened. "I remember her from Harrison Beck's party. She was the first one to get naked and jump into the pool."

Liza managed a half smile. "That's Billie."

"Not to worry, though. As far as memorable moments go, nothing trumps Harrison whipping out his cock for your benefit."

Liza made most of her drink disappear and already felt like asking Tom to fix her another one. She was going home to Justin tonight. But what she really wanted was to join Billie and Kellyanne in the Hamptons, no matter how late.

As much as she looked forward to the reunion, Liza had to admit that along with that came a nagging sense of irrational hope.

Maybe this time would be different.

God, she felt that way before every gathering with the girls. So much went into their escapes—meticulous planning, giddy anticipation—but the actual events never quite lived up to the hype.

Liza was always left with a certain longing. The bond they shared was never quite nourishing enough. It was empty-calorie companionship. She yearned for deeper connections, more stimulating exchanges, something . . . different.

Tom seemed to pick up on her inward distraction. "Are things better at home?"

She looked at him as she sipped. "You first. How are things at your house?"

"Lonely," Tom said quietly. "I haven't had a meaningful relationship since college, and that one was just my wasting an incredible girl's time. Now I don't even have meaningless affairs. They're too risky. Nothing is worth some one night stand's snapping a cell phone picture and running off to TMZ or Perez Hilton."

For a moment, Liza said nothing. She was stunned by his raw honesty. But it also made her feel good that he trusted her so much. "It sounds awful, Tom, but maybe it could be liberating. If people found out the truth, then you'd be free to live your life."

Tom drained the last of his drink and stared plaintively into the bottom of his glass. "That's not the sort of freedom I'm looking for. I want the career Anderson Cooper has. I want that kind of money. I want that kind of promotion. I want that kind of access to big interviews. I'll never get there by becoming the *gay* face of CNBC." He winced at the word. "And that's what will happen. It'll overshadow everything I've worked for." He glanced at her near-empty glass. "Another round?"

Liza nodded somberly. "Sometimes I hate America."

Tom chuckled. "Let's keep that between us. Can you imagine the campaign Sean Hannity would wage if that got out?"

Liza scowled. "He's a partisan pig."

Tom laughed, finishing up the new drinks. "These are a bit stronger."

"Good." Liza gamely accepted hers and chased down the first swallow, which practically set her throat on fire. "You know, you could be the one," she offered optimistically. "You could be the guy who changes everything."

Tom clinked her glass in a mock toast. "Nice try. But you really don't believe that."

Liza sighed. "No, I really don't. It sounded good, though." She drank up.

Tom looked melancholy. "If I came out, there'd be the inevitable torrent of attention. But all of it would be focused on the gay angle. How long have I been gay? Who am I dating? What's my position on same-sex marriage?"

Liza groaned. "Maybe staying in the closet isn't so confining after all. How pathetic is that?"

"Very," Tom murmured, drinking deep. "I don't want to end up on the cover of *People,* like Lance Bass. Being gay isn't the most interesting thing about me. It would follow me everywhere, though. The activists would be after me to take up all the gay causes, too. But I've never really identified with the culture-at-large. Most of my friends are straight. To me it's just a matter of sexuality, and that's such a private thing."

Liza could feel a definite buzz sensation from the alcohol. "It makes me sad that you don't feel comfortable dating. You deserve someone special."

"Don't feel too sad. I'm not exactly living the life of a monk."

Liza gazed at him with keen interest.

"There's something to be said for successful married men. They're discreet, and they have a great deal to lose. Sometimes that makes for a wonderful arrangement."

"*Tom Shapiro,*" Liza said in a faux scolding tone. "You're a home-wrecking slut."

He laughed sheepishly. "Actually, I've never wrecked a home . . . but I am a bit of a slut."

"Anyone I know?" Liza inquired silkily.

Tom named a major movie star, an international sex god married to a world-famous actress and humanitarian. Together they had the devotion of the media and an exotic coterie of adopted children from faraway countries.

Liza was thunderstruck. "You're joking."

Tom shook his head. "It happened at the Mercer."

"Okay, I'm no longer sad. Now I'm jealous."

"You should be," Tom said, raising his glass with a sexy grin. "That night with him was worth a lifetime of loneliness." He whistled at the memory. "So what about you? How's that fucking husband of yours?"

"He's the same," Liza said quietly. "He'll always be the same. That's the problem, I'm afraid."

"I imagine that most men would find you too intimidating. What's the joke? If a woman wants to turn a guy off completely, she just has to mention that she has an MBA from Harvard."

"Yeah." Liza laughed a little. "It's called dropping the H-bomb. Apparently, my husband's immune to its detonation."

Tom looked impressed. "That says something about him."

"What? That he's too stupid to realize?"

Tom gave her a strange look. "Man, you are brutal."

"I know," Liza sighed. She drank more and considered having a third. "Maybe I'm just frustrated. The claim to fame in our relationship had always been the sex, and now we don't have that, so . . . I'm wondering what's there."

"Do you think it could be a medical issue?" Tom asked.

Liza scoffed at the notion. "Justin treats his body like a holy temple. I don't think it's a physical problem."

"What about a porn addiction?"

Liza shook her head. "I've never seen him show an interest in anything like that. Ever."

For the next few miles, Tom just sat there in distracted silence. Finally, he spoke. "It's unlikely that he's lost interest in sex."

"So you're telling me that he's getting it somewhere else." Before Tom could answer, Liza finished her drink and passed him her empty glass. "Hit me again."

He hesitated and cocked an eyebrow, then went about the business of prepping their third round. "I just don't want you to get blind-sided. An FDNY calendar cover boy doesn't have to go looking for it. Be aware. Protect yourself."

"I don't care anymore," Liza said, only half-meaning the words. "Here I am on my last round of fertility drugs to freeze my eggs, and I'm so tender where it counts that I'd probably turn down sex with George Clooney. Maybe I should be grateful to the firefighter groupies for keeping him satisfied."

"That's certainly charitable."

"I know. Stick around. I'll probably get mean after this third drink."

Tom laughed at her and handed it over.

Suddenly, Liza gave him a penetrating gaze. "Let me ask you something, Tom. Do you think I'm a fraud?"

His answer was an expression of bewilderment.

"Harrison Beck thinks I am," Liza explained. "He says I pretend to be this power feminist, but then I run around dressing like a party girl and marrying firemen."

Tom shrugged. "How does that make you a fraud? All of those things can be true at the same time."

She nodded thoughtfully, appreciating his reasonable assessment.

"We're all hypocrites to a degree," Tom went on. "I consider my sex life a matter of absolute privacy, but *The Roundtable* dedicated significant airtime to the outing of that married senator from Louisiana. I rationalized it because he was such an aggressive opponent of gay marriage, gays in the military, and hate-crime legislation." He clinked his glass against hers and grinned. "Here's to two self-righteous frauds."

Liza laughed and raised her highballer in salute.

"It's surprising, though," Tom remarked.

Liza returned a quizzical look. "What is?"

"That Harrison Beck got to you this way. I thought you ate macho men like him for breakfast."

"I don't know. Maybe it's the extra hormones I'm injecting into my body." She drank, contemplating the situation as the limousine coasted toward Manhattan. "Sometimes I wonder what I really believe in, though. I rail against the medical establishment for propagandizing women's health care, and here I am with a syringe in my purse, frantic to beat the biological clock. I hardly ever eat and, when I do, I feel guilty and worry about getting fat. I've actually stood naked in the bathroom mirror and considered breast implants. And I fantasize about finding a rich husband and having a baby and never working again." She stopped and took in a deep breath. "Oh, and I'm generally attracted to men who are no more evolved than an ape at the Bronx Zoo."

Tom smiled easily. "You're being too hard on yourself."

"Am I?" Liza wondered. Suddenly, an internal thunderbolt hit, sending her mind into overdrive. She recalled a popular, hard-charging song by Pink and instantly conceived the second book concept that had been eluding her for months.

Stupid Girls.

That was a perfect title for her next polemic. She could write about the dichotomous roles that women end up playing in contemporary society. It'd be a more personal book than *Whore*. This time, she'd not only write about other women's stories but about her own. She just hoped that the self-examination would be therapeutic and cathartic as opposed to painful and debilitating.

Liza dug into her Miu Miu ostrich satchel and jotted a few notes into a small leather journal, confident that the idea would hold up even under the harsh glare of sobriety.

"A writer's work is never done," Tom mused, kicking off his shoes and slouching back against the plush seats.

"Something like that," Liza murmured. She put away the journal and slipped off her Christian Louboutin slingbacks, then tucked her feet underneath her legs and smiled tipsily at him.

Tom gestured to the privacy screen. "The driver probably thinks we're back here nailing each other."

"I bet limousine drivers gossip like sorority girls." Liza giggled. "You know what would be funny? If I left my panties behind."

Tom shook his head and pointed to her drink. "That's it," he scolded playfully. "I'm cutting you off."

She giggled again and touched his knee. "God, that sounded like something Billie Shelton would say."

"Not really," Tom countered. "When she stripped on the pool deck at Harrison's party, she wasn't wearing any underwear."

Liza busied herself with her drink to avoid comment. Sometimes it struck her . . . Billie's raunchy rock star excess . . . Kellyanne's willingness to live her life as a passive sexual vessel for a controlling rich man . . . what exactly was the common thread among them?

Tom took a break from personal confessions and brought up media gossip—the precipitous fall of the former morning show queen turned embattled evening news anchor, the surprise exit of an MSNBC star, and the rumored affair between an ABC White House correspondent and a high-ranking White House cabinet official.

When the limousine stopped in front of Liza's apartment building in TriBeCa, she was grateful for the time spent with Tom and reluctant to end it. "This was fun. We should carpool more often."

Tom smiled at her. "Anytime, my friend." Suddenly, he became distracted, shifting his gaze out the window and onto the sidewalk. "Now that's just wrong." His voice went thick with lust.

Liza turned to see Justin walking toward the building, shirtless and soaked in sweat, a small gym bag in one hand and a slim can of Red Bull in the other. His wet shorts clung to him like a second skin, and the imprint of his crotch bulge was impossible to ignore.

"That's my husband. I want you to meet him."

Justin was eyeballing the limousine just as Liza zipped down the window. "Hey, baby," he called out, strutting toward the curb and whistling at the conspicuousness of it all. "You're traveling like a star."

"Hardly!" Liza said, louder than she intended. The alcohol was really doing its number now. "I bummed this ride from a real star." She giggled longer than the joke warranted.

Justin zeroed in on her with a knowing half-smile, then bent down to peer into the cabin and make friendly eye contact with Tom. "I think my wife's hammered."

"I think you're right," Tom said, extending his hand as Liza struggled to get into her slingbacks. "Tom Shapiro."

Justin shook firm and fast. "Justin Beal."

Liza beamed at Tom. "Tom's the host of *The Roundtable*. He's a *major* rising star. I'm so proud of him." She leaned over to kiss Tom on the cheek.

Tom smiled uncomfortably.

"I should probably get you upstairs and into bed," Justin said.

"To sleep, right?" Liza asked. And then sotto voce to Tom she added, "All we do is sleep. We never fuck anymore."

Justin's jaw tightened as he opened the limousine door and pulled Liza onto the sidewalk.

She stumbled slightly, falling against his hard frame before turning back to her confidant. "Tom, I love you. Honestly, I do."

"I love you, too, Liza," Tom said, delivering the line in the patronizing tone one is forced to employ when dealing with an overly sentimental drunk. He gave Justin an apologetic look as he passed Liza's handbag through the window.

"Do you play racquetball?" Justin asked.

"Not regularly. But I can hold my own in the game. Why?"

Justin grinned. "I'll kick your ass sometime. It'll be payback for bringing my wife home wasted." His challenge was teeming with jock humor and devoid of any hostility.

"You're on." Tom laughed. "I might even let you win."

Justin shut the door and heartily slapped the roof of the limousine.

Liza watched as the gleaming black stretch weaved back into traffic and disappeared down the street. Instantly, she was overwhelmed by a sense of emptiness. The chatter with Tom had been nonstop. Now she was standing next to her husband, and they had nothing to say to each other.

Justin pitched his Red Bull into a waste bin. "Let's go upstairs." He reached for her elbow.

Liza reflexively pulled away and lost her balance, almost falling down.

Justin reacted fast to help her recover, then pulled her inside with a firm hand. "Stop acting like a dumb bitch."

Liza's head began to spin. Maybe it was the vodka. Or maybe it was the sudden and intense anger. No matter, she knew that it was going to be a long night.

The elevator ride seemed interminable. A seething silence settled in and never broke.

When they stepped inside the loft, Justin slammed the steel door with a pent-up fury. "Don't *ever* disrespect me like that again!" he roared.

Liza betrayed no reaction and walked toward the spiral staircase that led to the master bedroom. "I'm going to take a shower."

"It's none of that faggot's business what we do in bed."

Liza spun around hotly. "Then tell me whose business it is. I'm just trying to get a man involved here. And don't call my friend a faggot. As usual, you have no idea what you're talking about."

Justin's laugh was bitter. "Maybe you were too drunk to see the way he was looking at me. Given the chance, he would've sucked my dick right there on the sidewalk."

"You're disgusting."

"Who else have you told?" Justin demanded.

"Told what?"

"That we don't fuck."

At first, Liza just stared at him. "Unlike you, I'm more concerned about the problem than about who knows."

"I don't see it as a problem," Justin said.

"So this is your idea of a good marriage?"

He answered with a shrug. "You can't have it both ways. You want to wear the pants in this relationship. You want to make the big money and bark out orders and walk around like you've got a cock between your legs. That doesn't turn me on."

Liza gave him a sharp look. "I suppose I could quit everything that I'm doing. Then we could live on your salary. Maybe poverty would get you hot."

Justin glared at her.

Liza thundered on. "And while we're on the subject of roles, you should know that sometimes I feel like I've got a fourteen-year-old roommate instead of a husband. You're not responsible for a goddamn thing around here except yourself. You go to the fire station, you hang out with your buddies, and you play sports. That's it. So you're not exactly a turn-on, either."

Justin's face was impassive. None of this seemed to reach him. Or maybe he just didn't give a fuck.

"Are you sleeping around?" Liza asked. "If so, I should probably get tested."

Justin laughed at her. "Yeah, maybe you should."

A ferocious anger erupted within Liza. Her rage was so powerful that it actually made her dizzy. She felt a sudden compulsion for violence and frantically searched the immediate area for something to throw at him.

Before she could stop herself, a beautiful blown and acid-etched glass vase by Tommie Rush was in her hands and flying through the air.

Justin dodged it with little effort, sending the two-thousand-dollar decorative piece smashing against the wall behind him. A rainbow of shattered shards skated across the stained concrete floor.

"You fucking bastard!" Liza practically screamed her throat raw.

Justin moved in fast, pushing her against the wall and putting a hand to her neck.

For a microsecond, Liza experienced a cold fear, thinking that he might strangle her. But the feeling passed, and she knew instinctively that it was merely a show of dominance.

"You want to call all the shots all the time. Don't you, baby? But then when you don't get any dick, you want to make it out like something's wrong with me. What kind of bullshit is that?"

Liza squirmed to get away as Justin pushed up her Proenza

Schouler dress and cupped his hand between her legs. She winced. The hormone cocktail had made her so tender that his touch was painful.

"If you want me to fuck you, then tell me to. Bark out the order. Just like you do with everything else."

She wanted to push him away. He smelled like a locker room. But something about his attitude fascinated her. Justin's behavior was demeaning and disrespectful. In fact, it came close to promoting abuse. And yet a secret part of her was dazzled by it and found the act of surrendering strangely, blissfully erotic.

"Tell me," Justin insisted.

Liza could see and feel his erection straining against his gym shorts. And the realization hit her that she had truly missed his cock. It was an inch too big. Blow jobs were a workout. Vaginal sex was intense. "I can't," she heard herself say. "I'm too sore from the fertility drugs. You'll kill me."

He turned her around to face the wall, grabbed a fistful of hair, and snapped her head back with a brutal tug. "That's not the only hole I can use." His fingers played roughly with her ass.

No man had ever been granted access there. Liza was an anal virgin, thinking the act unhealthy and a gross example of sexual oppression and control . . . and yet the mere suggestion of the forbidden had stirred something within her. She could only describe it as a secret yearning for rebellion. But with this realization, the desire Justin had juiced up began to cool. She felt ashamed.

All of a sudden, Liza resented his attempt at domination. She twisted out of his grasp and smoothed down her dress. The spell was broken. "You stink. I mean that literally. Get your hands off me and go take a fucking shower."

He kicked his gym bag across the floor and started off. No doubt his limited mind was churning out a plan to cheat on her again as soon as possible.

It occurred to Liza that Justin was afraid of her. Even his attempt at roughness was a reaction to his fear. She'd embarrassed him in mixed company. Now he wanted to put it to her and show her what a man he was. But masculine desperation did nothing at all for her.

Liza found herself thinking about Harrison Beck. She marveled at the fact that he wasn't afraid of her, that he wasn't desperate, either.

She dug into her Miu Miu bag and pulled out the little journal again. Turning to the page where she'd scribbled her notes on *Stupid Girls,* she began to write. *This week I met the man who will make me end my marriage . . .*

Kellyanne

NINE

The three-hour flight from Miami International to JFK provided Kellyanne more time to think about the mess that was her life. Nothing in *Elle*, *Vanity Fair,* or *People* could pique even casual interest. Her inward distraction was total.

The hours that followed her retreat from the *Soul Mates* set had been difficult. Consecutive days of standby had effectively killed her cell phone battery. A flirtatious guard manning a massive security gate on a nearby Star Island property had offered his own phone.

On instinct, Kellyanne had called Walter first. He was her go-to man for everything. When the initial attempt went straight to voice mail, she tried again. And then a third time.

Finally, Walter had picked up and hissed, "What is it?"

Kellyanne had been stunned, hurt, and momentarily speechless. "Walter, it's me."

"I know that. You've called three times in as many minutes. I'm with my kids. What is it?" He'd spoken in a cold, hushed whisper.

"I just wanted you to know that I quit the reality show." She'd paused a beat. "And I'm leaving tonight for the Hamptons."

"Fine. We'll get together in New York." And then he'd hung up.

Instantly, tears had sprung to Kellyanne's eyes. Walter was somewhere with Allison, Brock, possibly even Cagle, his troubled youngest, and in that set of circumstances, she was absolutely nothing to him. Kellyanne had always known that. She knew it more now. Never in her life had she heard such dismissal in a man's voice. And that included every Hollywood casting agent who'd told her, "Hell, no!"

It was disturbing that Walter could react in such unpredictable ways. A vague conversation about Liza's East Hampton summer share invitation had ended with his scratching out a fifty-thousand-dollar check. And yet Kellyanne's frantic call to announce that she'd quit a television show had failed to conjure up even a simple question as to why.

Next, she'd reached out to Pommie, who was busy pinch-hitting as waitstaff for a caterer friend at a rich teenager's beach party. Pommie had informed her that Jab was off for the day and passed along his number.

Kellyanne's call had woken up Silk Electric's main bartender. His voice was thick and barely audible.

"Jab, it's Kellyanne. I'm stranded on Star Island."

"You poor thing," Jab had teased, showing signs of life. "That sounds like *Survivor.* I thought you were on a dating show." He'd laughed at his own joke.

Kellyanne had truly smiled for the first time in days. "More like *Fear Factor.* I'd rather eat dead bugs than stay here. Can you come get me? Are you okay to drive?"

"Yeah, I just need a Starbucks fix," Jab had said.

She could hear him yawning and stretching over the receiver. "I'm sorry to impose. I know you've got the day off, but—"

"It's no problem," Jab had assured her easily. "I need to get this skank out of my apartment anyway."

Kellyanne had shaken her head. When it came down to sex, men were such a combination of good and evil. "I'm at forty-five Star Island Drive. I'll be waiting outside the gate. Hurry, Jab." She'd hung up, her body flooding with relief as she returned the phone to the security guard.

The man, whose badge pronounced him Rockland, had continued raking her up and down with an indecent gaze.

"Thank you," Kellyanne had said earnestly, then left him there to guard his post and fantasize about what would never be. She'd taken off toward the street, located a nice spot in the sun, and sat down on her Vuitton beauty case, settling in for the wait.

When Jab had rolled up in his beaten down BMW 3-Series, it was a glorious sight for Kellyanne's eyes. She tossed her bags into the backseat and slid into the front like a teenager running away from home with a delinquent boyfriend. "Drive fast."

Jab had smiled, put the manual shift into gear, and roared off.

The jolt had slammed Kellyanne against the passenger seat. She buckled her safety belt as an afterthought, her head already splitting from the sonic blast of "Icky Thump" by the White Stripes.

"Where to, gorgeous?"

Kellyanne twisted down the stereo volume.

"You're my first damsel in distress of legal age. This is officially hot."

Kellyanne had laughed at him. Jab Hunter was the horniest guy she'd ever known. "What happened to your skank?"

"My roommate was heading out to work, so I pushed her off on him."

"You're a true romantic."

"Trust me. There was no romance involved. I picked her up at Nocturnal, brought her back to my place, and we're barely through the door when she starts yelling at me to fuck her in the ass. It was intense." He grinned and cast a sideways glance. "If you must know, I felt violated."

Kellyanne rolled her eyes. "Maybe you should file rape charges."

"Don't get me wrong. Ultimately, it was consensual." Jab hit the MacArthur Causeway and picked up speed, opening up the BMW's ancient engine to maximum revs. It barely performed. But at least they were moving away from Star Island.

"So . . . what happened back there?" Jab inquired.

Kellyanne sighed deeply. "It was awful. I'll tell you about it sometime. But right now I don't have the stomach to go into it."

"That fucker from the restaurant hit on you, didn't he?" Jab demanded, his voice filled with menace as he hit the steering wheel with a strong fist.

"Something like that," Kellyanne admitted, appreciating the fact that someone in her life actually gave a shit. "But it's over. I'm out of there." Disturbingly, a gut thing told her that it was only over for the moment. The situation would come back to haunt her. She just knew it.

Jab reached over to supportively pat Kellyanne's knee. "I knew that asshole was trouble."

In a gesture of thanks, she touched his hand. All of a sudden, she noticed the cell phone sitting in the console between them. "Do you mind?"

With Jab's sweet nod of permission, Kellyanne went to work securing a flight to New York for later that night. She'd been ferociously determined to leave Miami immediately and was lucky enough to secure a seat on Delta Airlines for less than three hundred dollars.

"Do you need a ride to the airport?" Jab offered.

Kellyanne's answer was a look of imploring gratitude. "If you could take me by the apartment to pack some things *and* do that, I'd love you forever."

"How much love?" Jab teased, winking at her.

"*Friend* love. Not skank love," Kellyanne clarified. "Are you sure that you have time for all of this?"

"My only plans for the day are to get drunk, get high, and get laid. I can fit it all in." And then Jab turned up the music volume, rocking out to Finger Eleven and Sick Puppies until they arrived at the Jade building on Brickell Bay.

When they walked through the expansive lobby, Julio, the typically warm and charming doorman, had reacted coolly toward Kellyanne and given off strong vibrations of disapproval.

It occurred to her that she never entertained company in her apartment. Now she'd suddenly turned up with Jab, who was young, blessed with a genetically perfect worked-out body, and so good looking that even in a city teeming with beautiful people, he earned whiplash-inducing double takes from women—and men— of all ages.

Kellyanne had no doubt that Walter paid Julio something extra to keep a watchful eye on her comings and goings . . . and, more important—her visitors. For the first time, he'd actually earned his money, because she lived like a fucking recluse otherwise.

"This is sick," Jab murmured as they stepped inside the ultramod elevator that would catapult them to the forty-first floor. "I can't believe you live here." He glanced at the control panel. "Forty-eight stories!"

"I'm still getting used to being up so high," Kellyanne answered.

On the journey up, Jab had been as wide-eyed as a tourist experiencing the natural wonder of Niagara Falls for the first time. He gasped as they entered the sleek apartment. The maid service had shown up regularly during Kellyanne's absence. Everything was spotless and gleaming.

"You should see my place," Jab said, checking out the waterfront views. "It's a shit hole compared to this. And I share it with a roommate."

"At least your name's on the lease," Kellyanne pointed out. "I could be homeless at any time. That's no way to live. Believe me. It looks more glamorous than it really is."

Jab was practically salivating over the plasma television when he muttered, "Let me know if it doesn't work out with your guy. I'd gladly blow him on a regular basis for the chance to live here."

Kellyanne cut a harsh look in his direction.

"That came out wrong," Jab said. "I didn't mean it that way."

Kellyanne had no trouble letting it go. "Don't worry about it."

"I'd never allow a guy to stick his dick in my mouth. You know that, right?"

Kellyanne had given Jab an amused glare. He was just messing with her. "Shut up. You can watch TV while I pack. Help yourself to anything in the kitchen. There's beer in the refrigerator, and the bar's fully stocked, too."

She disappeared into the master bedroom, pulled three large Vuitton suitcases from the closet, and proceeded to carefully arrange all of her clothes, shoes, electronic devices, photographs, and personal papers. Kellyanne packed as if she might not ever return to Miami. She hadn't planned to do that. The impulse was pure instinct.

"So how does this man feel about your going off to the Hamptons for the summer?" Jab called out from the living room. "If I had the money to keep a woman like you, I'd never let you out of my sight."

Kellyanne stepped out of the bedroom, holding her new favorite belt—a velvet piece by Chanel with a gorgeous crystal-and-resin buckle. Walter had bought it for her in Paris last month while vacationing there with his wife, Connie. "Jab, please. You'd get bored and start looking around for the next hot girl. That's the age-old story. Men chase, they catch, and then they start all over again."

For a moment, Jab just tipped back a bottle of Blue Marlin and stared at her. "I know I'm a pussy hound. But you'd be rehab for a guy like me."

Kellyanne considered him, wondering what it might feel like to be with a man closer to her own age again, instead of one thirty-plus years older. She'd been faithful to Walter all this time, so the idea was infinitely tempting.

Jab had cut quite a swath through the waitress pool at Silk Electric, and the reviews were wildly enthusiastic. Though the consensus had always been that he was a hopeless cad, there were rarely hard feelings toward him. His ex-lovers praised his amazingly fit body, his impressive endowment, and his incredible skills in bed.

"I'd just be one more waitress for you," Kellyanne told him lightly. "And then you'd become obsessed with getting Pommie into bed."

Jab quickly rose from the sofa and moved toward her. "That's crap." He closed in, wrapping his arms around her waist and resting the Blue Marlin bottle in the crack of her ass. "The first part, I mean. I'll always want to show Pommie what she's missing. People change. But I think that girl's a hard-core lesbian for life."

Kellyanne laughed, feeling torn, half of her wanting to extricate from his embrace, the other half enjoying the closeness and the erotic energy of a possible encounter. She was barely able to look at him. "I'm a mess, Jab."

"If that's the case, you're the most beautiful mess I've ever seen. I'll take my chances."

In that moment, Walter's rude dismissal had ricocheted in Kellyanne's mind. And now the notion of a zipless fuck with Jab, the kind she had read about in Erica Jong's *Fear of Flying*, seemed inevitable.

Jab put his mouth onto hers, softly at first, then with delicious passion and insistence. "I'm going to make you come," he whispered. "But not the short little climax you feel all in one place. That's the kind you're used to, isn't it? I'm going to make you come so hard that you feel it throughout your entire body."

As a general proposal, it was difficult to turn down. But Kellyanne gently pushed him away. "I can't, Jab . . . there's too much going on in my head. All I want to do right now is get out of Miami."

Jab grinned, shaking his head regretfully. "And I was so close."

Kellyanne laughed. "Honey, you have no idea."

Now she was storming through the Delta terminal at JFK, desperate to retrieve her checked baggage, make the trek to the Jitney airport connection, and board the night's final bus for Long Island. It was strange. But she felt like a new life was waiting for her there.

Kellyanne's recharged cell phone jingled to the music of Destiny's Child's "Independent Women," a ring tone dedicated exclusively to Liza. "I'm here! My plane just landed!"

"I'm on my way to the airport," Liza said. "Wait for me, and we'll drive in together."

"You don't have to do that!" Kellyanne wailed. "It's late. And I already made plans to take the Jitney."

"Cancel them," Liza insisted. "I pay a fortune every month to keep my car in a parking garage. I should get some use out of it. We'll be exhausted, but it'll be worth it to wake up in the Hamptons tomorrow morning."

A half hour later, Kellyanne was embracing her friend outside the ground transportation exit. Immediately, she was struck by Liza's gaunt look. Kellyanne had never seen her so thin. By comparison, Victoria Beckham was a heavy girl. And the smell of alcohol on Liza's breath concerned her.

"You look amazing, as always," Liza gushed. "You tanned, blond, fit, and flawless . . . *bitch.*"

Kellyanne laughed. "You look great, too, but you're so *skinny!* I'm going to make my mother's recipe for frozen peanut butter pie, and you're going to eat the whole thing. I insist!"

"I accept!" Liza shrieked. "As long as there's chocolate involved." She helped Kellyanne maneuver the cart that was overburdened with Vuitton cases. "My God, look at all this luggage. Are you moving here permanently?"

Kellyanne halted. "Honestly, I don't know where I'll end up after this."

Liza hooked an arm under hers. "Well, we've got the entire summer to figure that out."

They tumbled the luggage into the cargo area of Liza's black Lexus LX 470.

"Are you sure that you're okay to drive?" Kellyanne asked. "Don't take this the wrong way. But you look tired, and it's obvious that you've been drinking."

Liza's body tensed. She started to protest, then seemed to think better of it. "Follow the signs to the Long Island Expressway," she said, surrendering the keys.

Kellyanne accepted them gratefully. "Bless your heart. I've been a passenger all day. I'd *love* the chance to drive." She climbed behind the steering wheel and carefully adjusted the seat and mirrors. "It feels strange being up so high. But I kind of like it. Maybe I should trade in my little sports car for a monster SUV like this." But as she gave voice to the idea, it dawned on her that only Walter could make that decision. The Mercedes roadster was registered in his name only.

"I'm so glad that you're here," Liza trilled. "But be warned—it's going to take both of us to keep Billie in line."

Kellyanne's eyes widened. "Oh, God—how wild is she?"

"Worse than ever. Or maybe the same. Who knows? We're used to spending a long weekend together once a year. This is an entire season. I suppose it'll be a miracle if we're still friends by Labor Day. Veer to your right up ahead."

Kellyanne nodded, still trying to adjust to the road handling of the large vehicle. "Don't worry. We're going to have an amazing time. I just know it." She smiled at Liza to underscore her confidence on the matter.

Liza grinned in response, vaguely hopeful but certainly not convinced. "I got your text. What happened with the show?"

Kellyanne groaned. "I'll tell you everything—provided I'm at a pool or on a beach *and* have a drink in my hand."

"I'm sorry it was a bad experience . . . but I'm glad it got you here earlier than planned."

"Me, too," Kellyanne whispered, willing herself to banish all thoughts of Walter, Brad "Bonzi" Lucas, and Adam Griffie. She glanced over at Liza. "Am I *finally* going to meet Justin? I can't believe you've been married all this time, and I've never laid eyes on your husband."

Liza's mouth tightened. "When you finally meet him, he might be my ex-husband."

Kellyanne was stunned. "Sweetheart, I'm sorry. I didn't realize you were having problems."

Liza sighed. "We're too far apart, I guess. Intellectually . . . economically . . . it just doesn't work. And now we don't even connect sexually. I think he prefers his women dumb and poor."

"Really? Maybe *I* should marry him," Kellyanne cracked.

Liza managed a half-smile and waved her left hand. "You can have him. I'll even throw in the ring."

"Have you tried counseling?" Kellyanne asked, her tone more serious now.

"A man like Justin isn't hardwired for couples therapy. He considers psychiatry a threat to his masculinity. If the problem at home can't be solved with his dick, then it's not his problem."

"So . . . what do you do now?"

Liza gazed out at the dark road ahead. "I probably should see an attorney. I think he's cheating. He didn't admit to it outright, but he didn't deny it, either. And the truth is, I'm not sure that I even care one way or the other. Maybe I'm not cut out for marriage. Not in the traditional sense, anyway. My literary agent has been involved with the same man for twenty years. But they don't live together. And sometimes they take separate vacations. I can see myself in a relationship like that. With the right man, of course."

"But what if you wanted children?" Kellyanne wondered. "How would that arrangement work then?"

Liza's hands dropped to her lower abdomen. "Funny you should ask. I'm scheduled for my second egg retrieval next week."

Kellyanne shot her a look, a question in her eyes.

"The drugs are a real bitch," Liza confessed. "But when I do decide to get pregnant, then I'll have a greater chance of conceiving, whether that be with a man in my life or with a sperm donor."

"So you're stockpiling your eggs?" Kellyanne couldn't keep the incredulity out of her voice.

"Is something wrong with that?"

"No, of course not," Kellyanne answered quickly. "It just seems so . . . I don't know . . . calculating."

"You have to be. For the next ten years, I want to focus on my career and grab every opportunity that comes my way. I'll start thinking about a baby after I turn forty. But there's too much risk and uncertainty to rely on my body at that age. My eggs are vital now, and the freezing technology is incredibly sophisticated."

Kellyanne grew silent. It amazed her how Liza could sit there and announce what she'd be doing at forty. Meanwhile, Kellyanne was in the dark when it came down to simply predicting where her life might be after the summer. "It sounds like you have everything figured out."

"No, I'm just giving myself options," Liza said. "Believe me. I have *nothing* figured out."

"At least you have a ten-year plan," Kellyanne countered, revealing a bit of the awe that she felt toward Liza. "Plus, you have a real career and assets in your own name."

"Yeah, well, that's just a matter of being practical. Every woman in today's society should be financially independent. Otherwise, she's a fool."

Kellyanne winced at the words. They made her feel like an anachronism. Sometimes she considered herself a bimbo mistress relic from the eighties, a plaything to some money baron who kept her anxious for expensive gifts and lonely on important holidays. Girls like her never came out on top. They were usually left with nothing but the bitter regret of having wasted their most productive years.

The digital car clock tripped past midnight, and at least another ninety minutes of driving loomed ahead. Kellyanne's eyelids felt heavy. There'd be plenty of time for Liza to weigh in on her pathetic life and deliver her feminist firebrand robo-lecture in full. So at the moment, Kellyanne was desperate to change the subject.

"I wonder what Billie is doing right now."

Billie

TEN

She was drunk dialing Todd Bana. "Answer the phone, motherfucker!" Over and over again, she punched in the number, refusing to leave a message, knowing from personal observation that his BlackBerry was attached to him like nerve fibers.

Finally, Todd picked up, only to scream, "Jesus Christ, Billie! What the fuck do you want?"

His hostility barely registered. Billie was wasted. She was pissed off, too. So shouting was her preferred method of communication anyway. "I want some goddamn progress, you son of a bitch!"

"At one o'clock in the morning?" He laughed at her. "You're a nutcase. Hey, I've got an idea. Why don't you hang up and go boil a rabbit."

In the background, a woman cackled.

Billie could hear Todd inhaling sharply. The bastard was loaded and banging some stupid bitch. And here she was sitting alone in the dark like a fat girl on prom night, living on the hope that March Donaldson might call.

"Hold on." Todd's tone was curt. A moment later, Billie heard him murmuring in a thick, sexy voice. "No, no, no . . . snort it off my cock . . . get every bit . . . don't waste it, baby . . . good girl . . . very good girl."

Billie experienced an immediate white-hot rage. "You're with some slut getting coked out of your mind!"

"What's your point?"

She fought the urge to throw the phone against the wall. "My point is that I haven't heard a fucking thing about those songs you want me to record. I'm taking a big risk by going in this new direction. I don't mind my bass player partying like a rock star, but I wish my label president would act like a real suit."

"Be careful what you wish for," Todd said ominously.

"What the fuck is that supposed to mean?" Billie demanded.

"It means that a buttoned-down exec would look at your numbers and tell you to get lost."

Even in her alcohol-soaked haze, Billie knew to fold instead of fight. A few drinks and two Ambiens ago, the idea to call Todd and raise hell had seemed like a good one. She'd only lashed out at him because March was unreachable.

"I'm scared, Todd," Billie whined. "This is a new thing for me— recording someone else's songs. Maybe I'd relax a little if I heard the demos."

Todd sighed. "Two of the tracks were on Ariel's last album. 'Submission' and 'Naked in the Rain.' Check them out on iTunes. Van can e-mail you an audio file of the third song next week."

Billie's stomach lurched as the impact of Todd's words began to resonate. "You expect me to take sloppy seconds from *Ariel*?"

Ariel was a former Miss Teen USA who'd shot to worldwide fame after a star turn in a successful *High School Musical* rip-off called *Homecoming Dance*. But just as her first hit single was building, her career had been derailed by scandal. A DUI accident in Los Angeles had killed a pregnant woman and her two young children. Leaving an all-night party at seven in the morning, Ariel had driven the wrong way down an exit ramp, causing the head-on collision that also claimed the life of the twenty-two-year-old personal assistant traveling with her.

"White Tiger considers those tracks some of their best work," Todd assured her in a voice just patronizing enough to make her want to take a sledgehammer to his balls. "Ariel's album tanked after the accident. Nobody will identify those songs with her. Once you lay down the vocals, they'll be yours."

Billie was hardly convinced. "This is bullshit, Todd."

"I agree. Anything but sex or sleeping at this hour usually is."

"There's no way—"

"*Billie,*" Todd cut in savagely. "I'm with a gorgeous piece of ass, we're both on a coke high, and it's time for me to fuck her brains out."

Click.

She started to protest, then realized that the Napoleonic shit had hung up on her. "Cocksucker!" She hoped that bitch infected him with hepatitis tonight.

Billie considered calling Todd right back. But before she could act on that impulse, a stronger one sent the cellular device sailing across the room. It smashed against an antique mirror. A sickening crack fanned out like a spider's web and threatened seven years of bad luck.

She buried her face into the tangled sheets that had gone unlaundered all week, inhaling deeply, desperate to breathe in March's scent. When would he call her again? For a long time Billie just lay there, unable to erase the mental image of March spooned against Amaryllis, sleeping and satisfied. Is that what he was doing right now? The horrible possibility consumed her until she drifted into oblivion.

"*You* should sue for sexual harassment," Liza said.

Billie couldn't resist a slight roll of the eyes as she tried to factor the worst-case scenario. Was it her killer hangover, Kellyanne's reality TV woes, or Liza's feminist bullshit?

"I made a mistake," Kellyanne said matter-of-factly. "Nobody forced me to sign on for that show. Now I just want to move forward. Legal action would cost too much and take too long. I'm done with it. And I want things to stay that way."

"But it's not just about you," Liza argued. "Your case could spotlight the indignities that so many women face in that industry. I think the reality genre is a form of pornography."

Billie slathered on more bronzing oil, drank deep on her Bloody Mary, and chomped down on the celery stick garnish. "Yeah, Kellyanne could stand up for all the sad, single sluts of the world and become the Norma Rae of lame dating shows."

Liza, the self-righteous skeleton, shot her a polar look.

Billie ignored the silent reprimand, her gaze falling on Kellyanne's perfect tan. It was on glorious display in her Michael Kors white bikini with gold chain insets. The girl's beauty was so exquisite that it became impossible to ignore. And how fucking unfair that she had possession of such a gift yet squandered it on a rich old man and deadend career moves.

Liza rose up from the chaise, adjusting her white floppy hat and oversized Tom Ford sunglasses.

"Careful, Liza," Billie teased. "I think you might be burning."

Kellyanne grinned.

"Instant gratification isn't my thing," Liza said. "A tan looks great in the short run, but the sun damage will haunt you for the rest of your life."

In answer to the minilecture, Kellyanne stretched languidly, letting out a faint, almost orgasmic moan of pleasure. "Nothing natural that feels this good could be bad for you."

"I'm going inside to make more Bloody Marys," Liza announced. "Anybody?"

"Oh, I'm fine, thanks," Kellyanne said.

"Don't be such a pansy girl with the vodka," Billie complained. "That last round tasted like a virgin batch."

Liza slipped into her Manolo Blahnik yellow flat thong sandals and started for the house, laughing a little. "I could leave out the tomato juice altogether and give you a glass of straight vodka. I bet the drink still wouldn't be strong enough."

Kellyanne smiled absently at the remark. She was staring down at the intricate mosaic design on the bottom of the pool, completely lost in her own reverie. "Do you think she's right, Billie?"

"About what?"

"Am I letting down other women by walking away from this?"

"It's *your* life," Billie pointed out. "Besides, if you cared about other women so much, you wouldn't be fucking someone's husband."

Kellyanne's face registered real shock.

"Why do you look so surprised?" Billie challenged. "Did I say something inaccurate?"

"The situation is complicated," Kellyanne said quietly.

"It's not like I'm moralizing," Billie assured her. "I'm just saying that you don't owe anybody any explanations." She cut a glance back toward the house. "Liza's always going off about what women need to be doing for each other. I say the bitch should practice what she preaches. I mean, come on. Why not eat a bagel for sisterhood? That might actually do something for the body image crisis. Have you noticed how fucking skinny she is?"

Kellyanne nodded uncomfortably. "Some women have trouble keeping on weight. And it could be stress-related, too. Last night she mentioned problems at home with Justin. It sounds serious. She thinks he's cheating."

Billie shrugged. "From what I've seen so far, she won't be far behind him. I wonder if she made him sign a prenup. He's not earning shit as a fireman. She could be looking at paying out major alimony. Now that would really test her equality principles."

"Look!" Kellyanne suddenly exclaimed, pointing at the pool gate.

A beautiful golden retriever was propped up on its hind legs, negotiating the latch with nimble front paws until the gate fell open. Then the dog trotted across the deck, jumped into the crystal blue water with a loud splash, and swam the entire length of the pool, exiting at the opposite end to shake off and lick the faces and feet of Billie and Kellyanne.

"That's Annie," Billie explained. "She comes by every day for a morning and afternoon swim."

"Oh, bless her heart!" Kellyanne squealed. "She's precious! I wish we could keep her for the summer."

"She belongs to some big designer who lives down the street. He's got his own show on HGTV."

Liza was stepping out of the house just as Annie flitted through the gate as stealthily as she'd arrived. "Bye-bye, Annie!"

"That is *so* adorable," Kellyanne gushed. "Oh, I miss having a dog. I wanted to get a small breed, but Walter forbade it. He's allergic."

Billie moved fast to relieve Liza of her Bloody Mary and wasted no time in sipping greedily. The extra vodka gave the drink some necessary bite. "Oh, yes. Much better."

"K.K. just called about a party tonight," Liza announced. "He's hosting a cocktail hour and dinner for close friends and realized that he needs some authentic estrogen on the guest list."

Billie pulled an ugly face. "I'm in no mood to be a fag hag tonight."

"I know," Liza agreed, a bit guiltily. "I didn't commit us to anything. I only said we'd try to stop by for a drink." She turned to Kellyanne. "This is your first weekend. What do you feel like doing?"

"I'm open to *anything*," Kellyanne answered sincerely. "Honestly. I'm just thrilled to be out of Miami. You could tell me that we're going to search for ticks on Annie tonight, and I'd be fine with it."

Billie howled with laughter.

Liza chuckled as she perched down onto the edge of her chaise. "Well, I don't think it'll come to that. I was thinking we could do some shopping together at Citarella's this afternoon. We could pick out some great wine and load up on all kinds of gourmet munchies. Then tonight we could check out Sunset Beach on Shelter Island.

It's always a packed scene, and they make the best Mojitos I've ever had. March Donaldson will be there. He's the guy I spar with on *The Roundtable*."

Billie's stomach lurched at the mere mention of March's name. She hadn't heard anything from him in days, and now Liza was suddenly a fucking central intelligence agency about his social plans.

"Oh, he's hot," Kellyanne put in. "I never agree with what he has to say, but he's definitely fun to look at."

"How do you know that he'll be there?" Billie inquired, fighting to keep her tone casual. "Is that one of his regular hangouts?"

"I don't know," Liza said. "But he sent me a text this morning, so I know he'll be there." She gave Billie a wicked smile. "With Amaryllis, I'm sure."

"*Great,*" Billie managed to deadpan, still fuming internally. She checked her cell phone again to make certain she hadn't missed a call or a text. Not a goddamn thing.

"Who's Amaryllis?" Kellyanne asked.

"March's fiancée," Liza explained. "She's a Connecticut debutante."

"And we hate the bitch," Billie added.

"She works in PR for Stella McCartney," Liza continued evenly. "Her parents have a gorgeous estate in Watermill. The landscaping is immaculate. We should rev up the Vespas and ride over there for a look."

"Yeah," Billie snarled. "And maybe Amaryllis will invite us in for afternoon tea." Knowing that she was going to see March tonight had her completely fucked up. No guy had ever gotten to Billie quite like this. She downed what remained of her Bloody Mary, deciding that the only way to deal was to get fully loaded. And she had all day long to do it.

The stereo was blasting Jennifer Lopez at maximum volume. "You can turn me on, throw me off track/Boy, you do it well . . ."

Liza swiveled her hips and vamped in the mirror, whipping around her freshly blown-out hair. "How do I look?"

Billie surveyed Liza's ballerina-thin neck, her long chopstick legs, and the Diane von Furstenberg butterfly-print tank dress. "You look like a lollipop. If cock is the only meat you allow in your mouth, then you really need to start swallowing. You could use the calories."

With a measured calm, Liza sprayed her pulse points with Sarah Jessica Parker's Covet fragrance. "Billie, I think you need to see someone. A professional. I'm convinced you have some form of Tourette's."

Kellyanne appeared in the doorway of Liza's master bathroom, stunning in a Tory Burch silk tie halter top and second-skin tight jeans by a Swedish Denim company called Acne. "Don't laugh. I brought all that luggage, but I forgot to pack nipple covers."

Liza located a new strip of Nippets and handed the packet over.

"Thanks. You're a sweetheart," Kellyanne said. She seemed to speak in a perpetual breathy singsong. It was at once soothing and annoying. "I *love* that dress. It's genius."

Liza pursed her lips in triumph, as if validated. "Billie thinks I look like a lollipop."

"Billie!" Kellyanne admonished, half-laughing and clearly trying to stop. "That's mean."

Billie shrugged, taking a swig from the Voss water bottle that now contained X-rated premium vodka. "Do we really need to bullshit each other? Isn't that what the men in our lives are for?" She adjusted the neckline of her teal-colored Betsey Johnson dotted tunic and finger-combed her hair into place. "I'll say this, though, Liza. For an anorexic bitch, you look damn good. If I had a dick, I'd fuck you."

Liza delicately smoothed over an eyebrow with the tip of her ring finger. "Forget songs. You should write greeting cards."

Kellyanne laughed, putting another coat of gloss onto seemingly liquid lips.

"Look at us," Billie marveled as she stood in front of the full-length double vanity mirror, flanked by Liza on her right and Kellyanne on her left. "We weren't this hot in our college days." Suddenly, she swayed backward on her Brian Atwood platform sandals.

Liza reacted quickly to stop her fall. "Okay, you either need flats or a pot of coffee." She paused a beat. "Or rehab."

Billie steadied herself on the Plexiglas heels. "I just lost my balance for a second. I'm fine." She took in a deep breath and gave all of them a curious assessment, wondering how this group had made a friendship sealed in the crucible of a Cancún college party last almost ten fucking years.

Everybody wanted the *Sex and the City* girl clique model—sisterly love, emotional intimacy, loyalty, and all that shit. But Billie had rarely seen it work in the real world. Sure, some women tried. They even pretended. But shine a blue light on most girl posses, and the evidence was right there—the weak bonds, the blind determination to prove to themselves—to prove to the world—that they had their own Carrie, Samantha, Miranda, and Charlotte thing going on. Maybe the delusion made them feel less lonely.

Most women hated Billie. For starters, she was too honest. If a pair of jeans made a girl's ass look big, she said so without being asked. And no longtime crush, boyfriend, or husband was ever off limits. When Billie wanted to bang a guy, it was game on. Most women hated Kellyanne, too. She was too fucking beautiful. What other reason did they need? As for Liza, she was nobody's dream sorority sister—too intelligent, too ambitious, too opinionated. It was no wonder the three of them had glommed together over the years. They were settling for whatever was there.

Billie gave everyone a final once over in the mirror. "Bitches, I think we're ready."

Shelter Island was a remote and secluded jewel on the eastern end of Long Island. Part of its charm was the quaint isolation. The island was only accessible by an open-decked ferry that shuttled back and forth between the North and South forks. Throwback touches to an earlier, more innocent age were everywhere. Billie's favorite was a hand-stenciled sign nailed to a tree. It warned drivers of crossing turtles.

As Liza gunned the Lexus down Route 114, Billie lay slumped in the backseat, more than living up to her goal of being properly smashed in advance of the night's event. Her new plan was to pretend that March Donaldson didn't exist. Even if he walked up and slapped his dick across her face, she'd still ignore him. The asshole could rot in hell with that slab of dry ice from Connecticut. Billie didn't care anymore.

She listened with vague interest as Liza and Kellyanne blathered on about how beautiful everything was in the Hamptons. Billie's thoughts drifted to how nice it would be to have a second home in one of the hamlets, a peaceful place to escape from the city. Of course, Amy would tell her that she couldn't afford it. But if Todd's relaunch idea worked, then she'd be swimming in cash.

West Neck Road became Shore Road. Liza followed it to the beach and turned left into a parking lot. Billie swung out first, spotted a dingy waterfront restaurant, and murmured, "What's the big fucking deal?"

Venturing closer, it became clear. The sunset and harbor views were spectacular. Billie climbed the stairs to discover three outside decks, each one at full capacity and overflowing with kinetic social energy. The decor was simple—rattan chairs, benches, and strings of little white lights. Kat DeLuna's melodic Caribbean jam "Am I Dreaming?" percolated in the background.

The atmosphere made Billie ravenous for a cigarette. She dug into the crocodile hobo bag that had set her back two grand. Something to tell her kids if she ever had any: Never shop online late at night when you're drunk. "Fuck!"

"What's wrong?" Kellyanne asked.

Billie continued digging, even though she knew it was a futile effort. "I left my goddamn cigarettes back at the house." She spotted a hunky guy smoking in the sand and made an instant beeline for him. "Hey, can I bum one of those? I'm about to die."

He smiled at her with perfect teeth and tapped out a Parliament. "Do you need a light?"

Billie shook her head, whipped out a vintage Cartier lighter, dragged deep, and filled her lungs with the sweet poison. "Thanks."

"My pleasure." His hair was styled in a severe buzz cut, his body was lean and lanky, and he dressed down in a gray tank, camo cargo pants, and an orange cotton hoodie. The sum of it all was a poor girl's Justin Timberlake. He studied her for a moment. "You look familiar."

"That's because I'm a fucking rock star."

He laughed. "That's a good one. Do you mind if I steal that sometime?"

"Why? Do you think it'll get you laid?" She started off to catch up with Liza and Kellyanne.

"Maybe," he called out. "It'd sure work for you if you came back to my room tonight!"

Grinning, she took another drag and waved him off, trudging through the sand in her Brian Atwoods. Christ! She'd paid nine hundred bucks for these shoes. Did a girl have to be in fucking Cirque du Soleil to walk sexy in them?

She nearly tripped over a fat chocolate Labrador that was sacked out in the sand, no cares in the world. "Oops," she giggled, bending over to stroke the pooch's adorable face. "Sorry, sweetie."

The dog licked her hand and went back to sleep.

Billie glanced up at the obvious owners, an attractive older couple holding court just a few feet away. She smiled at them. "I'll have what he's having."

The husband laughed uproariously; the wife managed a tight smile and glared at Billie behind Fendi sunglasses.

The bistro's uncovered deck was packed. Liza and Kellyanne had secured what appeared to be the last table on earth. A first round of drinks had already been ordered, and a fresh Mojito sat waiting.

Billie gulped down the concoction of rum, sugar, lime, and mint as if it were Gatorade. The drink was beyond delicious. Instantly, she wanted another. She stopped a fast-moving waitress and pushed the empty glass into her hand. "Bring me two of these as soon as humanly possible and keep them coming after that."

Liza laughed. "I could have a word with management. Maybe they'll set up an IV drip."

Billie thrust out a forearm and made a fist. "I'm game for that." Anxiously, she scanned the crowd. March could be on one of the other decks. He could be inside the restaurant, too. She wanted the chance to ignore him. In fact, her body was burning for the opportunity.

"Kellyanne, I think you have some admirers," Liza observed, discreetly gesturing to a rowdy trio of twenty-something guys.

To say they were hammered would be the understatement of the night. The three stooges were laughing, gawking, and adjusting themselves over the sight of the blond goddess from Alabama. And in true testosterone posse fashion, there appeared to be a sexually confident leader, a funny dork, and a financially successful asshole.

Kellyanne rolled her eyes skyward as the ringleader approached, leaving his idiot friends behind to sort out the cash for whatever bet had been wagered.

He walked right up to Kellyanne and politely asked, "Do you clean houses?"

Kellyanne's model-perfect face became a masterpiece of bored disbelief. "Excuse me?"

"I'm looking for a housekeeper."

Kellyanne tossed an annoyed look to Billie and Liza, as if questioning her hearing. "Sorry. I guess your search continues."

He reached into his back pocket. "Let me give you one of my business cards just in case you change your mind."

"Don't bother. I won't." Kellyanne spun around, ignoring the lame offering.

Billie watched the interloper glance back at his buddies and shoot them a self-satisfied asshole grin. Actually, she thought the guy was sort of hot. His who-gives-a-fuck attitude gave him a certain sex appeal. But the smug shit needed to be schooled on the fact that all the gym work he put into his Vin Diesel arms would never compensate for the Stein Mart wardrobe, gay-porn-star goatee, and Johnny Knoxville idol worship.

"Oh, now I'm *really* going to need a drink." The voice booming behind her belonged to March Donaldson.

Billie experienced a powerful thump in her gut. It was fucking ridiculous. The bastard had her at "Oh." She turned slowly, intending to look fast, then look away. But she ended up just standing there, robbed of all breath, drinking in every detail and finding herself thirsting for more. Her desire for him seemed unquenchable.

She watched him play primarily to Liza while Billie got a casual, "Hello, nice to see you again." March was social maestro as introductions went back and forth with Kellyanne and Amaryllis. Another attractive couple entered the mix—Jay and Gopa Dobson. March announced that he and Amaryllis had flown in from Manhattan on Jay's helicopter. Billie had taken the goddamn Jitney bus. She was slowly boiling with fury now.

The loser who tried to hit on Kellyanne was still standing on the periphery, wondering what to do with the business card nobody wanted. He was five foot ten. He was only mildly handsome. It was so unfortunate. But when a March Donaldson entered the room, men of this caliber were rendered as meaningless as bugs on a windshield.

Billie knocked back Mojito after Mojito, her frustration building as the party mushroomed. MSNBC's Dan Abrams turned up with a pretty blonde, but his eyes tracked Kellyanne like heat-seeking lasers. The interior designers Jamie Drake and Peter Falk made their way over with shrewd housing investors Audrey and Phillip Davis. As Amaryllis glowered off to the side, Audrey openly swooned over March. The woman with the gorgeous turquoise choker was thrilled to encounter a fellow Republican who—like her—was proud to say so.

The more the evening progressed, the easier it was for March to ignore Billie. She left to bum another cigarette, finding her Timberlake clone in the same spot. His name was Shayne Cutter. He announced that he was staying on Shelter Island for the summer to finish a screenplay. The name Billie Shelton rang no bells for him. Without apology, he admitted to listening to only hip-hop since the age of twelve. She entertained the idea of fucking him later that night and wandered back to the group.

"Billie, where have you been?" Liza asked. "We ordered some food!"

She surveyed the crisp french fries, steamed mussels, shrimp rolls, and fried calamari. It looked delicious. It smelled divine. But all she wanted was another Mojito.

Amaryllis was engaged in a serious conference with Jamie and Peter. "If you saw what she did to my parents' pool house, then you would understand why I sent her a new set of cards with the title *inferior desecrator* under her name."

Casually, March sidled up to Billie, sipped his drink, and took in the scene. "Are we having fun yet?" He spoke in a deliberately low voice.

Billie's spirits were instantly buoyed by his acknowledgment. Her desperation was total. She hated him for that. And she would make him pay for it, too. "I'm not wearing any underwear."

March swallowed hard. "Don't tell me that. It's not fair."

"It's not supposed to be. But I did it for you."

He seemed to be concentrating on the situation as if it were hard science. "Go to the bathroom. I'll count to sixty and follow you there."

Billie liked his plan. It was hot and dangerous and risky. She had the son of a bitch exactly where she wanted him—horny enough to choose her even with his fiancée standing three feet away. A man's cock truly had a will all its own.

She walked inside the ladies room, only to find a trashy blonde in front of the mirror, touching up a makeup job that had been botched from the start. Billie checked the stalls. They were empty. Now she just needed this imitation Tara Reid to beat it.

"*Billie Shelton*? Oh, my God! I, like, love, love, *love* your music!"

Christ. Of all things to contend with at the moment—a fucking fan.

"I saw your concert at Jones Beach last year! It was awesome! Nobody's going to believe this! You've got to take a picture with me!" She rushed Billie, pressed against her cheek to cheek, and thrust out her right hand to frame them inside her cell phone camera's tiny lens. When she inspected the captured image, she beamed, displaying it with pride. "This rocks!"

Billie smiled weakly, growing increasingly anxious. Fans like this were usually good nourishment for the ego. But she had half a mind to flush this bitch down the toilet. March was probably loitering outside by now, feeling conspicuous and ready to bolt.

Thinking fast, Billie clutched her stomach with both hands. "Ugh . . . I think I'm going to be sick." She tilted her head toward the exit. "Do you mind?"

"Oh, God! No! Is there anything I can do?"

Billie shook her head. "I'll be fine. I just need a few minutes."

Finally, the girl got the hint and took off.

Billie paused for a count of ten before flinging open the door and pulling March inside with a degree of strength and power that surprised her.

He was caught off guard, too, losing his balance and bracing the sink to steady himself. He laughed and groped for her, kissing her neck, his fingers, lips, and tongue practically searing into her. "We should lock the door."

"Then we'll *definitely* get caught." Billie pushed him inside the last stall, shoved him onto the commode, and latched the door.

March flattened his feet against it, helping Billie climb onto the toilet and holding her legs as she struggled for traction.

"These goddamn shoes! I should take them off."

"No," March said quickly. "They're fucking hot. Keep them

on." He worked harder to steady her body, the proof of his effort in the corded veins popping out of his forearms. "Do you have any coke?"

She shook her head.

He groaned. "Fuck, I'd kill for a line right now."

Billie hiked up her Betsey Johnson dress and squatted over him. "I made a special trip into the city this week. I went to J. Sisters just like you said. Do you like it?"

March arched his back to inspect the work, then dipped two fingers into his mouth to moisten them before slowly tracing the outline of his meticulously sculpted initials, moaning his appreciation. "MDD . . . this is definitely my pussy now." He slid a finger inside, teasing her. "How'd you know my middle name was Douglas?"

"I Googled you."

He chuckled slightly, angling his neck to taste her.

Billie waited until his mouth was almost there. And then she unleashed a slap across his face with such force that she had to grab the top of the stall's side panel to keep from falling down.

March reeled from the impact, then rose up, grabbing her firmly by both arms and shoving her against the door. He was close enough to breathe her breath. He was red-faced and angry. He was still turned on. "What the fuck? Do you like to play rough? Is that it?"

Billie gave him a placid little smile. "That's not it at all. Do you actually think I'm going to let you treat me like some throwaway piece of ass?" She didn't wait for his answer. "You suck. And I can't wait to shave tonight."

March dropped a hand down and rested it between her thighs. "You don't mean that."

"Oh, yes I do." It took nearly everything that she had to ignore the exquisite heat of his palm as it inched upward.

"Liar." He smiled like the cocky bastard he was.

Billie reached up to touch March's cheek. For a half movement, she caressed it, but then she dug her freshly manicured nails into that gorgeous face that had been bronzed by a thousand Texas suns.

March froze. His eyes went wide with fear.

All of a sudden, Billie halted. Her claws were deeply imbedded but not ripping skin . . . *yet.* She had the entire left side of his face in play. Her arm was perfectly angled, the tension in it as tight as a drum. All she had to do was work her way down. "I could fuck you up so bad that you wouldn't be able to go on television for a month."

"You're crazy." He didn't mean it in a good way.

Billie smiled at him. "I know." With her free hand she reached down to stroke the crotch of his Rock & Republic jeans, finding him hard—and getting harder. "Nine out of ten men surveyed will say that the best sex they ever had was with a girl who was just a little bit psycho."

March took in a deep breath, stifling a moan.

"I want you to think about that when you're in bed with your frigid fiancée tonight." And then Billie pushed him onto the toilet, unlatched the stall door, and stalked out to search for Shayne Cutter.

She found him smoking on the beach. Where else? He was talking on his cell phone but ended the call when he saw the sexual determination in Billie's hooded eyes.

Shayne took her by the hand and led her to his room at Sunset Beach. They shared a cigarette on the way. Not a single word was spoken. His suite was warm, cozy, and inviting—white walls, a carpeted floor, a minibar, and a large private balcony with a beautiful view of the water.

Billie noticed an Apple laptop on the desk. Several red-lined script pages were scattered around it. He really was working on a screenplay. She ventured over to have a look, picking up one of the more marked-up sheets of paper. From what she could tell, his project was some kind of vampire movie called *Not Enough Blood.*

Shayne stepped over, removed the page from her hand, and kissed her with an insistent passion. He tasted of Parliaments and Mojitos. "Is there anything I should know?"

Billie just looked at him.

His hands found their way to her ass, cupping her cheeks and giving them a delicious little squeeze. "What you like . . . what you don't like . . ."

"You can put it anywhere," Billie said.

Liza

ELEVEN

The cramping had been intense. In fact, a day after Liza had been administered the HCG drug to promote egg release, she'd nearly doubled over in agony. The pressure on her ovaries had been unreal. But that was last night. This morning she was recovering nicely, having undergone her second egg retrieval at Reproductive Medicine Associates of New York, an approved partner center of the Boston-based Extend Fertility.

"Things couldn't have gone better," Dr. Allan Copperman said. "We have thirty-two eggs from this cycle." He patted her forearm. "Still a little groggy from the sedation?"

Liza nodded.

Dr. Copperman had harvested fluid from her ovaries using an ultrasound-guided needle. The eggs had been identified under a microscope. They would soon be flash-frozen and secured in a liquid-nitrogen storage tank. Recent advancements in cryopreservation—one being a technique to avoid the formation of ice crystals during the freezing and thawing processes—had greatly improved the success rate of pregnancies.

The procedure was high-tech baby insurance. Liza knew that her decision to go through with it was the right one. The prospect of motherhood no longer seemed like a fatalistic deadline. Now it was a personal reality *whenever* she wanted to choose it—ten years into the future, perhaps even later. From her vantage point, the biological clock was still running, but it had stopped ticking like a time bomb. The attendant sense of freedom was empowering.

"We're going to have you rest for another hour," Dr. Copperman said. "Then you'll be free to go. Do you have any questions?"

"You probably won't see me again for ten years," Liza said wryly. "Take good care of my eggs."

Dr. Copperman smiled. He was a kind man with thick dark hair, a big smile, and a comforting bedside manner. "They're in capable hands. I assure you."

Extend Fertility's storage facility was state-of-the-art and protected by a fail-safe backup system, round-the-clock security, and a triple-checked client identification procedure. Liza had once joked to Christy Jones, the company's founder and CEO, that she should consider heading up Homeland Security. On Christy's watch, the domestic threat of al Qaeda would probably disappear overnight.

Liza rested peacefully, taking in the antiseptic surroundings, realizing that the next time she passed through these doors, it'd be for ICSI. An embryologist would fertilize one of her eggs with the injection of a single sperm in preparation for transfer to her uterus. But whose sperm? That'd be the real question facing her.

Since she returned home from the most recent weekend in the Hamptons, Liza and Justin had barely spoken. It amazed her how disengaged she could feel from a man who slept in the same bed with her. Night after night, Justin simply rolled over to one side, tucked his body into the fetal position, and snoozed like a satisfied baby.

It was over with him. Intellectually, Liza knew that. But emotionally, no matter how dysfunctional the situation, she felt a strange reluctance about taking the necessary measures to put an official break into motion. Part of her still loved him. And another part of her wasn't quite ready to be alone again. She wondered how long she could endure this state of limbo.

She took a deep breath and pushed Justin out of her thoughts, firing up her MacBook Pro and accessing the clinic's Wi-Fi network. She could make better use of the downtime by checking her public e-mail account and updating her blog.

Scrolling through the new messages, Liza noticed the usual assortment. There were scores of reader comments on *Whore*. The trade paperback release had triggered a new wave of passionate interest. There were also requests for speaking engagements, which she automatically forwarded to her lecture agent, plus the odd marriage proposal.

Of course, the most disturbing aspect of having a Web presence—and a high-profile media one—was exposure to the vicious attacks that came with it. Within her first few weeks of appearing as a regular pundit on *The Roundtable,* a doctored photo of Liza with a noose around her neck and a muzzle over her mouth had turned up on various blogging sites. And just days after launching her own blog, someone had posted a comment detailing his fantasy of ejaculating into her face and then slitting her throat.

Liza tried to be philosophical about the issue. The anonymity of online posts allowed dark prejudices and sick anger to surface, particularly toward women. And it was not merely an appalling lack of civility. It was genuine harassment. As a result, she knew women who only blogged under a gender-neutral pseudonym. She also knew of colleagues who'd simply abandoned the practice altogether.

Liza refused to be silenced or sidelined by what she considered to be lowest-common-denominator intimidation. She was determined to gut it out. Besides, the worst offenders were no doubt cowardly creeps posting in their stained bathrobes. So it was her custom to give these messages no more time than it took to click the DELETE button. But this morning, one missive in particular captured her attention.

From: travisowen@yahoo.com
To: liza@lizapike.com
Subject: Watch Her Bleed

Shut up, bitch. Or you will be next.
Travis Owen

A palpable unease swept over Liza as she read the words once, twice, three times. It was the subtext—not the vague threat—that bothered her. *Watch Her Bleed* was the title of Harrison Beck's slasher movie. Travis Owen was the name of its psychopathic character who goes on a murder binge targeting powerful and influential women. And at the end of the film, he escapes from an asylum for the criminally insane and lives to kill again, ostensibly in the inevitable sequel.

Something about the message left a distinct chill. Perhaps it was the idea that someone had actually taken the deliberate measure to not only create an e-mail account under the name of a fictional character but to write a message from that character's point of view as well. That degree of intent made Liza uncomfortable, though she ultimately trashed the e-mail.

The incident triggered a recall of one of her peers, Tuesday Kent. They'd met while in graduate school at Brandeis University. Both Liza and Tuesday had earned the wrath of other would-be feminist scholars on campus. With their stunning looks, interest in and acceptance of fashion, and appreciation for relationships with men, they were openly disdained, considered dubious torchbearers for the cause, and dismissively chided as "lipstick feminists."

They were also fiercely competitive with each other. Liza and Tuesday had dueling columns in *The Justice,* the independent weekly student newspaper. When Liza upstaged Tuesday by securing a call-in radio show on the university station WBRS-FM, the race was on to become the next Naomi Wolf. Postgraduation, Tuesday had crossed the ticker tape first. She landed a big publishing deal for *The Baby Girl Diaries*, a personal manifesto about growing up in the confines of a strict, patriarchal, upper-class suburban household. It became a phenomenally successful bestseller.

Tuesday had been shrewd in using the Web to marshal a community of dedicated followers, building a network of like-minded Baby Girls all across the country with her online message board and sophisticated electronic newsletters. But then came the trouble.

What Tuesday had thought was the occasional random comment suddenly hardened into a sinister trend of violent threats and character-assassinating taunts. Posts began popping up online with increasing frequency, everything from the prediction that Tuesday would die from a chainsaw rape to the outrageous charge that her Baby Girl nickname stemmed from a long-term sexual relationship with her father. Law enforcement officials laughed it off, telling her that it was just harmless online talk.

Eventually, the Web-based terrorism pushed Tuesday over the edge. She cancelled public speaking engagements. She stopped writing. She developed agoraphobia. And the saddest irony of all was that, in the end, she returned home to Highland Park in Dallas, where she moved back in with her parents and once again became the Baby Girl that she'd made a career out of disavowing with such ferocious aplomb.

Curiously, Liza logged onto Tuesday's official Web site. With the exception of a few stray message board comments wishing her well and calling for her return, the site hadn't been updated in over two years. Tuesday Kent remained underground. It was such a sad and wasteful turn of events. Liza remembered her as being so vital.

A thought lanced her brain about the e-mail she'd received from this Travis Owen. It occurred to Liza that Harrison Beck could be the culprit. Perhaps his idea of an inside joke? Her suspicions began to mount. If it was his attempt at humor, then it was a thoroughly tasteless effort. But then again, this was the same man responsible for bringing *Watch Her Bleed* to the screen. What else could she possibly expect from him?

The hour passed quickly and, along with it, the lingering effects of the anesthesia. Liza checked out of the clinic and slowly negotiated her body into a cab. The tenderness would remain for the next few days. After taking a deep breath, she announced her address to the driver.

She switched her BlackBerry from silent mode and checked for missed calls. There were four—one from her literary agent, one from Tom Shapiro, and two from Kellyanne.

The device vibrated in Liza's hand. She smiled and answered the call before it had a chance to ring. "Third time's the charm. I just walked out."

"How did everything go?" Kellyanne asked.

"Thirty-two eggs," Liza said, groaning slightly.

"*Thirty-two?*" Kellyanne exclaimed. "In your itty-bitty body? I can't believe it."

Liza laughed. "They're not goose eggs. You can't even see them without a microscope."

"I know, but still. Was Justin with you?"

"No." She paused a beat. "He's at the fire station."

"So you were there all by yourself? Bless your heart! I knew that I should've insisted on coming with you."

"I'm fine," Liza assured her. "I was in and out within two hours. I don't even have an incision."

"Well, I didn't know what to do with myself, so I made my mother's frozen peanut butter pie. Part of your recovery is going to be eating the whole damn thing."

Liza grinned. "What are your plans for the rest of the day?"

"I'll probably go to the beach. And then I might do some shopping."

"I have a few calls to return. I'll check in with you later, okay?" Liza signed off and rang Tom Shapiro.

"You're a lightweight," Tom said right away. "I haven't seen a girl that drunk in a limousine since my junior prom."

"Well, I hope she got more action than I did."

He chuckled. "Actually, she cut my dick with her braces while attempting a blow job and threw up at the sight of the blood."

146

Liza laughed. "I assume that's the defining moment when you gave up on women."

"Yeah—that and Don Johnson. When I was ten years old, I liked *Miami Vice* way too much."

"Such a sweet, confused boy."

"Did you know that your husband challenged me to a racquetball game the other night?" Tom asked.

"That doesn't surprise me. He's always up for a game. Are you any good?"

"I can hold my own."

Liza smiled at the cocky edge in his voice. "Justin's an athletic cyborg, Tom. Even with a sport he's never played before. He could take up windsurfing tomorrow and make lifers look like first-timers. You'll be totally annihilated."

"Care to put some money down on that?" Tom challenged.

"That would be stealing," Liza teased. "I like you too much for that."

"You know, you really are a bitch. I'm going to stop defending you to other people."

Liza laughed again. "Before I forget—I've got a topic idea for the next show."

"Hold the thought," Tom said. "We're dark for the next three weeks."

"Oh, that's right," Liza murmured, recalling the on-and-off summer schedule. She felt an immediate sense of relief. This would allow her the flexibility to spend more time in the Hamptons. "Are you going anywhere fun?"

"To the West Coast for a few days. But it's work. We're shooting a Hollywood red and blue version of *The Roundtable*. Mel Gibson, Alec Baldwin, Susan Sarandon, and Bo Derek are already booked."

"That should be interesting. I hope Alec hasn't left you any voice mail messages. And don't let Mel drive."

"Yeah," Tom remarked wearily. "So far it's been a scheduling nightmare. Their publicists are making us crazy, too. They want all the questions in advance, and every day we get a new list of no-fly-zone topics. No one wants to come off looking like a dumb actor."

"That'll be the ultimate test of their thespian skills," Liza put in dryly. She sighed. "Well, I'm going to take a break from politics and relax. When you get back, you should come to East Hampton for a few days."

"Sounds like fun. And I've already seen Billie naked, so that awkwardness is out of the way."

Liza smiled. "Now, *she* could match you drink for drink. In a whiskey shot contest, I bet Billie could outlast a gunslinger from the Old West."

The cab jerked to a stop in front of Liza's building.

She pushed some cash into the driver's hand and swung out. "I just got home, Tom, and I always lose reception in the elevator. Call me when you're free. We'll set up a plan for East Hampton. I really want you to come."

Liza breezed past the doorman on her way to retrieve the mail. She bumped into a neighbor, Teddy Easton, at the boxes. "So make me feel like a slug. Tell me how far you rode this morning."

He smiled shyly, glancing down at the Cat Cheetah handmade carbon fiber bike that was easily ten thousand dollars. "Sixty miles."

"Only sixty? You're going to get *fat.*" She delivered the last bit in a singsong voice.

Teddy grinned. "Hey, you're one to talk, Mary-Kate."

He was a print and runway model, primarily for European fashion houses where the new hot look was stick-thin, tall, and gaunt. A Dior Homme representative had discovered him on a street-search talent mission called Boy Safari. The quarry that day happened to be a pedigreed male waif.

Teddy was a nineteen-year-old heir to the Easton Oil fortune. Money would never be an issue, and the idea of college bored him, so modeling seemed like a cool way to garner attention and make himself the It Boy among his friends. He hoped that it would lead to acting, too. With his extreme slenderness and androgynous features, Teddy rivaled many women, even with his severe buzz cut. A recent denim campaign that cast him in the role of faux concentration camp survivor had received a torrent of media outrage. But the jeans were still flying off the shelves.

As they walked toward the elevator, Liza regarded Teddy's physique with something close to envy. He was six foot two with a twenty-nine-inch waist. She guessed his body mass index to be eighteen or lower. "What's your exercise routine?"

"I get up, cycle anywhere between twenty and sixty miles, take a coffee break, run five miles, take another coffee break, swim half a mile, and then I try to get in a yoga class by the end of the day."

"I don't think I could get through one of those things," Liza grumbled.

"It's my job." He shrugged, then navigated his bike through the open elevator doors.

Liza followed him inside. "I didn't hear anything about food in your routine."

"Food? What's that?"

She grinned knowingly. This boy was skin and bones, and he didn't eat. They had more in common than she wanted to admit. "Eat a pizza, Teddy. I beg you."

He raised a thin eyebrow. "I will if you will. Let's share one."

They disembarked on the same floor. Teddy lived two apartments over in a smaller unit.

Liza waved him off and ventured inside the loft, surprised to hear the television blaring from the living room. She stepped closer and discovered Justin sprawled on the sofa, wearing nothing but boxer briefs and watching *Jackass Number Two*. Again. "I thought you were at the station."

Justin let out a deep belly laugh as someone's finger-puppet-covered penis got bitten by a snake. He didn't bother looking away from the giant screen. "Nope. I'm here."

Liza experienced a familiar firestorm of anger and resentment. She vaulted upstairs without a word and proceeded to pace the area like a panther in a cage, debating whether to throw the stupid bastard out on his ass. In the end, she decided to pack her things and take an extended break to sort through her true feelings.

She sank down onto the unmade bed and started to cry. Tears of frustration, regret, and uncertainty rained down her cheeks. A strong part of her yearned to engage him, to get a good fight started. But Justin had an infuriating ability to opt out of arguments and treat her like the most insignificant person on earth. It was a tactic that stirred her most violent impulses. In the right circumstances, Liza could envision herself actually hurting him, or at least attempting to. The thought frightened her.

She pulled herself together, retrieved two Prada wheel-away trolleys from the closet, and methodically gathered everything she'd need for the next three weeks. The focused nature of the task had a necessary calming effect.

Justin made no move to assist her as she brought the luggage pieces downstairs one at a time. His interest remained glued to the disgusting *Jackass* antics.

Liza set down the second and final bag with a loud thud, then stood directly in front of the television until Justin acknowledged her.

"What?"

"We need some space," Liza said evenly. "I'm going to stay in the Hamptons for the next three weeks."

"This is a funny part. Do you mind?"

She spun around and switched off the power. "*This* is not the funny part. This is the part where you act like you care even a little bit about us. Otherwise, it's over, Justin. We can end it. Right here, right now. And you can take the next three weeks to find a new place to live. One that you can actually afford. And I promise you that won't be in a Manhattan zip code."

Justin scratched his balls, kicked back, and cradled his head in his hands. "I'm not going anywhere."

Liza merely stared at him, amazed that she was in this kind of situation . . . with this kind of man. A surreal feeling swept over her. How could this be her existence? It should be some other woman's life. But right now it was hers.

Justin extended his right arm and aimed the remote control between her legs, zapping *Jackass Number Two* back into obstructed view.

Without a word, Liza rolled her luggage into the corridor and closed the door, her mind in tumult over what move to make next.

Teddy Easton appeared again and politely relieved her of one of the bags. He was suited up in a sleeveless tank and tiny running shorts, a black iPod strapped to his bony arm. "Escaping?"

"Only to the Hamptons," she replied quietly. "Not far enough, I'm afraid."

They rode the elevator in easy silence.

Liza could hear the music buzzing from Teddy's headphones. Fergie was singing, "It's time to be a big girl now/And big girls don't cry . . ."

Kellyanne

TWELVE

She was sunbathing on Georgica Beach when the call came through from Adam Griffie.

At first, Kellyanne hesitated to answer, fearing that Brad "Bonzi" Lucas had complained to the William Morris Agency about her abrupt exit. But something compelled her to pick up, if only to get the unpleasantness over with. Walter Isherwood's girl or not, she felt certain that Adam was striking her off his client list.

But his tone was uncharacteristically warm. In fact, Adam was downright chatty before delivering the bottom line. "I think I might have an acting job for you. A real one."

Kellyanne was stunned. Her mind took off in at least a dozen directions, all of them variations of her secret dream that this day might come. *The* call from out of the blue. An offer to play the ingenue in a big-budget action thriller starring Clive Owen. A character part in a Paul Haggis–scripted ensemble piece such as *Crash*. A plum new role on a megahit such as *Grey's Anatomy* or *Twenty-Four*. And so on.

"*As the World Turns* is hiring a new contract player," Adam explained. "They're looking for a beautiful blonde with an authentic Southern accent."

It sounded too good to be true. Kellyanne's stomach did a complete revolution.

"The character's an abstinence counselor with a dark past," Adam went on. "It's a great role that intersects with most of the main story arcs. Soap work is a grind, but this is a great opportunity for some major exposure."

"I . . . I don't . . . know what to say," Kellyanne stammered.

"Say you're interested."

She gripped the phone tighter. "I am!"

"The writers have worked up a full treatment for this Anna-Claire character. She's going to be revealed in layers, peeled away like an onion. If you nail it, this is the stuff of Daytime Emmys."

Kellyanne had never heard Adam sound so upbeat. It was a complete about-face. Maybe he'd believed in her talent all along. Everyone said the big break was always connected to the perfect role that allowed an actor to shine. And in more cases than not, it was a great agent who found it.

Adam cleared his throat. "Listen, Kellyanne, I don't know what your . . . *arrangement* is with Walter, but the show shoots in New York. It'll mean relocating from Miami."

"That's not a problem," she said quickly.

"Good to hear." He laughed a little. "Walter might stonewall me from getting that apartment I want at Indian Creek. But who gives a shit? I'd rather have a new star on my roster."

"I believe Walter will be happy for me. I truly do."

"Let's hope so," Adam murmured. His tone was skeptical. "Most men like him are only interested in their own dreams."

Kellyanne fell silent. Deep down, she knew Adam was right.

"Now this isn't exactly a done deal," Adam cautioned. "You still have to read for the part. But they went nuts over your head shots and reel, and I know that once they hear that sweet Southern twang in your voice, they won't be able to sign Kellyanne Downey fast enough."

"This is *amazing*!" she screamed, leaping to her feet and running toward the surf to kick around in the water.

The sky was a perfect periwinkle blue. The sun was a bright orange ball of rejuvenating heat. The beach was sparkling clean. And just beyond the dunes was a gorgeous backdrop of magnificent estates and fairy-tale mansions. This was a glorious moment that Kellyanne wanted to seal in her memory forever—the day she got *the* call . . . where she was . . . what she was thinking . . . how she was feeling.

"I'll be in touch as soon as I have details about the reading. Have a bag packed and your car gassed up for the airport."

"Actually, I'm in New York," Kellyanne said. "Well, East Hampton, to be exact. I'm here for the summer."

"Perfect. Be ready to move fast." He started to sign off.

"Adam!" Kellyanne blurted. "I almost forgot. Technically, I'm supposed to be in Miami shooting that reality show, *Soul Mates*."

"Oh, yeah, I forgot about that. What happened?" His interest in this new subject was so marginal that he sounded like the old Adam.

"I had a bad experience with the producer, and I quit," Kellyanne explained matter-of-factly. "He threatened to—"

"Summer reality shows are a joke," Adam cut in. There was a faraway quality to his voice and the distinct clacking of fingertips on a keyboard in the background. He had officially checked out. "The networks throw a bunch of shit on the schedule and hope some of it sticks. Most of those shows get yanked after a few airings. You probably won't get paid for whatever you did there. But who cares? We're moving on."

"Thank you, Adam," Kellyanne gushed, appreciating the inclusive pronoun. It closed out the conversation that made her feel like a real actress for the first time in her life.

She raced back to her spot on the sand, feeling as if she were floating on a cloud. Her heart was positively soaring. This was real happiness. And it belonged to her exclusively.

Desperate to share the news, she started to call her parents.

But then she stopped herself. It was too soon. Better to wait until the role had been officially offered and accepted. Spreading the word prematurely could jinx the situation. Kellyanne was superstitious that way.

Of course, she could tell her summer roommates. Liza and Billie understood the nuances of the business. They'd instantly realize what this call from her agent represented and how incredible a juicy role on *As the World Turns* could be for her career.

She dialed Billie first. When it went straight to voice mail, she hung up and tried Liza, who answered on the second ring in a voice only half its full compass. "Liza?"

"Hi, Kellyanne." Her tone was somber. "I'm sorry about not calling you back."

"No, it's okay. Where are you?"

"Somewhere on the Long Island Expressway. It turns out *The Roundtable* will be dark for the next few weeks, so I hired a car service to bring me back. I should be there in about two hours."

Kellyanne's excitement about Liza's early return was tempered by the depressive quality in her voice. "How are you feeling?"

"Good. Still a little sore, but . . ."

Kellyanne was hardly convinced. "You sound down, sweetheart. Talk to me."

Liza sighed deeply. "It's just my fucking husband. And he's not worth the airtime."

"Honey, there's no man issue that two pretty girls and a bottle of Pinot can't fix," Kellyanne said.

"Is that so?" Even through the phone, it was clear that Liza was almost smiling.

"Absolutely. It's obvious to me that if Justin isn't counting his blessings every day for you, then he's a complete idiot. I know the boy can put out a fire, but he probably couldn't pour rain out of his boot with a hole in the toe and directions on the heel."

Liza laughed. "What is this? Am I driving into *Petticoat Junction*?"

Kellyanne stretched her body in a show of worship to the relentless sun. "You're talking to an Alabama girl who's celebrating her roots today. They just might do me some good after all. I'll explain later. But here's the plan. I'm going to call my Uncle Kirby and get his recipe for shrimp and cheese grits. He owns a waterfront restaurant in Mobile, and people come from all over for that one dish. I'm cooking dinner for us tonight, and you're going to eat even if I have to tie you to a fence post and spoon-feed you like a fussy baby. Then we're going to drink a few bottles of wine and solve all the world's problems. Any questions?"

"No, ma'am."

"Good. Dinner's at six." Feeling infinitely competent and useful, Kellyanne hung up and tried to call Billie again. Once more, it rang directly into voice mail. But this time she left a message. "Hey, sweetheart, it's Kellyanne. Just wondering what your plans are for tonight. I'm making a big dinner. Let me hear from you."

She had a strong feeling that Billie would be MIA. There'd been a hushed phone call earlier that morning, and then Billie had rushed out of the house as if a three-alarm fire were blazing.

Kellyanne's cellular jingled to the music of Dr. Dre's hip-hop classic "Nuthin' but a 'G' Thang." It was Walter's dedicated ring tone and so ridiculously incongruous that she almost laughed every time it played. But today she was stone faced. "Hello?"

"How's my girl?" Walter asked.

Kellyanne bristled at his patronization. "Fine, thanks." She paused a beat. "How are your kids?"

"Doing *fantastic*. All of them. Just *fantastic*." He was trying too hard. There was obvious tension in his voice.

Kellyanne wanted to ask about Cagle, Walter's youngest son—a twenty-two-year-old college dropout. His transcript was checkered with false starts from at least half a dozen top schools all across the country. And as Jab had filled her in on the way to the airport, Cagle was recently arrested for drug possession and sexual assault.

"I'll be in New York for a few days starting tomorrow," Walter announced.

"That's great," Kellyanne lied, struggling to sound even mildly enthusiastic. Because inside she was thoroughly deflated. Her weekend with the girls would be ruined.

"I'm staying at the St. Regis. My schedule's crazy with back-to-back meetings and dinners, but I'll be able to break away here and there for some fun. My plane lands at eleven. Be at the hotel by noon. I'll want to put your special de-stressing talents to work before my first appointment. How does that sound?"

Worse than Abu Ghraib. That's the way Kellyanne longed to answer him, but she just held the line as a miserable feeling of dread spread over her. Finally, she spoke. "I heard from Adam today. I'm up for a role on a soap. It's a great part. But they want me to read, so I might be—"

"Tell Adam to put it off until next week," Walter cut in brusquely. "I'm paying a lot of money to let you play for the summer, so when I'm there I want you available."

Kellyanne experienced a wave of revulsion. He made her sound like some kind of sex slave. She fought the urge to slam the phone shut. In the end, she tried to reason with him. "Chances are I will be. It's just—"

"Why is Adam sending you out for that kind of work anyway?" Walter interrupted. "I'm not going to miss a good blow job just so you can audition for some crappy soap opera."

Kellyanne resigned herself to being at his beck and call. Fighting too hard against it might provoke him to seek out Adam and cause trouble. For once, her agent was regarding her as a marketable actress, as opposed to some old bastard's bored mistress. And she wanted to keep it that way. If the reading conflicted with Walter's visit, then she'd somehow figure out a way to make it work. The most important goal was landing the role of Anna-Claire. After that, everything would be on Kellyanne's terms.

In the meantime, she shut her eyes and prayed for Walter to be stricken with a bout of impotence that would resist every erectile dysfunction drug on the market. And then she prayed for world peace.

The engine's running but nobody's driving.

The voice of Kellyanne's father boomeranged in her mind. He was a man who never got lost and displayed little patience for people who did. Joe Downey could probably sniff out the right direction in a pitch black jungle. But this particular trait had skipped Kellyanne's genetic makeup.

For the last hour, she'd been driving up and down East Hampton streets and residential roads, trying to get her bearings for the area but coming up frustratingly short. Somewhere in between, she'd pulled over so that Uncle Kirby could dictate his recipe for shrimp and cheese grits. Now she was navigating Liza's Lexus down Jericho Road, eventually coasting onto Montauk Highway.

Kellyanne started to relax. These were familiar surroundings. She could easily find her way back to the house from here. Coming up on her right was a quaint white clapboard storefront called McGraw's Fish Market. Smiling at the country blue awning and the handmade sign advertising four lobsters for thirty-eight dollars, she made the split-second decision to turn into the white gravel drive.

It seemed like the logical thing to do. After all, she still needed shrimp for tonight's dinner, and the customer promise of this little place was, "The Finest Fish, The Freshest Choice." How could she possibly go wrong?

As Kellyanne pushed open the door, the jangle of a bell attached to it announced her arrival. The fishy odor practically knocked her over, but the shop was clean, tidy, and possessed an old-time charm.

A well-heeled woman in her mid-to-late sixties stood at the counter, breathlessly reciting an order to the man behind it. "Tucker, I need eight more lobsters. I just had an additional six people announce that they were coming for dinner, and I'm taking home two extra for good measure. Nobody RSVP's anymore. They just *assume.*"

"I've got you covered, Mrs. Gold. You must be having a big summer party. This morning you took home a ten-pack of these bad boys."

Kellyanne smiled to herself, finding the man's Long Island accent amusing. It was all twanging nasals, diphthong drawls, *er*'s coming out as *ah*'s, and *w*'s larding onto *a*'s. She absolutely adored it.

"Don't remind me," Mrs. Gold snarled good naturedly. "Half the people I'm feeding tonight, I don't even like."

He laughed gently. "Then I'm no longer offended about not being invited. I packed these in seawater-soaked newspaper. Remember to keep the cartons upright and put them in the refrigerator as soon as you get home."

"You already told me that this morning, Tucker. I'm not senile yet!" The woman spun around and gave Kellyanne a disapproving glance before stalking out.

Kellyanne got a better look at Tucker as he emerged from behind the counter. His deeply tanned muscular arms were loaded down with Mrs. Gold's lobsters, and he wore a smudged white apron, red T-shirt, khaki cargo shorts, and black Croc sandals.

He was thirty-something, six foot one, and ruggedly handsome with thick dirty blond hair, soulful green eyes, and a sexy two-day stubble. Rushing by her to keep up with his demanding customer, he grinned and rolled his eyes skyward in a way that communicated a certain joy in his beleaguered situation. "I'll be right with you."

Kellyanne watched him leave, observing as he carefully packed the trunk of Mrs. Gold's vintage Jaguar XJ6. She was struck by his intoxicating vibrations of strength, sweetness, virility . . . and decency. That was the quality that really killed her.

Tucker stepped back inside, smoothing his apron as he made his way around to the iced-down fish that was his livelihood. "Sorry about that. What can I get for you?" He rested his impressive forearms on the countertop, dangling hands that were large and wonderfully masculine. His fingernails were clean, short and square cut.

That's when Kellyanne noticed the simple white gold wedding ring. A tiny part of her was crestfallen. All the good ones—and the bad ones—were usually taken. And so went the story of her life. She took a deep breath. "I need some big-ass shrimp."

Tucker smiled at her with perfect teeth. "I've got plenty of big-ass shrimp. How much do you need?"

Kellyanne stared through the glass, considering the question as she noticed an owner's special on striped sea bass. "It's just dinner for me and a friend. I don't know. Maybe a dozen?"

He nodded in agreement and grabbed two handfuls from the jumbo shrimp pile.

"Oh," Kellyanne began helplessly. "Could you also cut off the heads and peel them and clean out the yucky stuff?"

"*Clean out the yucky stuff?*" he repeated, his tone teasing. "We call that deveining."

Kellyanne made a face. "Ugh—that sounds even worse." The bell jangled in perfect synchronization with a gorgeous little boy's exploding through the door. He had flowing blond surfer locks, the deep brown tan of a lifeguard, and the same green eyes as the man he was running toward. "Daddy, Daddy!" he called, racing around the counter to embrace his father's leg.

Tucker wiped his hands with a well-worn rag and bent down to kiss the top of his son's head. "Parks! What's going on, son?"

"I missed you, Daddy. You're my best friend."

"And you're my best friend. How cool is that?"

Kellyanne's hand covered her heart. She'd always thought that a father's devotion to a child was incredibly sexy. She thought even more so now. In fact, observing this rapport was devastating—in the very best way. "He's precious. How old is he?"

Tucker beamed with pride. "Almost four."

"Bless his heart."

"Parks, would you like to help me get this pretty lady's shrimp ready?"

In answer, Parks jumped up and down with delight.

Tucker quickly positioned a metal folding chair beside him and lifted Parks on top of it so that he could reach the counter. "Why don't you peel that pile right there, son. Help out your dad. I need a strong first mate to get this work done."

Kellyanne watched in wonder as the boy's tiny fingers removed the scales with expert precision, his face a masterpiece of pride, determination, and desire to please. It was the sweetest scene she'd ever witnessed.

Tucker shot a glance toward the door. "Where's your Aunt Rae?"

Parks remained focused on his task. "She's sitting in the car on her cell phone yelling at Uncle Scott."

Tucker laughed and stroked the boy's hair. He glanced back at Kellyanne and winked. "One thing about kids—they tell it like it is."

Kellyanne smiled warmly. A few minutes later her order was cleaned, packed, and ready. She paid in cash.

Parks bagged the purchase and presented it to her with a flourish.

"Tell the pretty lady what we tell all our customers," Tucker prompted.

"Thank you for shopping at McGraw's Fish Market! We hope to see you tomorrow!"

Tucker bit down on his lower lip, stifling a laugh. "That's a little pushy, son." He grinned at Kellyanne. "We hope to see you again."

Over the years, Kellyanne had heard some superlative lines from powerful and prominent men. The U.S. senator who told her she was the most beautiful woman he'd ever seen. The highest paid actor on television who told her she was the hottest girl in Hollywood. The Academy Award–winning producer who told her she was too gorgeous for celluloid.

So the simple irony wasn't lost on her. She'd stumbled across a fish market. An unassuming man—who was not trying to hit on her—had indirectly told her she was pretty. And yet it was the greatest flattery of all.

She extended a hand to Parks. "Thank you, kind sir. I'll definitely be back."

Billie

THIRTEEN

He slapped her ass so hard that the palm-to-cheek impact popped like a gunshot. "You like that, don't you, bitch?"

Billie managed to moan out a yes.

March relentlessly tore into her from behind, gripping her arms for balance as he increased his amperage with a selfishness that bordered on brutality. "What are you?"

"I'm your dirty little whore."

"And you like it when I fuck you this way, don't you?"

"Yes!"

Cocaine turned March into an animal. His stamina became almost more than she could endure, and the coke rush made him exponentially aggressive. He was demanding, firm handed, ruthless, and vulgar.

Billie's cock-tease act at Sunset Beach had done a real number on him. So had seeing her disappear with Shayne Cutter. She left the next move up to March, and he played it sooner than she ever expected.

He called three times on Monday. She refused to answer. He called five times on Tuesday. She ignored him. By the time Billie picked up his first call on Wednesday morning, March was in such a state that an elopement to Las Vegas could've been negotiated. He wanted her that bad. And when he finally got her, he was a bastard possessed.

"I want to come all over your face."

Of course, he did. Didn't they all?

One hand surfed down the slope of her back while the other pulled Billie up by her hair. He crushed his mouth onto hers. "Are you my slut?" His hips were thrusting at jackhammer speed, plowing so deep that he was bottoming out and bumping up against her cervix.

Billie nodded her answer, unable to speak as she climaxed and grimaced simultaneously, an exquisite duet of pleasure and pain.

March pushed Billie onto her knees and stood over her while he finished himself off, his breathing and moaning on a steady rise until he cried out with a wall-rattling, "Fuck!"

Billie closed her eyes as his warm semen splattered all over her forehead, nose, cheeks, mouth, and neck. The explosion seemed to go on and on.

When it was over, March cradled her face in his hands, admiring his pretty mess. "Jesus Christ. That's fucking beautiful."

"Would Focus on the Family agree?" Billie asked. But before he could answer, she was sucking him clean of every last drop.

March laughed the laugh of the satisfied, shuddering slightly, as he was sensitive to postorgasm ministrations. Still, he appreciated and expected such dedication to his cock.

Billie had seen bigger. In fact, March's dick was average. But at the end of the day, attitude trumped size, and he carried himself in a manner that added two inches, if not more. He loved his cock. He was tyrannical with it. He knew what it could do. Some men might be bigger, but they were almost always smug about the fact that they were packing more than the next guy. March didn't care about other men. He only cared about women. And there was the difference.

They were in a small room at the Hotel Elysée on East Fifty-fourth Street, a hideaway eclipsed between two huge office buildings.

Billie wiped her face with a towel and lit a cigarette. She loved fucking in hotels. Somehow the sex was always better.

With no offer to share, March snorted the last bit of cocaine and flung himself onto the bed, landing stomach first.

Billie blew smoke rings and stared at his amazing, muscular ass. "When are we going to be together again?"

"We're together now."

"I know, but . . . I'm just wondering. That's all."

"I'll be back on Friday. Maybe over the weekend."

Billie felt anxious. This wasn't enough. She wanted a firm plan about the next time.

He rolled over onto his back. "We'll see what happens."

Cigarette still in hand, she climbed on top of the bed and straddled his washboard abs.

March grinned lazily. "This is a nonsmoking room."

"So I'm a bad girl."

"A nasty girl." He took possession of her Marlboro Light, dragged deep, and returned it. "I want to fuck you again, but I have a flight to catch."

He was flying to Colorado Springs to speak at a dinner being hosted by Focus on the Family.

Billie shook her head. "That blows my mind."

"What?"

"That you're showing up to give some speech about conservative Christian values. It's like your navy suit is a costume." She laughed out loud. "Hey, you're Batman!"

"Just because I like to have a little fun doesn't mean I don't believe in my work."

"Oh, please. That crowd's idea of fun is a church picnic. You're cheating on your fiancée, snorting coke, and fucking like a porn star. Don't tell me there's not a difference."

March stole her cigarette again. "Maybe we're all hypocrites."

"Speak for yourself," Billie scoffed.

His eyes flashed irritation, and he blew smoke directly into her face. "Right now I'm speaking for you and me."

"How am *I* a hypocrite?" Billie demanded. "I'm the grand fucking marshal of the live-and-let-live parade! You go out there stumping to ban gay marriage. That's telling people how to live. Why should I care if a couple of fags want to get hitched? Hey, I'm no Diane Sawyer, but as I understand it, you Republican types are supposed to be probusiness. Well, shit! What's better for the economy than a bunch of gay weddings?"

March's jaw was clenched tight. "You're out of your element, Billie. You sound much more intelligent with my dick in your mouth." He pushed her off his body and over to the side of the bed. "I need to take a shower."

"Fuck you!" she screamed.

March stood up. "Most of my life is spent talking political shit. That's not why I called you. I thought you'd be a fun escape."

Billie was torn. She was alarmed by his sudden use of the past tense. But she was still pissed off about his insult. "I'm not some idiot slut! I've got a degree from goddamn Dartmouth!"

"Congratulations," March said. "But my point is that you don't read or keep up with any of the issues. If I wanted a debate, then I'd call your Hamptons roommate. Liza's my current events foil. You're my fuck toy."

She stared daggers at him. It always came down to the same slights. Men respected Liza for her intellect. They admired Kellyanne for her beauty. But they just used Billie and left her to rot on the side of the road.

March snatched her iPod from the nightstand and fingered the smudged video screen. "And back to the subject that got us here. You want to project yourself as a wild, edgy rocker chick, but you're heading into the studio to record Ariel covers." He paused a beat. "Welcome to the hypocrisy club." And then he tossed the device onto the bed, walked into the bathroom, and shut the door.

Billie waited until she heard the shower running. That's when she started to cry. Rivulets of angry, bitter, frustrated tears rolled down her cheeks as her mind raced with dark plots to make the son of a bitch pay for treating her this way.

She dressed quickly, then gathered up the clothes March had arrived in—shoes included—and stuffed them inside his wheeled Tumi travel case. With cold water cool, she rolled it into the hallway, onto the elevator, and out of the hotel.

A silver-haired executive type darted out of a cab, holding the hand of a girl young enough to be his granddaughter. They rushed inside the Hotel Elysée. Apparently, it was all the rage for secret trysts.

Billie shoved the Tumi into the backseat of the vacated cab. Then she tumbled in and told the driver to take her to Central Park. On the way, she removed March's identification tag from the luggage, laughing wickedly.

How did a good Christian man end up at a hotel in the middle of the day without any clothes? Hmm. Maybe March could explain that little riddle to all the assholes at the Focus on the Family dinner tonight. *If* he made it there.

Her cell phone vibrated to life. She checked the screen. Guess who? A glorious wave of comeuppance coursed through her. She let it ring a few times before picking up.

"Where the hell's my luggage?" March roared. "You crazy bitch! I'm going to miss my flight!"

She answered him in a calm, pleasant, almost detached voice. "You must have me confused with your travel assistant. I'm just your fuck toy." And then she hung up.

Billie left his Tumi in the cab and found herself strolling aimlessly through Central Park, falling deeper and deeper into a place where she simply wanted to forget who she was.

The password to such blissful ignorance was in the medicine cabinet at her apartment. She found her way there, peeled off her clothes, and stepped into a cold shower. It was a scorching June afternoon, and the window unit air conditioner could only do so much. She slammed back a few vodka drinks and swallowed a handful of Ambien. Those beautiful white babies always knocked her out.

And this afternoon she took a few extra to countervail any discomfort from the heat. She just longed to be completely out of it . . .

"Billie! Billie!"

Somewhere in the deepest recesses of her mind she could hear the sound of Amy Dando's voice. She could also feel the pinch of long nails digging into her exposed shoulders as someone shook her violently.

Billie managed to flutter her eyes open.

"What the fuck is wrong with you?" It *was* Amy. The perfect eye makeup distracted Billie from the blazing anger in her manager's gaze.

Oh, God, she was *so* tired. All Billie wanted to do was sleep. Just holding up her eyelids was an exhausting effort. She started to fall back into the silky folds of oblivion.

"Wake up, Billie!" Amy shrieked. "Wake up, or I'm calling 911 and having you taken to the goddamn emergency room!"

Billie groaned faintly in protest. Not the hospital. She didn't want to go there. Why had she ever given Amy the key to her apartment? Right now that seemed like the worst decision she'd ever made in her whole fucking life. "Stop yelling," she pleaded in a faint whisper, forcing her eyes open.

"How long have you been here like this?"

Billie just stared back at her blankly. She had no idea what time it was . . . or even what day it was. "I don't know."

"*You don't know.*" Amy shook her head in disgust.

"But I'm okay," Billie insisted weakly. "You can go."

"There's nothing I'd love more than to take you up on that offer," Amy hissed. And then she ferociously pulled Billie forward and up, yanking with great force until the object of her rage was standing on two feet.

Billie's body felt as limp as a rag doll. All she wanted was to be left alone. The Ambien daze was one stubborn bitch. Her head bobbed to one side. Maybe she could sleep this way . . .

"Goddamn you, Billie!" Amy screamed.

And then she felt herself being pushed . . . out of the living room . . . into the bathroom . . . the light was so bright . . . somebody turn off the fucking light . . . oh, shit . . . her head hit a hard surface . . . jets of freezing water began to soak her . . . it was a shock to the system.

"Are you awake now?" The tiled acoustics gave Amy's voice some added boom.

Billie kept her eyes open and met the lesbian bitch's gaze, holding up an arm in a silent plea for mercy from the water.

Amy cut off the shower. "I'm going downstairs to get you some coffee. There's nothing in this fucking apartment but liquor and cigarettes."

"By the way, I sure could use one," Billie croaked.

Amy disappeared, then returned a few moments later to throw a pack of Marlboro Lights and a matchbook from Butter in Billie's general direction. "Don't set yourself on fire." She left again.

Billie heard the slam of the apartment door and fumbled for the cigarettes in a near-catatonic daze. She lit one and brought it to her dry lips. The relief was sort of like heaven. Every drag seemed to slowly wake her up. She lay slumped in the tub, cold and soaking wet, fascinated by the subtle texture changes in the filter as she smoked it down.

Amy stormed back inside and pushed a tall Starbucks into her hand. "You're a goddamn mess."

Billie sipped gingerly on the hot liquid. Fuck. It was black. She hated it black. She liked it loaded with sugar and cream. First Amy ruins her nice long sleep, and then she brings her bad coffee. What the hell kind of management was that? "This tastes like shit."

"Then you must be drinking your career. That's the closest thing to total shit I can think of."

Billie fired up another cigarette.

"I got an earful from Todd Bana last night."

"Oh, yeah? What did that prick want?"

"You missed the first recording session with White Tiger."

Billie puffed away, nonplussed by the news. Those lazy mother-fuckers had only written one new song for her. They deserved to wait. "What day is this?"

"It's Friday morning."

Christ! Had she been sleeping for a day and a half? If Amy had left her alone, she probably could've gone a solid two days. "Oh, well. Tell Todd to reschedule."

"You tell him. I'm done." There was an ominous ring of finality in Amy's voice.

Billie looked at her with a wounded expression.

"I can't do this anymore. I've got clients who need my attention. Clients who actually care about the future of their career. You know, Billie, at first I didn't agree with this new direction that Todd suggested, but the more I thought about it, the more I came to believe that he was probably right. You're not a disciplined songwriter, and it's been a fast downhill slope since *Dick Magnet*. You have the rare opportunity to work with one of the hottest production teams in the business while you're at a low point, and you fucking blow them off."

"They expect me to sing backwash tracks from Ariel's last record," Billie spat. "I don't do retreads. And if you were any kind of manager, you wouldn't want me to."

"That CD dropped a few days after her DUI arrest, and it was dead on arrival. But it's still considered one of this industry's bigger could-have-beens. It was at least seven tracks deep with hit singles. Two of them could be yours. And the new White Tiger track is a radio-ready smash."

"Whatever." Billie rolled her eyes and blew smoke up toward the ceiling. "Who Is She?" was infectious, sure, but it was also repetitive. A hard-core Alzheimer's case could probably commit the lyrics to memory after one listen. And it was hardly an original. For the main hook, those White Tiger hacks had sampled the guitar riff from Rick Springfield's "Jessie's Girl."

"Whatever?" Amy repeated, leveling a look of disgust. "There are artists far more successful than you who'd kill for that track right now. Ashlee Simpson wants it. So do Rihanna and Kylie Minogue. But Todd convinced White Tiger to save it for your project."

Billie stubbed out her cigarette in the sink. "Big fucking deal." She peeled off her wet cotton tank and Hanky Panky underwear, then slipped on her robe.

"I wouldn't knock it," Amy warned her. "It's the best thing you've got going at the moment. Everyone thinks you're over, Billie. Some of your newer songs have leaked onto the Internet, and bloggers are ripping them to shreds. I don't think I could book a tour for you right now, even a short one. A twenty-five-hundred-seat theater would be too big. I'd be lucky to get interest from casinos in second- and third-tier markets." She shook her head regretfully. "It didn't have to be this way. But you're the architect of this train wreck, and this is where we part ways. I wish you luck. I really do." She started for the door.

"Amy!" Billie shrieked, her heart lurching with fear. "You can't be serious!"

"Oh, I'm very serious. You're the one who's fucking around. I'll put an official letter in the mail this afternoon."

"You can't cut me loose! I'm Billie Fucking Shelton!"

Amy looked at her with genuine sadness. "A few years ago that name actually meant something."

At first Billie couldn't believe it. But then Amy Dando walked out of her life.

Liza

FOURTEEN

She looked like hell—no makeup, unwashed hair stuffed into an old Brandeis baseball cap, battered Levi's, and a distressed SuperEXcellent yellow cotton tee emblazoned with the phrase YOU LOST ME AT HELLO in faded pink letters.

It was Liza's ritualistic writing costume. She'd been working like a demon for the last few days, trying to shape her *Stupid Girls* proposal into a presentable product. The intense focus on her new book helped to purge Justin from her mind, and it was a necessary emotional break. When she finally resurfaced, she knew that a clearer head would prevail.

Liza dashed into Citarella on Pantigo Road. Long writing hours always left her fatigued and hungry. Cravings for sweets were particularly insane. But rather than give in to the temptations of candy and chocolate, Liza chose the healthier path of natural sugar. She loaded up on strawberries, blackberries, raspberries, star fruit, mango, cantaloupe, honeydew, kiwi, pineapple, grapes, peaches, guava, and papaya.

"You have to stop doing this."

Startled by the voice, Liza spun around.

Harrison Beck stood behind her, holding a coffee in one hand and stuffing one of Citarella's famous doughnuts into his mouth with the other. "You show up at my party uninvited. Now you're stalking me in the market. It's ridiculous." He licked a tiny dust storm of powdered sugar from his lips and smiled.

Against every impulse to do otherwise, Liza found herself smiling back at him. "I don't know which is worse—your movies or your attempt at flirting."

"Definitely my flirting," Harrison said easily. "I should note, however, that so far in my lifetime two women have agreed to marry me."

"They've also agreed to divorce you," Liza pointed out.

Harrison shrugged. "That just means I'm road tested. At least I'm capable of commitment. And, obviously, I'm worthy of it. I've got the alimony expenses to prove it." He glanced down into her shopping cart. "Where's the real food?"

Liza gestured to the last bit of doughnut between Harrison's fingers. "Apparently, at the pastry counter."

Without warning, he pushed what remained of the treat into Liza's mouth, immediately laughing at his successful effort.

At first, she staged a shocked miniprotest, then simply gave in and enjoyed the small bite of sweet warm cake. It was delicious. She grinned at him. "You son of a bitch."

"That good, huh?"

"Better."

"Have a cup of coffee with me."

Liza hesitated. "I can't. I'm on deadline. I just ran in here for some sustenance. Maybe when I get out from under."

"How about dinner tonight?"

Even though Liza appreciated his persistence, she demurred. "I really need to work. I have an angry agent and a frustrated editor regularly checking in on my progress."

"Come on," Harrison said, swatting away her excuse like a gnat.

"I'm a writer, too. I know how it works. There are only so many good pages you can produce in a day, then it becomes diminishing returns. A nice meal will rejuvenate you. The Palm at eight o'clock. Consider it a working dinner. You can tell me all about your new book."

Liza regarded him carefully. If nothing else, the man had presented a slam-dunk case. There was every reason to say yes to his invitation. "Eight-thirty," she said. "I'll meet you there."

"And you'll pick up the check, too."

She gave him an incredulous look.

"You owe me at least that much for the crack about my dick."

"Fine," Liza agreed with faux exasperation. "As long as you promise not to whip it out in public again, I'll pay for your dinner."

"Deal." Harrison extended his hand.

Liza shook firm and fast.

He held the grip longer than the moment called for, and there was undeniable poetry in the pressure. "I'll be sitting at the bar around eight . . . should you decide to come early to join me for a drink."

The hours that followed were a total waste. Instead of sitting in front of her computer, she was standing in her bedroom, wishing that the Yves Saint Laurent hand-painted silk voile strapless number wasn't hanging in her closet back in Manhattan.

God, it was so critical that Liza be working, but her ass simply would *not* stay in the chair. She needed bum glue. That's what the Australian writer Bryce Courtenay called it. If only Liza could purchase such stuff by the ten-gallon drum.

Her BlackBerry vibrated, and she peered down to discover that—as expected—her agent was dialing in with a midafternoon call. "Hello, Linda."

"What are you answering the phone for? You should be writing," Linda Konner barked.

"I don't screen your calls. You could be ringing me up to extend my deadline."

"Dream on," Linda huffed. She was a great literary agent—a tough negotiator, a no-nonsense operator, and a shrewd mover in all areas of nonfiction. "How's the writing coming along?"

"Very well," Liza answered truthfully. She paused a beat. "And very slowly."

Linda sighed. "Speed it up. Kate's getting nervous. I want to show her something soon."

Kate Goodman was Liza's editor at New Woman Press, the first publishing imprint from mogul Toni Valentine, who was quickly rising among the corporate titan ranks to earn her media nickname as the female Rupert Murdoch. *Whore* had been the house's phenomenally successful launch title and solidified Toni Valentine's reputation as a Midas-touch cultural prognosticator. She'd conquered film, television, the Web, and now publishing.

"I don't want to stress you out," Linda continued. "But this needs to be your number one priority."

"I know, I know," Liza said quickly, feeling anxious.

"Everything else that you're doing is exciting, but those opportunities only happened because you wrote a bestseller. That's your product. That's also where the real money is. Don't lose sight of that. Your second book has been bumped from this fall to next spring to next summer, and now we're probably looking at next fall. It's time to go to contract again, and I don't want an unreliable delivery history to get in my way when it's time to talk numbers. We're going for a *major* deal. You put Toni in the publishing business, and it's time for her to pay up."

"This book is going to be *good*, Linda," Liza said passionately. "It's different than *Whore*. It's more personal. Women are going to relate. I'm calling it *Stupid Girls*."

"I love the title," Linda praised. "It's provocative. I'll call Kate and let her know that you're on the right track. Keep writing." And then Linda hung up.

The conversation kicked Liza into proper gear. She worked non-stop for the next several hours, breaking only to scoop up an occasional bowl of the colorful fruit medley she'd assembled from her earlier run to Citarella and speed surf her favorite Web sites for breaking news.

She checked her recent column on *The Huffington Post,* the left-leaning digital newspaper conceived by Arianna Huffington that had recently become the fifth-most-linked-to blog on the Internet. Liza had fired off a rant on right-wing female blowhards called "Conservative Women in the Media: The New Old White Guys." Periodically, she surveyed her entries for comment posts. Scrolling down, Liza scanned the feedback quickly, then stopped.

travisowen

This phony bitch needs to shut up. She's a lying whore. Her real name is Liza Beal. She married a fireman but won't take his last name. I guess she thinks no man's name is good enough. If she were my woman, I'd brand OWEN onto her ass like she was a head of cattle. The director Harrison Beck made a brilliant film with WATCH HER BLEED, and this slut trashed the movie and him on national television. She's a know-it-all cunt. I'd love to watch HER bleed.
posted 02:17 pm

The comment had already been flagged as abusive. In short order, it would be removed from the site. Liza zeroed in on the words. There was a disturbing quality to online attacks. They could easily give her the feeling of being stalked. But in reality, it was some bored asshole clicking the mouse and going from site to site, trying to come off sinister in their anonymity. They were just cyberspace punks. Nothing more.

She went back to work in earnest, framing the entire book, determining chapter subjects, drafting chapter titles, and making a list of essential interview subjects and research priorities. But the most satisfying task came from free-writing the sample chapter, "Will You Marry Me, Boy?"

Liza dug deep. She pushed past the denial and through the discomfort as she examined her relationship with Justin with brutal honesty. What had drawn her to him? What did that reveal about her? And why did the public perception of a divorce loom darker than the private unhappiness of a dead marriage? In unflinching prose, she put everything on the page. It read like the literary equivalent of an exposed nerve.

She also wrote about the disappearance of feminism from the public consciousness. The cause was no longer an organized social movement. Today it was being played out within personal relationships, a place where many women had put down their swords and abandoned the fight altogether. Liza admitted that in some ways she was one of them.

It was after seven o'clock when she stopped writing. She rushed into the shower, put the dryer to her hair, applied her makeup, threw on a Yohji Yamamoto silk-and-cotton sailor blouse over Odyn jeans, slipped a few Van Cleef & Arpels diamond bracelets over both wrists, stepped into a pair of spike-heeled Gucci white leather pumps, and raced out the door, spraying Viktor & Rolf's Flowerbomb into the air as she walked through the mist.

At eight o'clock sharp, Liza arrived at the Palm at the Huntting Inn. She encountered Sarah Jessica Parker, Matthew Broderick, and Jessica and Jerry Seinfeld leaving as she entered. Taking in the dark paneled decor, she smiled at the caricatures of local notables and international stars that lined the walls. Billy Joel was up there. So was Steven Spielberg.

She spotted Harrison at the bar. He looked hot-summer-night handsome in beige linen pants and a white embroidered camp shirt unbuttoned to reveal a thick mane of tangled chest hair.

Liza eased onto the stool next to him as he finished the last swallow of a deep amber liquid on the rocks. "You started early."

Harrison grinned. "It's called bracing myself." He signaled to the bartender. "What are you drinking?"

"A glass of the Marquis Phillips Shiraz would be perfect."

Harrison ordered another Scotch for himself. "Our table should be ready in a few minutes." He gave her an admiring glance. "You look beautiful tonight. You smell beautiful, too."

She smiled her thanks, relieved to see the wine arrive with such fast efficiency.

Harrison raised his short highballer. "To your new book."

"I can drink to that." She gently clinked her glass against his, appreciating the sentiment.

"Did you have a productive writing day?"

Liza could feel her own eyes shining. "One of my best ever. It all came together. Everything clicked."

He gave her a knowing nod. "There's no better feeling."

Almost instantly, she felt overwhelmed by his attentiveness— the compliments, the genuine interest in her work. It amplified the emptiness she felt with Justin in a way that made her feel unbearably lonely, even as she sat here with Harrison.

"Tell me about your new book."

"For starters, it's called *Stupid Girls*."

He smiled. "I've been with my fair share of those. Let me know if you need insight from the male perspective."

Liza gave him a quick roll of the eyes and practiced a cold run of an elevator speech that encapsulated the main premise of her project. Upon finishing, she was pleased with her delivery.

Harrison seemed visibly impressed. "It sounds very personal."

"It is," Liza agreed. "But it's also very universal. The most personal things almost always are." She sipped on her wine. "And what about you? Can I look forward to seeing *Watch Her Bleed Two*?" Her voice carried a tone of playful menace.

Guiltily, Harrison cast his eyes downward into his Scotch.

"Oh, God!" Liza exclaimed, punching his thickly muscled upper arm. "You're actually doing a sequel?"

"It's not official," Harrison said sheepishly. "But I gave my agent a magic number, and the studio's offer is getting close. Believe me, I tried to price myself out of it. Now I'm in a position where I won't be able to say no to that kind of money. I'd be a fool."

Suddenly, Liza remembered the creepy online messages that had been sent to her from Travis Owen, the movie's misogynistic psycho killer. "Did you send me an e-mail through my Web site recently?"

Harrison gave her a curious look, shaking his head. "No, why do you ask?"

Liza shrugged. "Never mind. It must've been a prank."

He opened his mouth to inquire further.

Liza cut him off. "Don't ever make a creative decision based solely on money. You'll always regret it."

"How about basing my decision on the fact that I have three children?" Harrison countered. "This deal could secure their futures for life. If the price for that is being called a sellout or taking some critical jabs when the sequel's released, then I'll pay it. The freedom and peace of mind will be worth that."

Liza fell silent. She could hardly judge him for putting his children's best interests first on his agenda.

"You can relax, though. It'll be at least a few years before a sequel hits theaters."

Liza breathed an exaggerated sigh of relief.

Harrison laughed, tipping back his glass. "I think you might actually like my next film. I just finished the script. It's a true story about a New Orleans doctor who was falsely accused of murdering patients in the aftermath of Hurricane Katrina." He crossed his fingers. "Jodie Foster is considering it."

"I've never read a screenplay before," Liza said.

"I'd love for you to take a look at it." His tone was earnest. "I mean that. You might have some notes on the female point of view. If Jodie passes, it's going out to Reese Witherspoon next, then Jennifer Connelly. The role is tough. I want an A-list actress in the part."

"Jodie Foster would be amazing. I haven't read it, of course, but she brings so much integrity to every role."

"I know. I'm having trouble with financing at the moment, and a marquee name like that would green light this picture in a heartbeat."

A host interrupted to inform them that their table was ready. Liza and Harrison were escorted to a cozy booth in the corner of the restaurant and seated directly behind a glowing Gwyneth Paltrow and her husband, Chris Martin of Coldplay.

Harrison selected a bottle of wine—a South American red—and proceeded to order up a feast that included oysters on the half shell, sesame seared ahi tuna, Caesar salad, steamed Nova Scotia lobsters, creamed spinach, sautéed wild mushrooms, and three-cheese potatoes au gratin.

Liza ate more than she could believe without even the faintest degree of reluctance or shame. The intense afternoon writing hours had left her positively ravenous.

It was a blissful evening—delectable food, fantastic wine, and animated conversation that flowed effortlessly. They talked more about her new book and his new screenplay, then moved on to discuss their favorite visual artists, all the exotic places they wanted to travel, and their eclectic tastes in music.

Harrison's eyes sparkled when he told her about his children. Cassandra was eighteen and starting her first year at Smith College in the fall. Mariah was sixteen and captain of her high school swim team. Alexis was four and obsessed with all things Hello Kitty.

As a busboy cleared the table, the white-jacketed waiter appeared to lobby them for dessert, but the idea of so much as a morsel of more food seemed impossible to comprehend. They declined the offer of an after-dinner drink as well and requested the check.

"I'm a terrible husband but a good father," Harrison announced with philosophical directness. "I love my girls. I love my ex-wives who gave them to me, too." He sighed heavily, pouring the last of the second bottle of the 1995 Faustino. "Divorce sucks. But sometimes it's the only way to keep your dignity and preserve what was good about things."

"Didn't it give you a crushing sense of failure?" Liza asked.

Harrison considered the question. "I wouldn't say that. There were elements of success in both of my marriages. I try to remember those aspects and fake amnesia to all the rest." He stared at her thoughtfully. "You haven't mentioned your husband all night."

Liza averted eye contact and busied herself with her napkin. "Is it that obvious?"

"Believe me, I hate to bring it up. I wish you didn't have one. But yes, it is."

She looked at him. "It's complicated."

"It always is." Harrison tilted his head, pursing his lips sympathetically as the waiter swooped in and discreetly left the check. He pushed the bill to her side of the table. "I believe we have a deal."

Liza reached into her red satin Zac Posen clutch and slapped her American Express Black on top of the leather guest check presenter.

He gave her a mischievous smile. "And just because you paid for dinner, don't expect to get laid tonight."

"You're enjoying this, aren't you?"

"I feel like the girl. I'm probably going to wait by the phone all day tomorrow, too. You know, hoping you'll call to ask me out again."

She laughed at him. Harrison was smart, funny, and sweet. Frankly, it amazed her that this was the same man who'd created the ugly gore on display in *Watch Her Bleed*.

Liza signed over a generous 30 percent tip, and they ventured out into the cool night. A galaxy of stars gleamed in the dark sky. There was a whipping breeze and a sharp tang in the air. It smelled like a beach town. She closed her eyes and took everything in. "I love it here. I should buy instead of rent."

All of a sudden, Harrison's hands were on her hips. He stood behind her, nuzzling her neck. "Come back to my house for a drink."

His cologne was strong in her nostrils—Tobacco Flower by

Fresh. She breathed in the heady, masculine hints of eucalyptus, mint, sun-kissed vines, and ripening olives. The fragrance was made for him. She reached back to stroke his cheek. "I can't."

He kissed her shoulder. "It's a beautiful night. We could sit out by the pool."

Liza hated the idea of going back to an empty house. Kellyanne was in the city with Walter, and Billie was God knows where. No one had heard from her in days. She found herself weakening to the idea of going home with him. But she knew where the night would inevitably lead. And she wasn't ready for it to go there.

"We could take a walk on the beach," Harrison murmured, continuing the hard sell.

"I had a wonderful evening, but it's time to say good night." Liza turned around, kissed his cheek, and walked to her car, fighting temptation the whole way. It dawned on her that she wasn't the kind of woman who could cheat on her husband, even one who'd cheated on her.

Stupid girl, Liza thought. And then she drove away.

"You've got to stop," Teddy Easton pleaded. "I can't take anymore."

Reluctantly, Justin pulled out. He could easily hold this pretty male model down and make him take it, but he was tired of the little bitch's whining.

Teddy rolled over onto his back. "Sorry. You're just too big. It hurts. I usually only have sex with Asian guys." He took a swig from the giant Dasani water bottle on the nightstand and raised a perfectly waxed eyebrow. "I couldn't turn you down, though. I had to try."

Mildly annoyed, Justin stripped off the condom and reached for his True Religion jeans. Being with Teddy was like fucking a skeleton. In fact, he was bonier than Liza. Still, Justin could've plowed his tight boy pussy for hours. All those cycling miles had built up a tiny ass of pure muscle. What a waste.

He checked the clock on his cell—just a few minutes past midnight. There was plenty of time to find a willing hole to take the pounding he wanted to give.

"I'd pop a few Vicodin and suffer through it if I didn't have to leave for the airport at four-thirty in the morning," Teddy said. "Can you imagine?" He laughed a little. "I'd be too fucked up to find my gate."

Justin managed a weak grin and slipped on his paint-splattered Salvage T-shirt. "Maybe next time." He stepped into his Cole Haan sandals and started for the door.

"Hey!" Teddy called, tossing something into the air. "A little happy for your trouble."

Justin caught the object with his right hand. It was a small, expensive looking scrap of burnt-orange leather. He gave Teddy a quizzical look.

"It's an Hermès condom holder. Very posh." He giggled. "A booker in Paris gave it to me."

"Thanks," Justin muttered. He transferred three Magnum XL rubbers from his front pocket into the sleek new case before walking out to hunt down his next prey.

He hit a Chelsea nightspot called the Secret Lounge and gave the stone-faced doorman a cool nod as he breezed past the industrial entryway into the dark-walled, dimly lit club.

The crowd was gay, good looking, and upscale. A glinting chandelier illuminated two velvet-bolted circular sofas. European house music pumped from the sound system. It was a million miles from Engine 40, Ladder 35 on Amsterdam and Sixty-sixth.

Justin headed straight for the bar and slid onto one of the few remaining pink-cushioned stools.

The bartender approached right away, giving him *that look* as he took note of his wedding ring. Without preamble, he set down a caipirinha with a splash of Red Bull. "This is our claim-to-fame *cock*tail. If you don't like it, you don't have to pay for it."

Justin sampled the offering and pushed it back. "I'll have a beer."

The bartender looked thunderstruck. "Really?"

Justin laughed and repossessed the drink. "No, I'm joking. It's good. Thanks."

The bartender winked and breathed a sigh of relief before moving on to an impatient Wall Street type.

"*Justin?*"

He turned to face the source of the surprised voice and couldn't believe his luck as he stared into the HDTV-perfect face of Tom Shapiro.

"What are you doing here?"

Justin shrugged easily. "I'm having a drink."

"Oh, well, that's . . . uh . . . great. I—I was just hanging out with one of my producers from the show. She likes the music here."

Justin glanced around. "Where is she?"

"She left," Tom answered, struggling to sustain direct eye contact. "She wasn't feeling that good."

"That's too bad," Justin said in a dull voice. And then he slipped off the barstool and strode over to an unoccupied black banquette in the corner. He looked up to see Tom staring at him with confused interest, wondering if the invitation to follow was there. In answer, Justin allowed his legs to fall open and dropped a hand to his inner thigh.

Tom hesitated, the moral debate all over his face.

Justin stroked a thumb across his denim crotch.

Tom swallowed hard and stepped over to join him. "I want to take you up on that racquetball game you mentioned."

Justin nodded vaguely, grooving to the ambient beat of the music that throbbed like a pulse, watching the flickering light of the votive candles that tossed shadows onto Tom's face.

"I should leave," Tom whispered. "Liza's a good friend."

Justin inched closer. "Liza's in the Hamptons."

Tom shook his head. There was a lustful longing in his eyes. But the loyal part of him still seemed to be winning the private war. "It doesn't feel right."

Justin leaned in to kiss Tom on the mouth. His lips were hard and unyielding, his tongue aggressive and probing, and nanosecond by nanosecond, Justin could feel all of Tom's reasons why not melting away. Suddenly, Justin drew back. "Trust me. When I'm fucking you over and over again in her bed, it's going to feel right."

Kellyanne

FIFTEEN

"I've been cheated/Been mistreated/When will I be loved?" The old country-rock nugget blared from the tinny speakers of the CD player as Linda Ronstadt belted out precisely what Kellyanne was feeling.

Bundled up in a terry-cloth robe, she sat miserably in the Astor Suite of the St. Regis Hotel, waiting for Walter to put in a cameo appearance between meetings.

Kellyanne had never resented him more. In fact, the change in area code had unleashed a hostility that she found impossible to contain. She responded to his selfish expectations by acting out in passive-aggressive ways.

She hit below the belt by not swallowing his cum. That was his favorite part of oral sex, too. When she took him out of her mouth and jerked him to a climax with her hand, forcing him to shoot all over his stomach, the disappointed look on Walter's face had been priceless. To add insult to injury, Kellyanne explained that his ejaculate had developed a horrible taste, then went on to speculate aloud whether his age might have something to do with it. Every day she prayed that he'd trade Levitra for Prozac and go back home to Miami.

But more disturbing than Walter's presence was the fact that Adam Griffie hadn't called. The waiting was slowly killing her. She even began to question her own sanity. Had Adam really talked to her about the perfect role of a Southerner on *As the World Turns,* or was that notion just the manifestation of a dream?

Being stuck in the city was wrecking her mood as well. Walter's visit for a few days had stretched into a full week. In any other circumstances, Kellyanne would've appreciated her surroundings. Though small at six hundred square feet, the Astor Suite was beautifully appointed with silk wall coverings, antiques, deeply carved crown moldings, and a full bathroom of Italian marble. There were French sliding doors between the bedroom and living area, plus a separate powder room. No matter the opulence, she was sick of the goddamn hotel and desperately longed for the Hamptons.

She gazed out the window at the bumper-to-bumper traffic on Fifty-fifth Street and finally noticed that the CD player had advanced to the next track. "Poor, poor pitiful me/Oh, these boys won't let me be." Once again, Linda Ronstadt was providing the soundtrack to her fucking life.

Kellyanne cut off the music and switched on the plasma television, clicking through the channels at breakneck speed. It was the same bullshit on every news network—the presidential election, the endless war in Iraq, the shaky economy, the gossip of another idiot star rushing off to rehab.

Suddenly, a promo captured her attention. She turned up the volume, and that generic male announcer voice—so ubiquitous and so familiar—filled the room.

"It's the hottest reality series of the summer . . . and it's only on Fox!" Images of Vlad Branigan canoodling with bikini-clad contestants—in the hot tub, on a boat, at the beach—filled the screen in a barrage of quick-cut edits. "Can one man find true love in the city of lust?"

Now Vlad was addressing the camera. "Miami is wild. I've never seen so many gorgeous women in one place. And they're willing to do *anything* for love."

Kellyanne watched with a surreal sense of detachment as her own likeness appeared—an excerpt from one of her video confessionals. "He's close enough to Brad Pitt for me. I'll get him. Just watch." A split-second night-cam vision scene hinted at a man and woman engaged in sex.

Her stomach dropped fast, and a sick feeling spread across her abdomen. She'd never spoken those words. Well, she'd said them, yes, but not in that particular order or context. A sense of helplessness swept over Kellyanne. This was the editing hatchet job that Bonzi had threatened her with.

The announcer was back, speaking over a montage of romantic interludes, cat fights, and emotional breakdowns. "For the most eligible bachelor in the country, bed buddies come and go, friends with benefits fade in and out . . . but *Soul Mates* are forever. Watch him make the biggest decision of his life, and brace yourself for the last minute surprise that will rock his world. *Soul Mates*. This summer. Only on Fox."

The hotel phone jangled, startling her and ringing several times before she had the presence of mind to answer. It was Walter. He was downstairs with an hour to kill. At the moment, Kellyanne preferred jumping out the window to entertaining him.

He crashed through the door a few minutes later, jerking off his tie and bitching at her for not having a drink ready.

Like a zombie, she poured his favorite—Dalwhinnie—over some half-melted ice and offered it to him.

Walter's face was splotched with red, and he was breathing hard as he drank deep on the Scotch. He untied Kellyanne's robe and pawed roughly at her breasts, kneading them like baker's dough.

She winced as he pinched a nipple.

He grinned with satisfaction, thinking she liked it.

What would the old bastard do if she told him the truth? And the truth was that she was no more aroused right now than she would be for a root canal. All she wanted to do was blow him fast and send him on his way. But Walter had other plans.

He put down his glass and unhooked his belt. "Bend over the sofa."

This encounter was more tedious than most. He was only semi-erect and had difficulty staying inside her. His cock flopped out like a wet noodle at least a dozen times.

Kellyanne submitted her body to his incompetent desire and teleported her mind to a different place. She thought about Tucker McGraw, the handsome fish market proprietor, and his precious mini-me, Parks. She found herself smiling as she pictured them— big man and little man in their matching Croc sandals—prepping her jumbo shrimp with old-fashioned masculine pride and pur-pose. The image was a sweet escape.

Finally, Walter climaxed with a grunt, then pulled up his pants and collapsed into an armchair. He was sweating profusely.

"You don't look well."

His rheumy eyes flashed irritation. "Just get me a towel and an-other drink."

Kellyanne slipped on her robe before freshening his Scotch and grabbing a hand towel from the powder room. "Maybe you should see a doctor."

"Why? Isn't going out with a bang the best way to expire?"

She thought about him dying in the middle of the act. It simul-taneously frightened and disgusted her. "Don't talk like that."

He sipped his drink and blotted his face with the towel, in-dulging in an inward distraction that appeared more troubling than usual. Business issues could always trigger a foul mood, but this was the worst shape Kellyanne had ever seen him in.

She'd picked up on the basics just from overhearing a few cell phone conversations. After several booming years, real estate was in crisis, and now the ax was falling on condominiums—Walter's primary vehicle. Miami, in particular, was taking quite a beating. Within the next few years, over twenty-four thousand new condo units would be flooding an inventory-heavy market. Falling prices were forcing appraisals down, and scores of presale buyers were suing Walter to get out of contracts.

"Things will turn around," Kellyanne told him. She squeezed his shoulder for emphasis.

He clasped her fingers, holding her there. "That fucking Arab got six hundred million in loans for more than twenty properties, and every single one is in foreclosure. Nobody seemed to notice that he didn't know shit about real estate. But they didn't know shit, either. So there you have it."

Kellyanne waited quietly for the moment to pass.

He could easily build to a boil on the subject of amateurs and the investors who poured money into their projects. Not long ago, there were limited sources for equity debt financing. But then hedge funds, special real estate funds, and community banks all jumped into the race, betting on unproven developers to win. Some did. Most didn't. And now it was a bloodbath. Though Walter knew that he'd be among the strong players who survived, he also realized that it might take years to dig out from the rubble.

"All these meetings are a pain in the ass," he said, still holding her hand. "It helps to have you waiting for me. I need the stress release."

"I'm shocked that you're still here," Kellyanne replied evenly. "It's been a whole week."

"I hope I can wrap this up in the next few days. I need to get home." He let go of her fingers. "And you probably want to get back to your girlfriends in the Hamptons, right?" There was a hint of derision in his delivery of *girlfriends*.

She said nothing.

Walter stood up to tuck in his still-crisp shirt and reknot his Mimi Fong tie. "I met an investor last night who just sent his girl in for anal bleaching. He says she's got the prettiest asshole he's ever seen. Why don't you check into that?"

Kellyanne turned on him hotly. She already spent enough time with two-blade razors and baby powder, dry shaving her bush into the perfect isosceles triangle that was his preference. But bleaching her anus was out of the question. "Get serious."

Walter narrowed his gaze. "I am. If you're not going to swallow, blow jobs aren't fun anymore. I need something to keep me interested. Giving it to you in the ass sounds like the ticket."

Kellyanne just stared back at him in disbelief.

"Don't look so surprised." His smile was nasty. "And don't let that Gloria Steinem wannabe fill your pretty little head with girl-power shit, either."

Kellyanne gave him a confused look. "What are you talking about?"

"I'm talking about your loudmouth feminist friend. Whenever that bitch comes on television, I scramble for the remote to press the MUTE button." He scoffed. "Don't listen to her. You've developed an attitude and a smart-ass mouth since you've been here. I don't like it. Remember—I put in fifty grand for this summer vacation. If that doesn't deserve an all-access pass to that body of yours, then what does?"

That night, she started swallowing again. And the son of a bitch stayed in New York for five more days.

When he left, Walter insisted that she accompany him to the airport. Just before boarding his flight, he announced that he'd be back in two weeks, possibly for another ten-day stay. If Kellyanne had been given a guarantee that Walter Isherwood would die from his next sex act, then she would've stripped down to nothing and fucked him right there in the Delta terminal at LaGuardia.

The days that followed brought the worst of all possible outcomes. *Soul Mates* launched to incredible ratings, demolishing its time slot's competition. The show's success drew headlines for a socko five-point rating with adults eighteen to forty-nine and 13 million viewers overall.

Fox marketing went into hyperdrive, declaring it the summer's first network megahit, scheduling an encore airing, and announcing one-week delay repurposing on sister channels Fox Reality and MyNetworkTV. Rabid fans flooded YouTube with clips of the show's saucier bits. TMZ broke the story that an ex-girlfriend was accusing Vlad Branigan of infecting her with herpes. *Soul Mates* was officially a phenomenon. And the hysteria continued to build. Episode two pulled in 14 million viewers, improving on the debut by an astonishing 1 million.

If the portrayal of Kellyanne had been damaging in the first hour, then it was totally devastating by the end of the second show. Slick-trick editing had managed to depict her fed-up exit midway into filming as petulant outrage over being told that sneaking into Vlad Branigan's bedroom after hours was forbidden. Footage of her yelling, "I quit the goddamn show!" was looped over and over again.

Reaction interviews with her former castmates only dug the knives in deeper. The most vicious of all came from Dee Lonergan, the proudly self-described bitch whom Kellyanne had barely tolerated during that miserable week on Star Island. "She found out that acting like a complete slut was against the rules, so she quit," Dee summarized for the camera, clearly relishing every syllable. "That's rich. If you ask me, this show was never a good fit for Kellyanne. When do they start shooting *Who Wants to Marry an Alabama Skank?*" I think she could actually do much better on something like that."

The campaign of personal destruction didn't end there. Throughout the program, viewers were prompted by the show's smarmy host—a cringe-inducing ex-NFL quarterback sporting new porcelain veneers too big for his mouth—to log onto the *Soul Mates* Web site and cast their votes in the "Slut-O-Meter" poll, which pitted Kellyanne against Hooters waitress Bunny Corvette. Results were updated live and scrolled onto the bottom of the screen. There was no contest. By an extreme margin, Kellyanne earned top honors.

She was devastated. Her cell phone exploded with calls— Pommie, Jab, her father, her mother, and Uncle Kirby, among others.

But she let them all go to voice mail. Right now there was only one person she wanted to hear from—Adam Griffie.

Finally, he called. "I thought this *Soul Mates* shit would die quickly. But *everybody's* talking about it."

Kellyanne groaned her displeasure as she entertained the idea of asking Walter to pay for a lawyer. There had to be a legal recourse for this kind of malicious deception. When Liza had suggested it weeks ago, Kellyanne refused to consider the idea, going on the long-held Downey principle that you don't pour gas onto a fire. But things were different now. She felt under attack more than ever. "What if I sued?"

"Sued who?" Adam balked.

"I don't know . . . Three Kegs Entertainment. That's Bonzi's production company. He threatened to humiliate me like this if I didn't sleep with him. That's sexual harassment."

"You signed a contract," Adam reminded her. "Those reality boilerplates waive any and all rights to legal action based on the outcome of the show."

"But it's all a lie!" Kellyanne cried. "This is my reputation!"

"Yeah, well, most people concerned about their reputations don't sign up for these shows. Exhibitionists who want attention do."

Kellyanne mentioned Gloria Allred, the high-profile superattorney who took on sensational victim's rights cases.

"You might get a press conference out of that," Adam surmised with little encouragement. "And the talk shows would pursue you for a day or two. But Bonzi and the network won't budge an inch. Besides, it'll be tough to cry sexual harassment when the die has already been cast with the actual show. He's putting you out there as a drunk slut. Whether that's true or not is irrelevant. Images are damning, and perception is reality. If you take them on, your relationship with Walter will become fair game, too. That's not an arrangement most people would find noble or sympathetic. My advice—just hope this goes away soon."

Kellyanne thought about fighting back. It'd take a will of iron, impossibly thick skin, deep financial resources, and a plan to win. At the moment, she had none of those things. She unleashed a dramatic sigh of defeat. "Have you heard anything from *As the World Turns*?"

"They want you in for a reading next week."

Her mood instantly brightened . . . but then it was darkened again by a subterranean uncertainty she picked up in Adam's voice. "Is something wrong?"

"This *Soul Mates* business makes me nervous," Adam admitted. "My gut tells me that all of the attention is going to be a liability. This isn't stunt casting. It's a legitimate role. They want a serious actress. Let's see what happens." His tone lacked even cautious optimism.

Kellyanne was crushed. Doomsday thoughts flooded her mind as angry tears watered her eyes. She wanted this part so bad that her body ached for it. Why not her? Goddammit! Why not? Considering all the users and humiliations over the years, she deserved this break.

Adam promised to e-mail details about the reading, then signed off.

Kellyanne barely said good-bye. She just tucked her legs underneath her chin and sat there on the bed, disturbed and distracted, her mind burning with regret for all the bad choices, missed chances, and crushed dreams. And, as it always did whenever she had the temerity to look back, there was one memory that scorched the most. Los Angeles, 2004 . . .

"*Everyone's* a whore in this town," Michelle Estes said. "The city is full of them. Studio execs, stars, producers, agents—everybody." She stabbed at the avocado in her Greek Californian Salad. "It's not just the call girls. It's a way of life here."

Kellyanne merely nodded as she sipped more kouros, a light Greek white wine.

"Do you see that guy in the white Prada shirt two tables to your right?" Michelle asked.

Kellyanne spotted him without appearing too obvious.

Michelle leaned in conspiratorially. "That's Robert Bradley. He's a plastic surgeon in Century City. Loves blondes. For a few fucks and a couple of blow jobs, he'll give you a new pair of tits. And he's the best in town." She smirked. "At breast augmentation. The man's a lousy lay. His dick is too small, and he sweats too much." Michelle made an ugly face. "He should really throw in some liposculpting to make it a fair deal."

Kellyanne found herself staring at Michelle's enhanced cleavage.

"Perfect Bs."

They were lunching on the sprawling patio of Taverna Tony's at the Malibu Country Mart, a casual yet chic outdoor shopping center situated with the roaring Pacific on one side and the scenic Santa Monica mountains and canyons on the other.

Kellyanne spread some hummus onto a small piece of grilled pita bread as she sorted out the new facts.

Michelle Estes, her friend from method class, was less struggling actress and more working high-class prostitute. And the half-truths didn't end there. The multimillion-dollar sand castle they were living in on Broad Beach was hardly an incredible sublease deal. It was an act of generosity from one of Michelle's regular johns, a top-tier actor currently on location in Australia.

Kellyanne had also discovered that Michelle worked for Judith Love, a discreet madam who managed a small group of meticulously selected, exceptional girls. For every appointment, Michelle easily made a few thousand dollars. Her nickname was Elvira, given not for anything to do with the Mistress of the Dark, but in tribute to her uncanny resemblance to Michelle Pfeiffer's character in the film *Scarface*. Michelle Estes had the same drop-dead ice blond looks and the same superior blond attitude. *I'm hot, and everybody wants to fuck me. What else is new?*

Kellyanne sipped more wine and regarded Michelle with on-the-sleeve resentment. She felt played. The lattes and girl talk after method class, the shopping excursions, the dinners out, the club adventures, the invitation to leave her dodgy apartment in a not-so-great neighborhood for a three-month free ride in a beachfront Malibu mansion—all of it had been part of a strategic campaign to recruit her.

Michelle's real agenda had started to spill last night. More details followed the next morning while they drank coffee on the waterfront deck. And the entire charade was on the table at the popular Greek restaurant where they sat now.

"You'd be a natural," Michelle insisted.

Kellyanne narrowed her gaze. "A natural hooker? You're such an angel to say that. Bless your heart."

"It's not a stigma," Michelle maintained. "It's a solution." She recited two famous names—an actress starring on a new hit television series about suburban housewives and the eco-friendly wife of a movie director. "Both of them used to work for Judith."

"That doesn't mean I'm willing to."

Michelle pushed her half-eaten salad over to the side. "You're practically doing what I'm doing already. You just haven't made it official yet. And you're not getting properly compensated."

Kellyanne started to protest.

"Come on, girl. Get real. You're a hurricane hooker, just like me. I'm from Florida. You're from Alabama. The wind blew us west, because we wanted to make it in Hollywood. How many horny producers and bullshit actors have you gone to dinner with—and slept with—in hopes of getting a part?"

Kellyanne just looked at her.

"Judith's a boutique madam for the power elite. You'll make top dollar *and* make some important introductions. This is how I landed that speaking part on *CSI* during February sweeps. If they pay to fuck you, they're more inclined to help you careerwise. It sounds weird, but it's true. Judith says it's because a successful business transaction has already taken place." Michelle laughed a little. "Personally? I think these men love the idea of getting pussy for nothing and fucking over naive girls. If they didn't pay for it on the front end, then they don't want to pay for it on the back end. But I'm in a different league. I get paid to get them off. But more important, I get paid to leave. So they're not on guard about my wanting more than what they intend to give. This relaxes them. And when these guys are relaxed and feeling like a stud, a real career boost has a better chance of coming my way. It's a win-win."

What frightened Kellyanne the most was that this was all starting to make sense to her. The fear triggered an impulse to bolt. "I'll be out of the house by midafternoon."

Michelle shook her head regretfully. "No one's asking you to move out."

"But that was part of the sweetener package for this pitch, right?" Kellyanne accused. "If I'm not going along, I should take off. You and Judith probably have another mark picked out."

"It's not like that," Michelle said quietly. "I consider you a real friend. We've talked for hours. I know about all the disappointments you've had to deal with since moving here. It's been one jerk off guy after another." She paused a beat. "And if you think that's going to change . . ."

"For me, the answer isn't—"

"Michael Zanker," Michelle cut in.

Kellyanne fell silent. She read *Variety* and *The Hollywood Reporter* to keep up with cocktail party conversation. Michael Zanker was a prolific producer and part of the town's unofficial yet prestigious Billionaire Boys Club. His recent string of high-octane blockbusters—a remake of *The Towering Inferno* set in Las Vegas, the vigilante drama *Bulletproof,* its sequel *Still Bulletproof,* and the terrorist thriller *Blast Point* had collectively racked up a cool billion in domestic box office receipts alone.

Michelle fingered the stem of her wineglass. "If you wanted to give this a try, you could see him tonight."

There was industry talk percolating about Michael Zanker's plans for a big-budget film based on the DC Comics heroine Batgirl. The word was out that he wanted an unknown to fill the spandex.

As if reading her mind, Michelle said, "By the way, all this talk about a Batgirl movie is bullshit." She rolled her eyes. "It's Zanker's cocaine project."

Kellyanne gave her a puzzled look.

"He only talks about it when he's high. Action movies with female leads rarely work, and he's already snorted the idea that the budget needs to be one hundred million. Don't believe anything he says about it. It'll never get out of development. Trust me." She laughed. "I can name three girls off the top of my head who are walking around telling everyone they're going to be the next Batgirl. I used to be the fourth. *Don't* fall for it. The real movie on his schedule is *Trigger Finger.* Matt Damon's already attached. It's about a bad cop. I've got the script at the house. There's a great innocent-girlfriend part that you'd be perfect for."

Kellyanne was instantly wary. "If it's such a great part, why aren't you going after it?"

Michelle smiled wryly. "I can't do innocent. I'm not that good an actress. Besides, Zanker has this thing about casting new talent. And by 'new talent' I mean girls he's recently *conditioned.* I saw him a few years ago. He ended up giving me the philandering bitch–wife role to Colin Farrell's demolition expert in *Blast Point,* but all of the domestic scenes ended up on the cutting-room floor. They eventually turned up in the special-features section of the deluxe DVD. But nobody has time to watch all of those extras." She shrugged helplessly. "What's a call girl to do?"

Kellyanne was up to speed on *Trigger Finger.* It'd been a buzz project in the trades for weeks. Michael Mann had just signed on to direct. And Denzel Washington was rumored to be in negotiations to play a tough police captain. In the general sense, Kellyanne had to admit that she'd easily sleep with a producer if it meant joining Damon, Washington, and Mann on a film project. So what was stopping her now?

Michelle seemed to pick up on the fact that Kellyanne was slowly warming to the idea. "Just think of tonight as a trial run. If you decide it's not for you, so be it. But you'll still make some good money and meet one of the most successful producers in the business."

Kellyanne could feel anxiety building. That she was actually considering this seemed crazy. Just recently she'd turned down an offer to pose for *Playboy*. And yet here she was close to saying yes to prostitution.

"It's not a dark path," Michelle said. "*If* you stay away from drugs. Judith says that's where most girls go wrong. They get stuck doing it for the cocaine and needing the cocaine to do it." She reached out to squeeze Kellyanne's hand. "Don't overthink this. It's not an indictment on your morals. It's a strategic move. And working for Judith, you'll only go out on dates with the upper echelon. I'm talking about the men who make it onto those annual Hollywood power lists in magazines."

Kellyanne took a deep breath. She swallowed hard. She swore to herself that, in a town full of users, this was nothing more than a shrewd way for someone like her to operate. "What's the split?"

Michelle smiled triumphantly. "Judith gets thirty percent."

Michael Zanker lived in a gorgeous home on Stone Canyon in Bel Air. When he opened the door, Kellyanne was surprised to see how short he was—five foot six.

He raked her up and down with obvious appreciation. "Judith said she was sending over a knockout. You're much more than that."

Kellyanne smiled her thanks, nervously taking in the minimalist Japanese-inspired decor.

"May I offer you a drink?"

She politely declined, wondering how one thing would lead to another. Michelle had told her that Zanker was a time management obsessive. He wanted his girls to arrive and depart in punctual two-hour blocks.

He was in his midthirties, physically fit, and handsome in that effective sales representative sort of way—attractive, sexually appealing, but ultimately unmemorable.

"I want to show you something." His voice was tender. He took her by the hand and led her through the impeccable house and into a dedicated screening room.

At first, Kellyanne assumed that he wanted to show off a rough cut of a new film. But the entertainment was something else entirely. What filled the massive screen was crude hidden-camera footage of Zanker interviewing a young actress for a role in one of his movies. It ended with her taking off her clothes and performing fellatio on him. And then another one played—same story, same setup.

Kellyanne sat through at least half a dozen of these clips, betraying no reaction even as Zanker closely monitored her for one.

Mercifully, the screen went blank.

"What do you think?" he asked.

She looked at him. "I think after the second interview, it all became rather predictable."

He grinned. "Those are utility girls. I just use them for pleasure. They aren't worthy of a part in one of my movies. Only the women I choose to condition are elevated to that status."

Kellyanne recalled Michelle using the term *condition*, too. "What does that mean exactly?"

"Come with me." He took her hand again and this time ushered her into a small guest room that contained little more than a low platform bed. "Take off your clothes."

Kellyanne braced herself. She'd slept with worse. And for less. If Michelle was right about his time issues, then she only had about an hour left. *Yes.* She could do this. Slowly, she untied the Diane von Furstenberg wrap dress, let it fall to the floor, and stood there in her La Perla best.

Zanker took Kellyanne's face in his hands, gazing at her in a state of absolute marvel. "You are truly exquisite. The word *beautiful* is almost too ordinary to describe you."

She hoped he'd remember that speech when the studio wanted a name actress for the part of Matt Damon's girlfriend in *Trigger Finger.*

Suddenly, Zanker reached down to grab something on the edge of the bed. "I want you to wear this." He presented her with a black hood fitted with breathing holes around the nose and mouth.

Kellyanne looked at him in disbelief.

"This is part of your conditioning." Zanker's smile was as cold as his voice. He slipped the hood over her head.

Kellyanne experienced a mounting panic as everything turned pitch black. She could breathe, but the instant blindness scared the hell out of her. "No! I can't—"

Zanker shoved a rubber ball into her mouth and strapped it tightly around the hood.

Kellyanne tried to stop him, but he grabbed her by both wrists and pushed her down onto the bed. She could hear the crinkling of a Mylar-wrapped condom being ripped open.

"Stop fighting me," Zanker hissed. "I'm not going to hurt you. This is *conditioning.*"

Kellyanne's fear intensified. And she felt played all over again. Michelle had given her no hint as to this rich asshole's perversions.

"Your beauty makes no difference right now. You can't be seen. You can't be heard. You're just a receptacle." He pushed himself inside her. "I hate actresses. You're all selfish, greedy bitches who want something for nothing."

Unable to scream or beg him to stop, Kellyanne just laid there motionless, counting the seconds, counting the minutes . . . until the hour was up.

Zanker used her sexually, violating her with his body and various toys as he taunted her with the constant refrain, "Do you feel beautiful?" When it was over, he told her that she had three minutes to get dressed and leave.

The moment she heard him exit the room, Kellyanne yanked the rubber ball out of her mouth and tore off the black hood, crying hysterically as she scrambled for her dress and shoes.

There was an envelope of cash on the pillow. She counted three thousand dollars in crisp hundred-dollar bills. But that wasn't nearly enough for what she'd just been through.

Kellyanne made her way to the front of the house. She found Zanker kicked back on the sleek living room sofa, drinking a beer and talking on his cell phone.

For a moment, she stood there, staring daggers at him.

Casually, he dropped the mobile to his side. "I'll set up a screen test with Matt. Leave me your number."

The rage that coursed through her rattled her bones. "Rot in hell, you sick fuck!"

Zanker was unfazed and returned to his conversation.

She stormed out and raced back to Malibu. The house was empty. Michelle had left a note on the counter, promising to be back at midnight. Below the clumsily drawn heart that closed the message, Kellyanne scribbled "Judith's share" and dropped nine hundred dollars. She owed them nothing. It was a clean break.

By the time midnight ticked around, she was already on a red-eye flight to New York, desperate to leave behind the Hollywood meatgrinder, Michelle Estes, and the horrific memory that she knew would last forever . . .

And so far it had. She wiped away a tear. The emotional wounds remained raw. Years later, the episode still represented Kellyanne's lowest point in life. The reality-show fiasco paled in comparison. Part of her had been permanently damaged that night in Bel Air. There was a crack in her soul. And this had set her up as perfect prey for a controlling man like Walter Isherwood. She'd been weak, she'd been broken, and she'd wanted so desperately to believe that being taken care of was the answer.

Do you feel beautiful?

She could still hear Zanker's voice inside her head. Or was it Walter's now? Did it even matter anymore? Sometimes Kellyanne wondered what her life might've been today if she'd stayed in Los Angeles, if she'd left her number with that sick bastard, if she'd done the screen test with Matt Damon, if she'd never met Walter.

Oh, God, if only . . .

Billie

SIXTEEN

"I missed my flight because of that crap you pulled at the Hotel . . . Elysée! Do you realize I lost . . . a twenty-five-thousand-dollar . . . speaking fee?" March's breathing was labored, and his hazel eyes blazed with renewed rage.

Billie smiled. She could feel his hands tighten around her throat. The sensation was thrilling. March might be pissed off and twenty-five grand poorer, but he was back where he belonged—deep inside her. And anger meant that he actually felt something. Love could come later.

For now, it was pure, hot, jackhammer sex.

Billie put her strongly responsive vaginal muscles to effective use. Without warning, she contracted them, squeezing March's cock like a Venus flytrap.

He cried out in astonished pleasure. And his amazing hands— that only moments before had hinted at killing—were now caressing as he collapsed on top of her in an exhausted, satisfied, sweat-slicked heap.

Billie played with March's dirty blond hair, blissfully content to have him all to herself again. She wanted to bask in the sensual nirvana. He was still inside her. They were skin on skin, body on body. His intoxicating, manly scent was potent in her nostrils.

Oh, God, she tried to just enjoy the moment. In fact, she gave it her goddamn best effort. But the familiar anxieties began to build. How long would this moment last? When would she see him again? Why did he want to marry that bitch Amaryllis?

Rolling over and onto his back, March moaned with erotic contentment, placing a proprietary hand on the inside of Billie's thigh. "It's hard to stay mad at a woman with a trick pussy." He sighed. "Do you have any coke?"

"I wish."

With his free hand, March reached for a silver case on the nightstand. "Then this will have to do." He tapped out a fresh joint, fired it up, and inhaled deeply, displaying more ganja know-how than a lifetime subscriber to *High Times*.

They were at the Hudson on West Fifty-eighth. Mr. Political Superstar had gone all out, splurging on a standard room just shy of 150 square feet. The matchbox was only big enough for a double bed and a stainless-steel desk and chair.

Billie took a hit of the weed and stared at the dark-paneled African wood walls. "You really know how to impress a girl."

"What?"

"I've stayed at Comfort Inns that had bigger rooms."

March repossessed the joint. "This is a hot hotel. It's got style."

"Whatever."

"Does it matter? We just needed a clean bed for a few hours."

"Yeah, God forbid you treat me to a meal before or after. I might get confused and think you want to start picking out china patterns."

"Call room service."

"It's not the same."

He passed the joint. "Here. You obviously need this more than I do."

Billie didn't refuse. She sucked the magic smoke straight into her lungs. "Would it kill you to take me out to dinner sometime?"

March laughed and snatched back his herb. "Where's this shit coming from? We just fucked our brains out, and now you're making noises like a nagging housewife."

"So I'm not supposed to want anything more? Being treated like a slut is all I should aspire to when it comes to the fabulous March Donaldson?"

"You're ruining my high." He took another deep drag and closed his eyes.

"Go to hell." She rose up to bolt from the bed.

But March grabbed her arm. "Billie, come on, what's wrong with you?"

"Quite a bit, obviously." She twisted free of his grasp. "I bet you wouldn't think twice about taking Liza out for dinner."

"You're right," he said simply. "I wouldn't. But we work together. There's a difference."

Billie fought the urge to spit in his face. "You suck."

He laughed at her in frustration. "You know what my situation is. I'm engaged. I've got a politically sensitive career. Nothing's changed for me."

"But what about *me*?" Billie cried. "I'm supposed to just wait around and jump whenever you throw a scrap of time my way?"

"Well, shit, Billie. You're a rock star. Call up Nickelback. Ask them to take you to lunch. I can't be everything for you."

Now it was Billie's turn to laugh. "Oh, please, get over yourself. I don't want you to be my everything. But you could be *something*."

March smiled and shook his head, then pulled her down to kiss her on the mouth and wrestle playfully. "This bitch drives me crazy!" he yelled out. It was exasperation. It was admiration. It was something else, too . . . affection. Real, unguarded affection.

Billie saw an opening and went for it. "I was watching you and Amaryllis at Sunset Beach," she began quietly. "She doesn't excite you."

"Billie . . ."

"I've never had sex like this before. Have you?" She didn't wait for him to answer. "It surprises me every time. We're electric together. You can't deny that."

"I don't. And it works." He patted the mattress. "But right here. Nowhere else." His tone was absolute.

Billie tried to conceal her disappointment but couldn't help the hurt being telegraphed all over her face.

March sighed. "Don't look at me that way."

She felt the tears building in her eyes. Only her anger kept her from breaking down. "You're such a bastard."

He smiled, almost as if it was a private joke. "I'll write you a poem. Will that help?"

Before Billie realized it, her hand lashed out against his face. "Don't mock me!"

March barely reacted. He just smoothed the point of impact with his palm and looked at her. "I can't keep up, Billie. One minute you're the good-time hookup, and the next minute you're this lovesick schoolgirl. What the hell do you want from me?"

"I want some goddamn honesty."

"Okay, I'll start. You're taking the fun out of this. And when it stops being fun, I'm gone." He paused a beat. "Your turn."

His answer crushed her. Billie got the strong sense that his coldness ran deeper than she could imagine. A part of him was so unreachable. But still, she wanted to try. "I wish you'd treat me like you treat Liza. She's a real person to you. You respect her. I want that."

March's smile was almost sad. "You want a relationship."

Billie just stared at him.

His eyes were candid. "I can't offer that. I can't offer you anything other than . . . *this*."

She shook her head mutely.

March grinned at Billie for a long moment before finally pulling her down into his arms for a tender embrace.

She thought about resisting him, if only because she didn't want to know what it felt like to be held this way. But she succumbed to

207

her naked need and allowed it to happen. Right away, she regretted the indulgence. It felt too damn good. And Billie knew that she'd never stop wanting more of it.

He kissed her shoulder, and almost against his will, he said, "I think about you, too. The other night I was with a group of people, and I was bored out of my mind. I wanted you there. Sometimes I wish . . ."

Billie held her breath for the rest.

But March's voice just trailed off into silence. He traced her torso with his fingertips.

"What do you wish?" Billie prompted.

He hesitated. "I wish you were my type."

"Judging by Amaryllis, your type is frigid and dull."

He smiled wanly. "I run a conservative think tank. There are certain expectations that go along with that. And if I ever run for public office, I'll need the right partner."

"So marrying her is a business arrangement."

March winced at the crude assessment. "I wouldn't put it that way."

"How would you put it?"

"We complement each other."

"I guess Tina Turner was right all along. 'What's Love Got to Do with It?'"

March nuzzled her neck. "Maybe you should do a remake. You could sing the hell out of that song. When was that a hit—eighty-four, eighty-five? It's time for a new version."

Billie tangled her leg around his, loving the intimacy, hating herself even more for allowing it, but still wishing it could linger for hours, for days, for weeks . . . forever. "Oh, so you're giving me career advice now? Maybe you should be my manager. I'm in the market for one."

"Clean up your act. I can guarantee you a gig singing 'God Bless America' at the next Republican convention."

"I'll keep looking," Billie deadpanned.

March laughed. "Hey, I almost forgot. Kip mentioned that you owe him some money. He says you've been dodging his calls, too."

Billie tensed immediately. Kip was the dealer with the Wall Street vibe that March had referred her to during their first rendezvous. "I'm not dodging him. He called once. I was in the shower. Right now I'm trying to sort out my money situation. My ex-manager used to handle all of that. He'll get the cash."

"Make sure that he does. Kip may look clean cut and wear expensive suits, but he's still a fucking drug dealer. Don't forget that."

"Is that a warning?" she trilled lightly.

"No, Billie, that's good advice." His tone was serious.

The truth was, Billie had started using a new dealer, because it was either pay Kip what she owed him or get more drugs from another source. Now she just wanted to change the subject. "I went to your Web site."

March's eyes widened. "OurAmerica.com?"

Billie nodded. "The extreme right side of things must be a lucrative racket. You can't really believe most of that shit."

"I'll admit there's a certain business advantage to courting the values crowd. But I'm also a white guy from Texas. At the end of the day, it's not such a stretch."

"I guess it's sort of like me going pop," Billie reasoned philosophically. "I have a certain contempt for it, but at the same time, I need to make real money. Maybe we're not hypocrites after all, you and I. Maybe we're just pragmatists."

March smiled. "Yeah, well, don't be offended if I decline to make that one of the talking points in my next Rotary Club speech." He checked the clock on his iPhone and groaned. A hot second later, he was on his feet, shoving peppermint into his mouth and throwing on his clothes. "Are you really sure about this?"

"About what?"

"Going Celine." He grinned. "I think I might miss my raunchy rocker bitch."

Billie shrugged. "I need a radio hit. When I hear Alicia Keys singing 'No One,' that works for me. Doing what I've been doing has put me in a spot where I can't pay my dealer on time. Fuck that."

"I hear you. That's why I'm about to go tell a group of rich evangelicals that prayer in school is the most important issue facing our country today."

He rolled his eyes and slipped on a diamond-striped Stefano Ricci dress shirt, working the buttons with lightening speed. "You know, I just read that Madonna dumped her record label to sign with Live Nation, the concert promoters. And Apple's starting up a music division. Everything's changing. I think it's a smart move to widen your audience."

March stepped into his pants and fastened his belt, then leaned down to kiss her on the mouth. "But when I come to see your next concert, you have to do 'Make Me Laugh and Make Me Come and I'll Fucking Marry You,' even if the audience is full of teenagers." He scanned the room quickly for any leave-behinds.

Billie reached for his hand as he started for the door. March could make her laugh. He could make her come, too. So why wouldn't he fucking marry her? "Don't rush off like this." Her voice was almost pleading.

He gave her a strange look.

"I've heard some great things about the food at Cafeteria downstairs. I thought we could—"

"Billie, didn't we just go through this?" His voice was annoyed and impatient. "I can't be seen with someone like you."

The words sliced into her and cut deep.

March sighed his regret, ostensibly for the insensitive phrasing. "You know what I mean. How would I explain being spotted with a wild music scene chick like you? Unless you plan to announce that you're switching over to Christian rock. Then maybe we could make a go of it." He smiled at his own joke.

She glared at him with fresh tears in her eyes. "Take off then, you son of a bitch. I'll even give you a thirty-minute head start. That way we won't be on the sidewalk at the same time. I wouldn't want you to risk staining that squeaky clean reputation of yours."

March stepped toward the door and suddenly turned back to face her. "Listen, Billie, this is what it is. I've been clear about that from the beginning. But if we have to constantly redefine things every time we get together, then I think we should just end it."

Something in his voice told her that he already had. But she wanted to be sure. "When will I see you again?"

"I don't know." March opened the door. "I'll call you." And then he walked out for good.

Liza

SEVENTEEN

 Liza observed Kellyanne stretched out by the pool, sacrificing her body to the sun in a gold-foil Norma Kamali bikini.

Having just completed her morning swim, Annie the golden retriever lumbered over to lick Kellyanne's face and feet.

"Hello, sweetheart," Kellyanne gushed in an uninspired happy-talk voice that unsuccessfully disguised the darkness of her true mood. But she seemed genuinely grateful for the animal distraction.

As Annie trotted away, Liza stepped onto the deck in a white cut-out swimsuit by Dolce and Gabbana that emphasized her thin body, protected from those aging UV rays by a wide-brimmed white floppy hat and loads of SPF 45. Behind the giant Dior rimless shield sunglasses, there was deep concern in her eyes. She offered up a tall glass loaded with crushed ice and filled to the top with Bolthouse Farms Prickly Pear Cactus Lemonade.

"Bless your heart," Kellyanne murmured.

"This morning marks a brand-new day," Liza announced with her best Zen-like spin, settling into the chair next to Kellyanne.

"Any word from Billie?"

Liza shook her head. "And I'm done leaving messages. She has our numbers. She knows where the house is."

Kellyanne made a helpless gesture.

Where once Liza had been preoccupied with worry, she was now annoyed and insulted. Billie had been MIA for weeks, refusing to return calls and answer texts. Even urgent messages imploring her to get in touch were ignored.

"I think she's shacked up with some guy."

"Probably," Liza agreed. "But it's not the boy from Sunset Beach. Like an idiot, I drove to Shelter Island last week to see if he was still hanging around."

"And?"

"He was. But he hasn't seen or heard from Billie since that night."

"I just hope it's not drug related," Kellyanne said. "If so, a disappearing act like this is a bad sign. She could be on a bender. Walter's youngest son has a problem. For the most part, he's functional with it. But when he falls out of contact, everyone in the family starts to worry." She paused a beat. "Of course, Billie could also be off recording or performing somewhere. It'd be just like her not to mention that and make us feel like fools for worrying."

Liza shrugged. "Maybe. I did call Amy Dando—her manager . . . or more accurately, *ex*-manager."

Kellyanne looked up in surprise. *"Really?"*

Liza nodded. "You know, I'm not sure how accurate it would be to refer to Billie as a rock star in the present tense."

Kellyanne sighed. "Well, I'll still trade places with her. Better a career on the skids than no career at all."

"You're going to be a soap star," Liza declared with upbeat cheer. "That part on *As the World Turns* is yours. I can feel it."

Kellyanne made a show out of covering her ears.

"You can't let your mind be poisoned by what's going on," Liza said fiercely. "Just go in there and *knock them out*. You know that you can."

Somewhere in Kellyanne's eyes was a sign of confidence regenerating.

Liza tilted down her sunglasses and gave her a determined look. "I can't imagine how excruciating it must be to see yourself being exploited this way. This *Soul Mates* business is disgusting. But it's a temporary storm. You just have to ride it out. I see this in politics all the time. A scandal hits and there's an intense focus, a relentless piling on. Then the interest shifts to something else, and everything becomes quiet again. Don't lose sight of the fact that memories are short, either. This will pass."

"God, I hope you're right," Kellyanne whispered. "I want that job. I *need* that job. It could really mean a fresh start for me . . . without Walter."

Liza gave her a probing ray-gun gaze. "Run for your life. I think you could be happier in a rathole apartment living off cash advances from credit cards. At least you'd have your freedom."

Kellyanne brought a hand to her mouth, then seemed to think better of it. Her nails were down to the quick and cracked with dried blood from her nervous biting. *Soul Mates* had her fraying at the edges.

For several long seconds, Kellyanne just lay there. But finally, she began to speak. "Sometimes I wonder how I got here. I'm almost thirty. And I'm living this *dumb* life. It's hard to look back, because it's so pathetic. I haven't accomplished anything."

"That's not true," Liza said. "You went to college. You have your de—"

"Oh, big deal," Kellyanne cut in. "So I went to college. I got my diploma." She twirled a hand in the air. "Whoop-dee-fucking-do. What can I do with a degree in *theater*?"

"What do you want to do?" Liza challenged.

"I want to act!" Kellyanne shrieked.

"Then *do it*. But nothing's going to happen for you in Miami. Move back to Los Angeles."

Kellyanne winced at the suggestion.

"Or move here to New York again," Liza suggested. "Just don't give up until you're making a living at it."

Kellyanne stared at the sun. "Cue the theme from *Rocky*."

"Maybe I'm oversimplifying the idea," Liza admitted. "But people have landed in both places with less than thirty dollars in their pocket and made it work. Talent and looks have always been there for you. It's the focus and drive that you're missing. And if you could only break this habit of getting steered off course by men who are completely unworthy . . . my God, you'd probably have a fucking Oscar by now."

Kellyanne smiled wanly. "That's so true."

"But you've been this way ever since I can remember," Liza went on. "Who was that asshole you were dating when we met in Cancún for the first time?"

Liza sat there as Kellyanne put her sex memory chip to work, rewinding past Walter to name the manic-depressive musician in New York, certain jerky actors, egocentric producers, and high-strung directors in Hollywood, then on to her college lovers. And there'd been a reasonable number—the Crimson Tide's quarterback, an assistant football coach, a delicious tennis player on scholarship from South Africa, a hot fraternity guy, later his hotter older brother . . .

"Okay, slut, enough already!" Liza cut in with exasperated good humor. "It was March of 1999!"

Kellyanne laughed, covering her face in her hands.

All of a sudden, the name seemed to come to her. She grabbed Liza's wrist and squealed, "*Heath Warren!*"

"That's him!"

"Oh, God, I haven't thought about him in ages. He was one of my English professors. I thought he was *so* hot!"

Liza stole a look to the heavens, as if pleading for divine mercy. "I hated that pompous prick. You were a college girl on spring break in Cancún, and he wanted you to stay cooped up in the hotel room with him while he wrote his *literary novel*."

Kellyanne giggled. "He said I was his inspiration. He couldn't write unless I was around."

"Oh, please. That bullshit was all about control. By the way, I don't think his book was ever published."

"I don't think he ever finished it. I broke up with him that summer, and he still had at least one hundred pages to go." Kellyanne gasped. "Do you remember that dinner all of us had at La Madonna? I thought the two of you were going to kill each other!"

Liza traveled back. "Ugh! I wanted to stab him in the head with a fork! Monica Lewinsky's book had just been released, and Heath said something so unbelievably sexist."

Kellyanne laughed at the memory. "You really got the best of him that night. The entire table was speechless. I think he was pissed off for the rest of the trip."

Liza shook her head in disbelief. "What did you ever see in that guy? He was so full of himself."

"I know," Kellyanne murmured. "Heath thought the sun came up just to hear him crow." She finished the Prickly Pear Lemonade as they enjoyed the glorious sunshine in easy silence. "God, that seems like so long ago. And yet here we are . . . still friends." She turned to make eye contact. "Thank you."

Liza met her gaze with curiosity.

"For sticking with me all these years," Kellyanne clarified softly. "I've been on such a dead-end path, and you've been on such an ambitious one. You could've dumped me a long time ago. I wouldn't have blamed you. And watching your success has been inspiring. It's made me think about my own life, my own choices." Her smile was shy. "I guess you're my hero."

Liza glanced down. It was so true. They were worlds apart. Kellyanne believed it was Liza's loyalty that kept their relationship intact. But shamefully, Liza wondered if it might be something else entirely—a chance to feel superior . . . smarter, stronger, more successful. She never threw that back in Kellyanne's face—or Billie's, for that matter—but there was a certain lazy comfort in being around them. Liza didn't have to compete.

This realization stung. It was a quality she didn't like about herself. And Kellyanne, in particular, deserved better. She was kind, thoughtful, consistent, caring, a good listener, and more intelligent than she gave herself credit for. If Liza took months to return a call, Kellyanne never took it as a personal affront. She was always just happy to hear from her, and they picked right back up without a beat of awkwardness, as if no time had passed between them.

"I don't mean to embarrass you," Kellyanne said.

"I'm not embarrassed," Liza replied quietly. "I'm just not quite worthy." She looked at her. "I might seem like I have it all together, but you're a better person than I am. And frankly, I'm lucky to have you as a friend."

Kellyanne reached out to squeeze her hand. "Enough of that. It doesn't take much to have me bawling my eyes out. And enough about *me*. Let's move on to you. Have you talked to Justin?"

"Not about anything significant. I'm not sure there will be a *talk* per se. I'll probably just serve him with papers after Labor Day."

"Billie says he could get alimony."

Liza shook her head. "Over my dead body."

"And what about Harrison?" Kellyanne inquired. "How are things there?"

"We're . . . *friends*," Liza replied pointedly. "And we'll remain that way until I finalize the situation with Justin."

Suddenly, Liza rose up and dipped feet first into the pool, shivering instantly. "Oh, my God! The water's *freezing*!"

Kellyanne grinned from the chaise like the bathing beauty she was.

"Harrison and I are going out to dinner one night this week. Probably Nick and Toni's. You should join us. It'd be good for you to get out."

Kellyanne's reluctance was transparent. It was clear that the idea of company appealed to her. But it was also clear that the idea of being in public after last night's *Soul Mates* did not. "What if I made dinner for us here?" she suggested. "I could do shrimp and grits again."

Liza nodded enthusiastically. "I think Harrison would love that. We're meeting for lunch later on. I'll tell him to plan on it." And then she carefully placed her Dior shades onto the deck and submerged herself into the water with a graceful half-dive.

Cittanuova was the next best thing to a sidewalk café in Rome . . . or Hollywood.

Liza and Harrison were on the outdoor terrace at the contemporary trattoria, dining al fresco on the De Padova table and chairs. The Italian restaurant was in the heart of East Hampton village on Newtown Lane, and the atmosphere was casual, animated, celebratory, and *rich*.

An ultratan and ultratoned Kelly Ripa sat at the next table, laughing infectiously as she twirled pasta on her fork. Nearby was Renée Zellwegger, eating alone and deeply engrossed in a book— David Halberstam's *The Coldest Winter: America and the Korean War*.

Harrison had insisted that they try a bottle of wine from the Long Island–based Channing Daughters Winery, a 2006 Vino Bianco with delicious aromatic notes of white peaches, honey, and vanilla.

Having just finished the last of a roasted chicken panini, Harrison sat there, drinking his wine and smiling as if he had a secret to tell.

"What?" Liza wanted to know as she pushed aside her Insalata Cesare.

"Nothing," Harrison murmured, still grinning. But it was so clearly *something*. "I like this. I like you. I like . . . *us*."

She was affected by the sexy gleam in his eyes. Cittanuova scene seekers were humming all around them but, at the same time, the strangers were all invisible. Liza and Harrison were tucked away in a private world. A realization began to spread through Liza that something big—and something she couldn't deal with—would happen very soon. She gave him a cautious look.

"Don't get uptight. I'm not going to ask you to wear my class ring . . . *yet*."

Liza smiled.

"I'm just letting you know that I'm not going anywhere." His hand found hers across the table.

Something in her quickened as she sipped her wine and gazed back at him. It was the most unexpected of alliances. Liza Pike and Harrison Beck. And yet here they were. The mere idea of them scared her. But she was determined to feel the fear and move forward nonetheless.

"I know your situation is complicated. But I'm a patient man."

Liza took a deep breath. "I made a commitment to myself to table the divorce until after Labor Day. This has nothing to do with any second thoughts and everything to do with my book. I have to finish it." She gave him a faux glare. "In fact, I should be working on it right now instead of having this three-hour lunch with you."

Harrison smiled. "If you need to take off, go. Don't stay on my account." He chose that moment to flag down the waiter and order the house gelato.

"Well, I'm not going to leave now," Liza huffed. And she meant it. Her relationship with Harrison had changed her relationship with food. Sharing meals with him had become an indulgent, enjoyable ritual. And he was quite decadent about it, perfectly content to linger at a restaurant for hours.

This was so different from her experience with Justin, who ran out of conversational energy before the first course arrived, ate fast, and then gave off anxious signals that he was ready to leave.

What you don't know will end up hurting you.

That was so true in life. And especially true in love. The next time around, if there was a next time, Liza would *know* the man she was going to marry. Every critical question would be asked, too—about children, financial goals, family history, spirituality, commitment to fidelity, sexual needs, the whole gamut. Leaping in was no longer an option when it came to husbands.

Harrison stared at her with a certain lustful longing. For several seconds, he seemed to vibrate with it.

His look was so steady and sure that it practically engulfed Liza. Pure desire swept through her, almost forcing her out of her chair and onto his lap. But the moment thankfully passed.

"Harrison, I can't be starting up with the next to come while I'm waiting to finish up with the last to go. That's not how I want to live my life. And that's not how I want to start over. So until I'm *legally* a single woman, I think we should just . . . enjoy each other as friends."

"Do you mind if I sleep with other women?"

The question stunned Liza into silence.

Harrison held a straight face for as long as he could before breaking into a laugh. "Gotcha!"

She shook her head in exasperation just as her BlackBerry vibrated and chimed to announce a new e-mail message. Instinctively, Liza reached for it.

"I hate those things," Harrison complained. "I check e-mail once a day. That's enough."

But she could no longer hear him. Liza's distraction was total as she scanned the new message.

From: travisowen@yahoo.com
To: lizapike@mac.com
Subject: WHORE

I read your book, WHORE. I guess it was an autobiography? Ha! Stop trying to protect the future sluts of America. Just let the little bitches dress like prostitutes and grow up too fast. Ask any guy. Baby pussy is a good thing. So shut the fuck up. You don't want me to get pissed off.
Travis Owen

The communication was all too familiar now. The threats had been showing up with disturbing regularity on her Web site, and in the comment section of her blogs on *The Huffington Post*. But this was the first one to hit her personal e-mail address, which was known only to key business associates and close friends.

"Everything okay?" Harrison asked.

"Oh, it's nothing," Liza murmured. "Just some meaningless propaganda." And then she prayed that it was.

Kellyanne

EIGHTEEN

Kellyanne returned to McGraw's Fish Market with a certain girlish anticipation. There was no denying it. She had an innocent crush—on the shop's owner *and* his son.

Stepping inside to the chime of the bell on the door, she waited patiently for Tucker to finish up with a chatty grandmother type. The woman reeked of old money and lovingly clutched an impeccably groomed Maltese accessorized with bright pink bows and a flashy jeweled collar.

"Give me a pound of your crab salad, too. I served that at my last garden club meeting, and everybody thought it was delicious."

"Happy to hear that." As Tucker turned around to flash his customer a quick smile, he noticed Kellyanne for the first time and acknowledged her with a sly wink.

A flurry of butterflies went loose in her stomach. His on-the-sleeve kindness and integrity put her in a state of awe. There was no trace of a come-on in his gesture. The man positively oozed goodness.

"I ran into your sister and that darling boy of yours at Scoop du Jour," the woman said. "He's a fine young man. Excellent manners."

Tucker beamed as he reached for a plastic container. "He's been after me all summer to let him learn how to surf. The kid's got no fear of the water at all."

"You're doing an amazing job with him. But I know how difficult it must be for you. Holly was dearly loved by so many here."

Tucker nodded somberly and scooped the crab salad into the container.

"Parks is so happy and well adjusted, though," the woman went on. "That's a blessing to see."

Tucker went through the process of bagging and ringing up, then insisted on taking the small package out to the woman's car.

He stepped back inside and halted, grinning and shaking an accusing finger at Kellyanne. "You're the lady who likes the big-ass shrimp."

She laughed. "Guilty as charged."

"Another dozen for you?" He took long strides to return behind the counter.

"Eighteen this time, and—"

"Clean out the yucky stuff?" Tucker finished. "I got it covered." He grinned and went to work.

Even in his bulky cargo shorts, Kellyanne could tell that Tucker had the most amazing ass she'd ever seen on a man. "Where's your little helper today?"

"You just missed him. He usually pops in around lunch. My sister keeps him during the day. They're off to a birthday party that'll have a space jump. So he's stoked." Tucker turned back and smiled.

"Forgive me for prying, but I . . . I couldn't help overhearing . . ."

He stopped working. "Yeah, I, uh, lost my wife about two years ago. A drunk driver smashed her head-on, right out there on Montauk Highway."

Kellyanne could feel the blood drain from her face. "I'm so sorry."

"Day by day. You know?"

She nodded, completely at a loss for words.

Tucker returned to the business of the shrimp.

A thought occurred to her. She knew it was too forward and grossly presumptuous, but she gave voice to it anyway. "I have an embarrassingly flexible schedule. If your sister ever needs a break or has a conflict . . . I'd adore the chance to look after Parks."

He spun around, regarding her with an amused curiosity.

Suddenly, she felt supremely foolish and extended her hand. "By the way, I'm Kellyanne Downey. I probably should've introduced myself *before* offering to assume responsibility for your child."

He laughed, wiped his hands, and shook gently. "Tucker McGraw. I appreciate it, but I can't just hand off my son to the big-ass shrimp lady. We'll have to get to know you a little better first."

It was a no. Yet Kellyanne felt not even the slightest hint of a rebuke. There was a soothing quality to Tucker's voice and a soulful sensitivity in his eyes. He treated her with a quiet dignity and respect, a circumstance so alien coming from a man that she briefly wondered whether she deserved it.

"I don't open the shop until noon on Mondays. Parks and I usually hit Flying Point in the morning and check out the surfers. Maybe you could join us next time."

Kellyanne smiled. This was the first time a man had ever asked for the privilege of her company without the implication or expectation of sex being part of the equation. It was the most wonderful feeling. "I'd love to."

Adam rang just as she was starting the car. "You have two hours to get to Brooklyn for the reading," he announced without preamble.

Kellyanne's heartbeat surged. "You've *got* to be kidding me."

"I don't know what happened. I've been trading voice mails with the casting director for weeks to stay current on this, but I just got a call from an assistant. They've broadened the search. Readings are going on right now."

A hopeless feeling shot through Kellyanne's solar plexus, and she let out a defeated sigh.

"Just go. They want a real beauty. I think you still have a good shot. Who knows? The *Soul Mates* baggage could work in your favor. Notoriety might be an asset, especially since you'll be playing against type. That's a good publicity angle."

"You say that as if slut is my default position," Kellyanne shot back. She glanced down at her vintage Bruce Springsteen T-shirt and cut-off denim shorts. "Adam, I'm not even properly dressed."

"Don't worry about it," Adam barked. "You barely have enough time to just get there and be seen." He gave her the Brooklyn address for JC Studios, then hung up.

Kellyanne programmed the destination into the GPS system of Liza's Lexus. As she gunned it down Montauk Highway, waves of alarm coursed through her.

Nothing about this felt like the beginning stages of a career break. Instead, it smelled suspiciously like more desperation all over again.

Kellyanne called Liza to explain about taking off with the car and bailing on dinner. She signed off and glanced over to notice the McGraw's Fish Market bag on the passenger seat.

The shrimp would spoil without a cooler, and letting it go to waste struck her as disrespectful to Tucker, so she stopped at the next available gas station for a quick Styrofoam and ice fix to rescue the seafood he'd prepared with his own hands.

For the rest of the way, Kellyanne fought hard to reinforce the situation with positive energy. *As the World Turns* was the second-longest-running soap opera in history and had churned out such stars as Meg Ryan, Julianne Moore, Courteney Cox-Arquette, and Dana Delany. Landing a contract player role would mean a grueling twelve-hour schedule and twenty to forty script pages to memorize for a single day's shooting. But it would also mean claiming a professional stake of her own. At last!

Upon reaching JC Studios, Kellyanne felt suddenly emboldened.

It could happen. It *would* happen. She had to believe that more than anyone.

She dashed inside, slightly feverish and scarcely aware of anything beyond her own success-oriented agenda. But her optimism was put to the test when she discovered a room spilling over with blondes almost like herself—thirty years old (or close to it on either side), attractive, and fit. The only upside was that many of them had a brittle East Coast look about them. And as for the few Southern transplants in the running, none of them were a match for the Alabama goddess of sun and sand.

A ripple of awareness seemed to roll over several of the assembled soap dreamers. There were rude double takes and bitchy whispers all around.

"Are you *that girl* from *Soul Mates*?" one out-of-work actress asked.

"You do know you're auditioning to play an abstinence counselor, right?" another inquired.

As she sweated out the humiliation, Kellyanne delivered a silent stream of vile imprecations to Brad "Bonzi" Lucas.

Suddenly, a pretty, obese, apple-cheeked woman in her mid-thirties approached, clipboard in hand. "I did something awful. I hope you'll forgive me." She had an eager-to-please, rapid-fire delivery. "One of the supervising producers canceled you off the reading list, but I *had* to meet you. I'm *so* obsessed with *Soul Mates*. That's why I called Adam at the last minute. Is Dee really an evil bitch?"

A certain panic surged into Kellyanne's brain. "Do you mean I'm not even supposed to be here?"

"That's right, honey," an actress with pockmarked skin called out. "They cast for *Law and Order* hookers on the other side of the bridge."

The cacophony of laughter that came next instantly flushed Kellyanne's face. She knew it was scarlet. If the opportunity to exit the room via astral projection had been available, she would've jumped at the chance.

The heavy girl just stared back guiltily. "I can still get you in," she said in a hushed whisper. "I'll just say I never connected with your agent. You should totally read for this part. You're prettier than anyone else here."

Kellyanne cut a glance to the other actresses. They were dressed in character for Anna-Claire. She was dressed for a barbecue. Her heart drummed away. But what the fuck did she have to lose? If nothing else, she'd stand out from this gaggle of blond she-beasts.

"Yes, Dee really is an evil bitch," Kellyanne answered finally, taking pity on the TV junkie. "And Vlad is a total pig, not to mention a complete bore. If you have a crush, you can dream much better."

The woman seemed lit from within after receiving this nugget of inside reality wisdom. She pressed a script page into Kellyanne's hand and pointed to the door. "They still have your résumé and head shot."

She could feel an uptick of adrenaline as she entered the audition room to find three men and one woman seated behind a long rectangular table.

The hawk-faced man whose name plate pronounced him the head writer scowled at her attire right away. He looked impossible to charm or amuse.

Kellyanne's mind spun with positive computations. She'd read countless stories about seemingly disastrous auditions that resulted in actors actually getting the role. And that knowledge kept her planted in the room.

"Good afternoon, y'all. I'm Kellyanne Downey." She poured on the accent a bit thickly. But it was authentic.

"*Kellyanne Downey,*" the supervising producer repeated, and not in a way that made anyone think he was happy to hear the name again.

He staged a hushed miniconference with the casting director and executive producer, both of whom lobbed back unencouraging looks.

"We tried to get word to your agent," the supervising producer said. "But since you're already here. Go ahead and read."

Kellyanne glanced at the first line of dialogue. "Just because you're physically ready for sex doesn't necessarily mean that you're emotionally ready." Her delivery was warm and earnest, as if talking to a niece.

"Okay, thank you," he called out, dismissively.

For one second, Kellyanne just closed her eyes and listened to her heartbeat and sweated and congratulated herself on having the temerity to walk into that room in the first place. It was a familiar place in her head. She'd been there far too many times.

And now it was over . . . so, so *over.*

Billie

NINETEEN

Billie had never been so fucked up. There was a little bit of everything in her system—alcohol, cocaine, crystal meth, Ambien, Vicodin, even a handful of over-the-counter diet pills. Amazingly, she could still function.

"Play it back," Babydoll commanded from the studio.

The engineer in the control room obeyed the rude order. Within seconds, an urgent rock beat exploded through the monitors.

Babydoll and Tigger were the freakishly goth twenty-something fraternal twins who made up the production team known as White Tiger. While the music blared, their darkly painted eyes remained tightly closed, and their black-clad bodies swayed in a spastic, rhythm-obsessed groove. They were in some kind of hypnotic trance, at once listening for what they loved and hated about the track. It was creepy.

With fingernails that looked like they'd been polished with a nail color called Crude Oil, Tigger pantomimed slicing his neck.

The engineer killed the playback.

"You caught a decent mood on that, but the vocal's not quite there," Babydoll said. "Try it again."

Simultaneously pissed off and insecure, Billie waited for the engineer to restart the prerecorded backup.

Once again, high-energy bubblegum rock—reminiscent of Rick Springfield's 1981 hit "Jessie's Girl"—blared from the monitors.

Billie gripped the RE-20 mic as if her life depended on it, ripping into another vocal pass.

Does she know that I'm your lover?
Or do you keep that undercover?
Why don't you tell her I'm your side thing?
Your after-midnight nasty plaything
I know why you want me, I know why you need me
Cuz she's not sleazy, Cuz she's not easy
Princess likes it sweet, Princess likes it nice
But I like it rough, and I let you do it twice
Who is she?
I bet she's asking
Who is she?
What do you tell her?
Who is she?
I'm the bitch from your honeymoon
Who is she?
I did your husband in the very next room
Who is she?
Just me

Babydoll signaled for the engineer to stop recording, then conferred with her brother and Todd Bana for a long exchange that Billie couldn't hear.

Finally, Tigger's voice crackled through the monitors. "You're not living it yet. Take a break. Get inspired. We'll try again."

Billie shot a look of dismay to the engineer. "What the fuck? That was a good vocal, right?"

The handsome, easygoing black man with one-carat diamonds gleaming from each ear merely grinned. "I've worked with them before. This could go all night."

Christ! It was nine o'clock in the evening. She was at Monster Island Recording Studio on West Twenty-first Street. And she was about to fall over. "Do *you* think my vocal was off?" Billie asked the engineer again.

He gave her a diffident shrug.

"Maybe it's their bullshit song!" She stalked out of the control room, meandering around until she found a bathroom.

There was a nice hit of coke in the pocket of her Rich & Skinny high-waist jeans. Yes! She needed something to get through the session. She snorted the powder off her long pinkie nail, lit a cigarette, and slid down the wall until she was sitting straight-legged on the floor. God, she wanted to sleep. But the cocaine would kick in any minute. It had to. Otherwise, she was fucked.

Todd Bana pushed open the door and stepped inside, closing it behind him. "You look like shit. And you sound like shit."

Billie struggled to glance upward.

Todd's face was dark, his eyes blazing. "You're fucking loaded."

"So?" Billie shot back, blowing smoke in his direction. "Is that only allowed when Mr. President is shooting it up my ass? You're the one who got me into meth."

He gave her a disgusted look. "It's supposed to be an *occasional* tool. I didn't realize you were an addict. I thought you had some backbone."

"Oh, I've got plenty of backbone," Billie snarled, feeling some definite oomph from the coke. "How else could I stand in that control room and sing that crap?"

His smile was cruel. "Is that your idea of singing these days? We thought you were vomiting."

"Fuck you!"

Todd snatched her Fendi bag.

"Hey, give that back!" She lunged for him, losing her cigarette in the process.

But he moved too fast, sidestepping her, rifling through the satchel, finding her pills, and one by one, throwing the plastic bottles onto the floor with an echoing clatter. "What the fuck, Billie? Look at all this shit!"

"It's from a doctor! I had a toothache! I needed something for the pain! And sometimes I have trouble getting to sleep!" She grabbed her purse from his hands and crawled around, desperately reclaiming her medicine.

"Go home," Todd said acidly. "You're in no shape to record. You're in no shape to do anything."

Billie stood up defiantly. "I'm fine! It's not me! It's them!" She pointed at the door. "It's those fucking freaks! This isn't how I record! I usually lay down vocals live with my musicians! This is fucked up! What kind of producers are they, anyway? They don't even work the boards! They just sit there looking like Marilyn Manson groupies! I bet they're fucking each other! Two sick incestuous Satan worshipers! That's what they are!"

Todd laughed at her. "It's no wonder Amy dumped you. You're out of your goddamn mind."

"That dyke didn't cut me loose! I fired her!"

"Sure, baby, sure." He sighed impatiently. "Just get yourself cleaned up, okay? They'll be in town over the next several days to work with Gwen Stefani. We can reschedule the session."

"I said I'm fine!" Billie insisted. "Let's just nail this fucking track down!"

Todd held up his hands in mock surrender. "Okay, bitch. If you think you can. Don't let me stand in your way."

Billie studied him for a long moment.

Todd was such an arrogant bastard. And sexy in the way that only certain asshole guys could be. March Donaldson might be light years ahead of him sexually, but Todd still packed a big cock, and he knew how to use it. In the area of consolation lovers, a girl could do worse.

Billie pressed up against him and slipped a hand underneath the waistband of his jeans, pouting the luscious lips that had sucked him all the way to heaven and back on more than one sober and drugged out occasion. "Tigger told me to get inspired," she whispered. "I have a delicious idea on how to do that . . ."

Todd attempted to extricate himself.

But Billie clung to him with an almost savage intensity. The rush-rush of the coke was peaking. Oh, God, she felt as if she were the queen of the universe, or at the very least, the only bona fide rock goddess who could resuscitate Olympic Records from an industry-wide slump.

She toyed with the button and zipper on Todd's fly. "Fuck my throat. Come on. I want the taste of your cock in my mouth when I lay down this track." Slowly, she sank to her knees and peered up at him with hungry, determined eyes.

Todd groaned helplessly, pushing down his jeans and freeing his erection through the slit of his Thomas Pink boxers. His voice was thick with lust. "I am here to serve the artist." And then he shoved her head down with both hands . . .

A short time later Billie was back in the control room. There was a strange motor inside her, and it was running completely separate from her free will. She belted out the lyrics with a coke-fueled ferocity that bordered on the certifiable.

Does she know I keep you up every night?
Thinking 'bout our next time, you know that ain't right
What would happen if she read your e-mails?
All those dirty things you write to me without fail
I know why you call me, I know why you text me
Cuz she's not horny, Cuz she's not sexy

Princess likes romance, Princess likes to make love
But I don't need flowers, I just want to fu—
Who is she?
I bet she wonders
Who is she?
I think she knows
Who is she?
I'm the one who gets his booty calls
Who is she?
I'm the reason why he climbs the walls
Who is she?
Just me

Billie sang to that right-wing bastard March Donaldson. She sang to his blue-blood bitch fiancée Amaryllis Hartman, too. Line by line, she inhabited the lyrics, every note bubbling over with gut-filled rage. Her vocals were raw, impassioned, and better than any singer had a right to be. If ever there was a second coming of Janis Joplin, then it was Billie Shelton at Monster Island on this track.

When she finished, Babydoll and Tigger were staring at her in slack-jawed amazement.

Todd Bana gave her a self-satisfied smile. No doubt he thought his impressive anatomy had something to do with the talent she'd just displayed.

Even the engineer was blown away. "Damn, girl, where'd you get those pipes?"

Billie popped her hips and cooed, "I got it from my mama," coyly aping the smash hit by will.i.am.

The engineer cackled. "Miss Thang!"

Billie grinned before turning to address the studio with a new-found smug confidence. "That was just a scratch vocal, but I think you can use it as a final take."

Babydoll nodded. "It doesn't get any better than that, Billie. You rock."

"Yeah, that's what they tell me." She stepped outside to get some fresh air and smoke a cigarette. Her nose was runny, and there was drainage going down the back of her throat like a goddamn faucet. Suddenly, a wave of sickness overwhelmed her. She wretched on the sidewalk, gagging violently as she puked up what felt like the entire contents of her stomach. An instant film of sweat prickled her face and body. But she was better.

Part of the vomit had dribbled onto her AC/DC cap-sleeved vintage Trunk tee and stained the LOCK on the LOCK UP YOUR DAUGHTER banner. Billie smeared the mess with her palm and wiped her hand clean on her jeans. Shit. This crash was going to be one mean bitch. She fired up a Marlboro Light, pacing the sidewalk as her mind raced on all cylinders.

It was time to get her shit together career-wise. No more fucking around. But everything appeared to be falling into place. After all, she'd just recorded her first number one record. "Who Is She?" possessed the same quality as Avril Lavigne's "Girlfriend." Love it or hate it, the hook dug into the brain and stuck there like Krazy Glue.

Her mind shifted. She stewed about Todd Bana. Sometimes that five-foot-five fuck came off shortsighted and desperate. It was always White Tiger this and White Tiger that. Could Olympic really take her all the way? Billie began to wonder.

There used to be a proven system. A single got pushed to radio. Tower Records sold it. MTV played the video. The cover of *Rolling Stone* actually mattered. But everything was different now. Nobody listened to the radio anymore. Tower had gone bankrupt. MTV showed reality crap in 24-hour blocks. And a plug from that piggy pink-haired faggot Perez Hilton could do more for an artist than a dinosaur rag like *Rolling Stone*.

She tossed her cigarette stub into the gutter and lit another one, still ruminating. It was a brand-new world. Companies like Olympic were no longer the gatekeepers. They'd lost control. Todd could be on his way out, too. Sure, he was young. But he was also old school. Christ, Todd talked about MySpace as if it were a hot new thing. Even Billie realized that the social network site had lost its cool factor.

When her cell phone rang, she knew it was him.

"White Tiger is going fucking crazy!" Todd gushed. "They want to write more songs for you."

"You make it sound like such an honor. Maybe those freak twins are the lucky ones. Have you ever thought about that? Billie Shelton is singing *their* songs."

"It's a win-win," Todd said.

"Don't talk like a schmuck. I can hear that kind of shit in a one-day business seminar at the Learning Annex. Think big, mother-fucker. Find a way to get my music in a movie or on a TV show like *Grey's Anatomy*. Or maybe you should slap your big cock across Ryan Seacrest's face until he says yes to a guest spot on *Idol*. And I want to record a remake of 'What's Love Got to Do with It?' Ask those freaks to produce. Call me when there's real news to report. I'll be in the Hamptons."

She hung up and flagged down a cab. There was still time to catch the Jitney at Lexington. The last connection left around eleven. Billie hopped on bus number seventy-three with minutes to spare and settled in for the three-hour ride.

Trying to sleep proved futile, even after swallowing two Ambien pills. Some kook in the row ahead was playing a vampire movie on a Sony VAIO. It was the 1922 silent classic *Nosferatu*. Billie pressed her face between the space in the cushions and watched the entire film, thinking about Shayne Cutter and wondering if he'd finished his screenplay.

The bus was half-empty. Billie stretched out on her row of three seats and gave napping another shot. She was just drifting off when a stupid bitch across the aisle distracted her.

"I want to do the show," the girl said loudly into her cell phone. "I know another girl who's interested, too. She's about five-ten, really hot, looks like me . . . The thing is, I can't get off work until four-thirty, and I can't, like, not work. I would really love to do it. I mean, it sounds awesome. A shoot for *Hamptons* magazine? I want to be in that magazine! Oh, my God . . . Oh, my God . . . Okay, so I'll be in touch. Ciao."

She hung up and made another call. And then another one after that. It was the same shit over and over again about some two-bit modeling gig that she was obviously not getting paid for.

Finally, the Jitney driver made an announcement. "The rule is one phone call—no more than three minutes. We have one passenger who's been on three calls lasting at least five minutes each."

"The phone is off!" the girl screamed. "Okay? So let's chill out."

Billie glared at her, making a quick assessment. The girl was an unremarkable beauty of indeterminate origin and no discernable talent—a total waste of human matter. "Fucking bitch," she muttered.

"Excuse me?" the twit challenged. "I don't appreciate that. I was on a *business* call."

"It sounded like volunteer work to me," Billie fired back. "Real models don't have to beg for gigs after midnight. They have agents."

The few passengers within earshot broke up into fits of laughter.

Humiliated, the girl covered her face with a pageboy cap and pretended to fall asleep for the remainder of the journey.

A short time later, the driver began to make all the tedious stops—Manorville, Southampton, Water Mill, Bridgehampton, Wainscott, and, finally, East Hampton.

Billie stepped off the bus and called Liza right away.

She answered with a groggy, "Hello?"

"I'm back!"

"Billie?"

"Which one of you lazy bitches is going to come pick me up? I'm at the Jitney stop."

"It's two o'clock in the morning," Liza croaked.

"Then you should get here in a flash. There's no traffic to fight."

Liza sighed. "Where have you been? We've tried calling you a million times. Is everything okay?"

Billie laughed. "Why wouldn't it be? I'm a rock star."

Liza

TWENTY

"Where's your sense of romance?" March challenged. "This is a fairy tale—a rich prince, a glass slipper. Maybe it's been updated to conflate with some of the raunchier elements of today's culture, but it's a classic setup. That's the reason for its success."

The Roundtable was back. *Soul Mates* was Topic A. And the gloves were off. This was bare-knuckled political debate, a verbal blood sport that took no prisoners.

Liza lunged forward. If she could've choked March with his own Armani tie and not been arrested for it, she would have. "What little girl dreams about a herpes-infected jerk sticking his tongue in twenty other women's mouths while she sits around and waits on him to decide whether he's interested—*or not?*"

Tom Shapiro raised a cautious hand. "Hold on, Liza. There's no medical confirmation regarding Vlad Branigan and any STD. At this point, it's only being reported as an accusation."

"I didn't mention anyone by name. I was speaking figuratively."

Tom remained firm. "We're talking about *Soul Mates*. He's the star of the show. And this allegation is in the headlines. Your implication is transparent. I have to insist that this program be fair and responsible."

Liza was shocked. Tom had never road-blocked her with such stridency. In fact, his treatment toward her bordered on hostile. But she charged forward anyway. "March, when you have children, is this the sick fairy tale you have in mind for your own daughter?"

March disarmed the masses with his trademark sexy grin. "What I have in mind for my own daughter is no dating until she's thirty. By then, I figure she'll be too old for a reality show like this."

The crew erupted with laughter, followed by Tom, and finally, even Liza herself.

If she could say nothing else for him, March Donaldson was a charming son of a bitch. Liza imagined that one day he'd run for high public office—and win.

"In the interest of full disclosure, I should say that I'm close friends with one of the show's cast members. She's been treated horribly by the producers and network involved, so my opinions on this subject might be stronger than usual. But I think most people who know me would agree that, personal connection or not, *Soul Mates* is a show that I'd find repugnant on even my most generous day."

March tilted his head and opened up his hands. "I just don't see the overarching danger here. It's a dumb reality show. To hold it up as a window into society is ridiculous."

Liza saw a chance to knock him down. "That's a lame cop-out, March. Even for you. Popular programs *are* a window into society. That's why we're here every week to provide commentary. It's not just an excuse to get your teeth whitened."

March's jaw went tight as he absorbed the vanity dig.

Liza thundered on. "My concern is the larger message that gets floated with crap like *Soul Mates*. There are millions of young women watching this show with uncritical eyes, and what seeps into their psyches is this notion that the brass ring for them is male validation. Don't sit here and tell me that's not dangerous for certain viewers. And I shudder to factor the impact on the women who actually participate in this contrived sexist garbage."

Tom interjected. "Let's bring in one of the show's behind-the-scenes consultants. If you've been watching *Soul Mates,* you'll recognize her as Dr. Deb, but in her professional civilian capacity she's Dr. Debra Brunman, now joining us via satellite from Culver City, California. Dr. Brunman, do shows like this dangerously reinforce female insecurities?"

"Tom, I'm a mental health professional, and there is nothing remotely dangerous about this program, whether participating as a viewer at home or as a contestant on the actual show." Bleached and Botoxed to the *n*th degree, the good doctor spoke in a gratingly robotic Elizabeth Dole–like cadence. "In my experience, it's the viewpoint of feminists like Liza who inflict the most harm on our young women. She makes them feel less than for wanting to fall in love, get married, and raise a family. It's my position that we need to support *all* of girls' dreams and aspirations."

Liza launched into full attack mode. "I'm curious about your credentials, *Dr. Deb.* Where did you attend medical school?"

"I have a PhD in counseling," she replied crisply.

"From what school?" Liza demanded.

"West Coast College of Art and Science."

"And is that an *accredited* institution?"

Dr. Brunman hesitated. "Yes, I believe that it is."

Tom started to protest Liza's line of questioning.

She cut him off with a polar look. "Actually, you're wrong about that, *Dr. Deb.* The West Coast College of Art and Science is an *unaccredited* diploma mill that requires no academic study at all for its degrees. So in light of your inadequate educational platform, I'll excuse your ignorance on today's subject."

Dr. Brunman's face turned scarlet.

Tom jumped in. "And that's it for our Culture Wars segment.

We'll be back next week with more fireworks, I'm sure." He nodded intimately to the camera. "This is Tom Shapiro. Please join us again."

"And we're out!" the producer shouted.

March laughed uproariously. "Please—somebody put the last guest on suicide watch!"

Crew members chuckled at the suggestion.

"Damn!" March went on. "And here I thought the first ten minutes of *Saving Private Ryan* were tough to sit through." He turned to Liza. "Does the military know about you?"

Tom lashed out. "What the hell was that? This isn't your show. You can't just take down one of my guests."

Once again, his behavior mystified her. "Tom, when people attack me, I shut them down. That's how I operate. You know this. The real concern is the person who booked that idiot. Last night it took me thirty seconds on Google to find out she was a fraud."

"She's got you there, buddy," March chimed in. "Let's face it. This is Liza's world, and we're just visiting."

Tom stormed off without a word.

Liza and March shared a dismayed look.

"Do gay men have a menstrual cycle?" March whispered.

Against all impulses of political correctness and good taste, Liza laughed. "You are *so* annoying."

"Thank you. I try."

She rolled her eyes and started walking out.

March fell into step beside her. "Maybe the ratings are slipping. I do a lot of these shows, and that can make a host pretty uptight."

"It's not that," Liza said. "The numbers are up. Tom has improved on year-ago averages by over thirty percent."

"What do you do—subscribe to Nielsen?"

"No, I just happen to expand my reading beyond *The Weekly Standard* and *Sports Illustrated*."

"Don't forget *Maxim*. I need something for the bathroom."

Liza put her hand on the exit door, then suddenly halted, the bizarre situation with Tom heavy on her mind. She looked back in the direction of the studio. "I don't want to leave like this. I should go talk to him."

"Maybe you should ask Dr. Deb for advice on how to handle it."

Liza tugged playfully at the Armani tie she'd pondered as an instrument of death just minutes before. "One day I think I might actually kill you." She smiled with exaggerated sweetness and started off.

March held out a hand to stop her. "Can I ask you something?" He cleared his throat. "About a friend of yours?"

Liza gave him a curious look. She had a feeling . . .

"What's the deal with Billie?"

And the feeling was spot on. "In what context?"

"Is she crazy?"

"She's a rock star. She has to be a little bit crazy. Otherwise, what's the point?"

March shrugged in tacit agreement and glanced down at his Gucci loafers. He laughed to himself and shook his head as if to say, "What the fuck am I thinking?"

If Liza wasn't exactly sure a moment ago, then she was now. "You're having an affair with her."

March returned a guilty look. "You're trying to class it up."

"I was giving you the benefit of the doubt. My mistake."

"A few weeks ago she got pissed off and stole my luggage. I missed a flight to Colorado Springs and had to bail out on a speech that night. It cost me twenty-five thousand dollars."

Liza smiled wryly. "That sounds like Billie. So was it worth it?"

"I'm still thinking about her."

"Why are you telling me this?"

"I don't know. It's not a confessional . . . I just wanted some insight, I guess. There's a danger to her that I find . . . that I *found* appealing."

"In other words, you were addicted to the sex."

He smiled at her and nodded. "You see, this is why I like feminists. At times like these, it's almost the same as having a beer with a guy."

"Billie needs to be loved," Liza said earnestly.

"Okay, now you've ruined it. You sound like a chick again."

She leveled a serious look.

"At first, I thought she was just a wild time. I mean, come on, she's a rock singer. But she's just so needy."

"You're talking about a girl who lost both of her parents—one of them to suicide—before she got out of high school."

March blanched, every flippant instinct flash-frozen on his tanned and handsome face. "I didn't know that."

"There are obviously some substance abuse issues, too," Liza continued. "It's strange. I think she craves and despises the love of an audience at the same time, which would explain the hot and cold nature of her career. That kind of acceptance must be intoxicating, but after a concert, when no one's around . . . I can't imagine a lonelier feeling. So if you're just looking to get in the occasional grudge fuck for that twenty-five grand, show a little humanity and leave her alone." She observed him for a moment, picking up on his discomfort. "I take it this is more than you wanted to know."

"Yeah," he admitted quietly. "You could say that."

"Every girl has a story, March. That's Billie's. I'm sure you have no plans to break off your engagement with Amaryllis and appear in public with someone like her. That would be a disconnect to your family values image." Liza's eyes hardened.

He smiled without showing his teeth.

For the first time, Liza stared back at March . . . and didn't like him. "It's sad. Billie probably thinks that she's not good enough for you. But the real truth is, you're not good enough for her."

March looked exposed.

What an asshole. Choking him was too kind. He should be pushed cock-first through the wood chipper on George W.'s ranch in Crawford, Texas. But by next week, Liza would no doubt be laughing at March's dumb jokes again.

She left to seek out Tom Shapiro, scrolling her BlackBerry for new e-mails on the way. The most recent message brought her to a halt.

From: travisowen@yahoo.com
To: lizapike@mac.com
Subject: Favorite Song.

I've been playing that old song by Blondie over and over again. Do you remember how it goes? "I will drive past your house. One way or another I'm gonna find ya."
Thinking of you, Travis Owen

"Sick fuck!" Liza hissed under her breath, giving serious thought to changing her e-mail address as she deleted the message.

The door to Tom's dressing room hung open, and he sat on a small sofa, desperately texting on his BlackBerry.

Liza pushed the e-mail terrorist out of mind and knocked twice to announce herself. "I think we were all much better off before we had those things."

Startled, Tom glanced up with a jolt. He seemed nervous, almost guilty, but not angry.

She stepped inside his sanctuary. "Are we okay? I tried calling you over the hiatus. I thought we had a plan for the Hamptons."

"Yeah . . . I meant to call you back, but . . . things got crazy." He glanced at his watch and avoided eye contact, as if already anxious for her to leave.

"Tom, it's been weeks since we've talked. That's unheard of for us. And you singled me out on today's show. What's going on?"

"Nothing," he answered. "I'm just in the middle of some . . . personal stuff. You're catching shrapnel. But it's not just you. Everyone around here is."

"Well, I'm a good listener," Liza said, easing down beside him. "And not a bad problem solver for life issues that aren't my own. Maybe we should take advantage of that limousine bar again."

Tom gave up a weak smile. His BlackBerry vibrated. Stealthily, he turned the device facedown.

In the corner, Liza noticed a gym bag half open and spilling over with racquetball gear. "Did you ever take on my jockstrap husband?"

"No, I've been playing with Jim Cramer, the *Mad Money* guy. He's an animal on the court."

Liza grinned. "Let me know if you want Justin's number. He could definitely give you a workout."

"He's probably too much for me," Tom murmured. His Black-Berry vibrated again. This time he stood up. "Listen, I'm in a text war with one of my producers over this immigration special we're trying to set up."

She took the cue. "The invitation to the Hamptons still stands. I'll be there through Labor Day, working on my new book. You're welcome anytime."

Tom nodded noncommittally.

Liza left feeling confused, sad, and unsettled. The relationship dynamic she shared with Tom had shifted on a dime. Something— or someone—had come between them.

Justin lived for action. The hotter it was, the better it was. When the three-tone alarm sounded, he knew he was going to get some good stuff. Oh, baby. He loved a triple.

The fire burned out of control—orange flames, black smoke, poison gas. And somewhere in this apartment was an eight-year-old girl named Addison.

Her stupid cunt of a mother—the one who'd fallen asleep smoking a cigarette and caused this shit—was downstairs on the sidewalk losing her mind.

Justin moved on one knee, shuffling one boot ahead, feeling his way through the dark, staying low. Above the floor, the difference between two and five feet could be four hundred fucking degrees.

"Hot enough, Calvin Klein?" It was Dick Flick, his rescue partner. Everybody called him that because his favorite movie of all time was *My Big Fat Greek Wedding.*

Justin whacked the bedroom door with a Haligan until it burst open. The heat was more intense, the smoke thicker. He heard a choking, sobbing shriek. "Addison?"

No one answered.

Justin moved along the wall, crawled to another closed door, and attacked it. Once inside, he found his reason for being there screaming in the bathtub. "I've got her!"

Fearfully, the girl shrunk away.

"It's okay," Justin said soothingly, scooping her up in one quick sweep. "Your mom's waiting for you downstairs. Let's go see her."

One little hand dug into his Nomex coat, the other grabbed the harness of his air tank and tripped the panic button on his PASS alarm.

Justin quickly reset it. His gut twitched. He could hear the fire eating through the ceiling, melting the staples and joists of the electrical system. "Let's go, DF. Get down first and tell the news crew to shoot my best side."

"That'd be your ass, right?"

Justin laughed and moved quickly, following his partner out along the same path that they used coming in.

Two men—nicknamed Pit Bull and Indiana Jones—were on the scene, working water lines that could spit two hundred and fifty gallons a minute. They sprayed defiantly into the flames, creating a steaming mist.

"Who's cooking back at the house, boys?" Justin asked. "I'm starving!"

"Hey, Mrs. Pike!" Indiana Jones called out. "You owe me five bucks from last week! Pay up!"

"Yeah, what's the problem?" Pit Bull put in. "Don't your TV star husband give you milk money no more?"

Justin shook his head. All the guys gave him hell, either for his underwear-model looks or for his liberated wife. Sometimes he hated them for it. But he'd still die for them . . . any fucking minute, any fucking day, any fucking fire.

There was enough smoke to lure WNBC, WCBS, plus a photographer from the *New York Post.* Channel Four's news chopper hovered over the blaze. Channel Five's film crew shot the happy ending. And the tabloid's lensman framed Justin and Addison in his best shot. Tomorrow's headline would scream HOT RESCUE and feature that picture, along with a beefcake inset of Justin's FDNY calendar cover.

Oh, man, it felt awesome to get up close and personal with a big fire again. For weeks, Justin had been stuck doing glorified milk runs like stabilizing car accident victims and breaking dogs out of locked-up cars. But this call had provided real action without serious injuries. And that was a damn good day at the office.

"Is your photo shoot over, Calvin Klein?" Dick Flick asked with a snort.

"Shut up and get on the fucking rig," Justin shouted. "You're just jealous because nobody wants to see your ugly mug in the papers!"

He smiled. It was nice to have that retard back on the job. Dick Flick had been recently forced off duty to deal with a breathing ailment after flunking the department's lung exam.

Justin loved him like an uncle. Even when Dick Flick dumped his wife and two kids to take up with the newly rich 9/11 widow of one of their own brethren, Justin stuck by him. He and Dick Flick had almost died together while buddy-breathing and awaiting rescue themselves during a hellacious skyscraper fire. As far as Justin was concerned, the man could do no wrong.

When Justin and the rest of the engine and ladder crews stormed the firehouse kitchen, Danny Boy was busy chopping beef for cheese steaks. "How was the fire?"

Justin grabbed a handful of meat and stuffed it into his mouth. "Hot and smoky, you stupid twat. So we put it out."

The burst of macho laughter that came next shook the wood paneling on the cheap rec-room walls.

"Get fucked," Danny Boy shot back.

"He already did," Dick Flick put in. "On the way back. By the way, your sister says hello."

Everybody howled.

Danny Boy raised his carving knife in a mock threat.

They ate like pigs and complained like bitches. Pissed off at the union. Pissed off at the city. Pissed off at Rudy Giuliani. They'd forever be pissed off at that money-grubbing motherfucker.

Talk turned to sex—a wish list of the five celebrities they wanted to bang. Somebody joked that Scarlett Johansson would need a scheduling secretary to deal with all of them. It was the same conversation at the end of every meal. But Justin never tired of the banter. He loved the camaraderie. He loved these guys. He loved this life.

There was something soul-affirming about saving people. And he also appreciated the finality of a firefighter's community work. A cop could arrest a thug but see him out on the streets a few days later. But once Justin and his brothers put out a fire, it stopped burning.

He slipped out of the room to check his cell phone, grinning as he read the text from Tom Shapiro.

Anytime, anyplace. It's yours. Call me.

Justin tapped out a reply.

I might use you later tonight.

He waited. One thousand one . . . one thousand two.

What time???

The desperation revealed in the speed of the reply—not to mention the extra question marks—made him smile. His thumbs moved over the keyboard to answer.

Not sure. Just be ready.

It was amazing how much power Justin wielded over Tom Shapiro. He lorded over him. He fucking *owned* him. God, the feeling was fantastic.

This didn't mean that Justin was queer, though, or even bi. He still considered himself very hetero. Gay sex was just a hobby. Some men played golf. Some men watched NASCAR. Justin fucked guys into total submission.

The first incident happened a few years after he married Liza. He was helping the new engineman—a battalion chief's handsome nephew they'd nicknamed Hollywood—move into his first hole-in-the-wall apartment in Queens.

Justin joked about not getting any head at home and advised the young guy to stay single as long as possible. And then Hollywood offered to give him a blow job. Justin laughed it off. But a few minutes later, the determined dude was sucking his cock like a champ, better than any woman ever had. When it was over, they stepped out for chili and beer. Not much was said about what happened. But they expanded on the sessions until Hollywood died in the same skyscraper blaze that had almost killed Justin and Dick Flick.

In the beginning, he loved Liza. September 11 had done a number on both of them. She wanted a hero. He needed a damsel in distress. But how could a man stay in love with a woman who wanted him to be someone else? It's not as if he tricked her to the altar. From the jump, he was a fireman making a shit salary. But one day, Liza just decided that he was no longer good enough. Suddenly, she wanted him to make more, say more, do more, feel more. And the bitch had a subtle way of showing contempt that made him want to punish her in secret.

So Justin did. By neglecting her sexually and choosing to satisfy his own needs with other men, he was playing out the ultimate rejection. Liza had no clue, not even the slightest suspicion. That's what thrilled him the most. She walked around—so superior, so intelligent—yet all of this was happening right under her nose . . . with her neighbor Teddy Easton a few doors down, with her good friend Tom Shapiro at CNBC, and with others, too—the fitness trainer at Equinox, the famous New York Yankee, the divorce attorney who billed at a thousand bucks an hour. Yet she still thought he was the dumb fuck in the marriage. Fancy that.

His Nokia sang to life with Elton John's "The Bitch Is Back," a ring tone dedicated exclusively to her. "Hey."

"This won't take long," Liza began. "I'm on my way to the apartment to pick up some things. I've decided to stay in the Hamptons until Labor Day."

"Okay."

"That should give you plenty of time."

"For what?"

She sighed. "*Justin.*"

"What does that give me time for? I'm stupid, remember?"

"It gives you time to move out," Liza said firmly. "Mature relationships require effort. They also require mature people who are willing to try. I can't do this anymore. I don't want to do it anymore."

Justin thought about Harper Ward, the divorce attorney. He had a socialite wife, four perfect children, and a weekly addiction to Justin in full firefighter gear, pillaging his ass.

"If you ever split up, I'll represent you as counsel," Harper had promised recently, after a particularly intense session. "I'll get you this loft. I'll get you alimony. I'll get you everything . . ."

Evenings on the beach had become Liza and Harrison's ritual. Sunsets and Merlot. That was their thing. Physically, it got no more intimate than him threading his hand through hers at some point as they walked. But emotionally, she was already a goner.

Liza could relax with Harrison in a way that she never had been able to with any other man. To make other relationships with men work—and this went as far back as college—there had always been an instinctive impulse to reduce her own stature to accommodate them in some way. But Harrison never transmitted the implicit signals that triggered those feelings. He was openly proud of her accomplishments, keenly interested in her work, and infinitely curious about the way that her mind went about its many calculations on issues of the day.

Liza had thought such a creature didn't exist. But, in fact, there *was* a straight, successful man who wanted a fiercely opinionated, highly principled woman, even a woman who cared as deeply about her career as he did about his.

Liza knew that she was strong and viable on her own. But with Harrison by her side, she already felt as if her world were expanding. And she knew with absolute certainty that she could do more with him than she could ever do on her own. It was a strange, new, yet wonderful feeling.

She shivered slightly. The breeze off the Atlantic was whipping up her pleated shimmer dress by 3.1 Phillip Lim.

"Are you cold?" Harrison asked. But before she could answer, he stopped in the sand, pulling her close and wrapping his arms around her.

Liza experienced an instant warmth.

"I want you to meet my girls." His whisper was in her ear. "And they want to meet you, too. Especially Cassandra, my oldest. She's a little feminist. She's read *Whore* cover to cover at least twice. I'm supposed to visit her at Smith College this fall, and I've been informed that if you don't arrive with me, then there's no reason for me to come."

Liza drew back a little. "I like her already."

"Yeah, I'm not so sure I want the two of you to get together, though. It could spell doom for me at the dinner table. I think Cassandra hated *Watch Her Bleed* more than you did." He kissed her forehead.

As her mind shifted to the most recent e-mail from Travis Owen, Liza managed a distant smile. She'd shielded Harrison from the disturbing messages, knowing that his natural instinct would be to worry, overreact, and smother her with manly protection. Even though part of her longed for that, Liza resisted, hoping the creep would grow bored with his own antics and just recede from memory. But if the pattern continued, she would tell Harrison.

He was regarding her with concern. "What's wrong? You seem distracted."

"I'm just worried about Billie," Liza murmured. It was the truth . . . just not the whole truth.

Kellyanne

TWENTY-ONE

Parks McGraw bobbed in the swell of the Atlantic surf, riding a wave on his boogie board. It might've been a mere ankle-buster for a hot pro like Kelly Slater but, for the little boy, it was a tidal surge of big-man magnitude.

"Daddy, that wave was *epic*!" he shouted from the beach. He was clad in ultra-rad Quicksilver swim trunks, his shaggy blond hair was slick with salt water, and a messy triangle of zinc oxide was smeared across the nose of his sun-blasted face.

Kellyanne had never seen a happier, more gorgeous child. "Bless his heart. He's starting to sound like them, too."

Tucker laughed.

Parks idolized the Flying Point Crew, a group of guys in their midteens to late twenties who ran the Flying Point Summer School Surf Camp in Southampton. He made every attempt to look, talk, and dress just like them.

"And here comes the million-dollar question," Tucker predicted.

Parks ran over to them. "Daddy, how many summers before I do the surf camp?"

"You have to be seven years old, son. That's about three summers away."

Parks accepted the answer with a serious, upbeat nod, just as he had every other Monday morning for the last six weeks. Then he raced back to attack the waves again.

Kellyanne observed him with unabashed adoration. Her heart swelled as she fought the impulse to grab him, squeeze him, and smother him with kisses. "Look at that little butt!" she squealed in delight as Parks lost his board at the water's edge and bent over to retrieve it. "He's got your butt!"

Tucker smiled. "Leave my butt out of this."

"But he does," Kellyanne insisted lightly. "He's got your butt, your eyes, your hands, your walk. That boy's the spitting image of you."

"He's got his mother's mouth," Tucker said. "Holly had lips just like his."

Kellyanne fell silent.

And then Tucker did something that literally took her breath away . . . he slipped his hand into hers. It was such a simple, innocent display of affection. But tears still sprang to Kellyanne's eyes. The gesture meant more to her than she wanted to admit.

Oh, God, she'd been craving this for weeks. A touch, a kiss, a look—any sign at all that Tucker thought of her as more than the big-ass shrimp lady who tagged along on his Monday morning ritual with Parks. And the fact that he'd made such a move within the same breath of mentioning his late wife wasn't lost on her.

Kellyanne squeezed Tucker's hand, and they stood there on the beach, on this sparkling August day, watching Parks mimic the paddle movements of the older surfers surrounding him.

Ford Stewart, the member of the Flying Point Crew whom Parks regarded as nothing less than a superhero, swam over to give his board an encouraging little push.

"Take it away, Oakley!" Ford bellowed. He'd given him the insider nickname because Parks drooled over the display of Oakley sunglasses whenever he ventured inside the Flying Point Surf and Sport Shop.

Ford was nineteen, the son of two schoolteachers, and a popular, swoon-inducing instructor for the young girl campers, not to mention the mothers, nannies, and au pairs who dropped them off. With his laid-back stoner charm, surfer dude hair, and tattooed torso, he was beach stud personified.

Parks roared with excitement, beaming from the Ford Stewart assist as he rode the crest of the wave, having the time of his life.

Tucker smiled broadly as the scene unfolded. With an enviable masculine cool that came naturally to both of them, he traded long-distance air knuckles with Ford, then pointed at Parks. "Look at him go!"

She watched him watch his son. If ever there was any greater joy on a man's face, then Kellyanne had yet to witness it. The moment was glorious.

Parks wiped out on the wet sand, recovered in a flash, and dashed toward them. "Daddy, did you see me? That ride was *ill*!"

"It sure was," Tucker said, laughing gently.

"You were awesome!" Kellyanne praised.

Parks moved in close, wrapping one arm around Tucker's knee and his other arm around Kellyanne's thigh, squeezing them all together in a group hug. He gazed up. "Watch me again!" And he took off toward the water.

"One more time!" Tucker called out. "And then we've got to go!" He shook his head in bemused wonder, releasing Kellyanne's hand and looping an arm around her waist as his father's pride gaze stayed locked onto Parks like a tractor beam. "That boy."

She leaned into Tucker. This was the closest they'd ever been, and the proximity nourished her in the most profound way. It was like nothing she'd ever felt before. It was love. Deep love. The kind of love that filled every sense of emptiness she'd ever known.

"Thank you," Kellyanne whispered. She clutched both hands around his muscular arm and pressed her cheek against his broad shoulder.

He glanced at her curiously. "What are you thanking me for?"

"For letting me share this time with you and Parks. It makes me happy. I don't think I've ever been so content."

"This is the real Hamptons. There's a slogan around here—'Your vacation is our life.'"

"I could get used to this life," Kellyanne murmured.

Tucker chuckled. "A glamour girl like you? I can't see it. You'd get bored here after the summer."

"That's not true!" she protested, stomping a foot in the sand to drive her point home.

Now he was laughing. "What would you do? You couldn't work at the fish market. I'd end up firing you."

Kellyanne was instantly offended. "Why?"

There was a flirtatious gleam in Tucker's eyes. "I don't know. Probably for sexual harassment."

Kellyanne could hardly believe it. The man was *finally* making his move. "Oh, so you think *I'd* be harassing *you*?"

He opened up his hands in a smug I'm-God's-gift gesture. "Obviously."

"Maybe you'd be the one harassing me."

He shook his head, and a sly grin spread across his face. "I'd keep you in the back cleaning fish. That way you'd smell too bad to fool around with." But all of a sudden, Tucker's expression turned serious. He licked his bottom lip and brushed a windblown strand of hair away from her eyes. "God, you're beautiful."

Kellyanne could hardly look at him. She wanted him so badly that she feared all her desire might be telegraphed in her eyes . . . and possibly scare him away. There'd been no woman in his life since Holly. She'd be the first. And instinct told her that it was important to let Tucker set the pace for everything. Unfortunately, the man moved slower than cold molasses running uphill in the wintertime.

He held her face in both hands, running sandy thumbs across her cheeks. "They say it doesn't matter how long it's been . . . that it's kind of like riding a bike." And then his mouth closed over hers.

Kellyanne shut her eyes. For the first time in her life, she imagined herself as a heroine in a romantic epic. It felt that spectacular to be in his arms.

Tucker's kiss plundered on, and she yielded to him with complete and total abandon. He was so good, so pure, so decent. No better man could be out there. She felt certain of that. This guy was gold.

His approach to life was amazingly simple. He loved Long Island and had grown up in Hampton Bays, mowing lawns and building roofs on the mansions of Gin Lane until he saved enough money to start his own business. McGraw's Fish Market was a modest success, and Tucker lived with frugal discipline. He paid cash for everything, refused to own a credit card, and believed that the only loan a man should ever take on was for a home mortgage. His small cottage in Sag Harbor suited him fine.

The only TV program he watched regularly was *The Suite Life of Zack and Cody* on the Disney Channel, because it was Parks's favorite show, and he loved the sound of his son's laugh. Tucker owned a computer but rarely turned it on, thinking the Internet overrated and preferring the grit of newsprint between his fingertips when he read the paper with his morning coffee.

He thought politicians were in it for themselves, that paying a star 20 million a picture was obscene, that music got no better than the Eagles in perfect harmony, and that gossip was a waste of time.

Kellyanne stayed lost in the best kiss she could ever imagine, with the best man she would ever know. She felt truly, divinely, exquisitely . . . blessed.

If only to breathe, Tucker drew back, pecking the tip of her nose and tracing the outline of her upper lip with his index finger. "Have dinner with us tonight. At the house. I'll throw something on the grill."

Kellyanne nodded yes. It was easy. Because she would've said yes to anything he asked.

"If you feel like it . . . maybe you could stay over."

Her heart soared. "That sounds nice."

Tucker grinned and threaded his hand through hers, leading her down the beach toward Parks, who was listening with rapt attention to the surfing wisdom of Ford Stewart.

"Daddy!" Parks shouted. "Ford says I don't have to wait three more summers to do camp!"

Tucker and Ford engaged in a cool handshake, then bumped shoulders in a macho man-hug.

"I think we can relax that age rule for Oakley," Ford said. "He might be ready next summer. But if not then, *definitely* the summer after that."

Parks twirled around with his boogie board and started to sing. "I'm so happy, I'm so happy, I'm so happy."

Ford grinned. "This little dude's a trip. I could give him a private lesson in the afternoon. Nothing major. Just show him a few tricks."

"Daddy! Private lessons are the best!"

Tucker looked at Ford. "I know you get a hundred bucks an hour from the rich kids. How much for a fellow townie?"

Ford considered the question, scratching the faint stubble on his chin. "Hook me up with four lobsters. I need to impress my girlfriend's parents."

Tucker put out a deal-closing hand. "Done."

"*Sweet.*" Ford shook hard and fast and gave the whooping Parks an energetic high-five. He shot Tucker a teasing glance and zeroed in on Kellyanne. "Your lessons are free, by the way."

Tucker laughed. "It's bad enough you're corrupting my son. I can't have you doing the same to my girl."

The two little words thrilled her. *My girl.* Kellyanne experienced a weightless sensation. And when Tucker's warmly possessive hand claimed her lower back, and his calloused fingertips skated down to the top of her Juicy Couture terry eyelet string bikini bottom, she was flying above the clouds.

They managed to nudge Parks toward the beachfront lot, where luxury vehicles like Liza's Lexus LX 470 were parked alongside the beaten-down vans and pickups driven by the surfers.

Parks bobbed his head up and down. The Flying Point Surf and Sport Shop was ready for business, and the music of Linkin Park was rocking from inside. The little boy stared longingly at the open door.

"Let's move, Parks," Tucker said sternly. "We have to get you over to Aunt Rae's, so I can get to work."

"Why not let me take him for the day?" Kellyanne suggested quietly. "I'll let him hang out here for a little while and then take him back to the house."

Tucker appeared uncertain. "Rae has him on a schedule."

"I'll make sure he has a good lunch and gets in a nap," Kellyanne promised. "And later tonight we'll both drive over."

He still hesitated. "Are you sure about this?"

"*Yes*. Besides, your sister could use the break. And I could use the company. Liza works on her book all day, and Billie usually sleeps in the afternoon." She gave Tucker an imploring look.

"Okay." He shared the new plan with Parks.

The boy pumped his fist in the air with a loud hoot and grabbed Kellyanne's hand to pull her inside the shop.

Tucker grinned and started for his Jeep Wrangler, then turned back to yell, "Don't let him talk you into buying him anything in that store!"

But Kellyanne couldn't resist. If Parks coveted something, she added it to the pile, which now included patchwork Billabong shorts, a Quicksilver tee, Reef sandals, a dive watch, and even a new style of Oakley sunglasses called Monster Dog. They were too big for his little face—ridiculously so—but Parks thought they were the coolest shades in the world.

Tucker would be furious. But Kellyanne decided to deal with that later. Spoiling Parks gave her such a wonderful feeling inside. The damage came to over four hundred dollars. Out of sheer habit, she put down the credit card that billed directly to Walter's corporate office. Suddenly, she snatched it back and wrote out a personal check drawn on the bank account that stashed her Silk Electric earnings and paltry commercial residuals.

Head to toe, Parks wore everything out of the store and insisted that they find Ford to show him the new sunglasses. "Now I'm *really* Oakley!"

"You sure are, dude." Ford tried on the Monster Dogs and struck a cool pose. "Nah. They look better on you."

Parks slipped them back on, glowing with pride.

Kellyanne was helpless again when he led her to the Fudge Company next door for ice cream. Over an enormous scoop of chocolate chip cookie dough, he talked nonstop about his upcoming private lesson with Ford, his desire for a puppy, and his wish that everyone start calling him Oakley instead of Parks.

Several times, Kellyanne had to stop from laughing at the way he went on and on about himself. It was hilarious. Only on the edge of four and already just like a man. As soon as they arrived at the summer share, Parks discovered the pool. She helped him change back into his swim trunks, and he jumped in with his boogie board, splashing with wild glee.

A few minutes later, Billie shuffled out, looking terminally hungover. She scowled at Parks. "What the fuck is that?"

Kellyanne glared at her. "A child."

"What's it doing here?"

"*He* is Tucker's son, Parks."

Billie covered her bloodshot eyes with jumbo Chanels. "I take it the fisherman's too poor to afford day care." And then she flopped down onto a chaise, fiddled with her iPod, and began flipping through *Us Weekly,* muttering curses about Lindsay Lohan.

Kellyanne gave full consideration to pushing Billie into the pool. But in the end, she told herself that all the alcohol toxins still lurking in Billie's skin pores might upset the water's sensitive chemical balance. With a positive psychology mind-set, Kellyanne focused every bit of her attention on Parks.

Until her cell phone began to play Dr. Dre's "Nuthin' but a 'G' Thang." Oh, God, she hated that song. It was Walter.

Kellyanne hadn't seen him for more than six weeks. For her, the hiatus had been paradise found. But for Walter, it was only a series of calamitous events that kept him away. The storm of lawsuits from presale buyers looking to get out of their contracts had intensified, forcing one of his condo projects into foreclosure. His wife, Connie, had fallen off the ladder in the library of their Key Biscayne home and broken her hip. And Cagle, his youngest son, had been despondent over a breakup with a girlfriend and nearly overdosed on liquid heroin; now he was recovering in a Malibu rehab facility that would cost Walter eighty thousand dollars a month.

The absence was heaven, but enduring regular phone calls had become an underestimated chore. Walter droned on endlessly about his problems—the relentless real estate lawyers, Connie's constant bitching about pain, Cagle's rehab bills, even his own back trouble. Kellyanne forced herself to listen with vague interest, offering occasional platitudes of encouragement. Her plan was to enjoy the summer and make a clean break from Walter after Labor Day.

"How's my girl?"

The question sickened her. Walter Isherwood could go to hell. She was Tucker McGraw's girl now.

"I just passed the Jade building on my way to a meeting, and I thought, 'I can't wait until my girl's back in that swanky pussy palace where she belongs.'"

Kellyanne fought the urge to vomit.

"I'll be in New York . . . where the hell are you?"

She made a half-hearted attempt to hush Parks. "I'm babysitting for a friend."

"It sounds like you're at a Chuck E. Cheese's. Go someplace where you can talk."

"Hold on," Kellyanne said acidly, hating it when he snapped out orders. She covered the phone with her hand. "Parks, I have to take this call inside. Don't go near the deep end, okay? Stay right where you are."

He nodded obediently, then paddled away on his boogie board.

Kellyanne stalked over to tap Billie on the shoulder.

The perpetual party casualty looked up with an annoyed expression, making a show out of removing the earpods that were booming Kanye West's "Stronger" at deafening volume. "What do you want? You know I'm a total bitch until at least three in the afternoon."

"It's five, actually," Kellyanne corrected. "I need you to watch Parks for a few minutes. Make sure he doesn't go into the deep end."

"What am I? Super Nanny?"

"Billie, *please*. I'll be right back." She dashed inside and padded into her bedroom, praying desperately that a minute ago she had *not* heard Walter utter the words *I'll be in New York*. "Okay. It's quiet here."

"As I was saying, I'll be in New York at the end of the week."

Shit. Kellyanne closed her eyes.

"I booked the same suite at the St. Regis. I'm just there for one night, but I'll be making up for lost time with you. Count on that."

The mere thought repulsed her. His life had been in such continual discord that she never expected this to happen. Kellyanne honestly believed that she'd get through the remainder of the summer without being beckoned to the city and forced to serve out another term as Walter's hotel sex prisoner.

"You must be hungry," Walter said thickly. "I bet you've missed daddy's big dick."

Kellyanne recoiled. "Please don't talk dirty over the phone, Walter. You know how much I hate that. It's disgusting."

"You spoiled little bitch!" Walter exploded. "I've been going without it for six weeks! You'd be *here* to get me off if I hadn't been so fucking gullible as to bankroll this summer escape of yours! Show some goddamn appreciation!"

Kellyanne could visualize the fat vein that throbbed on Walter's forehead whenever he got angry. She knew it was being put through a serious workout right now. "Calm down."

"*Calm down?*" His voice was seething. "No, you *get down* . . . on your knees and suck my dick! That's how I expect to be thanked for all the things I do for you. And if you don't want to do it, I can find a replacement *like that.*" He snapped his fingers. "Don't think that being branded this summer's most famous reality TV whore makes you special. I could pop a Levitra and find ten girls just like you before my cock gets hard. But *me*? I'm one in a goddamn million. There's not another sucker in the world who'd pay fifty grand to let his mistress play Barbie's beach house for three fucking months. Believe that."

There was a beat of silence.

"Are you finished?" Kellyanne asked coldly.

"No, I'm not finished. In fact, I haven't even started yet." His voice painted a dark threat. "Your feminist friend can pull off that empowerment bullshit, but you can't, baby. My flight lands at eleven on Friday. Be at the hotel by noon." And then Walter hung up.

Kellyanne's eyes welled up with tears as the anger, bitterness, and resentment crystallized in a torrent of emotion. All these wasted years with him . . . and for what? To be regarded like a street hooker. And to hate the bastard so much that she secretly wanted him to die.

The *Soul Mates* insult was the lowest blow. Walter knew first-hand how excruciating those few weeks had been for her. Not to mention for her parents. But just as Liza had predicted, the storm winds eventually shifted as other scandals rose up to assume media domination. Thank God for the conservative senator's airport bathroom gay sex frolic. His personal Waterloo had eclipsed everything for days. After that came the comedy superstar's suicide attempt, then the leaked hotel security video of the trashy pop star physically abusing her children.

The relief was also aided by the fact that the success of *Soul Mates* had been short-lived. It burned hot and fast, like a hot pink meteorite flashing through the night sky and extinguishing before hitting the ground. In fact, ratings erosion had been so severe that Fox yanked the show off the schedule and posted the last few episodes online to placate the few remaining die-hard viewers.

Bonzi's next effort, *America's Hottest Bartenders,* had suffered a worse fate—premiering to abysmal numbers and getting the official ax the very next day.

So just as quickly as she'd become a scandal culture icon, Kellyanne was dismissed as a forgotten footnote of tabloid excess. In the weeks that followed, she'd fashioned her own spiritual retreat. She took long walks on the beach. She read self-help books like *Happier: Learn the Secrets to Greater Joy and Lasting Fulfillment.* She sipped coffee by the pool with Liza every morning. She made a regular Vespa ride to Wainscott to shop at Lisa and Bill's produce stand and indulge in the cheese Danish at Breadzilla. She joined Liza and Harrison for regular dinners at Nichols for seafood pie, never once feeling like the proverbial fifth wheel. And she made the magical discovery that was Tucker and Parks McGraw. The sum of it all sealed off the hurt of being rejected by *As the World Turns.*

My flight lands at eleven on Friday.

So fucking what? She no longer had any use for that information. Her disconnection to Walter—to everything and everyone in Miami—was total. He could burn the contents of her apartment. He could drive her Mercedes into Biscayne Bay. Kellyanne would start over with nothing. Correction. She would start over with *everything.* Because all she needed was her self-respect.

Be at the hotel by noon.

"Never again, you son of a bitch," she whispered. "You better hope that the St. Regis butler gives good head."

She blotted her eyes with a tissue and dashed back to relieve Billie. With every step, she felt the most delicious sense of freedom. From now on, it'd be a whole new way of living, dreaming, and loving.

Kellyanne stopped. Her heart lurched. Her stomach twisted. Her mouth gaped open. She took in all the scenes at once.

Billie sunbathing in complete oblivion as she lay flat out on the chaise, her eyes shielded by gigantic pitch black plastic lenses, her ears plugged tight by bud headphones.

Parks facedown near the bottom of the pool's deep end, his Sunkist orange boogie board drifting on the surface, in the corner, so far from his reach.

Kellyanne fell to her knees. Because she knew. And the agony of the reality took her down. The sound that came next was primal. It was her heart shattering into a million pieces. She screamed louder than she ever thought humanly possible.

Billie never heard a thing.

And Parks never moved. He was motionless. He was lifeless. He was already dead.

Billie

TWENTY-TWO

Billie was lost in the lazy Dirty South hip-hop of Kanye West's "Can't Tell Me Nothing," her head bobbing to the beat as her mind related to the lyrics.

"I feel the pressure, under more scrutiny," Kanye rapped. "And what I do? Act more stupidly."

She grooved to the music. Fuck, yeah. Billie was into this shit. Suddenly, an idea dawned on her. Maybe she should take her sound in a more rhythmic direction. A sexy urban vibe could generate real career heat. Nelly Furtado had glommed onto Timbaland, and the rest of that story was platinum.

Billie grimaced. Why hadn't Todd suggested this? Did she have to think of every fucking thing? Sure, the White Tiger session had produced a solid winner. "Who Is She?" was a hot-ass track. But the rest of their songs were so *craptacular* that Billie had refused to show up to record them.

Internet freaks were still pissing on the tunes from her third—and permanently shelved—CD that had leaked online. It was the same old shit. Everybody accusing her of phoning it in since *Dick Magnet.* Everybody grousing about "Make Me Laugh and Make Me

Come and I'll Fucking Marry You" being her only great song. What-ever. Those screen suckers didn't pay for music anyway. They stole it through illegal downloads. And why record substandard White Tiger drivel and give those cheap fucks more grist for the bad-buzz mill?

Billie thought about calling Todd Bana and telling him to get his goddamn head in the game. She'd put her future in his hands. And so far, all she had to show for it was one single in the vault. Better material existed out there for her. Did she have to find it, sing it, *and* promote it? Screw Todd Bana!

Maybe she should start her own fucking record label. Plenty of independent acts were doing it. But the thought instantly ex-hausted her. Billie was an artist, not an entrepreneur. Plus, there were certain things that only a major label could make happen. When all was said and done, the big corporate giant had her in a sling. Christ!

She tapped her iPod, killing Kanye West and giving life to 50 Cent. The mogul thug's swaggering, filthy slab of sultry beats called "Ayo Technology" blasted loud enough to cause brain damage. When Justin Timberlake started cooing the hook, Billie was in hip-hop heaven. She dreamed a little. It'd be an awesome coup if JT pro-duced a cut for her. Any linkage to that sexy motherfucker was hotness guaranteed.

Billie jolted violently as the music stopped cold.

Liza had ripped the headphones from her ears and slung the iPod across the deck. "Call 911!" she shouted, then raced to the pool's edge and dove in with her clothes on.

Kellyanne was collapsed on the other side, screaming her vocal chords to shreds.

What the fuck was happening?

Billie saw the little boy sunken at the bottom . . . like a pebble. Why were they freaking out? He had to be playing dead. Kids pulled that kind of shit all the time.

Liza pulled him out of the water, gingerly placing him face up on the concrete. She glanced at Billie. "Call the fucking ambu-lance!"

Billie fumbled for her cell phone and dialed. The emergency bitch seemed to have a million dumb questions. "Where the hell are we?" Billie shrieked.

Liza yelled out the North Bay Lane address as she tilted back the boy's head and lifted his jaw to open his airway.

Billie relayed the information and tossed down the phone. She stood up, not sure of what to do, feeling useless.

Liza seemed to be examining the child for any sign of life, first with her ear to his mouth, then with just her hand. "He's not breathing."

Kellyanne's screams turned to eerie silence. As tears rolled down her cheeks, she stared with the blankest eyes Billie had ever seen.

Liza pinched the boy's nose, closed her lips around his mouth, and breathed in two slow breaths. She placed her hand on the inside of his wrist. And then she waited. "There's no pulse. I'm starting CPR."

Oh, shit. Billie clutched her stomach.

Liza placed the heel of her hand between the boy's nipples, compressed his chest at least thirty times, and again gave him two breaths, this time more significant ones.

Nothing happened.

Billie blanched. If the kid died, everybody would blame her. She knew that. Well, fuck. How was this *her* fault? If the little brat couldn't swim, then he shouldn't have been in the goddamn pool.

Liza started to repeat the CPR pattern. Suddenly, she halted. "He's breathing!"

Billie experienced a wave of relief.

Kellyanne shut her eyes, pressed her hands together in prayer, and thanked God over and over again.

Billie thought it was *Liza's* rescue. Southerners! They loved to cook the books and give Jesus credit for just about everything.

The boy opened his eyes and coughed up water. He appeared weak and disoriented . . . but he was alive.

Liza maintained a steady hand on his pulse.

From a distance came the sound of an advancing siren.

"Kellyanne," Liza said firmly, "Parks is shivering. Go inside and get him a blanket from the linen closet."

Kellyanne broke out of her trance. She disappeared into the house, returning with a cream-colored fleece throw just seconds later.

The ambulance arrived, and paramedics rushed the scene in full emergency response mode. The boy was lifted onto a stretcher. When someone announced that he'd be taken to Southampton Hospital, Kellyanne insisted on riding with him.

"I'll call his father," Liza said. "We'll meet you at the hospital."

Kellyanne mouthed a silent, desperately grateful, "Thank you."

Billie watched them go. It was crazy. Just a few minutes earlier, everything was fine. But now that annoying kid had almost drowned, and Kellyanne had suffered some kind of psychotic break.

She braced herself for the blame game. It was coming. Billie could feel it. As soon as the initial shock and drama subsided, everybody would start in with the finger-pointing. Liza's Wonder Woman act made her bulletproof. And Kellyanne was too beautiful and too damaged to attack. So the default maneuver would be to bash Billie. What fucking bullshit!

Now Billie found herself in the passenger seat of the Lexus. She was still in her Michael Kors chain lace-up one-piece. Liza was still in her lived-in jeans and L.A.M.B. tee, soaking wet.

They drove in hot pursuit of the ambulance. Liza had one white-knuckled hand on the steering wheel, the other on Black-Berry duty. She dialed Information for the number to McGraw's Fish Market, then followed up with a call to the boy's father, breaking the news in a calm, measured tone.

Billie wished she'd stayed back at the house. All the hullabaloo had her itching for a couple of drinks and some pills. The kid was going to be just fine. Why did they all have to do the hospital vigil bit?

Liza was speeding. She veered slightly to the right as Old Northwest Road became Stephen Hands Path. "What happened back there?"

"I was watching him," Billie lied. God, she needed a cigarette. "He was fine. I just closed my eyes for a minute, and then . . ."

"*A minute?*"

Billie said nothing.

"You were *completely* out of it. The entire population of East Hampton could've been drowning in that pool, and you wouldn't have known it."

"Oh, come on!" Billie raged. "Don't try to put this shit all on me! What about Kellyanne? She shows up with this kid who can't swim, and the first thing she does is turn him loose in the pool! Then she pulls a disappearing act like fucking Criss Angel!"

It was a silent ride for the next ten minutes.

When they arrived at Southampton Hospital, Liza parked illegally and rushed inside the emergency room entrance.

Billie noticed an older woman smoking outside and stopped to bum a cigarette.

The woman quietly obliged.

"We smoke the same brand," Billie observed. She put the Marlboro Light between her lips and allowed her new best friend to fire it up. "This is better medicine than anything they've got inside."

The woman grinned, appearing tense but still grateful for the company and the distraction. "I've always hated hospitals," she said.

Billie took a meaningful drag. "Yeah, they suck."

The woman was attractive, probably in her midfifties, and sporting the largest solitaire diamond on her left hand that Billie had ever seen. No doubt she lived in one of those massive estates hidden behind twelve-foot privet hedges.

The woman's husband was having heart surgery—a triple bypass. The doctors said he'd die if he didn't quit smoking. But he couldn't kick the habit. Neither could she.

Billie told her about the near drowning.

The woman took a long drag, shaking her head. "There was an angel looking out for that child today. Last summer, my daughter's best friend lost her seven-year-old in a pool accident. It's not like on television where there's screaming and splashing. Drowning is a silent killer. A child can slip underwater and sink straight to the bottom. Only takes a minute."

Billie felt emboldened. None of this was her fault. The woman's story proved that. She walked inside to find Liza, Kellyanne, and Tucker in close conference with a young female doctor wearing green scrubs. From a distance, the news looked good. There were thankful smiles, sighs of relief, and warm, celebratory embraces.

But when Kellyanne saw Billie, the expression on her face turned to ice. She fought Liza's attempt to hold her back and came vaulting toward Billie, eyes blazing. "I'll never forgive you for this! Never! You make me sick!"

Liza moved fast to intercede. "Kellyanne, this isn't the time or the place."

Billie glared at both of them. "And there won't ever be a time or a place. Nobody's going to blame me. This shit happens all the time. It was an *accident*."

"God!" Kellyanne cried. "You're the most selfish person I've ever met in my life! I asked you to watch him for a few minutes! Just a few minutes! But you can't be bothered to do anything for anyone but yourself! And you don't even care! A precious little boy almost died, and you don't even care! What kind of monster are you?"

"Maybe you're the monster," Billie shot back. "Stop trying to pass the buck and think about that for a minute. If the brat couldn't swim, then at the very least he should've been wearing a pair of those floaties. Seems to me like five bucks and a trip to Target would've kept him out of this hospital. But what do I know?"

Liza attempted to pull Kellyanne away.

But Billie bulldozed on. "And why did you push him off on me anyway? Why was that phone call so fucking important? Who was it?"

Kellyanne didn't respond. She didn't have to. The ugly answer was all over her beautiful face.

"It was him," Billie said. "Your rich old married sugar daddy from Miami called, and you couldn't get rid of that kid fast enough. That's the reason he almost died."

Kellyanne turned ghostly white. She seemed fatally stricken by the accusation. Glancing over her shoulder, she froze.

Tucker was staring, his granite face immobile. He'd heard every single word. And he looked impaled by them. "Is this true?" His voice was equal parts surprise and disgust. "I trusted you with my boy, and as soon as the telephone rings, you hand him over to *this woman*?" He pointed at her as if she were some kind of degenerate.

Billie wanted to kick him in the balls. No way was a fucking fisherman going to pass judgment on her. She opened her mouth to protest.

But Tucker waved all of them off and stalked down the corridor, shaking his head with self-loathing. He stopped suddenly and punched a wall with a balled-up fist. "I should've known!"

Shamefully, Kellyanne buried her face in her hands.

Billie didn't stick around to survey the rest of the damage. She found Liza's keys in one of the waiting room chairs and took off with the Lexus, driving aimlessly as the deeper truths presented themselves.

A little boy had come close to dying. Because of her. And Kellyanne's future with a decent guy was shot to hell. Because of her.

Billie tried to reach March. His phone rang straight to voice mail. He never answered her calls. She knew that contact was on his terms only, and ever since their last encounter at the Hudson, he'd cut it off entirely. But she dialed back several times anyway, just to hear him recite the outgoing message.

Tears rained down Billie's cheeks as she pulled into a gas station to buy cigarettes and whatever alcohol she could find.

That night she hit Stereo by the Shore, the former Tavern space along Tuckahoe Road. It was the beach sister to Stereo NYC and the hottest dance club in the Hamptons.

Billie needed to party. But more important, she needed to forget. And it had nothing to do with the almost-drowning. That episode was already a distant memory. Right now what she wanted to crash out of her mind was anything associated with Todd Bana.

His call had come through just a few hours ago. "Billie, it's over. White Tiger's sick of your bullshit. They're done."

"What do you mean *done*?"

"They want out of the Billie Shelton business."

Billie had snorted. WHITE TIGER SCRATCHES OFF SHELTON! DROWNING KID SAVED IN THE NICK OF TIME! Even with those dopey headlines, it was still a slow news day. "Who cares? I'm better off without those goth freaks. They only gave me one decent song anyway."

"Which is no longer yours," Todd had announced. " 'Who Is She?' went to Ashlee Simpson."

That little slam had truly enraged Billie. "They can't give my fucking song to that lip-synching bitch!"

"It's not *your* song. It's theirs. And now it's hers."

"Whose side are you on?" Billie had demanded. "This is bullshit!"

"*Was* bullshit." Todd's tone had been flat, the words hitting with frigid finality. "I want out of the Billie Shelton business, too. You're off the Olympic roster."

And before she could launch into a spew of venomous curses, the line had gone dead. It was over. She was out. The motherfucker had actually dropped her from the label.

Billie tried not to think about it as she held court in one of the freestanding pagodas in the VIP area. She was downing Dom

Perignon and snorting strawberry cocaine, courtesy of a brilliant thug known as Domestic Violence.

She was crushed up against his two-man posse—one an ugly errand boy called Sea Biscuit on account of his twelve-inch dick, the other a statuesque bodyguard and near clone to actor Djimon Hounsou. They called him Big Smurf because his skin was so black it looked blue.

Stereo by the Shore was full, frantic, and loud. The party carnage could only be described as heavy-duty. And Billie was right in the middle of the so-hot-it-must-be-lethal riot, sex-scamping her way to career resurrection.

Big Smurf's big hands were working their way up her Derek Lam silk camisole dress. And she let them. There was no Amy Dando to clean up after her this time. Billie had to find a new way to make the deal happen.

"I sound like Joplin!" she shouted over the stripped-down beat of Lil Mama's "Lip Gloss."

Domestic Violence chugged the Dom straight from the bottle. "Who?"

"Janis Joplin!"

"Never heard of that bitch." He glanced at Sea Biscuit and Big Smurf, who offered clueless shrugs.

Billie could hardly believe their ignorance. Hip-hop was a whole new world. Obviously, she'd have to adjust. "I guess you could say I sort of sound like Amy Winehouse!"

Domestic Violence perked up. "Oh, damn, so you got some bluesy shit going on! That's hot!"

"Real hot," Big Smurf echoed.

The only reason the ex-cons had ever heard the name Amy Winehouse at all was because Jay-Z provided the guest rap on her "Rehab" remix.

Domestic Violence was nodding. "I could work with some shit like that."

He was a second-tier artist/producer, nowhere close to the level of a Timbaland, Pharrell, Swizz Beatz, or Danja, but still considered a name. His biggest success to date had been his own hit, "Yeah, I Did That," which offered the backstory for his stage name in graphic detail—the girlfriend he pushed out of a moving car, the girlfriend he sent to the emergency room twice in one night, the girlfriend he put in a wheelchair. And that was just the first verse.

Since the age of eighteen, Rikers Island had been his home away from home. The essence of *authentic thug* emanated from Domestic Violence like kettle steam. His tattoos had been carved in with straight razors, his muscles built up in the prison yard. He was the kind of man who made people instinctively power-lock their car doors, even if he was on the other side of the street. And all of that could only do Billie good.

She grinned. Running into this walking rap sheet outside the club had been deliciously serendipitous. She had no intention of placing drummer ads in music papers and tacking BASS PLAYER WANTED flyers in guitar shop windows. That was the old rock direction. She was taking a new street path. Because a white hip-hop bitch *always* got attention. That was provocative, rebellious, print-worthy, *forbidden.* And Billie needed to stand out like neon to get a major label's attention.

Right now the business was tense, reactionary, and in constant panic mode about a feared free fall. Execs were signing and cutting artists for the wrong reasons. The music was secondary. Selling it was all the suits cared about—having it out by a certain release date, getting it in a movie or on a TV show. She included White Tiger in that group. Babydoll and Tigger might wear makeup and dress like morticians on acid, but they still had the musical souls of McDonald's CEOs.

Billie went back and forth constantly, embracing the idea of selling out one minute, then reacting against it the very next. Was she a musical purist? Was it the drugs? Who knew? And who fucking cared? If she wanted to make a decent living in this business, she would have to bend over. Literally, no doubt. That much was obvious. And to make some real money, she'd probably have to launch one of those cheap fashion lines.

Christ! Did raw talent even matter anymore? And goddamn the iPod! The concept of buying an album was on the way out thanks to that fucking device. People just wanted to download a few good tracks, if that many. All of this made the portals of the major league music industry practically impenetrable. But Billie would find a way back in. She had to.

Sea Biscuit was pouring Dom straight down her throat as Billie lay flat-out on the VIP table with her head hanging over the edge. Big Smurf had her dress pulled up to her waist and was giving her a gynecological exam. Domestic Violence was probing her mouth with his fingers. She could taste the metal of his bling jewelry.

DJ AM did his thing. At Sea Biscuit's persistent request, the mixmaster was finally blasting Domestic Violence's trademark smash and claim to fame. The music beat its way into Billie's coked out skull. Upside down, she watched Amaryllis Hartman make her way to a pagoda nearby with an armada of doe-eyed, waiflike, size zero-to-two shop girls in close pursuit.

"Hey, bitch!" Billie called out. "I fucked your fiancé."

Amaryllis flashed Billie a look that translated to seeing garbage on the side of the road. "Maybe you did," she said. "But he would never admit to it." Before disappearing into the crowd, Amaryllis held up the hand that sparkled three-carat proof of March Donaldson's commitment to her.

The confrontation wrecked Billie into a night of excess that would become her all-time personal best—or worst—depending on the view. She went back to being a human Dom Perignon funnel. She inhaled more strawberry coke. She popped Ecstasy. She mixed in some marijuana.

While Sea Biscuit drove and Big Smurf captured grainy stills of the action on his cell phone camera, Billie sucked Domestic Violence in the backseat of his Bentley.

They rode to Gerard Point, a secluded bayside spot that separated Accabonic Harbor from Gardiners Bay. Billie's new hip-hop Svengali carved an old-school prison-style tattoo with the initials FTW between her shoulder blades. It stood for FUCK THE WORLD. She didn't feel a thing. Even when she took off her dress and let all three of them have their kicks with her on the deserted pebble and rock beach.

Everybody had left her—Amy, Todd, March, Liza, Kellyanne. But everybody always did. From high school on, it'd been Billie and Billie alone. It was still that way. She'd show them, though. Hell yeah. She'd show them good. After all, she was Billie Fucking Shelton . . .

Kellyanne

TWENTY-THREE

When Tucker calmed down, she told him everything.

And in keeping with the kind of man that he was, Tucker wasn't interested in the details. He didn't blame her for the accident. He didn't judge her morals. He didn't lob intrusive questions. It was enough for him that the relationship with Walter Isherwood was behind her.

He only asked Kellyanne to promise that she'd never see Walter again. And if there was any business left to be done in Miami regarding her personal things, Tucker wanted to be the one to handle that.

Kellyanne had never seen him drink before, but tonight he'd consumed three Corona Lights. Meanwhile, she'd sloshed back an entire bottle of Merlot to wine up the courage to tell him about her sordid past. And then he hadn't even blinked once about any of it. Honesty was his steadfast rule. "I don't like secrets," he'd told her.

Now Tucker was turning the 2004 Cosentino bottle upside down and pulling a funny, shocked face on the fact that it was empty. He smiled easily. "Don't get smashed. I've got plans for you later on."

Kellyanne felt exhilarated. Luck was raining down and positively soaking her. Tomorrow she'd be waking up in the arms of Tucker McGraw for the very first time. Because she was here, at Tucker's cozy house in Sag Harbor, watching him shovel in his third piece of the frozen peanut butter pie she'd made. "You're going to get sick!"

"I don't care." He ate some more.

She laughed. They'd enjoyed a wonderful dinner—grilled steaks and salad for them, a hot dog and Tater Tots for Parks, who had fallen asleep earlier watching a Disney Channel marathon of *The Suite Life of Zack and Cody*.

Parks was home now. Safe and sound. He'd been kept over for observation at Southampton Hospital. Though he'd been alert and in typically ebullient spirits just hours after being revived, the doctor had warned of a secondary drowning syndrome that could occur after a submersion accident—as late as seventy-two hours later. And there were other complications to fear—acute respiratory distress, neurological impairment, pneumonia, and bronchospasms.

Beyond the initial ET intubation, the battery of tests on Parks had been frighteningly extensive—an arterial blood gas analysis, chest radiograph, urinalysis, electrolyte-level readings, coagulation profile, a rapid glucose determination, and hypoxia concerns.

Thankfully, every report had been relayed with superlative news. But it never left Kellyanne's awareness that the situation so easily could've gone the other way. Had she been one minute or even thirty seconds later in making that horrible discovery in the pool, had Liza not responded with such immediate competence . . . God, she couldn't bear to think of it.

None of the circumstances had brooked any lingering hostility or resentment from Tucker. He'd been up front about his own relaxed ways with Parks around water—Rae's, too—admitting that the boy's fearless approach to swimming made it easy for them to forget how young he was and how closely he must be watched.

But Kellyanne would never forgive herself for letting Parks out of her sight for those critical minutes. It was the single most shameful mistake she'd ever made in her life. That Tucker had forgiven her almost seemed impossible. And sometimes she wondered if she deserved a man so good.

The Eagles were singing about "Life in the Fast Lane."

Tucker gave her what he called a "ten-cent tour" of the house. They crept into Parks's bedroom and spoke in hushed whispers, giggling like coconspirators as Tucker gingerly removed the Oakley Monster Dogs from the boy's face and returned them to their case on the nightstand.

"He'll wake up and put these on again," Tucker whispered. "But if I hide them, he'll come wake *me* up." He pointed an accusing finger at her. "This is all your fault."

She covered her mouth to muzzle her laughter.

"And how much did those cost anyway?" Tucker asked. "They look expensive."

"Oh, they were only ten dollars," Kellyanne lied.

"*Ten dollars?* That's too much. You're spoiling him. He's only four." Tucker held up three fingers. "I'd never spend any more than two ninety-nine for something like that."

She prayed he'd never find out that the sunglasses actually cost one hundred dollars.

Tucker showed her the bathroom he intended to remodel, the kitchen that he already had, and the sketches for a wall unit he had in mind for the living room.

It was so easy just being with him. Kellyanne imagined that days, weeks, even months could stretch on in total bliss—with Tucker as her only company. She clung to him as he closed his eyes and listened to Timothy B. Schmit croon "I Can't Tell You Why."

When the ballad ended, he took her hand and led her into the bedroom. A framed portrait from his wedding sat on top of the dresser. He was younger, thinner, with shorter hair. And Holly was beautiful—a stunning brunette in the league of a young Teri Hatcher. They looked happy and hopelessly in love. Kellyanne couldn't stop staring at the photograph.

"You two would've gotten on like a house on fire," Tucker said, wrapping his arms around her from behind.

Kellyanne turned to face him and stroked his cheek, smiling. It was the sweetest sentiment . . . from the sweetest man. She wondered how she'd lived all these years without him in her life.

That night Tucker made love to her four times.

During his first attempt, he came faster than a teenage boy on prom night. For a moment, she worried that he might be upset or embarrassed. But he cracked an easy self-deprecating joke and just held her in his arms until he was ready again.

On the second try, Tucker revealed an amazing stamina. His skills as a lover were unmatched. He played her body like a flamenco guitar, going back and forth between softly tender and passionately insistent. He whispered sweet endearments, marveling at her beauty and how good she made him feel.

It was as if Kellyanne were a virgin. And maybe she was. Because this had been the first time a man truly communicated love for her in a sexual way. She fell asleep in rapturous exhaustion.

Tucker gently woke her twice in the night to ravish her again, and Kellyanne eagerly indulged his every desire, thrilled to discover that all the pleasure she gave to him came right back to her, only stronger. It was a physical, emotional, and spiritual miracle.

When she opened her eyes the next morning, the first thing she saw was the impossibly tan sole of Parks's little foot. Sometime in the early morning he'd slipped into the bed and found a place between them in the twisted sheets, upside down. One arm was slung over Tucker's leg, the other resting against Kellyanne's calf. He was zonked out on his stomach, exactly like his father.

Tucker stirred and reached out to thread a hand through hers, grinning the grin of a truly satisfied man. He raised his head slightly and glanced back at Parks. "That sneaky rascal. Where'd he come from?"

Kellyanne just smiled and patted the boy's butt.

Parks shifted restlessly in his sleep, nearly kicking both of them in the face.

They laughed together, joking about their narrow escape of two matching black eyes.

He yawned and reached down to stroke his son's back. "That stinker won't stay in his own bed for anything. You better get used to this."

Kellyanne gazed into Tucker's gorgeous eyes. She saw love in them. And she knew the same thing was shining from her own. "Believe me. I want to."

Rae Danes was already apologizing for running late as she entered through the front door. She started a loud rant that began in the living room. "Scott misplaced my keys *again*! I don't know how he stays organized at work. At home he can't put anything back where he found it." When she reached the kitchen, the spiel ended.

Kellyanne and Parks were sitting at the small table, poring over action photographs of Ford Stewart in the September issue of *Eastern Surf* magazine.

"Oh." Tucker's sister looked surprised. And then again, she didn't look surprised at all.

Parks jumped up to embrace her.

Kellyanne smiled. "Tucker just left five minutes ago. Would you like some coffee?"

Rae shook her head. She was four years younger than Tucker, married to a contractor, and lived ten minutes away in an identically framed house with no children and three cats. They were trying for a baby. Six months ago she'd suffered her second miscarriage. She enjoyed a growing business making jewelry with crystals, minerals, and semiprecious stones. Kellyanne was wearing one of her necklaces—a gorgeous sterling piece with glass beads. In look and manner, Rae reminded her of Calista Flockhart.

Kellyanne sat there in an old McGraw's Fish Market T-shirt and a pair of Tucker's boxer shorts, not quite knowing what to say.

Rae dispatched Parks to seek out his backpack and gather the things that he wanted to take with him for the day. "I assume my brother left with a smile on his face this morning."

Kellyanne shrugged sheepishly.

"Good for him. Two years is a long time." Rae glanced at the refrigerator door that was covered with Parks's artwork, then stepped over to straighten out a crooked ocean drawing that depicted three people on the beach—a man, a woman, and a child. She pointed to the scribble of yellow hair on the female figure. "This is you."

As Kellyanne took in the full import of the meaning, an immediate knot of emotion formed in her throat. "Bless his heart." It came out as a whisper. She put both hands to her chest, and a single tear rolled down her cheek.

"Listen," Rae began cautiously, "I don't know what your intentions are, but I do know that this is very sensitive ground you're walking on."

Kellyanne nodded mutely.

"This isn't a summer reality show that you can quit. We're talking about a single father and a little boy here. If you decide to just take off after Labor Day and leave my brother with a stack of medical bills he can't afford and my nephew wondering where the hell you are . . . well, that wouldn't be fair."

"I love them, Rae. And I'm staying. I'm staying for good."

"That's all I need to know, I guess . . . I just had to get that on the table."

Kellyanne absently toyed with the glass beads of the Rae Danes original looped around her neck.

"I have a bracelet that goes with that," Rae said casually. "If you're interested."

"Yes, I am. In fact, I'd love it." The offer touched her. But Kellyanne's thoughts were preoccupied by something else. "What medical bills are you talking about?"

"From the accident," Rae explained. She shook her head, as if embroiled in an internal debate. "Tucker would never mention this. He's too proud. He considers the responsibility completely his own. And he doesn't want you to feel any worse about what happened than you already do."

"Tell me, Rae," Kellyanne insisted.

She bit down on her lower lip and sighed. "Tucker's got medical insurance, but the coverage isn't great. He talked to a friend of mine who works in the hospital's administration office. There could be a bill coming as high as twenty thousand dollars."

Kellyanne could never allow him to absorb that. Not for an accident that happened on her watch. A heartbeat later, she came up with a plan. It'd mean breaking her promise to Tucker. It'd mean doing something she swore she'd never do again. It'd mean beginning the big lies as soon as the morning after.

She arrived at the St. Regis a few minutes past eleven. Check-in time was three, but Walter always booked a day before and after his main itinerary to avoid the hotel clock.

The Astor Suite was the same as she remembered it—small but sumptuous. She loaded a CD into the stereo and played a dulcet, lilting Ingrid Michaelson track over and over again. "All that I know is I'm breathing/All I can do is keep breathing . . ."

When Walter walked through the door, he looked old. Maybe it was the cumulative effects of his sickly wife, addicted son, and stressful career. Or maybe it was the initial juxtapositional shock of seeing the sixty-four-year-old after so many uninterrupted weeks with the younger, more vital Tucker.

Kellyanne poured him a Dalwhinnie over fresh ice while he went about the business of putting aside his luggage, removing his jacket, and loosening his Hugo Boss tie.

Walter accepted the drink, embraced her, and kissed her on the mouth.

Instinctively, Kellyanne resisted him. His lips were fleshy, his breath stale, and his body felt alien to her.

Walter drew back. "It's been a long time. And after our last conversation, I wasn't sure if you'd be here or not."

She grinned coyly. "You know what they say about long-distance relationships."

He took her in appreciatively. "You look beautiful, as always." Then he fingered the purple silk faille of her Oscar de la Renta dress. "This is nice." He let a beat pass as he searched her eyes for something. "Take it off." His fingers started undoing his belt.

Kellyanne couldn't edit the reluctance on her face.

"That dress makes you look too much like a lady. I've got a lady at home. I want to see a naked whore sucking my cock." Curling his lips into a supercilious smile, he pushed down his pants.

She stripped as if the purpose for doing so were a clinical one. Off went the de la Renta, the Chantelle bra, the lacy La Perla boy shorts. But rolling around in her mind as each piece went down was her reason for being there. The ultimate goal. She experienced a flashback to Michael Zanker. But she pushed it out of mind.

Kellyanne dredged all of her available resources for a final gust of control. It was no wonder they referred to the act as a job. She approached the task as if it were housework—mopping the kitchen floor, scrubbing the toilet, vacuuming the rug. And like those dreary chores, the shit got done if a girl just kept at it.

"Oh, baby, I've missed this!" Walter cried out, climaxing a moment later. He seemed more than satisfied as he murmured breathless praises and finished his Scotch.

She stepped into the powder room and emerged wearing one of the plush terry cloth robes that the hotel provided.

"What'd you do that for?" Walter complained. "I haven't seen you in six weeks. I don't want to look at you all bunched up in a robe. Strut around here bare-ass like God intended."

Kellyanne didn't argue.

"Good girl. No reason to cover up your tits and ass while I'm around." He gave her a scrutinizing gaze. "Have you put on weight?"

She thought about all those seafood pie nights at Nichols with Liza and Harrison. She thought about all the sinful ice cream at the Fudge Company with Parks. "Maybe a little."

He nodded approvingly. "It looks good on you. Come over here."

Thinking fiercely about the larger purpose, she obliged.

Walter began to paw at her, grabbing her buttocks and popping her cheeks until they splotched red. "I see some jiggle. And I think it's all going right here." He laughed.

Kellyanne wanted so badly to slap him across the face. So it required the full engagement of every cell in her body for her to mollify him with a faint smile and an affectionate hand through his thin silver hair.

He tweaked a nipple. *Hard.*

She winced, giving him a harsh, reproachful look.

"Sensitive?"

"You know that hurts."

"It hurts, huh? That's too bad. I wouldn't want to hurt you. Would you want to hurt me?"

Kellyanne felt certain that the question was loaded. She wondered what he knew. Or what he thought he knew. "Why would I want to hurt you, Walter?" Her tone was dull. It was simply the best that she could do. "You take care of me. When I need you, you're there."

"That's right." He pulled her down onto his lap and began stroking the inside of her thigh. "I've always taken good care of you, haven't I?" His tone was softer, bordering on the indulgent.

Kellyanne relaxed a little. Maybe the underlying tension was just the awkwardness of being apart for so long.

Walter played gently with her breast now, circling her areola with his finger. "Have you missed me?"

"Of course." She hooked her arms around his neck and stared plaintively out the window. Miserably, it dawned on her. She couldn't have felt more like a whore if she'd been parading around Hunts Point in fishnets and stilettos. "I have to ask you something . . . a favor."

"What kind of favor?"

She drew back and caressed his cheek as she looked at him,

really looked at him, in a way that she probably hadn't since the blush of their first few months together. It was the best fucking acting job she'd ever done in her life. "I feel bad about asking. You've already been so generous to me this summer."

Walter ran a hand across her hip and gave her a comforting smile.

Kellyanne experienced a sweeping sense of shame. There was a wounded tenderness in his eyes, and for a moment, she saw the man who'd endeared himself to her a million years ago, when she'd been schlepping lattes at the Coffee Shop on Union Square.

"I'll give you whatever it is that you need. You know that, right?"

She nodded gratefully, placing a hand on his chest.

He ran his fingers over hers. "You stopped biting your nails." It was strange. There was almost a hint of sadness in his voice.

Kellyanne grinned, admiring them herself. For the first time since grade school, she had significant nail growth. They were short and neat now, but she planned to have a real manicured look one day—something pretty, perhaps a soft pink polish, or maybe even the French style with white tips. Tucker had instilled the will for her to kick the nasty lifetime habit. He made her want every part of herself to be as beautiful as possible.

Thinking of him gave her the courage to make the ask. "I need money, Walter . . . but maybe you can't help me right now. I'm sure with the foreclosure—"

"I'm not strapped for cash."

Kellyanne smiled inwardly. She'd expected him to react that way. There was only one thing left to do—announce how much. Then he'd scratch out a check just to prove that Walter Isherwood, Master of the Universe, was still that, even while facing a brutal downturn in the market. "I need twenty thousand dollars."

Wordlessly, he reached for his jacket. A loose check and a Mont Blanc pen were in the inside pocket. He scribbled out the request, using her slim thigh as an impromptu writing surface. "I assume this is for that widowed fish shack owner you're fucking." His voice was casual.

Kellyanne froze.

Walter signed his name with a bitter flourish, piercing the paper with the pen's sharp point, staining her leg with ink. He pushed her onto the couch and stood up. His hand gripped the check tightly as he waved it in front of her shocked face. "Nothing's free, you manipulative little bitch. If you really want this, you're going to have to earn it. Just like any other whore would."

Everything around her blistered and burned.

"You must think I'm a senile old fart."

"Walter . . . I—"

"Shut the fuck up." He crossed over to the telephone and called the front desk. "Steve Bell's room . . . Thank you . . . Steve, it's Walter . . . I'm staring at her right now . . . Let's have some fun." The receiver went down with a bang. He turned on her viciously.

Kellyanne felt a frisson of absolute fear.

"Did you really think that I'd front the bills for your summer getaway and not keep an eye on you?" He ripped a manila envelope from the side pocket of his luggage and tossed out several long-lens surveillance photographs of Tucker kissing her on the beach.

She looked back at Walter in complete astonishment.

"So what's the money for?" he sneered. "Does this guy need a new fishing boat? Or is he one of these sad-sack Americans without health insurance? I know his kid got waterlogged this week. That must've cost a small fortune at the emergency room."

Kellyanne hated that Walter knew anything at all about Tucker and Parks. They were too good. And he was too full of ugliness.

"You won't last with that loser. A spoiled whore like you? No way. I thought your feminazi friend was teaching you how to live a life on your own. But you can't last ten minutes without a man—a rich one or a poor one."

Kellyanne picked up the de la Renta and covered herself with the dress. It had a high neckline, cap sleeves, and cinched waist.

Tucker had seen her wearing it once and told her that she "looked like that lady from the *Breakfast at Tiffany's* movie." At the time, the comparison had thrilled her. But she didn't feel like Audrey Hepburn right now.

Walter waved the check again, taunting her. "I bet another one of these that you'll be back in Miami before Thanksgiving."

She stared at him defiantly. "I'm never coming back. I never was."

His smile was nasty. "That's good. Because I've already got another girl living in the condo. She's driving the same car, too."

"What's her name? I should send her a sympathy card."

He snatched the dress and threw it down onto the floor, leaving her exposed. "I paid for that. I think I'll have it cleaned and take it home to her."

"I don't mind walking out of here naked. As long as I know that I'll never have to see you again." The room was suddenly cold.

"You can still walk out wearing this." He dropped the check onto the cocktail table.

Kellyanne glanced down at it. *Twenty thousand dollars.* She could make all the arrangements with Southampton Hospital's finance department. Tucker would never even have to see the bills.

Three quiet knocks rapped the door.

Walter stepped over to answer it. He put his hand on the latch, then hesitated, turning back. "I think I'm just going to watch. I've never had a front-row seat to see a real whore in action." And then he opened the door.

Steve Bell ran a New York–based real estate group that had invested heavily in two of Walter's Miami developments. He was in his midfifties, thirty pounds overweight, and wore his hair in a stubborn comb-over similar to Donald Trump's.

With him was Vanessa Bradley, a twenty-three-year-old massage therapist who'd recently been voted off the VH-1 reality dating series *Rock of Love,* featuring Bret Michaels of the rock group Poison. She had that porn star chic look—bleached hair, wet lips, and a tanning bed pallor.

"She's the girl I was telling you about," Walter said.

"Show us, baby," Steve prompted.

Vanessa beamed proudly, then bent over to spread her ass cheeks and display her freshly bleached pucker.

Walter poured himself a Scotch and settled back to enjoy the entertainment.

Kellyanne kept telling herself that she was doing it for Tucker. The constant reminder was the only thing that got her through the ordeal. And somehow she still felt faithful to him because her body never responded to the worshipful and relentless attentions of Steve and Vanessa. It was as if Kellyanne's sexual nerve endings had shut down. Only Tucker could activate that part of her now.

I don't like secrets.

Her heart broke a little bit as the voice of the man she loved so dearly played in her mind. Oh, God! If only they could've started their new life together with nothing but the truth between them.

Everyone had their secrets, though. For Kellyanne, there was the encounter with Michael Zanker and now this last freak show involving Walter. She planned on taking both of them to her grave . . .

Liza

TWENTY-FOUR

Harrison couldn't stop reading the most recent one.

From: travisowen@yahoo.com
To: lizapike@mac.com
Subject: Watch YOU Bleed.

Shut up, bitch. If I've told you once, I've told you a thou-
sand times. But you just won't listen. Now it's official.
YOU are next.
Travis Owen

Liza regretted ever telling him about the e-mails.

"I think you should have a gun."

At first, she just looked at him. "Harrison, I've never even held
a can of pepper spray. What am I going to do with a gun?"

"That's what classes are for. And I could show you, too."

Liza shut off the MacBook Pro and folded down the screen. "If I
armed myself every time an angry man with a computer and too

much time on his hands sent a hostile message over the Internet, I'd be a one-woman militia."

He nodded with sarcastic enthusiasm and took a frustrated bite out of his Dreesen's doughnut. "I like the sound of that!" He yelled this with his mouth full.

She rolled her eyes and continued to work around him, gathering up her things for the drive into the city.

He watched her while he finished his doughnut, then said, "When are you going to start taking these threats seriously?"

Liza looked at him evenly. "Honestly? Never."

He held her eyes for a moment. His expression was worried.

But she began ticking off an obscene greatest hits list in a tone that conveyed her tedium for the subject. "Let's see . . . in the past, there have been pictures posted of me with a noose around my neck and a muzzle over my mouth. Oh, and there was the lovely gentleman who fantasized about jacking off in my face and then cutting my throat. That's a personal favorite. Apparently, he didn't like my review of *The Passion of the Christ.* Go figure." She rolled her eyes. "I've been lucky enough to achieve a degree of prominence. Add the fact that I'm a woman. Now throw in that I happen to be very opinionated. What do you have? A perfect recipe for moronic and misogynistic vitriol." She moved closer to him and touched his knee for emphasis. "You know this. That's what your film was about."

He groaned at the reference to *Watch Her Bleed.* "I'll never live down that fucking movie where you're concerned."

Liza squeezed his kneecap. "This isn't as sinister as it appears. In some ways, today's Internet is yesterday's bathroom wall." She shrugged. "It's an ugly part of society we just have to deal with."

Harrison still looked worried and refused to relent. "I might buy that if we were talking about some asshole in a chat room. But this guy has your *personal* e-mail address."

"So does a Nigerian who needs my urgent help transferring overseas funds."

He managed a faint smile at her crack about the ubiquitous e-mail scam.

"On the surface, this is disturbing. I'll give you that. The first time one of those e-mails pushed down on my BlackBerry . . . it really got to me. But what am I supposed to do? Stop writing? Stop talking?"

There was a stubborn look in his eyes. *"Get a gun."*

"Oh, God! We're back to that?" Liza walked away from him to fill a glass with ice and pour a Diet Coke. "You're driving me crazy." She said it through gritted teeth, but she kept her tone affectionate. There was a brief silence as she waited for the fizz to die down. "There's no way to police something like this. It's not like I can narrow down the list of possible suspects. Conservatives hate me. Christians hate me. I realize that's oxymoronic, but it's the truth. I mean, aren't they supposed to have love in their hearts for all of God's creatures?" She paused to drink some soda. "Muslims aren't too thrilled with me after my last column. And speaking of guns, the NRA wouldn't mind using me for target practice. Everyone in the adult video industry would cheer if I perished in a tragic dildo accident. Am I leaving anyone out? Oh, yes—Opie and Anthony, the idiot shock jocks. They call their fans '*Pests.*' And they live up to the name. A few months ago, I had to disengage the comment section on my Web site for two weeks because of those fuckers." She sighed. "And did I mention Tom DeLay?"

His expression remained grim. "It only takes *one* wacko."

Liza gave him a pointed look. "Yes . . . that's becoming abundantly clear."

Harrison was *not* amused.

"*So* protective," she teased. "And we're not even sleeping together yet."

"Yeah, well, whose fault is that?"

She smiled, leaning into the counter in her tight Nudie jeans, setting the angle of her denim butt with perfect precision.

He noticed.

She knew that he would. More Diet Coke went down the hatch.

Liza had every intention of doing this relationship right. They'd become friends first. Done. She'd get divorced. Coming soon. They'd start officially dating. After the third dinner, she'd break down and have sex with him. And then she'd probably end up becoming his third wife. God. A man's *third* wife. She never would've imagined that for herself.

Harrison tossed a resentful glance to her bulging Jean Paul Gaultier white leather tote. "I still don't understand why you have to go in to the city."

"I have to print out my book. I can't proofread on the screen. I need the actual pages in my hands for that."

"Use my printer. I've got a brand new HP at the house."

"Not the same," Liza insisted. "I want to use the printer that spit out *Whore,* which is my old clunker at the loft. It's superstitious, I know. But writers have weird little rituals. You know that."

"It's Labor Day," Harrison complained.

"And I'll be back in time for dinner at Della Femina. What time is our reservation again?"

"Eight." His voice was a grumble. He slurped his coffee and gazed out at the pool.

"You know, I should've done this yesterday, but instead I let you drag me to that *awful* party."

Harrison looked put upon. "I'm never going to live that down, either."

"No, you're not. But if it's any consolation, I think I had a better time watching your horrible movie."

Harrison had convinced her to attend P. Diddy's annual White Party at his East Hampton palace. The Labor Day bash was famous for its fall-in-line or hit-the-road fashion edict: ALL WHITE AND ONLY WHITE. From headwear to footwear and everything in between—including jewelry—monochromatic ensembles ruled. Violators were asked to leave by thick-muscled security guards.

Yesterday Billie had been part of this unfortunate group. She'd shown up in a shade of cream and been denied entry. Her escort, Domestic Violence, had gone in without her and latched onto

Mariah Carey, who was half dressed and probably exhausted this morning from sucking in her stomach for so long.

Everything had been beautifully decorated and lavishly appointed with food and liquor, but the overall affair was a total ratfuck—shoulder to shoulder with the likes of Tommy Lee, Bruce Willis, Pamela Anderson, and *The View* cast-off Star Jones alongside her is-he-or-isn't-he husband, Al Reynolds.

Harrison had cajoled her into going by talking up what was supposed to have been an incredible fireworks display of white-only explosions. But the East Hampton Town Council had squashed that, citing safety concerns about the light show's potentially drawing too many boats and ships to the rocky waters in the Hedges Bank area.

They'd ended up leaving early and found themselves in the cramped living room of Tucker's house in Sag Harbor. Until his bedtime, Parks had entertained them, parading around in his Oakley Monster Dogs and rhapsodizing about his private surfing lesson from Ford Stewart. And then there'd been too much wine and a spirited couple-against-couple game of Trivial Pursuit.

"I still can't believe we lost that game last night," Harrison said.

Liza smirked as she sipped her Diet Coke. "That's the third time you've mentioned this since showing up here." She checked her watch. "An hour or so ago. Get over it!"

He shook his head. "I can't. We're two smart people. We went to Eastern schools. I'm a filmmaker. You're a writer. And we got our asses handed to us by a girl from Alabama and a guy who rings up dead fish all day. I can't get it out of my mind."

Liza laughed at him. "You're such an intellectual snob. This is not an attractive quality."

"I want a rematch," he said, not hearing her. "I wonder if they're up for it tonight." His face was determined. "Call—"

"I'm not calling anyone. Anyway, I think Kellyanne mentioned something about going to his sister's for a big barbecue."

But Harrison continued to stew. "I'm pissed at myself for missing that baseball question. I *knew* Hank Aaron's final game was with the Milwaukee Brewers. Why'd I say Braves?"

Liza gave him a look. "Don't you have a script to rewrite?"

Jodie Foster had said yes to star in *Mercy Killer,* Harrison's new movie about the New Orleans doctor accused of murdering her patients. Foster wanted a major rewrite to punch up the film's female point of view. Liza's publisher, media mogul Toni Valentine, had put the project on the fast track at Valentine Features after the two-time Academy Award–winner signed on.

In *Watch Her Bleed,* Harrison had depicted strong, accomplished, ambitious, and opinionated women as murder victims in scenes of brutal, almost orgiastic violence. Now he was—sort of—dating one in Liza. He'd be directing one in Jodie Foster. And he'd also be answering to one in Toni Valentine. The irony made Liza smile to herself.

"I should go." She kissed him on the cheek and slung the heavy Gaultier tote over her shoulder.

"Think about the gun." He was serious.

"No." And so was she. "Besides, if I had one, I'd probably shoot *you* with it right now. And that's not the point, is it?" Liza started for the door. "I'll meet you at the restaurant."

"Call from the road to let me know that you're okay."

She smiled at him. "Get some work done."

There was a glint in his eyes as she mentioned this.

Liza hesitated. She became suspicious. "What's going on?"

"I got an e-mail from Toni Valentine early this morning."

"On Labor Day? Does she ever *not* work?"

He shrugged. "I guess there's a reason why some people become moguls." He gestured toward her.

Liza scoffed at the implication. "Please. Compared to Toni I'm just a girl with a few part-time jobs. What'd she say?"

"She suggested you as a script doctor for *Mercy Killer.*" The look on his face told her that he liked the idea.

Liza was shocked. "*Me?* What do I know about scripts? I've never written a screenplay!"

Harrison waved off the concern. "Doesn't matter. You have a

strong female voice. Toni thinks that bringing you on board will make Jodie happy, too." He paused a beat. "And I really like the idea of us working together to create something." His excitement was real.

"Let me think about it." But in her mind Liza already knew that the answer would be yes. The movie would film on location in New Orleans. With preproduction, production, and post, that'd mean several months there. It'd also mean quitting *The Round-table*. But it was time. Her relationship with Tom Shapiro had deteriorated for inexplicable reasons. And frankly, the he said/she said routine with March Donaldson had grown tiresome.

Harrison followed her out to the Lexus. "I don't like it that you're driving back and forth alone. I could ride along and keep—"

"Harrison, you have to stop. If I do it your way, I'll end up like Tuesday Kent."

His face was blank.

"*The Baby Girl Diaries*."

The light of recognition sparkled in his eyes. "Yeah, of course. Whatever happened to her?"

"She let Internet threats get to her to such a degree that she had a breakdown. Her career disappeared overnight. And she ended up moving back in with her parents. Is that what you want for me? Because I'd rather take my chances with a mystery psycho than live with two known crazies."

He stepped away from the SUV, shaking his head and smiling as she drove away.

Before she reached Montauk Highway, Liza was cell-to-cell with Kellyanne. "Harrison is *wrecked* about losing Trivial Pursuit last night."

"Oh, my God," Kellyanne replied. "Are you serious? Bless his heart. Tucker's acting just as stupid, though. He's strutting around like he's the new Super Bowl champ."

"Harrison's a bigger idiot. He wanted a rematch tonight."

"Well, I think they're even. Tucker wants to win again just to prove it wasn't a fluke. Men!"

"Correction—*boys!*"

Liza and Kellyanne laughed, then glossed over the subject of Billie, whom they both considered a lost cause. She'd moved out of the summer share and cut off both of them after the confrontation in the hospital. Now she was shacking up with Domestic Violence at his New Jersey compound. Her lifestyle had become anathema to them. Perhaps it always had been.

Liza hung up and drove the rest of the way in indulgent silence, basking in the euphoria that was the relief of knowing her book was *done*. What a fantastic feeling!

She was ferociously proud of the manuscript, too. The contents were certain to stir controversy. Liza anticipated that many women would take umbrage at the notion of her calling out all of them as stupid girls. But she included herself in that group. Liza owned the label for some of her more fucked-up choices in life. And any woman out there who couldn't do the same was just floating down a river called Denial.

As she turned the key to let herself into the loft, Liza heard the throbbing pulse of a dance beat. Instantly, she bristled with anger. If her fucking husband was having some kind of party . . .

But the downstairs living and kitchen areas were empty. Accepting reality but feeling nothing, she rolled her eyes. So the party was going on upstairs. Big shock.

Liza hadn't spoken to Justin in almost a month. There was nothing to say. Her focus had been finishing her book by Labor Day. And her next goal would be finishing this marriage by Christmas.

She glowered at the spiral staircase. Her office was upstairs. And she'd have to walk through the bedroom to get there. Putting her things down on the console table, she decided to have a drink and wait. But after a moment of smoldering rage, she reconsidered. This was her goddamn apartment! Justin and his groupie whore could go somewhere else.

She snatched her tote and started up, determined to print her manuscript and get the hell out. The Euro disco music boomed louder and louder.

And then Liza saw them . . . in her bedroom . . . on her bed.

The shock knocked the breath from her body. For long seconds, she couldn't look away.

"Say it!" Justin panted. "I want to hear you say it!"

"You wear the ring, but he fucks me," Tom Shapiro grunted.

"Louder!" Justin demanded, tearing into him as he pinned down Tom's arms. "Louder, or I'll stop!"

"You wear the ring, but he fucks me!" Tom cried out.

"That's what you should tell the bitch next time you see her," Justin growled.

And by then Liza was quietly descending the stairs. They never even knew she was there.

She made it back to East Hampton in record time, driving like a demon and blasting Marie Digby's acoustic version of Rihanna's "Umbrella" like a broken record. As the betrayal and her own ignorance burned deeper and deeper into her brain, a strange kind of madness began to set in.

Marie's luminous voice and the trite-but-true lyric had saved her from insanity. "Know that we still have each other/You can stand under my umbrella . . ."

All she could think about was Harrison—getting back to him in the Hamptons, working with him on *Mercy Killer,* and one day . . . *marrying* him on her second try. He was her best friend. And she was his. The first time around, Liza had missed looking for that essential ingredient. *Stupid girl.*

Her stomach tightened with anxiety. Almost three hours without her BlackBerry. That was a lifetime record. But in her agitated haste to leave the TriBeCa loft, Liza had left it on the console table of the entryway, only to discover her mistake more than halfway to Long Island. No doubt Harrison had been trying to reach her numerous times.

Liza dashed inside through the front door to call him from the landline and put his worried mind at ease. She stopped suddenly. Her heart bolted in her chest.

There was a stranger in the living room. A thin, handsome, college-age boy with sandy-colored hair. He wore jeans and a Hunter College Hawks T-shirt. His blue-green eyes zeroed in on her with a disturbing intensity. "I'm Travis Owen." The voice was flat.

Everything that happened next was like a reenactment from the movie she hated . . . by the man she loved. And like she always did whenever under attack, she fought back. Because when they found her dead, as she knew that they would, she wanted them to know . . .

Liza Pike was a fighter . . .

Epilogue

Faye Hudson was startled by the sound of a splash as she prepared to read Page Six. Rising with a start, she peered out at the pool.

The sight provided instant calm and momentary comfort. It was Annie, the golden retriever, dog paddling away on her regular morning swim. Some things *were* the same at this house on North Bay Lane.

"Excuse me, Miss Hudson?"

She turned expectantly on Scott Danes, the contractor leading the retinue of workers rebuilding the living room. His brother-in-law was the future husband of Kellyanne Downey, the woman who had discovered the body of Liza Pike. It was a small world in the Hamptons.

"I just want to be clear. You want *all* of the living room furniture taken away?"

She nodded. Symbolically, it was important to her that everything be stripped—the floors, the walls, even the vents and fixtures. Would it make a difference? Could this place ever feel like

Cocaine and opiates were found in Shelton's system after her arrest.

WE HEAR

That **Ashlee Simpson**'s fire-breathing **White Tiger**–produced single "Who Is She?" is a lock to top the charts . . . That **Tom Shapiro,** host of CNBC's *The Roundtable,* just inked a book deal with media mogul **Toni Valentine** to answer all those curious questions about his personal life . . . That last week's death of Miami real estate developer **Walter Isherwood** at the St. Regis was discreetly handled by hotel management so as not to add to his wife's grief . . . That the engagement between political talking stud **March Donaldson** and **Stella McCartney** PR priestess **Amaryllis Hartman** is officially ka-put . . . That FDNY hunk and young widower **Justin Beal** is shopping for rings and close to popping the question to *The Sex Factor* authoress **Pila Anderson** . . . That **Jodie Foster** dropping out of the Hurricane Katrina medical drama *Mercy Killer* has put the troubled Valentine Features film out of its misery and permanently shut down production.

SIGHTINGS

Reality TV producer **Brad "Bonzi" Lucas** complaining to others on line for the loo at Bungalow 8 about his ouster from Fox . . . Manorexic male model and oil heir **Teddy Easton** cycling on the George Washington Bridge . . . Jewelry designer **Rae Danes** launching her exclusive line of crystal charm bracelets at Henri Bendel . . . Fashion stylist **K.K. Vermorel** huddling with **Jenny Barlow** at Bette to strategize the star's look for Cannes . . . New Hollywood scribe **Shayne Cutter** celebrating his first two-film pact with the Weinstein Company at Sunset Beach on Shelter Island . . . Olympic Records honcho **Todd Bana** leaving Whiskey Blue with a gorgeous blonde on each arm . . . Film director **Harrison Beck** knocking back Scotch after Scotch alone at Murf's Backstreet Tavern in Sag Harbor until closing time.